SADLIER-OXFORD
Algebra 1
SOURCEBOOK

R. James Milgram

Alfred S. Posamentier

Catherine D. LeTourneau

Edward William Quinn

Program Consultants

Joanne Mellia
Technology Consultant
Hommocks Middle School
Larchmont, NY

Alice Russo Dunning
Adjunct Associate Professor
Westchester Graduate Campus
Long Island University
Purchase, NY

Vern Williams
Mathematics Department
Longfellow Middle School
Fairfax County, VA

Daniel Jaye
Principal and Director
Bergen County Academies
Hackensack, NJ

Marilyn Occhiogrosso
Former Assistant Principal
Mathematics Supervision
Erasmus Hall High School
Brooklyn, NY

Paul M. Beaudin
Professor of Education
Iona College
New Rochelle, NY

Regina Panasuk
Professor of
Mathematics Education
University of Massachusetts
Lowell, MA

Sadlier-Oxford
A Division of William H. Sadlier, Inc.
www.sadlier-oxford.com

Reviewers

The publisher wishes to thank the following teachers and administrators, who read portions of the series prior to publication, for their valuable contributions.

Dennis Montone
Supervisor of Math and Science
Bergen County, NJ

Susan Blumberg
Mathematics Teacher
Coordinator, Grades 1–8
Merrick, NY

John Negherbon Jr.
Grades 7, 8, & Algebra 1
Teacher
Vero Beach, FL

Gary Rubinstein
Grades 9–12
Teacher
New York, NY

Sean Corcoran
Grades 7 & 8
Teacher
Philadelphia, PA

Francis P. Franklin
Grade 8
Math/Algebra Teacher
Newport, OR

Katherine Herbst
Grades 7–12
Supervisor of Mathematics
Ridgefield Park, NJ

Richard L. Cotten
Grades 9–12
Mathematics Teacher
Oviedo, FL

Sylvia Anna Nomikos
Math Teacher/Coordinator
Brooklyn, NY

Marie Bicsak
Grades 7–9
Instructor/Consultant
Harrison Twp., MI

Br. Ralph Darmento, FSC
Deputy Superintendent
Newark, NJ

Dr. Jeanne Rast
Grades K–8
Teacher
Hapeville, GA

Amy Talley
Middle School
Math Teacher
San Antonio, TX

Valery Melnick
Grade 7
Math Teacher
Havertown, PA

Marcia Escandar
Middle School
Math Teacher
Miami, FL

Maureen Thorley
Grades 6–8
Mathematics Specialist
Bethlehem, PA

Maureen Barnhart
Grades 6–8
Teacher
Hillsboro, OR

Sr. Agnes White
Principal
Rockaway Park, NY

Thomas R. Filippi
Dean of Academics
Aventura, FL

Bernadette Dougherty
Principal
Wayne, PA

Peggy Barrie
Grades 7 & 8
Math/Algebra Teacher
Belmar, NJ

Elizabeth Warren
Grades 7 & 8
Math/Algebra Teacher
Eagle Creek, OR

Margaret Clinton
Teacher
Philadelphia, PA

Emily Sheridan
Grade 8
Teacher
Hicksville, NY

Mary Anne Corcoran
Grade 8
Teacher
Philadelphia, PA

Joanne DeMizio
Associate Superintendent
Curriculum & Staff Development
New York, NY

Judith A. Devine
Educational Consultant
Springfield, PA

Stephanie D. Garland
Educational Consultant
St. Loius, MO

Printed in the United State s of America
ISBN: 978-0-8215-8209-1
1 2 3 4 5 WEBC 19 18 17 16 15

Mathematics Advisory Board

A Mathematics Advisory Board consisting of highly distinguished math educators from across the country was established to review the curriculum and pedagogy of *Progress in Mathematics*, Grades K–8. The recommendations they provided were invaluable to the development of the program.

Contents

Chapter

Basic Concepts of Algebra

 PRACTICE BOOK for all exercise sets.

Chapter

Linear Equations

Go to PRACTICE BOOK for all exercise sets.

Chapter 3

Linear Inequalities

Go to **PRACTICE BOOK** for all exercise sets.

Chapter 4

Relations and Functions

Go to **PRACTICE BOOK** for all exercise sets.

Chapter 5

Linear Functions

Go to **PRACTICE BOOK for all exercise sets.**

Chapter 6

Systems of Linear Equations and Inequalities

Go to **PRACTICE BOOK for all exercise sets.**

Chapter 7

Operations with Polynomials

Go to **PRACTICE BOOK** for all exercise sets.

Chapter 8

Factoring Polynomials

Go to **PRACTICE BOOK** for all exercise sets.

Radical Expressions and Equations

Go to PRACTICE BOOK for all exercise sets.

Quadratic Functions and Equations

Go to PRACTICE BOOK for all exercise sets.

Chapter

Ratio, Proportion, and Trigonometry

Go to **PRACTICE BOOK** for all exercise sets.

Chapter

Rational Expressions and Equations

Go to **PRACTICE BOOK** for all exercise sets.

Go to PRACTICE BOOK for all exercise sets.

Go to PRACTICE BOOK for all exercise sets.

End-of-Book Materials

Skills Update

Algebra 1

Dear Students,

You are about to begin a very important year in your study of mathematics. Algebra 1 is the gateway to all higher mathematics, and an essential part of your future education. The skills and concepts you learn this year will help you think logically, problem-solve, recognize relationships and patterns, and represent verbal situations as equations, both in mathematics and in other subjects.

Many students think that success in mathematics is just a matter of talent. Yet we know from research studies that success in mathematics results from the effort you make and the learning habits you develop. Make it a routine to check your understanding of each key concept before moving on to the next one. One way to test whether you really understand a concept is to explain it to someone else in your own way, using the precise language of algebra. Also develop the habit of thinking of specific examples and counterexamples to test and justify your reasoning. Remember also that the more complex the key concept or problem you encounter, the more self-checking you will need to do. Finally, make it a habit to think strategically about which methods of representing and solving problems work best for you. To help you develop your problem-solving skills, we have included lessons on problem-solving strategies in every chapter. Think of these strategies as important tools you can use in your daily mathematics work and in your everyday life.

The study of mathematics offers more than the reward of mastering computational and problem-solving skills, as you will learn in the *Enrichment* feature in each chapter. The topics covered in these features will illuminate the mathematics curriculum and give valuable insight into the special beauty of mathematics.

We know that this book can help you appreciate mathematics, develop confidence about your mathematical work, and learn to reason and communicate more effectively, which is essential for everyday life. We wish you all the best this year.

The Authors

R. James Milgram
Professor of Mathematics
Stanford University
Palo Alto, CA

Alfred S. Posamentier
Dean, School of Education and
Professor of Mathematics Education
The City College, The City University of New York
New York, NY

Catherine D. LeTourneau
Department Chairperson of Accelerated Mathematics
Faculty Mathematics Curriculum Advisor
St. Catharine of Siena School
Reading, PA

Edward William Quinn
Director of Curriculum, Instruction and
Staff Development, PK–8
Archdiocese of Philadelphia
Philadelphia, PA

Your Problem-Solving Adventure

Practically every moment of our lives, we are faced with decisions about what to do and how to do it. Sometimes these decisions require a lot of thought; other times, they are instinctive reactions. But in almost all cases, they can be considered to be problem-solving experiences.

Mastery in problem solving depends on critical thinking. To think critically, you must be able to organize your thoughts. The problem-solving steps outlined above will help you do just that.

Consider the following problem.

Problem: Ray has $6.15 in dimes and quarters. If he has five more quarters than dimes, how many of each does he have?

Solution: You could list every single dime and quarter combination, but by turning to a problem-solving strategy called *Guess and Test*, which taps into your knowledge of number sense, you can answer this problem in a more efficient way. Try each guess in a mathematical sentence, and then adjust your next guess on the basis of the results.

Start with 10 dimes and 15 quarters.

$10(\$0.10) + 15(\$0.25) = \$4.75$: This answer is too small, so the number of coins must be too small also. Try a larger number of coins.
$20(\$0.10) + 25(\$0.25) = \$8.25$: Too large! The third estimate must be about halfway between the numbers in your first 2 guesses. Try again.

$14(\$0.10) + 19(\$0.25) = \$6.15$: So Ray has 14 dimes and 19 quarters. Problem solved!

With this example, you can see the power that some problem-solving strategies can have. Our objective in this book is to introduce you to ten problem-solving strategies that will be invaluable not only when you work with mathematics, but also in other situations, both in and out of school. One caution: Just reading these problem-solving strategy sections diligently will not guarantee that these methods will become part of your regular thought processes. You must apply these problem-solving techniques as often as you can so that they *do* become part of your regular thought processes.

Problem-Solving Strategies

Using Your SourceBook

Skills update references direct you to previously learned skills that will be called on as you work through the current lesson.

Clear, concise mathematical **objectives** list the points you will cover in the lesson.

Many lessons use more than one **method** to address the fact that not everyone learns the same way. No matter what method is used, the instruction is developed **step-by-step**.

Key concepts summarize important facts, definitions, and mathematical properties that can be used as helpful reinforcements.

The use of **color** helps emphasize key steps in the instruction.

Update your skills. See page 403, I.

1-5 Integer Exponents

Objective To write repeated multiplication in exponential form and vice versa • To apply the Laws of Exponents for Multiplication and Division • To apply the definitions of zero and negative exponents

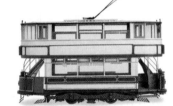

Mr. Toppler's miniature trolley model has 2 levels and 2 tracks per level. There are 2 trolleys per track, and each trolley has 2 cars. Each car has 2 pairs of wheels. How would you represent the total number of wheels the cars have using exponents?

To represent the total number of wheels using exponents, write the number as an expression involving repeated multiplication.

number of levels	number of tracks	number of trolleys	number of cars	number of wheels in one car
↓	↓	↓	↓	↓
2 •	2 •	2 •	2 •	2 • 2

▶ You can write a repeated multiplication expression as an expression using exponents. An exponent tells how many times a number, called the base, is used as a factor. A number in exponent form, or its equivalent standard form, is a power of that number.

$$2^6 = 2 \cdot 2 \cdot 2 \cdot 2 \cdot 2 \cdot 2 = 64 \leftarrow \text{power of 2}$$

base   exponent

2 is a factor 6 times

power of 2

Read 2^6 as:
"two to the sixth power" or "the sixth power of two."

The cars have a total number of 2^6 wheels.

▶ The exponents 2 and 3 have special names.

$$11^2 = 11 \cdot 11 = 121$$

exponential form   standard form

Read 11^2 as:
"11 squared," "11 to the second power," or "the second power of 11."

$$(-3)^3 = -3 \cdot -3 \cdot -3 = -27$$

exponential form   standard form

Read $(-3)^3$ as:
"negative three cubed," "negative three to the third power," or "the third power of negative three."

▶ To mul... with the *same base*, add the exponents.

Simplify using a single exp... $(-5)^2(-5)^3$

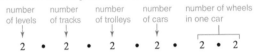

$$(-5)^2(-5)^3 = (-5 \cdot -5)(-5 \cdot -5 \cdot -5) \quad \leftarrow \text{...t the factors.}$$

2 factors   3 factors

$$= (-5 \cdot -5 \cdot -5 \cdot -5 \cdot -5) \quad \leftarrow \text{Group the factors.}$$

(2 + 3) factors

$$= (-5)^{2+3} \quad \leftarrow \text{Write in exponential form.}$$

$$= (-5)^5 \quad \leftarrow \text{Simplify the exponent.}$$

Key Concept

Law of Exponents for Multiplication

For any real number a, $a \neq 0$, and integers m and n, $a^m \cdot a^n = a^{m+n}$.

The **Online** logo points you to the Web-based components of the program. Here you will find helpful resources and engaging activities.

▶ To divide powers with the *same base*, subtract the exponents.

Simplify using a single exponent: $9^5 \div 9^2$

$$\frac{9^5}{9^2} = \frac{\overset{1}{\cancel{9}} \bullet \overset{1}{\cancel{9}} \bullet 9 \bullet 9 \bullet 9}{\underset{1}{\cancel{9}} \bullet \underset{1}{\cancel{9}}} = \frac{9 \bullet 9 \bullet 9}{1} \quad \longleftarrow \text{List the factors and simplify.}$$

$$= \frac{9^3}{1} = 9^3 \quad \longleftarrow \text{Write in exponential form and simplify.}$$

So $\frac{9^5}{9^2} = 9^{5-2} = 9^3$.

> **Key Concept**
>
> **Law of Exponents for Division**
> For any real number a, $a \neq 0$, and integers m and n,
> $$a^m \div a^n = \frac{a^m}{a^n} = a^{m-n}.$$

Think boxes model the reasoning and mental computation involved in computing and solving problems.

▶ Study the pattern below. Note that the exponents of successive expressions decrease by 1 and the value of each exponential expression is one-third of the previous expression. The pattern shows that exponents can also be *zero* or *negative*.

$3^3 = 3 \bullet 3 \bullet 3$

$3^2 = 3 \bullet 3$

$3^1 = 3$

$3^0 = \frac{3}{3} = 1 \longleftarrow$

> A zero exponent means the expression has a value of 1.

$3^{-1} = \frac{1}{3} = \frac{1}{3^1}$

> A negative exponent means the multiplicative inverse or reciprocal of the expression.

$3^{-2} = \frac{1}{3 \bullet 3} = \frac{1}{3^2} = \frac{1}{9}$

Additional **examples** model variations of the lesson objectives.

$3^{-3} = \frac{1}{3 \bullet 3 \bullet 3} = \frac{1}{3^3} = \frac{1}{27}$

> **Key Concept**
>
> **Zero and Negative Exponents**
> • For any nonzero number a, $a^0 = 1$.
> • For any nonzero number a and any integer n, $a^{-n} = \frac{1}{a^n}$.

Try These prepares you for the types of exercises you will encounter in the Practice Book.

Examples

Simplify.

1 $5 \bullet 5^{-4} \bullet 5^3$ *Think* $5 = 5^1$

$5^1 \bullet 5^{-4} \bullet 5^3 = 5^{1+(-4)+3} \longleftarrow$ Add the exponents with the same base.

$= 5^0 \longleftarrow$ Simplify exponents.

$= 1 \longleftarrow$ Apply the definition of zero exponent.

2 $\frac{5^4 \bullet 5^{-2}}{5^3}$

$\frac{5^4 \bullet 5^{-2}}{5^3} = \frac{5^{4+(-2)}}{5^3} = \frac{5^2}{5^3} \longleftarrow$ Add the exponents with the same base.

$= 5^{2-3} = 5^{-1} \longleftarrow$ Subtract the exponents with the same base.

$= \frac{1}{5} \longleftarrow$ Apply the definition of negative exponent.

Discuss and Write questions help underscore the concepts of the lesson as you write about them in your own words.

Try These

Simplify.

1. $6^2 \bullet 6 \bullet 6^{-4}$ **2.** $(-3)^5 \bullet (-3)^0 \bullet (-3)^{-6}$ **3.** $\frac{4 \bullet 4^0}{4^3 \bullet 4^{-1}}$ **4.** $\frac{\left(\frac{2}{3}\right)^3 \bullet \left(\frac{2}{3}\right)^{-7} \bullet \left(\frac{2}{3}\right)}{\left(\frac{2}{3}\right)^{-4} \bullet \left(\frac{2}{3}\right)^0}$

5. Discuss and Write Al correctly calculates that $2^4 = 4^2$, and assumes that $a^b = b^a$ is always true for $a, b \neq 0$. Is Al's assumption correct? Justify your answer.

Follow the reference in the *Go To* logo to find the exercise sets that you will complete in the Practice Book.

Go to ▶ **PRACTICE BOOK Lesson 1-5 for exercise sets.**

Algebra 1 Student SourceBook

Using Your Practice Book

Read the instruction in the **teaching display** before you begin the exercises.

Your SourceBook instruction is summarized and illustrated to help you with the exercises in the Practice Book.

1-5 Integer Exponents

Name _____ Date _____

Simplify: $5^{-2} + 5^0$

$5^{-2} + 5^0$ ← Identify the bases with negative and zero exponents.

$\frac{1}{5^2} + 1$ ← Use the rules for negative and zero exponents.

$\frac{1}{25} + 1 = 1\frac{1}{25}$ ← Simplify.

> **Remember:** Any nonzero exponent raised to the zero power equals 1. If $a \neq 0$, $a^0 = 1$.

> **Remember:** For any nonzero number a and any integer n, $a^{-n} = \frac{1}{a^n}$.

Simplify: $\frac{2^3 \cdot 2^5}{2^6}$

$\frac{2^{3+5}}{2^6}$ ← Add exponents to multiply powers with the same base.

$\frac{2^8}{2^6}$ ← Simplify.

2^{8-6} ← Subtract exponents to divide powers with the same base.

2^2 ← Write in exponential form.

4 ← Write in standard form and simplify.

> **Remember:** For any real number a, $a \neq 0$, and integers m and n:
> $$a^m \cdot a^n = a^{m+n}$$
> $$a^m \div a^n = a^{m-n}$$

Write each expression as repeated multiplication and in exponential form. Then simplify in standard form.

1. 3^4 **2.** 5^0 **3.** $5 \cdot 5 \cdot 5$ **4.** 10^4

$3 \cdot 3 \cdot 3 \cdot 3$
81
_____ _____ _____ _____

5. $-10 \cdot (-10) \cdot (-10)$ **6.** -4^4 **7.** $(-5)^2 \cdot (-5)^4$ **8.** $6^6 \div 6^2$

_____ _____ _____ _____

Find the value of each expression. Express answers in standard form.

9. 2^{-4} **10.** 6^0 **11.** 3^{-2} **12.** 5^{-3}

$2^{-4} = \frac{1}{2^4} = \frac{1}{16}$
_____ _____ _____ _____

13. 6^{-2} **14.** $\left(\frac{2}{3}\right)^3$ **15.** $\left(\frac{1}{4}\right)^4$ **16.** $\left(\frac{-3}{-5}\right)^2$

_____ _____ _____ _____

17. $\left(\frac{2}{7}\right)^{-2}$ **18.** $\left(\frac{3}{2}\right)^{-3}$ **19.** $\left(-\frac{1}{5}\right)^3$ **20.** $\left(-\frac{2}{9}\right)^4$

_____ _____ _____ _____

The **Use With** logo helps you easily locate the pages in the SourceBook that correspond to the current Practice Book lesson.

Use with SOURCEBOOK Lesson 1-5, pages 10–11.

Chapter 1   9

Algebra 1 Student Practice Book

The **Online** logo reminds you that there are more Practice exercises and activities on the Web site.

Your teacher may create customized worksheets and tests using the **Practice/Test Generator**.

For More Practice Go To:

ONLINE → www.progressinmathematics.com   ◉ Practice/Test Generator

Simplify. Express answers in standard form.

21. $6^2 + 4^0 - 2^3$

$36 + 1 - 8$
$37 - 8$
29
_____

22. $5^2 - 7^0 + 3^3$

23. $8^3 - (0.3)^4$

24. $7^2 - (0.4)^3$

25. $2^7 - 8^2 - 1^{10}$

26. $9^3 - 6^2 + 1^{23}$

27. $4 \cdot 4^2 + 3^2$

28. $6 \cdot 6^2 + 2^3$

29. $3^2 \cdot 3^{-4} \cdot 3^6$

30. $5^3 \cdot 5^5 \cdot 5^{-6}$

31. $2^2 \cdot 3^2 \cdot 8$

32. $3^3 \cdot 5^2 \cdot 6^0$

33. $\dfrac{6 \cdot 3^4}{6^2 \cdot 3^2}$

34. $\dfrac{2^4 \cdot 4^2}{2^2 \cdot 4^4}$

35. $\dfrac{3^3}{3^{-2}}$

36. $\dfrac{5^2}{5^{-2}}$

37. $\dfrac{7^2 \cdot 7^5}{7^7 \cdot 7^{-2}}$

38. $\dfrac{6^5 \cdot 6^{-4}}{6^{-2} \cdot 6^3}$

39. $8^3 \cdot \dfrac{1}{8^{-1}}$

40. $4^5 \cdot \dfrac{1}{4^{-2}}$

In every lesson, you will have the opportunity to apply your **problem-solving** skills.

41. $2^{-5} \div \dfrac{1}{4^{-3}}$

42. $5^{-1} \div \dfrac{1}{25^{-2}}$

43. $\dfrac{\left(\frac{2}{5}\right)^3 \cdot \left(\frac{2}{5}\right)^0 \cdot \left(\frac{2}{5}\right)^{-4}}{\left(\frac{2}{5}\right)^{-5} \cdot \left(\frac{2}{5}\right)^2 \cdot \left(\frac{2}{5}\right)^3}$

44. $\dfrac{\left(\frac{3}{4}\right)^0 \cdot \left(\frac{3}{4}\right) \cdot \left(\frac{3}{4}\right)^{-2}}{\left(\frac{3}{4}\right) \cdot \left(\frac{3}{4}\right)^{-5} \cdot \left(\frac{3}{4}\right)^4}$

Problem Solving

45. An ant is 6 feet from a wall. The first day, it walks half the distance to the wall. Each day, it walks half the remaining distance to the wall. How many feet does it walk each of the first five days? If it walked forever in this pattern, would it ever reach the wall?

46. Maria collected 3 cans on day 1, 6 cans on day 2, 12 cans on day 3, and 24 cans on day 4. Let d be the day. Write an expression for the number of cans she collects on day d. Then find the number of cans she collects on the 10th day.

Test Preparation is just one of many end-of-lesson features that encourage you to use higher-order thinking skills. Additional end-of-lesson features include Critical Thinking, Spiral Review, Challenge, Write About It, Mental Math, and others.

TEST PREPARATION

47. Which expression below is equivalent to $4^3 \cdot 4 \cdot 4^5$?

A. $\dfrac{4^{10}}{4^2}$ **B.** $\dfrac{4^2}{4^{10}}$ **C.** $\dfrac{4}{4^{10}}$ **D.** $\dfrac{4^{10}}{4}$

Algebra 1 Student Practice Book

Your Enrichment Journey

In this textbook, we provide some real topics of enrichment. You may wonder what we mean by this, since we are sure you have been told many times that you are being "enriched." Well, we are going to present topics that are not part of the regular curriculum but that are within the scope of your course of study. Some of these topics may be encountered in later years, but others may be missed if we do not include them now. In all cases, we hope you enjoy them. To really do that, however, you must read them with an extra degree of enthusiasm!

Accelerate　　**Expand**　　**Extend**

In each chapter, the Enrichment topic is appropriate to the material you have been taught, and it will enrich you in one of three ways: It will *accelerate* instruction to expose you to concepts that await you in the not-too-distant future; it will *expand* on a presented topic; or it will *extend* a topic already taught and will apply it to a closely related theme. The common thread is that the topics can be briefly, yet reasonably, and completely presented to you in a friendly fashion.

Some topics present mathematics in a historical context, which adds a great deal of interest and insight to the topic, while others may be more of a challenge that is intended to motivate you. In all cases, we hope you will find these Enrichment topics enjoyable so that you see mathematics as a subject that can be fun, as well as extremely practical and useful.

These Enrichment topics go a long way to ensuring that you will be able to see the beauty of mathematics. It is your teacher's goal to have you appreciate mathematics. We feel these Enrichment topics will help you reach that goal.

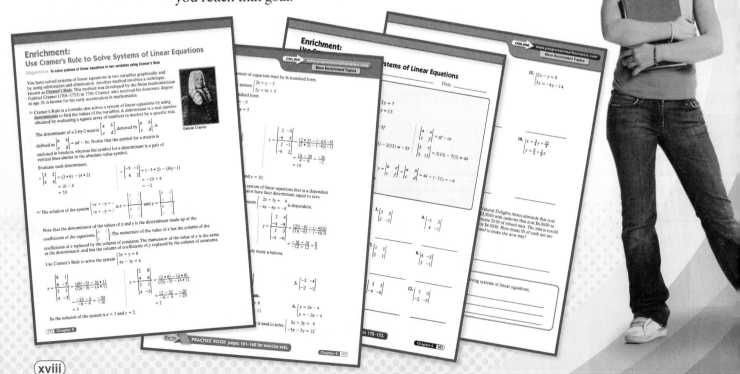

Basic Concepts of Algebra

In This Chapter You Will:

- Identify types of rational numbers and recognize irrational numbers
- Find square roots of perfect squares and approximate square roots of nonperfect squares
- Add, subtract, multiply, and divide signed numbers
- Classify and graph real numbers
- Simplify numerical expressions using the order of operations
- Perform operations on numbers in scientific notation
- Apply set operations of intersection and union
- Use matrices to organize data and perform operations on matrices
- Apply the strategy: *Make a Drawing*
- Look for new vocabulary words **highlighted** in each lesson

Do You Remember?

- A number is a mathematical concept used to describe and assess quantity.
- Addition and subtraction are inverse operations, as are multiplication and division.
- The prime factorization of a number shows the number as a product of prime factors.
- A fraction is in simplest form when its numerator and denominator have no common factor other than 1.

For Practice Exercises:

 PRACTICE BOOK, pp. 1–38

For Chapter Support: ONLINE

 www.progressinmathematics.com

- Skills Update Practice
- Practice Activities
- Audio Glossary
- Vocabulary Activities
- Technology Videos
- Enrichment Activities
- Electronic SourceBook

 VIRTUAL MANIPULATIVES

Critical Thinking

The Groth family pays 10.86 cents per kilowatt-hour for electricity in their home. Their total monthly usage in June was 888 kilowatt-hours. To save energy in July, the Groths want to cut their monthly usage by $\frac{1}{5}$. If they succeed, how much less will the family pay for electricity for the month of July than they would have paid for June?

Update your skills. See page 404 III, IV.

1-1

Rational and Irrational Numbers

Objective To identify types of rational numbers • To find square roots of perfect squares • To approximate square roots of nonperfect squares • To recognize irrational numbers

During a 4-month period, an environmentalist recorded the following changes to a lake's water level: 4 in., $-2\frac{1}{4}$ in., 0.41 in., and $\frac{3}{8}$ in.

The numbers recorded above are *rational numbers*.

► A rational number is the quotient of two integers, a and b, written $\frac{a}{b}$, with $b \neq 0$.

All of the following types of numbers are rational numbers.

- *Integers*, which are whole numbers and their opposites, are represented by the set $\{\ldots, -3, -2, -1, 0, 1, 2, 3, \ldots\}$.

- *Fractions* and *mixed numbers*, such as $\frac{3}{8}$, $-\frac{11}{7}$, and $2\frac{1}{4}$, can be positive or negative.

- *Decimals* can also be positive or negative. They are either *terminating* or *repeating*.

  Terminating decimals, such as $0.41, 3.0, -5.7$, have a finite number of digits.

  Repeating decimals, like the examples that follow, have a sequence of one or more digits that repeat indefinitely.

  $2.333\ldots$, which can be written as $2.\overline{3}$, and $-0.636363\ldots$, or $-0.\overline{63}$ ◄———

> **Remember:**
> Natural, or Counting, Numbers: $\{1, 2, 3, 4, \ldots\}$
> Whole Numbers: $\{0, 1, 2, 3, 4, \ldots\}$
> Every integer a can be written as $\frac{a}{1}$.

> Use an *ellipsis* (three dots) or use an overbar to show that one or more digits repeat in a decimal.

► Multiplying a number by itself, or raising it to the second power, is finding the *square* of that number. Some examples are given below.

square of $\frac{3}{8}$ ⟶ $\left(\frac{3}{8}\right)^2 = \frac{3}{8} \cdot \frac{3}{8} = \frac{9}{64}$ square of -7 ⟶ $(-7)^2 = -7 \cdot -7 = 49$

square of 0.5 ⟶ $(0.5)^2 = 0.5 \cdot 0.5 = 0.25$ opposite of the square of 4 ⟶ $-4^2 = -(4 \cdot 4) = -16$

Perfect squares, or square numbers, are the squares of natural numbers. Some examples of perfect squares are shown in the table below.

Natural Number	1	2	3	4	5	6	7	8	9	10
Square of the Number	1^2	2^2	3^2	4^2	5^2	6^2	7^2	8^2	9^2	10^2
Perfect Square	1	4	9	16	25	36	49	64	81	100

The set of perfect squares is $\{1, 4, 9, 16, 25, 36, 49, 64, 81, 100, \ldots\}$.

► A square root of a number is one of two equal factors of that number. The positive square root of a number is called the principal square root. It is indicated with the symbol $\sqrt{}$, called a radical sign. The expression under a radical sign is called the radicand. The negative square root of a number is indicated by writing a negative sign in front of the radical.

$\sqrt{25} = \sqrt{5 \cdot 5} = 5$ ◄— principal square root $-\sqrt{25} = -5$ ◄— negative square root

Read as "the principal square root of 25."

Read as "the negative square root of 25."

Examples

Find each square root.

1 $-\sqrt{225}$

$$-\sqrt{225} = -\sqrt{3 \cdot 3 \cdot 5 \cdot 5}$$
$$= -\sqrt{(3 \cdot 5)(3 \cdot 5)}$$
$$= -(3 \cdot 5) = -15$$

> **Remember:** The prime factorization of a number shows the number as the product of prime factors.

2 $\sqrt{\dfrac{4}{9}}$

$$\sqrt{\dfrac{4}{9}} = \sqrt{\left(\dfrac{2}{3}\right)^2}$$
$$= \sqrt{\dfrac{2}{3} \cdot \dfrac{2}{3}} = \dfrac{2}{3}$$

> **Think**
> What number squared equals $\dfrac{4}{9}$?

▶ To *approximate* the square root of a nonperfect square, a number that is not the square of a natural number, find two consecutive integers that the square root is between.

Between what two consecutive integers is $\sqrt{19}$?

19 is between 16 and 25. ◀—Find two nearby perfect squares that 19 is between.

$\sqrt{19}$ is between $\sqrt{16}$ and $\sqrt{25}$.

$\sqrt{16} = 4$ and $\sqrt{25} = 5$ ◀—Find each square root.

So $\sqrt{19}$ is between 4 and 5.

> **Think**
> The perfect squares in order are 1, 4, 9, 16, 25, ...
> 19 is between 16 and 25.

▶ Square roots of nonperfect squares are examples of numbers that are not rational. Numbers that are not rational are called *irrational*. The following are irrational numbers.

- positive or negative decimals that are *nonterminating* and *nonrepeating* or have a pattern in their digits but do not repeat exactly.

  4.13216582 . . . , −0.5050050005 . . .

- square roots of nonperfect squares

  $\sqrt{42}, -\sqrt{250}$

- pi, symbolized by the Greek letter π (3.14 and $\dfrac{22}{7}$ are rational *approximate* values.)

> **Key Concept**
> **Irrational Numbers**
> Irrational numbers are numbers that *cannot* be expressed in the form $\dfrac{a}{b}$, where a and b are integers and $b \neq 0$.

Try These

For each number, list all the terms that apply: *whole number*, *integer*, *rational number*, and *irrational number*.

1. -321.11
2. 45
3. $0.010203 . . .$
4. $1.\overline{358}$
5. $\dfrac{22}{7}$
6. $\sqrt{144}$
7. $-\sqrt{36}$
8. $\sqrt{102}$

Find each square root. If the radicand is a nonperfect square, between which two consecutive integers would the square root fall?

9. $\sqrt{400}$
10. $\sqrt{205}$
11. $-\sqrt{\dfrac{49}{81}}$
12. $-\sqrt{77}$

13. A contractor is building a patio in the shape of a square. The patio will cover 945 square feet. Estimate the length of the side of the patio to the nearest integer.

14. **Discuss and Write** Which of these numbers is irrational: $\sqrt{36}, \sqrt{\dfrac{1}{36}}, \sqrt{3.6}$? Explain.

Go to ▶ PRACTICE BOOK **Lesson 1-1 for exercise sets.**

1-2

The Set of Real Numbers

Objective To classify real numbers • To graph real numbers on a number line • To compare and order real numbers • To find the absolute value and additive inverse of a real number • To understand and apply the Closure Property

The set of real numbers consists of all rational numbers and irrational numbers. The Venn diagram at the right shows the relationships among natural numbers, whole numbers, integers, rational numbers, and irrational numbers.

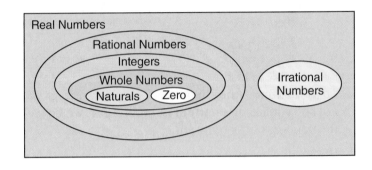

To which sets of numbers does each one of these real numbers belong:
$0.5\overline{4}, -\sqrt{81}, \frac{44}{11},$ and $\sqrt{98}$?

▶ To decide to which sets of numbers a real number belongs, you may need to rename the number in a different form.

- $0.5\overline{4} = 0.5444\ldots$ ◀—a repeating decimal

  rational number

- $\frac{44}{11} = 4$ ◀—a natural number

  natural number; whole number; integer; rational number

- $-\sqrt{81} = -9$ ◀—an integer

  integer; rational number

- $\sqrt{6}$ ◀—a nonperfect square radicand

  irrational number

▶ There is a *one-to-one correspondence* between the set of real numbers and the points on a number line. This is illustrated by the Completeness Property for Points on the Number Line.

___ **Key Concept** ___

Completeness Property for Points on the Number Line

Every real number corresponds to exactly one point on a number line, and every point on the number line corresponds to exactly one real number.

The *origin* of a number line is zero. Points to the right of zero correspond to *positive numbers*. Points to the left of zero correspond to *negative numbers*. Positive and negative numbers are often called *signed numbers*. The number zero is neither positive nor negative.

The point that corresponds to a real number is called the *graph of the number*. The number line below shows the graph of $\sqrt{2}, -3\frac{4}{5}, \pi, 2,$ and -1.7.

▶ A number line can help you compare and order real numbers. The farther to the right a number is on the number line, the greater it is.

Use the number line above to compare and order the following numbers from least to greatest.

$$-1.7 > -3\frac{4}{5} \qquad\qquad \sqrt{2} < \pi \qquad\qquad 2 \text{ is between } \sqrt{2} \text{ and } \pi.$$

In order from least to greatest: $-3\frac{4}{5}, -1.7, \sqrt{2}, 2, \pi$

▶ The absolute value of a real number, n, written $|n|$, is the distance from 0 to n on a number line. Since distance is always positive, the absolute value of a nonzero number is always positive.

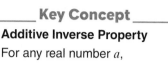

3.5 units   3.5 units

−4 −3 −2 −1 0 1 2 3 4

Opposites

The absolute value of 3.5 is 3.5.   **Write:** $|3.5| = 3.5$

The absolute value of −3.5 is 3.5.   **Write:** $|-3.5| = 3.5$

▶ Two real numbers are *opposites* (or additive inverses) if they are on opposite sides of 0 and they are the same distance from 0 on a number line. The sum of a real number and its additive inverse is 0.

Key Concept

Additive Inverse Property
For any real number a,
$a + (-a) = 0$ and $-a + a = 0$.

The opposite (or additive inverse) of 3.5 is −3.5.   **Write:** $-(3.5) = -3.5$
$3.5 + (-3.5) = 0$

The opposite (or additive inverse) of −3.5 is 3.5.   **Write:** $-(-3.5) = 3.5$
$-3.5 + [-(-3.5)] = 0$

The opposite (or additive inverse) of 0 is 0.   **Write:** $-(0) = 0$
$0 + 0 = 0$

▶ You can find the value of an expression involving absolute values or additive inverses of real numbers.

Find the value of each expression.

$-(-30) \cdot -(-12)$
    $30 \cdot 12$ ◀— Find the opposite
              of each factor.

     360

$|-6.9| - |2.9|$
    $6.9 - 2.9$ ◀— Find the absolute value
               of each number.

     4

▶ When you apply an operation (for example, addition) to any numbers in a set and the result is also a number of that set, the set is said to be *closed* under the operation. This is called the Closure Property.

Finding a counterexample that shows that a set of numbers is *not* closed under a given operation is one way to test closure for that set under the given operation. A single counterexample proves that a statement is false.

• The set of real numbers is closed under addition.
  True, whenever you add two real numbers, the sum is always a real number.

• The set of integers is closed under division.
  False, $3 \div 5 = \frac{3}{5}$ ◀— $\frac{3}{5}$ is *not* an integer.

Try These

Give an example to illustrate the type of number described.

1. a real number that is not rational

2. a rational number that is not an integer

Graph the numbers on a number line. Then write the numbers in order from least to greatest.

3. $-2.2, \sqrt{9}, 0, -\frac{5}{2}, -1.\overline{3}$

Find the value of the expression.

4. $-|9 \cdot 75|$

5. $-|3.9 + 5.2|$

6. Discuss and Write Explain why $\{-1, 1\}$ is closed under division.

Go to PRACTICE BOOK Lesson 1-2 for exercise sets.

1-3

Add and Subtract Real Numbers

Objective To model addition of signed numbers on a number line • To apply rules for adding and subtracting signed numbers

An oil well has been dug to a depth of 1.7 miles. Additional drilling makes the well 1.2 miles deeper. What signed number expresses the final depth of the well?

To find the signed number, add: $-1.7 + (-1.2)$

First estimate by rounding to the nearest integer: $-1.7 + (-1.2) \approx -3$

Think
$-2 + (-1) = -3$

Then add the actual numbers.

► You can add signed numbers by using a number line.

• Start at 0.
• Move *left* for negative numbers. Move *right* for positive numbers.

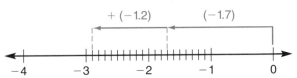

► Add signed numbers the same way you add integers.

Add with Like Signs

Add: $-1.7 + (-1.2)$

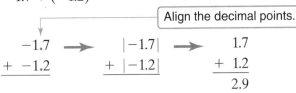

Align the decimal points.

$$-1.7 \rightarrow |-1.7| \rightarrow 1.7$$
$$+\ -1.2 \quad +\ |-1.2| \quad +\ 1.2$$
$$2.9$$

So $-1.7 + (-1.2) = -2.9$ ◄—Both addends are negative. The sum is negative.

_____ **Key Concept** _____

Adding Signed Numbers

To add signed numbers with <u>like signs</u>:
• Add their absolute values.
• Use the sign of the addends for the sum.

To add signed numbers with <u>unlike signs</u>:
• Subtract the lesser absolute value from the greater absolute value.
  $$|\text{greater}| - |\text{lesser}|$$
• Use the sign of the addend with the greater absolute value for the sum.

The final depth of the well is 2.9 miles (-2.9).

Think
-2.9 is close to the estimate of -3. The answer is reasonable.

Add with Unlike Signs

Add: $1\frac{7}{8} + \left(-3\frac{2}{3}\right)$

First estimate by rounding: $1\frac{7}{8} + \left(-3\frac{2}{3}\right) \approx -2$

Think
$2 + (-4) = -2$

Then add the actual numbers.

$1\frac{7}{8} + \left(-3\frac{2}{3}\right) \longrightarrow \left|-3\frac{2}{3}\right| - \left|1\frac{7}{8}\right| = 3\frac{2}{3} - 1\frac{7}{8}$ ◄— $\left|-3\frac{2}{3}\right| > \left|1\frac{7}{8}\right|$ Subtract $1\frac{7}{8}$ from $3\frac{2}{3}$.

$= 3\frac{16}{24} - 1\frac{21}{24}$ ◄—Rename the fractions using the LCD, 24.

$= 2\frac{40}{24} - 1\frac{21}{24} = 1\frac{19}{24}$ ◄—Regroup $3\frac{16}{24}$ as $2\frac{40}{24}$.

So $1\frac{7}{8} + \left(-3\frac{2}{3}\right) = -1\frac{19}{24}$ ◄—The addend with the greater absolute value is negative. The sum is negative.

Think
$-1\frac{19}{24}$ is close to the estimate of -2. The answer is reasonable.

▶Subtract signed numbers the same way you subtract integers. Use the Subtraction Principle.

____Key Concept____

Subtraction Principle

To subtract any signed number, add its opposite.

Subtract with Like Signs

Subtract: $-20.2 - (-7.33)$

First estimate by rounding: $-20.2 - (-7.33) \approx 13$

Then subtract the actual numbers.

.Think.........
$-20 - (-7) = -13$

| Align the decimal points. | Add the opposite of the subtrahend. | Apply the rule for adding with unlike signs. |

$$\begin{array}{r} -20.2 \\ -\quad -7.33 \\ \hline \end{array} \rightarrow \begin{array}{r} -20.2 \\ +\quad 7.33 \\ \hline \end{array} \rightarrow \begin{array}{r} |-20.2| \\ -\quad |7.33| \\ \hline \end{array} \rightarrow \begin{array}{r} 20.20 \\ -\quad 7.33 \\ \hline 12.87 \end{array}$$

$-20.2 - (-7.33) = -12.87$ ◀—The addend with the greater absolute value is negative. The sum is negative.

So $-20.2 - (-7.33) = -12.87$.

.Think..................
-12.87 is close to the estimate of -13. The answer is reasonable.

Subtract with Unlike Signs

Find the difference: $2\frac{5}{6} - \left(-4\frac{1}{3}\right)$

First estimate by rounding: $2\frac{5}{6} - \left(-4\frac{1}{3}\right) \approx 7$

.Think.........
$3 - (-4) = 7$

Then subtract the actual numbers.

$2\frac{5}{6} - \left(-4\frac{1}{3}\right) = 2\frac{5}{6} + 4\frac{1}{3}$ ◀—Add the opposite of the subtrahend.

$\left|2\frac{5}{6}\right| + \left|-4\frac{1}{3}\right| = 2\frac{5}{6} + 4\frac{2}{6} =$ ◀—Add the numbers in absolute value.
Rename the fractions using the LCD, 6.

$= 6\frac{5+2}{6} = 6\frac{7}{6}$ ◀—Add the integers. Then add the fractions.

$= 6 + 1\frac{1}{6} = 7\frac{1}{6}$ ◀—Rename the sum.

$2\frac{5}{6} + 4\frac{1}{3} = 7\frac{1}{6}$ ◀—Both addends are positive. The sum is positive.

So $2\frac{5}{6} - \left(-4\frac{1}{3}\right) = 7\frac{1}{6}$.

.Think..................
$7\frac{1}{6}$ is close to the estimate of 7. The answer is reasonable.

Try These

Add or subtract. Watch for the signs.

1. $8.4 + (-12.63)$ **2.** $-4.93 + \frac{1}{4}$ **3.** $-6.34 - (-10.4)$ **4.** $7.54 - 8.4 - 4$

5. $-2\frac{1}{9} + \left(-7\frac{1}{3}\right)$ **6.** $\frac{1}{2} - \left(-5\frac{1}{2}\right)$ **7.** $-2\frac{3}{5} - \left(-1\frac{1}{10}\right) - \frac{2}{5}$ **8.** $-6.2 - (-1.1) + 6.41$

9. Discuss and Write How would you model $2\frac{3}{4} + 1\frac{1}{2} - \left(-2\frac{1}{4}\right)$ on a number line?

Go to   **PRACTICE BOOK Lesson 1-3 for exercise sets.**

Update your skills. See pages 405, VI; 406, IX.

1-4

Multiply and Divide Real Numbers

Objective To model multiplication of signed numbers on a number line
• To multiply and divide signed numbers

A diver descended into the ocean at a rate of 2.1 meters per minute over a 3-minute period. What signed number represents the diver's final depth at the end of the 3 minutes?

To find the diver's final depth, multiply: $3(-2.1)$

First estimate by rounding: $3(-2.1) \approx -6$
Then multiply the actual numbers.

> **Think**
> $3(-2) = -6$

Multiplying Decimals

To multiply signed decimals, multiply as you would with whole numbers, and then use the total number of decimal places in the factors for the number of decimal places in the product.

Multiply: $3(-2.1)$

> _____ **Key Concept** _____
>
> **Multiplying Two Signed Numbers**
> • If the factors have *like signs*, the product is *positive*.
> • If the factors have *unlike signs*, the product is *negative*.

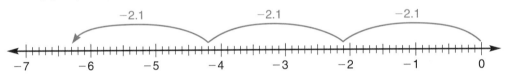

$3(-2.1) = -6.3$ ← Factors have *unlike signs*, so their product is negative.

1 decimal place   1 decimal place

So $3(-2.1) = -6.3$.

> **Think**
> -6.3 is close to the estimate of -6.
> The answer is reasonable.

Multiplying Fractions or Mixed Numbers

Find the product: $\left(-1\frac{2}{3}\right)\left(-2\frac{1}{4}\right)$

First estimate by rounding: $\left(-1\frac{2}{3}\right)\left(-2\frac{1}{4}\right) \approx 4$

> **Think**
> $(-2)(-2) = 4$

Then multiply the actual numbers.

$$\left|-1\frac{2}{3}\right| \bullet \left|-2\frac{1}{4}\right| = \frac{5}{3} \bullet \frac{9}{4}$$ ← Multiply the absolute values of the numbers. Rename each factor as a fraction greater than 1.

$$= \frac{5 \bullet \overset{3}{\cancel{9}}}{\underset{1}{\cancel{3}} \bullet 4} = \frac{15}{4}$$ ← Divide by the GCF to simplify. Then multiply the numerators and then the denominators.

$$= 3\frac{3}{4}$$ ← Rename the product as a mixed number.

So $\left(-1\frac{2}{3}\right)\left(-2\frac{1}{4}\right) = 3\frac{3}{4}$ ← Factors have *like signs*. The product is positive.

> **Think**
> $3\frac{3}{4}$ is close to the estimate of 4.
> The answer is reasonable.

Dividing Decimals

To divide signed decimals, divide as with whole numbers. Multiply both the dividend and the divisor by the power of ten that will make the divisor a whole number.

Find each quotient.

$\dfrac{-0.0141}{-4.7}$

> **Remember:** A fraction bar is a division symbol.

$|-0.0141| \div |-4.7| = 0.0414 \div 4.7$ ◀—Divide the absolute values of the numbers.

$$4.7\overline{)0.0.141} \longrightarrow 47\overline{)0.141}^{\,0.003}$$ ◀—Write 2 zeros in the quotient as placeholders.

Multiply by 10. Move each decimal point 1 place to the right.

So $-0.0141 \div (-4.7) = 0.003$ ◀—The dividend and divisor have *like signs*, so the quotient is positive.

_____ **Key Concept** _____

Dividing Signed Numbers
- If the dividend and divisor have *like signs*, the quotient is *positive*.
- If the dividend and divisor have *unlike signs*, the quotient is *negative*.

$2.2 \div (-0.055)$

$|2.2| \div |-0.055| = 2.2 \div 0.055$ ◀—Divide the absolute values of the numbers.

$$0.055\overline{)2.200.} \longrightarrow 55\overline{)2200.}^{\,40.}$$ ◀

Multiply by 1000. Move each decimal point 3 places to the right. Write 2 zeros in the dividend as placeholders.

So $2.2 \div (-0.055) = -40$ ◀—The dividend and divisor have *unlike signs*, so the quotient is negative.

Dividing Fractions or Mixed Numbers

When dividing with fractions, whole numbers, and mixed numbers, rename the whole numbers and mixed numbers as fractions.

Divide: $-3\frac{3}{5} \div \left(-\frac{3}{20}\right)$

$\left|-3\frac{3}{5}\right| \div \left|-\frac{3}{20}\right| = \dfrac{18}{5} \div \dfrac{3}{20}$ ◀—Rename as fractions greater than 1. Divide the absolute values.

$= \dfrac{\overset{6}{\cancel{18}}}{\underset{1}{\cancel{5}}} \cdot \dfrac{\overset{4}{\cancel{20}}}{\underset{1}{\cancel{3}}}$ ◀—Multiply by the reciprocal of $\frac{3}{20}$. Simplify using the GCF.

$= \dfrac{24}{1} = 24$ ◀—Rename the product as a whole number.

So $-3\frac{3}{5} \div \left(-\frac{3}{20}\right) = 24$ ◀—The dividend and divisor have *like signs*, so the quotient is positive.

_____ **Key Concept** _____

Dividing Fractions
- To divide real numbers as fractions, multiply by the reciprocal of the divisor.

$$\dfrac{a}{b} \div \dfrac{c}{d} = \dfrac{a}{b} \cdot \dfrac{d}{c}, \quad b, c, d \neq 0$$

reciprocals

$\cdot \dfrac{c}{d}\left(\dfrac{d}{c}\right) = 1$

Try These

Multiply or divide. Watch for the signs.

1. $0.9(-4.82)$
2. $\left(-\frac{1}{9}\right)\left(-\frac{3}{7}\right)$
3. $-4.8 \div (-0.5)$
4. $-0.45 \div \frac{3}{5}$
5. $1\frac{1}{2} \cdot 2\frac{3}{4}$

6. $0 \cdot (-171)$
7. $0 \div \left(-9\frac{1}{3}\right)$
8. $-12\frac{1}{2} \div \left(4\frac{1}{2}\right)$
9. $-8\frac{1}{2} \div 4$
10. $-\frac{3}{4} \div 0.5$

11. $-\frac{4}{5}\left(-1\frac{1}{4} \cdot \frac{5}{8}\right)$
12. $(3.564 \div 3) \div 0.5$
13. $-5\left(-\frac{3}{5} \div \frac{13}{20}\right)$

14. **Discuss and Write** Explain what steps you would take to multiply $4 \cdot -1\frac{1}{2}$.

Go to   PRACTICE BOOK **Lesson 1-4 for exercise sets.**

1-5

Integer Exponents

Objective To write repeated multiplication in exponential form and vice versa • To apply the Laws of Exponents for Multiplication and Division • To apply the definitions of zero and negative exponents

Mr. Toppler's miniature trolley model has 2 levels and 2 tracks per level. There are 2 trolleys per track, and each trolley has 2 cars. Each car has 2 pairs of wheels. How would you represent the total number of wheels the cars have using exponents?

To represent the total number of wheels using exponents, write the number as an expression involving repeated multiplication.

number of levels	number of tracks	number of trolleys	number of cars	number of wheels in one car

$$2 \cdot 2 \cdot 2 \cdot 2 \cdot 2 \cdot 2$$

▶ You can write a repeated multiplication expression as an expression using exponents. An **exponent** tells how many times a number, called the **base**, is used as a factor. A number in exponent form, or its equivalent standard form, is a **power** of that number.

base exponent

$$2^6 = 2 \cdot 2 \cdot 2 \cdot 2 \cdot 2 \cdot 2 = 64 \quad \leftarrow \text{power of 2}$$

2 is a factor 6 times

power of 2

Read 2^6 as:
"two to the sixth power" or "the sixth power of two."

The cars have a total number of 2^6 wheels.

▶ The exponents 2 and 3 have special names.

$$11^2 = 11 \cdot 11 = 121$$

exponential form   standard form

Read 11^2 as:
"11 squared,"
"11 to the second power," or "the second power of 11."

$$(-3)^3 = -3 \cdot -3 \cdot -3 = -27$$

exponential form   standard form

Read $(-3)^3$ as:
"negative three cubed,"
"negative three to the third power," or "the third power of negative three."

▶ To multiply powers with the *same base*, add the exponents.

Simplify using a single exponent: $(-5)^2(-5)^3$

$$(-5)^2(-5)^3 = (-5 \cdot -5)(-5 \cdot -5 \cdot -5) \quad \leftarrow \text{List the factors.}$$

2 factors   3 factors

$$= (-5 \cdot -5 \cdot -5 \cdot -5 \cdot -5) \quad \leftarrow \text{Group the factors.}$$

$(2 + 3)$ factors

$$= (-5)^{2+3} \quad \leftarrow \text{Write in exponential form.}$$

$$= (-5)^5 \quad \leftarrow \text{Simplify the exponent.}$$

_____ **Key Concept** _____

Law of Exponents for Multiplication

For any real number a, $a \neq 0$, and integers m and n, $a^m \cdot a^n = a^{m+n}$.

▶ To divide powers with the *same base*, subtract the exponents.

Simplify using a single exponent: $9^5 \div 9^2$

$$\frac{9^5}{9^2} = \frac{\overset{1}{\cancel{9}} \cdot \overset{1}{\cancel{9}} \cdot 9 \cdot 9 \cdot 9}{\underset{1}{\cancel{9}} \cdot \underset{1}{\cancel{9}}} = \frac{9 \cdot 9 \cdot 9}{1} \quad \longleftarrow \text{List the factors and simplify.}$$

$$= \frac{9^3}{1} = 9^3 \quad \longleftarrow \text{Write in exponential form and simplify.}$$

So $\dfrac{9^5}{9^2} = 9^{5-2} = 9^3$.

> **Key Concept**
>
> **Law of Exponents for Division**
> For any real number a, $a \neq 0$, and integers m and n,
> $$a^m \div a^n = \frac{a^m}{a^n} = a^{m-n}.$$

▶ Study the pattern below. Note that the exponents of successive expressions decrease by 1 and the value of each exponential expression is one-third of the previous expression. The pattern shows that exponents can also be *zero* or *negative*.

$$3^3 = 3 \cdot 3 \cdot 3$$

$$3^2 = 3 \cdot 3$$

$$3^1 = 3$$

$$3^0 = \frac{3}{3} = 1$$

$$3^{-1} = \frac{1}{3} = \frac{1}{3^1}$$

$$3^{-2} = \frac{1}{3 \cdot 3} = \frac{1}{3^2} = \frac{1}{9}$$

$$3^{-3} = \frac{1}{3 \cdot 3 \cdot 3} = \frac{1}{3^3} = \frac{1}{27}$$

> A zero exponent means the expression has a value of 1.

> A negative exponent means the multiplicative inverse or reciprocal of the expression.

> **Key Concept**
>
> **Zero and Negative Exponents**
> • For any nonzero number a, $a^0 = 1$.
> • For any nonzero number a and any integer n, $a^{-n} = \dfrac{1}{a^n}$.

Examples

Simplify.

1 $5 \cdot 5^{-4} \cdot 5^3$ **Think** $5 = 5^1$

$5^1 \cdot 5^{-4} \cdot 5^3 = 5^{1+(-4)+3} \quad \longleftarrow$ Add the exponents with the same base.

$= 5^0 \quad \longleftarrow$ Simplify exponents.

$= 1 \quad \longleftarrow$ Apply the definition of zero exponent.

2 $\dfrac{5^4 \cdot 5^{-2}}{5^3}$

$\dfrac{5^4 \cdot 5^{-2}}{5^3} = \dfrac{5^{4+(-2)}}{5^3} = \dfrac{5^2}{5^3} \quad \longleftarrow$ Add the exponents with the same base.

$= 5^{2-3} = 5^{-1} \quad \longleftarrow$ Subtract the exponents with the same base.

$= \dfrac{1}{5} \quad \longleftarrow$ Apply the definition of negative exponent.

Try These

Simplify.

1. $6^2 \cdot 6 \cdot 6^{-4}$

2. $(-3)^5 \cdot (-3)^0 \cdot (-3)^{-6}$

3. $\dfrac{4 \cdot 4^0}{4^3 \cdot 4^{-1}}$

4. $\dfrac{\left(\frac{2}{3}\right)^3 \cdot \left(\frac{2}{3}\right)^{-7} \cdot \left(\frac{2}{3}\right)}{\left(\frac{2}{3}\right)^{-4} \cdot \left(\frac{2}{3}\right)^0}$

5. Discuss and Write Al correctly calculates that $2^4 = 4^2$, and assumes that $a^b = b^a$ is always true for $a, b \neq 0$. Is Al's assumption correct? Justify your answer.

Go to PRACTICE BOOK **Lesson 1-5 for exercise sets.**

The Order of Operations

Objective To simplify numerical expressions using the order of operations

At the far end of a park is a meditation garden. The width of the garden is 13.4 meters, and the length is 2.5 meters more than the width. If a new semicircular entrance to the garden will be added, as shown in the diagram at the right, what will be the total area of the new garden to the nearest hundredth?

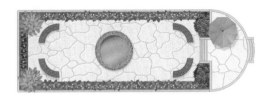

To find the total area, write an expression to represent it, and then simplify by using the order of operations.

___Key Concept___

Order of Operations

1. Grouping Symbols—parentheses ( ), brackets [ ], braces { }, fraction bar —
2. Exponents
3. Multiply or divide from left to right.
4. Add or subtract from left to right.

area of meditation garden → area of new entrance →

.Think..............
Area of semicircle:
$A = \frac{1}{2}\pi r^2$

$13.4(13.4 + 2.5) \quad + \quad \frac{1}{2}(3.14)(6.7^2)$

$13.4(13.4 + 2.5) \quad + \quad \frac{1}{2}(3.14)(6.7^2)$ ←Compute within parentheses first, then compute exponents.

$13.4(15.9) \quad + \quad \frac{1}{2}(3.14)(44.89)$ ←Multiply next.

$213.06 \quad + \quad 70.4773$ ←Add last.

283.5373

.Think................
283.5373 ≈ 283.54

Check:

13.4 × (13.4 + 2.5) + (1 ÷ 2)
× 3.14 × 6.7 x² enter

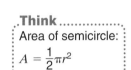

1.1 RAD AUTO REAL

$13.4 \cdot (13.4+2.5) + \dfrac{1}{2} \cdot 3.14 \cdot (6.7)^2 \qquad 283.537$

So the total area of the new garden is 283.54 square meters.

▶ When an expression has several grouping symbols, simplify the expression within the *innermost grouping symbols* first.

Simplify: $-2[-6 - 5(1.2 + 2^2 \bullet 3.5) - 8]$

$-2[-6 - 5(1.2 + 2^2 \bullet 3.5) - 8] = -2[-6 - 5(1.2 + 4 \bullet 3.5) - 8]$ ←Compute exponent within parentheses.

innermost grouping symbols

$= -2[-6 - 5(1.2 + 14) - 8]$ ←Next, multiply within parentheses.

$= -2[-6 - 5(15.2) - 8]$ ←Then add within parentheses.

$= -2[-6 - 76 - 8]$ ←Next, multiply within brackets.

$= -2[-90]$ ←Then subtract within brackets.

$= 180$ ←Finally, multiply.

▶ A fraction bar is also a grouping symbol. Do any computation above or below the fraction bar before simplifying the fraction.

Simplify: $\dfrac{(11-2)^2}{3(2+1.5)-1.5} - 3$

$\dfrac{(11-2)^2}{3(2+1.5)-1.5} - 3 = \dfrac{(9)^2}{3(3.5)-1.5} - 3$ ◀ Compute within parentheses first.

$= \dfrac{81}{10.5-1.5} - 3$ ◀ Next, compute the exponent above, and multiply below the fraction bar.

$= \dfrac{81}{9} - 3 = 9 - 3$ ◀ Subtract below the fraction bar. Divide next.

$= 6$ ◀ Subtract last.

Examples

1 Simplify: $\frac{3}{4}[2(5\frac{1}{2} - 3.5)]^3$

.Think....
$3.5 = 3\frac{1}{2}$

$\frac{3}{4}[2(5\frac{1}{2} - 3.5)]^3 = \frac{3}{4}[2(2)]^3$

$= \frac{3}{4}[4]^3$

$= \frac{3}{\cancel{4}_{1}}[\overset{16}{\cancel{64}}]$

$= \frac{48}{1} = 48$

2 Simplify: $\dfrac{[(3.2+4.8)^2 + (5+1)^2] + 30}{[(7-4)^4 - (8.5-6.5)^4]}$

$\dfrac{[(3.2+4.8)^2 + (5+1)^2] + 30}{[(7-4)^4 - (8.5-6.5)^4]} = \dfrac{[(8)^2 + (6)^2] + 30}{[(3)^4 - (2)^4]}$

$= \dfrac{[64+36] + 30}{[81-16]}$

$= \dfrac{100+30}{65}$

$= \dfrac{130}{65} = 2$

3 Simplify: $\dfrac{4|7-11|}{|6+2| \bullet |6-9|}$

$\dfrac{4|7-11|}{|6+2| \bullet |6-9|} = \dfrac{4|-4|}{|8| \bullet |-3|}$

$= \dfrac{4 \bullet 4}{8 \bullet 3}$ ◀ Calculate within the absolute-value symbols. Next, evaluate the absolute values.

$= \dfrac{\overset{2}{\cancel{16}}}{\underset{3}{\cancel{24}}} = \dfrac{2}{3}$ ◀ Multiply, then use common factors to simplify the fraction.

Try These

Simplify.

1. $-(-6) + 3(2+15) \div \sqrt{9}$

2. $5^2[-2 + (-5)] \div 5 + 2$

3. $[(-15.2 + 5.2)^4 + 0.47] - 10^3$

4. $\dfrac{6 + 4 \bullet (-2^3)}{2 \bullet 25 + 2} + 2\frac{1}{2}$

5. $\dfrac{[(11-2)^2 + 3^3 + 12]}{0.5 + 1.5} - 2^4$

6. $\dfrac{|-4 + 4(6-8)^2| \bullet |(3 - 2 \bullet 8)|}{2^2 \bullet |5 - 2^3|}$

7. **Discuss and Write** Karen simplified the expression $12^2 \div 2^4 + 9 \div (2+1) + 12$, and her result was 18. Was her answer correct? Explain your answer.

Go to ▸ **PRACTICE BOOK Lesson 1-6 for exercise sets.**

Scientific Notation

Objective To write numbers in standard notation as numbers in scientific notation, and vice versa • To perform operations in scientific notation

A mature male elephant can weigh as much as 24,750 pounds, which is 396,000 ounces. The weight of a feather is about 0.0125 ounces. You can write these numbers in scientific notation.

▶ Very large or very small numbers can be rewritten in scientific notation so that they are in the form of $a \times 10^n$, where $a \geq 1$ and $a < 10$, and n is an integer.

• To write a *number greater than 1* in scientific notation, move the decimal point to the left.

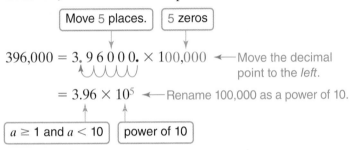

In scientific notation, $396,000 = 3.96 \times 10^5$.

• To write a *decimal between 0 and 1* in scientific notation, move the decimal point to the right.

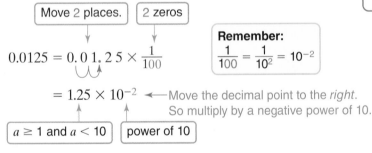

Remember:
$$\frac{1}{100} = \frac{1}{10^2} = 10^{-2}$$

In scientific notation, $0.0125 = 1.25 \times 10^{-2}$.

Key Concept

Writing a Number in Scientific Notation

To write a number in scientific notation, express it as a product of two factors.

1. Express one factor as a number greater than or equal to 1 but less than 10. Move the decimal point to the *left* or *right*.

2. Express the other factor as a power of 10. Count the number of places the decimal point was moved to the left or right, and use this number as the *exponent* of the power of 10.

▶ To write a number expressed in scientific notation as a number in standard form, multiply the factors.

Scientific Notation

$2.98 \times 10^5 = 2.98 \times 100,000 = 2.98000. =$

Standard Form

$298,000$ ←To multiply by 10^5, move the decimal point 5 places to the *right*.

$7.08 \times 10^{-3} = 7.08 \times \frac{1}{1000} = 0.007.08 =$

0.00708 ←To multiply by 10^{-3}, move the decimal point 3 places to the *left*.

▶ To add or subtract numbers in scientific notation, add the decimal factors, then multiply the sum by the common power of 10. Write the result in scientific notation.

Simplify: $9.7 \times 10^5 + 7.3 \times 10^5 - 2 \times 10^5$

$9.7 \times 10^5 + 7.3 \times 10^5 - 2 \times 10^5$ ◄—All the terms have the same power of 10.

$(9.7 + 7.3 - 2) \times 10^5$ ◄—Group the decimal factors; keep the common power of 10.

15×10^5 ◄—Simplify the decimal factors.

$(1.5 \times 10^1) \times 10^5$ ◄—Write 15 in scientific notation.

1.5×10^6 ◄—Multiply the powers of 10 by adding their exponents.

So $9.7 \times 10^5 + 7.3 \times 10^5 - 2 \times 10^5 = 1.5 \times 10^6$.

▶ To multiply or divide numbers in scientific notation, multiply or divide the decimal factors, then multiply or divide the powers of 10. Simplify and write the product in scientific notation.

• Multiply: $(6.1 \times 10^7)(2.3 \times 10^4)$

$(6.1 \times 2.3)(10^7 \times 10^4)$ ◄—Group like factors.

14.03×10^{11} ◄—Multiply the decimal factors. Then multiply the powers of 10 by adding their exponents.

$(1.403 \times 10^1) \times 10^{11}$ ◄—Write 14.03 in scientific notation.

1.403×10^{12} ◄—Multiply the powers of 10 by adding their exponents.

So $(6.1 \times 10^7)(2.3 \times 10^4) = 1.403 \times 10^{12}$.

• Divide: $\dfrac{4.731 \times 10^8}{5.7 \times 10^3}$

$\dfrac{4.731}{5.7} \times \dfrac{10^8}{10^3}$ ◄—Group like factors.

0.83×10^5 ◄—Divide the decimal factors. Then divide the powers of 10 by subtracting their exponents.

$(8.3 \times 10^{-1}) \times 10^5$ ◄—Write 0.83 in scientific notation.

8.3×10^4 ◄—Multiply the powers of 10 by adding their exponents.

So $(4.731 \times 10^8) \div (5.7 \times 10^3) = 8.3 \times 10^4$.

Try These

Write in scientific notation.

1. 751,000,000,000

2. 0.0000000589

Write in standard form.

3. 1.34×10^{-9}

4. 7.123×10^8

Perform the indicated operations. Express answers in scientific notation.

5. $6.9 \times 10^{-6} + 5 \times 10^{-6}$

6. $9.2 \times 10^8 + 6.4 \times 10^8 - 2 \times 10^8$

7. $(3.65 \times 10^{12})(4.7 \times 10^5)$

8. $(6.174 \times 10^{11}) \div (6.3 \times 10^6)$

9. $(9 \times 10^7)(4.1 \times 10^4) \div (3 \times 10^5)$

10. $6 \times 10^{13} + (4 \times 10^8)(1.1 \times 10^5)$

11. **Discuss and Write** Explain how to add 4.77×10^9 and 7.35×10^8 even though the given powers of 10 are not the same.

Go to PRACTICE BOOK Lesson 1-7 for exercise sets.

Algebraic Expressions

Objective To write algebraic expressions as word phrases, and vice versa • To identify the coefficients of a term of an algebraic expression • To evaluate algebraic expressions by using the order of operations

Alana works at a beach arcade during summer vacation. Her salary is $7.25 an hour plus a one-time summer bonus of $75. What algebraic expression represents how much Alana will earn over the summer?

▶ To write the algebraic, or variable, expression that corresponds to the amount of money Alana will earn over the summer:

* Represent the unknown quantity with a variable.

* Write an expression in terms of the same variable for any other unknown quantities.

Alana's hourly salary	times	number of worked hours	plus	one-time summer bonus
7.25	•	h	+	75

> A *variable* is a symbol, usually a letter, representing one or more numbers.
>
> An *algebraic*, or a *variable*, *expression* is a mathematical expression consisting of numbers, variables, and operations.

So $7.25h + 75$ is the algebraic expression that represents how much Alana will earn over the summer.

▶ A term of an algebraic expression is a number, a variable, or a product or quotient of numbers and variables. The numerical part of a term that contains variables is the numerical coefficient of the term. The variable, or variables, of a term is called the literal coefficient of the term. A term that does not have variables is called a constant.

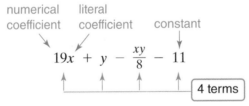

$$19x + y - \frac{xy}{8} - 11$$

4 terms

When the word *coefficient* is used alone, it usually means the numerical coefficient. The coefficient of x is 19 in $19x$. The coefficient of y is 1, since $y = 1y$. The coefficient of xy is $\frac{1}{8}$ in $\frac{xy}{8}$, since $\frac{xy}{8} = \frac{1}{8}xy$.

▶ To write an algebraic expression as a *word phrase*, you must be able to determine the mathematical operation(s) associated with the word phrase. The table below shows common word phrases that you can associate with each of the four basic operations.

Addition $a + b$	Subtraction $a - b$	Multiplication $ab, a \times b, a \bullet b,$ $a(b)$ or $(a)(b)$	Division $a \div b$ or $\frac{a}{b}$
a plus b the sum of a and b a and b are added a is increased by b b is added to a b more than a the number that exceeds a by b	a minus b the difference between a and b b subtracted from a a decreased by b a diminished by b b less than a a reduced by b	a times b the product of a and b b multiplied by a	a divided by b the quotient of a and b

Write each as an algebraic expression.

a. the number of minutes, m, increased by 10
    $m + 10$

b. 28 subtracted from y
    $y - 28$

c. twice the number of apples, a
    $2a$

d. the number of girls, g, divided by 5
    $g \div 5$ or $\frac{g}{5}$

▶ Algebraic expressions may contain more than one operation and may involve the use of grouping symbols. The table below shows some examples of these expressions.

Let n = the number.

Word Phrase	Algebraic Expression
• 38 *diminished* by the absolute value of the *product* of 7 and a number	$38 - |7n|$
• 11 *more than* *one fourth* of a number	$11 + \frac{n}{4}$ or $11 + \frac{1}{4}n$
• 10 *times* the *difference* of 15 and a number • 10 times the *quantity* 15 minus n	$10(15 - n)$
• double the *sum* of 8 and the *square* of a number • 2 times the quantity 8 plus n squared	$2(8 + n^2)$
• the *sum* of the opposite of a number and 12, *divided* by 9	$\frac{-n + 12}{9}$ or $(-n + 12) \div 9$
• the *difference* when 3 cubed is *subtracted* from a number that is tripled	$3n - 3^3$
• 26 *less than* the *product* of a number and its opposite	$n(-n) - 26$

▶ Not all word phrases translate *directly* into algebraic expressions. Sometimes you need to interpret a situation and apply a familiar fact.

Write as an algebraic expression.

a. the total value in cents of d dimes and n nickels

    The value of one dime is 10 cents, so the value of d dimes is $10d$ cents.
    The value of one nickel is 5 cents, so the value n nickels is $5n$ cents.
    The word *total* indicates addition, so the total value in cents is $10d + 5n$.

b. the number of days in w weeks

    The number of days in 1 week is 7, so the number of days in w weeks is $7w$.

▶ To evaluate an algebraic expression, substitute numbers for the variables in the expression, and then compute using the order of operations. This is called the Substitution Principle.

—————— **Key Concept** ——————

The Substitution Principle

For any numbers a and b, if $a = b$, then a may be replaced with b.

Continue Lesson ➡

Evaluate $4d - 2500$, when $d = 5000$.

$4d - 2500 = 4 \bullet 5000 - 2500$ ←Substitute 5000 for d.

$= 20{,}000 - 2500$ ←Simplify using the order of operations.

$= 17{,}500$

▶ The value of an algebraic expression varies, or changes, depending upon the value of the variable.

Jane orders some books from an online store. She pays $12 per book and $8.95 for shipping and handling. Write an algebraic expression for the total cost of Jane's book order, and then evaluate the expression for orders of 1–4 books.

Let b = the number of books that Jane orders.

total cost of books in dollars	*plus*	shipping and handling in dollars
↓	↓	↓
$12b$	$+$	8.95 ← total cost of Jane's book order in dollars

To find the total cost, in dollars, for each book order, evaluate the expression $12b + 8.95$ using the values 1–4 for b. Make a table to organize the results.

b	$12b + 8.95$	Total Cost (in dollars)
1	$12 \bullet 1 + 8.95$	20.95
2	$12 \bullet 2 + 8.95$	32.95
3	$12 \bullet 3 + 8.95$	44.95
4	$12 \bullet 4 + 8.95$	56.95

▶ You can use a handheld to evaluate an algebraic expression.

Evaluate $5.7c - 3.58$, when $c = 1.2$ using a handheld.

1.2 [ctrl] [sto▶ var] [C] [≈ enter] ←Enter the value of c.

5.7 [×] [C] [−] 3.58 [≈ enter] ←Enter and evaluate the expression.

So $5.7c - 3.58 = 3.26$, when $c = 1.2$.

▶ You can also use the order of operations to evaluate algebraic expressions and then use a handheld to check.

Evaluate: $5a^2 - 18 \div b$, when $a = 3$ and $b = 9$.
Use a handheld to check.

$5a^2 - 18 \div b = 5(3)^2 - 18 \div 9$ ←Replace a with 3 and b with 9.

$= 5(9) - 18 \div 9 = 45 - 2$ ←Simplify using the order of operations.

$= 43$

Check:

3 [ctrl] [sto▶ var] [A] [≈ enter] ←Enter the value of a.

9 [ctrl] [sto▶ var] [B] [≈ enter] ←Enter the value of b.

5 [×] [A] [x²] [−] 18 [÷] [B] [≈ enter]

So $5a^2 - 18 \div b = 43$, when $a = 3$ and $b = 9$.

Example

1 Evaluate $m(p^3 - q)$, when $m = 2, p = 4$, and $q = 8$.
Use a handheld to check.

$m(p^3 - q) = 2(4^3 - 8)$ ←——Substitute 2 for m, 4 for p, and 8 for q.

$\qquad = 2(64 - 8) = 2(56)$ ←——Simplify using the order of operations.

$\qquad = 112$

Check:

2 [ctrl] [sto▶ var] [M] [≈ enter] ←——Enter the value of m.

4 [ctrl] [sto▶ var] [P] [≈ enter] ←——Enter the value of p.

8 [ctrl] [sto▶ var] [Q] [≈ enter] ←——Enter the value of q.

[M] [×] [(] [P] [^] [3] [−] [Q] [)] [≈ enter] [=] 112

1.1	RAD AUTO REAL	
$2 \to m$		2
$4 \to p$		4
$8 \to q$		8
$m \cdot (p^3 - q)$		112
		4/99

So $m(p^3 - q) = 112$, when $m = 2, p = 4$, and $q = 8$.

Try These

Name the coefficient of each term.

1. $3xb + \frac{2}{3}cd$

2. $-ny + \frac{wt}{5}$

3. $r^2 - v^3 + 9rv$

4. $-\frac{n}{10} + 0.5tp$

Write each as an algebraic expression.

5. 18 more than twice a number

6. the quotient when 37 added to twice a number is divided by 9

7. the value in cents of q quarters and p pennies

Write each as a word phrase.

8. $13(n + 7)$

9. $\frac{27 - n}{3}$

10. $77 + 3n$

Write an algebraic expression to represent each situation.

11. Robert is now 10 years old. How old will he be y years from now?

12. What is the length (in terms of w) of a rectangle when the length, ℓ, is 6 more than the width, w?

Evaluate each algebraic expression for the given values of the variables.

13. $9z + 4(z - 5)$, when $z = 2$

14. $(-a)^3 + 5ab$, when $a = 2, b = -3$

15. $\frac{(3m - n)^2}{(m + n)^3}$, when $m = \frac{1}{3}, n = -\frac{2}{3}$

Evaluate each expression when $t = 40$, $u = 120$, $v = 100$, and $w = 75$. Use a handheld to check.

16. $(2u - v) + 2w$

17. $\frac{v^2}{40} + 3w$

18. $2t \div \frac{3v}{w}$

19. $2w - (u \div t)$

20. Discuss and Write Evaluate the expressions $6a + 3$ and $6(a + 3)$, when $a = 3$. Explain why the results differ.

Go to **PRACTICE BOOK Lesson 1-8 for exercise sets.**

Properties of Real Numbers

Objective To identify the properties of real numbers in addition and multiplication
- To justify the simplification of algebraic expressions by applying the properties of real numbers

The following are properties of real numbers in addition and multiplication.

Let a, b, and c represent real numbers.

Property	Addition	Multiplication
Closure	$a + b$ is a unique real number.	$a \bullet b$ is a unique real number.
Commutative	$a + b = b + a$	$a \bullet b = b \bullet a$
Associative	$a + b + c = (a + b) + c$ $= a + (b + c)$	$a \bullet b \bullet c = (a \bullet b) \bullet c$ $= a \bullet (b \bullet c)$
Identity	$a + 0 = a$ and $0 + a = a$ 0 is the *additive identity* element.	$a \bullet 1 = a$ and $1 \bullet a = a$ 1 is the *multiplicative identity* element.
Inverse	For every real number a, there is a unique real number $-a$ such that $a + (-a) = 0$ and $-a + a = 0$. $-a$ is the *additive inverse* of a, or the *opposite* of a.	For every nonzero real number a, there is a unique real number $\frac{1}{a}$ such that $a \bullet \frac{1}{a} = 1$ and $\frac{1}{a} \bullet a = 1$. $\frac{1}{a}$ is the *multiplicative inverse* of a, or the *reciprocal* of a.
Distributive	$a \bullet (b + c) = a \bullet b + a \bullet c$ and $(b + c) \bullet a = b \bullet a + c \bullet a$ Multiplication is distributive over addition.	

▶ You can simplify an algebraic expression by applying the properties of real numbers and combining like terms. Terms that have exactly the same literal coefficients that are raised to the same power are called like terms.

Like terms: $2a$ and a
xy^2 and $-2xy^2$

Unlike terms: mn and $-3mn^2$

.Think.................................
The variables are *not raised to the same powers*.
....

Use the properties of real numbers to justify the steps of a simplification process.

Simplify: $3(m + 9) + 2m$

$[3(m) + 3(9)] + 2m$ ←—Apply the Distributive Property.

$3m + 27 + 2m$ ←—Multiply.

$3m + 2m + 27$ ←—Apply the Commutative Property to get like terms near each other.

$(3m + 2m) + 27$ ←—Apply the Associative Property to group the like terms.

$(3 + 2)m + 27$ ←—Apply the Distributive Property to combine like terms.

$5m + 27$ ←—Add the coefficients of the like terms.

Examples

1 Simplify: $7(y + 2) - 5(y + 8)$

$7(y + 2) + (-5)(y + 8)$ ← Apply the definition of subtraction: $a - b = a + (-b)$

$[7(y) + 7(2)] + [(-5)(y) + (-5)(8)]$ ← Apply the Distributive Property.

$[7y + 14] + [(-5y) + (-40)]$ ← Multiply.

$[7y + 14 + (-5y)] + (-40)$ ← Apply the Associative Property.

$[7y + (-5y) + 14] + (-40)$ ← Apply the Commutative Property.

$[7y + (-5y)] + [14 + (-40)]$ ← Apply the Associative Property.

$[7 + (-5)]y + [14 + (-40)]$ ← Apply the Distributive Property.

$2y + (-26)$ ← Combine like terms.

$2y - 26$ ← Apply the definition of subtraction: $a + (-b) = a - b$

2 Simplify: $2z - (z + 3)$

$2z - 1(z + 3)$ ← Apply the Identity Property for Multiplication.

$2z + (-1)(z + 3)$ ← Apply the definition of subtraction.

$2z + [(-1 \bullet z) + (-1 \bullet 3)]$ ← Apply the Distributive Property.

$2z + [(-1z) + (-3)]$ ← Multiply.

$[2z + (-1z)] + (-3)$ ← Apply the Associative Property.

$[2 + (-1)]z + (-3)$ ← Apply the Distributive Property.

$1z + (-3)$ ← Combine like terms.

$z - 3$ ← Apply the Identity Property for Multiplication and the definition of subtraction.

Try These

Substitute a number for *n* to make each statement true. Identify the property or definition that is illustrated.

1. $7(10 + 1) = 7(10) + 7n$

2. $8 + n = 9 + 8$

3. $(3 + 4) + 8 = 3 + (n + 8)$

4. $7n = 1$

5. $9 \bullet \frac{1}{9} = n$

6. $n \bullet 12 = 12$

7. $6 + n = 0$

8. $16 - (-5) = 16 + n$

9. $8 \div 4 = 8n$

Write a justification for each step of the given simplification process.

10. Simplify: $7w - 5(3 + w)$

a. $7w + (-5)(3 + w)$

b. $7w + (-5)(3) + (-5)(w)$

c. $7w + (-15) + (-5w)$

d. $7w + (-5w) + (-15)$

e. $[7w + (-5w)] + (-15)$

f. $[7 + (-5)]w + (-15)$

g. $2w + (-15)$

h. $2w - 15$

11. Discuss and Write Explain how to simplify $4x + 6y + 3x - 2y + 8$. Show all steps.

Go to PRACTICE BOOK **Lesson 1-9 for exercise sets.**

Sets and Operations

Objective To apply Venn diagrams in problem solving • To use roster and set-builder notations • To find the complement of a set • To apply the set operations of intersection and union • To identify disjoint sets

 Of 250 people surveyed, 175 have brown hair, 110 have brown eyes, and 85 have both brown hair and brown eyes. How many of these people have neither brown hair nor brown eyes?

To find how many have neither brown hair nor brown eyes, draw a Venn diagram to model the situation.

▶ A Venn diagram shows relationships among *sets*. A set is a collection of objects, called elements. The elements could be numbers, letters, or physical objects (such as a set of people with brown hair). The elements of a set are written between braces, { }. Two sets are equal *if and only if* they have the same elements.

To draw a Venn diagram, represent the *universal set*, denoted by U, as a rectangle, and show the number of elements in that universe. The universal set, or universe, is the set of all elements being considered, such as the number of people in a survey. Inside the rectangle of a Venn diagram, *subsets* are often represented by circles. A subset, denoted by the symbol $\subset$, is a set contained within a set.

In the given problem, the universe, U, contains 250 people and has two subsets, A and B:

* $A = \{$people with brown hair$\}$
  A contains 175 elements.
  $A \subset U$

* $B = \{$people with brown eyes$\}$
  B contains 110 elements.
  $B \subset U$

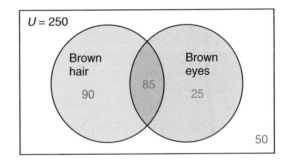

The circles overlap to show that some people are in both sets. That is, 85 people have both brown hair and brown eyes.

* The number of people who have brown hair but not brown eyes:
  $175 - 85 = 90$

* The number of people who have brown eyes but not brown hair:
  $110 - 85 = 25$

* The total number of people represented inside the circles:
  $90 + 25 + 85 = 200$

* The number of people outside the circles but still in the rectangle:
  $250 - 200 = 50$

So of the 250 people surveyed, 50 have neither brown hair nor brown eyes.

▶ You can write sets using two different notations: roster or set-builder.

  • **Roster notation** lists the elements of the set.

    The set of whole numbers greater than 10 is written as: $\{11, 12, 13, 14, \ldots\}$

    > **Remember:** An *ellipsis* (three dots) is used to show that the numbers in the set continue without end and follow the pattern established by the first four numbers.

  • **Set-builder notation** describes a set by stating the properties that its elements must satisfy.

    In set-builder notation, the set of whole numbers greater than 10 is written as:

    $\{x \mid x$ is a whole number and $x > 10\}$ ◀── Read as: "The set of all x such that x is a whole number and x is greater than 10."

    ↑
    such that

The following symbols are often used with set-builder notation.

  • $\in$ ◀── Read as: "is an element of, or belongs to"

    $50 \in \{x \mid x$ is a whole number and $x > 10\}$

  • $\notin$ ◀── Read as: "is *not* an element of, or does *not* belong to"

    $7 \notin \{x \mid x$ is a whole number and $x > 10\}$

▶ A set that has no elements is called the **empty set**, or the **null set**, and it is denoted by the symbol $\varnothing$ or $\{\ \}$.

  $\{x \mid x$ is an odd number that is divisible by 2$\}$ is $\varnothing$. ◀── There is no odd number that can be exactly divided by 2.

Examples

1 List the elements in the set: $T = \{t \mid t$ is an integer and $t < 0\}$

  $\{t \mid t$ is an integer and $t < 0\}$ ◀── the set of all t such that t is an integer and t *is less than* 0

  $\{\ldots, -4, -3, -2, -1\}$ ◀── Use an *ellipsis* to show that the numbers follow the pattern and continue without end in the negative direction.

2 List the elements in the set: $N = \{n \mid n \in$ the set of natural numbers and $n < 0\}$

  $\{n \mid n \in$ the set of natural numbers and $n < 0\}$ ◀── the set of all n such that n belongs to the set of natural numbers and n is less than 0

  $\varnothing$ ◀── Since there are no values that satisfy the given conditions, the result is the *null set*.

▶ When a subset is defined within a universe, its *complement* is also defined.

The **complement of a set** A, denoted by A', is the set of all elements that belong to the universe U but do not belong to set A.

If $U = \{0, 1, 2, 3, 4\}$ and $A = \{0, 1, 3\}$, what is the complement of A?

$A' = \{2, 4\}$ ◀── The complement contains those elements in U that are not in A.

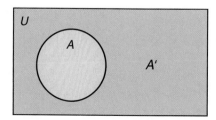

Continue Lesson ➡

▶ Just as there are operations in arithmetic and algebra, there are operations with sets.

Operation	Venn Diagram	Example
Intersection of Sets The *intersection*, ∩, of two sets is the set of all elements that are common to both sets.	U (Venn diagram of A and B with intersection shaded)	$A = \{1, 2, 3, 4, 5\}$ $B = \{2, 5, 6, 7\}$ $A \cap B = \{2, 5\}$
Union of Sets The *union*, ∪, of two sets is the set of all elements that are in either or both sets.	U (Venn diagram of A and B both shaded)	$A = \{1, 2, 3, 4, 5\}$ $B = \{2, 5, 6, 7\}$ $A \cup B = \{1, 2, 3, 4, 5, 6, 7\}$ When the sets intersect, the elements in the intersection are listed only once.

Example

1 Refer to the diagram, and specify each set by roster.

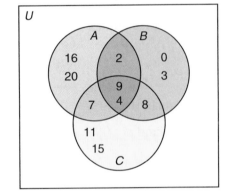

a. $A \cup B$ ◄── elements in either A or B
$A = \{2, 4, 7, 9, 16, 20\}$
$B = \{0, 2, 3, 4, 8, 9\}$
$A \cup B = \{0, 2, 3, 4, 7, 8, 9, 16, 20\}$

b. $A \cap C$ ◄── elements common to both A and C
$A = \{2, 4, 7, 9, 16, 20\}$, $C = \{4, 7, 8, 9, 11, 15\}$
$A \cap C = \{4, 7, 9\}$

c. $B \cup C$ ◄── elements in either B or C
$B = \{0, 2, 3, 4, 8, 9\}$
$C = \{4, 7, 8, 9, 11, 15\}$
$B \cup C = \{0, 2, 3, 4, 7, 8, 9, 11, 15\}$

d. $A \cap B \cap C$ ◄── First find $A \cap B$.
$A = \{2, 4, 7, 9, 16, 20\}$, $B = \{0, 2, 3, 4, 8, 9\}$; so $A \cap B = \{2, 4, 9\}$
and $C = \{4, 7, 8, 9, 11, 15\}$, so $A \cap B \cap C = \{4, 9\}$

e. $A \cap (B \cup C)$ ◄── First find $B \cup C$.
$B = \{0, 2, 3, 4, 8, 9\}$, $C = \{4, 7, 8, 9, 11, 15\}$; so $B \cup C = \{0, 2, 3, 4, 7, 8, 9, 11, 15\}$
and $A = \{2, 4, 7, 9, 16, 20\}$, so $A \cap (B \cup C) = \{2, 4, 7, 9\}$

f. $A \cup (B \cap C)$ ◄── First find $B \cap C$.
$B = \{0, 2, 3, 4, 8, 9\}$, $C = \{4, 7, 8, 9, 11, 15\}$; so $B \cap C = \{4, 8, 9\}$
and $A = \{2, 4, 7, 9, 16, 20\}$, so $A \cup B \cap C = \{2, 4, 7, 8, 9, 16, 20\}$

▶ Sets that have no elements in common or that do not intersect are called **disjoint sets**.

For $M = \{2, 3, 5, 7\}$ and $N = \{1, 4, 6, 8\}$, $M \cap N = \varnothing$.
So M and N are disjoint sets.

Example

1 Refer to the diagram, and determine each resulting set.

a. $A \cap C = \varnothing$ ←—The intersection of disjoint
sets is the null set.

b. $A \cup B = A$ ←—B is a proper subset of A,
so all of the elements in B
are contained in A.

c. $A \cap B = B$ ←—The intersection of a set
and its proper subset is
the proper subset.

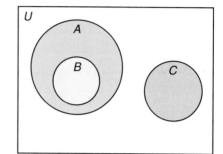

Try These

List the elements of each set.

1. $\{q \mid q$ is a whole number and $q < 0\}$ **2.** $\{v \mid v \in$ the set of integers and $v > 20\}$

List the elements of the complement of each set A, given its universe U.

3. $U = \{$integers$\}$, $A = \{0\}$ **4.** $U = \{$real numbers$\}$, $A = \varnothing$ **5.** $U = \{1, 2, 3\}$, $A = \{1, 2, 3\}$

Refer to the diagram, and specify each set by roster.

6. $A \cap (B \cup C)$

7. $A \cup (B \cap C)$

8. $A' \cup B$

9. $A' \cap C'$

10. $(A \cup B) \cap C'$

11. $(A' \cap B')'$

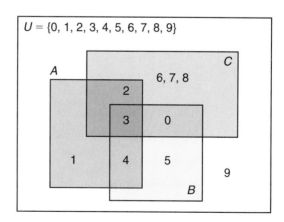

Solve using a Venn diagram.

12. Thirty students were asked about their participation in a sport. Of these students, 24 either play soccer or tennis. Six of the students play soccer but do not play tennis. Fourteen of the students play tennis and also play soccer. How many of the students play tennis but do *not* play soccer?

13. Discuss and Write The "union of sets" is an operation. Do you think that the Commutative Property and Associative Property hold for this operation? Explain. Give examples with specific sets.

Operations with Matrices: Addition and Subtraction

Objective To use matrices to organize data • To add and subtract matrices

A chain of retail stores that sell big-screen TVs offers both LCD and Plasma screens in these sizes: 32-inch, 37-inch, 39-inch, and 42-inch. The table below shows the data for the in-stock inventory of these products.

Number of TVs				
	32-in.	**37-in.**	**39-in.**	**42-in.**
LCD	240	186	320	225
Plasma	256	125	195	173

You can use a *matrix* to organize, combine, and compare data.

▶ A matrix (plural: *matrices*) is a rectangular arrangement of data in rows and columns.

The matrix at the right shows the above data. The matrix has 2 rows and 4 columns. Its dimensions are 2 by 4, or 2 × 4.

Each number in the matrix is called an element. The entry 320 is the element in Row 1 Column 3. This number represents the number of 39-in. LCD TVs in inventory.

$$\begin{array}{c} \text{Column 3} \\ \downarrow \end{array}$$

$$\begin{bmatrix} 240 & 186 & 320 & 225 \\ 256 & 125 & 195 & 173 \end{bmatrix} \leftarrow \text{Row 1}$$

2 × 4 matrix

Examples

Write the dimensions of each matrix.

1
$$\begin{bmatrix} 16 & -2 \\ 4 & 35 \\ 0 & 2.7 \end{bmatrix} \leftarrow \begin{array}{l} 3 \text{ rows,} \\ 2 \text{ columns} \end{array}$$

This matrix is 3 × 2.

2
$$\begin{bmatrix} 6 \\ 3.2 \\ -1 \\ 0 \end{bmatrix} \leftarrow \begin{array}{l} 4 \text{ rows,} \\ 1 \text{ column} \end{array}$$

This matrix is 4 × 1.

3
$$\begin{bmatrix} 2 & 3 & 8 & 4 \end{bmatrix} \leftarrow \begin{array}{l} 1 \text{ row,} \\ 4 \text{ columns} \end{array}$$

This matrix is 1 × 4.

▶ Only matrices that *have the same dimensions* can be added or subtracted. Add or subtract the elements that are in the same position in each matrix. Elements in the same position are called the corresponding elements.

• Given: $A = \begin{bmatrix} 7.4 & -4 \\ -5 & 2 \\ 0 & 1.72 \end{bmatrix}$ and $B = \begin{bmatrix} 6.1 & -2 \\ 7 & -8 \\ 10 & 12 \end{bmatrix}$

7.4 and 6.1 are corresponding elements.

Find $A + B$.

$$A + B = \begin{bmatrix} 7.4 + 6.1 & -4 + (-2) \\ -5 + 7 & 2 + (-8) \\ 0 + 10 & 1.72 + 12 \end{bmatrix} = \begin{bmatrix} 13.5 & -6 \\ 2 & -6 \\ 10 & 13.72 \end{bmatrix} \leftarrow \begin{array}{l} \text{Add the corresponding} \\ \text{elements. Then simplify.} \end{array}$$

• Given: $A = \begin{bmatrix} 9.25 & -7 \\ -8 & 3 \end{bmatrix}$ and $B = \begin{bmatrix} 1.12 & -9 \\ 1 & 0.4 \end{bmatrix}$

Find $A - B$.

$A - B = \begin{bmatrix} 9.25 - 1.12 & -7 - (-9) \\ -8 - 1 & 3 - 0.4 \end{bmatrix} = \begin{bmatrix} 8.13 & 2 \\ -9 & 2.6 \end{bmatrix}$ ←— Subtract the corresponding elements, then simplify.

Examples

1 Find: $\begin{bmatrix} -0.5 & 3 & 4.1 \\ 21.3 & 1.8 & 0.32 \end{bmatrix} + \begin{bmatrix} -0.7 & 3.3 & 1.2 \\ 0.01 & 2.5 & 1 \end{bmatrix} - \begin{bmatrix} 0.5 & 1.4 & -5 \\ 18.81 & 0.8 & -2 \end{bmatrix}$

$\begin{bmatrix} -0.5 + (-0.7) - 0.5 & 3 + 3.3 - 1.4 & 4.1 + 1.2 - (-5) \\ 21.3 + 0.01 - 18.81 & 1.8 + 2.5 - 0.8 & 0.32 + 1 - (-2) \end{bmatrix} = \begin{bmatrix} -1.7 & 4.9 & 10.3 \\ 2.5 & 3.5 & 3.32 \end{bmatrix}$

2 Find X to make a true statement: $\begin{bmatrix} -0.9 \\ 5.4 \end{bmatrix} + X = \begin{bmatrix} -2.5 \\ 0.6 \end{bmatrix}$

$X = \begin{bmatrix} -2.5 \\ 0.6 \end{bmatrix} - \begin{bmatrix} -0.9 \\ 5.4 \end{bmatrix} = \begin{bmatrix} -2.5 - (-0.9) \\ 0.6 - 5.4 \end{bmatrix} = \begin{bmatrix} -1.6 \\ -4.8 \end{bmatrix}$

Try These

Write the dimensions of each matrix.

1. $\begin{bmatrix} 5 & 8 & 3 \\ -2 & 7 & 6 \end{bmatrix}$

2. $[4 \quad 3 \quad 8 \quad 0 \quad -2]$

3. $\begin{bmatrix} 1 & 4 & -7 \\ 0 & 0 & 0 \\ 12 & 1 & 12 \end{bmatrix}$

4. $[17]$

Add or subtract, as indicated.

5. $\begin{bmatrix} 8 & 7 \\ -2.2 & -9 \\ 18 & -4 \end{bmatrix} - \begin{bmatrix} 4 & -2 \\ 0 & -1.3 \\ -9 & 7.2 \end{bmatrix} + \begin{bmatrix} 3 & -5 \\ -8 & 5 \\ 3 & 0 \end{bmatrix}$

6. $\begin{bmatrix} 6 & -9 \\ 2.35 & 8.1 \\ 17.9 & 0 \\ -7 & -7 \end{bmatrix} + \begin{bmatrix} 12 & 4 \\ -2 & -7.1 \\ 12 & -9 \\ 11 & 8 \end{bmatrix} - \begin{bmatrix} 9 & -6.5 \\ 8 & 8 \\ -10 & 0 \\ 3.2 & -6 \end{bmatrix}$

Find matrix X that results in a true statement.

7. $\begin{bmatrix} 17 & 4 & -1 \\ 8.1 & 0 & 9 \end{bmatrix} + X = \begin{bmatrix} 17 & 8 & -9 \\ 0.1 & 0 & 0 \end{bmatrix}$

8. $X - \begin{bmatrix} -1 & 6 \\ 4.3 & 0 \\ 8 & -9 \end{bmatrix} = \begin{bmatrix} -1 & -6 \\ 8.2 & 3 \\ 0 & 0 \end{bmatrix}$

9. The table at the right shows the data on the inventory of yoga pants at the north and south locations of a spa at the beginning of August. Write the data in a matrix.

Yoga Pants August Inventory				
	S	M	L	XL
North	16	9	7	12
South	2	15	0	3

10. Discuss and Write Do you think that the Commutative Property applies to the operation of matrix addition? Explain. Give examples with specific matrices.

Go to PRACTICE BOOK **Lesson 1-11 for exercise sets.**

Operations with Matrices: Multiplication

Objective To perform scalar multiplication • To multiply two matrices

The matrix below shows the monthly payments of six homeowners who took home-improvement loans for a period of 2 years at an annual interest rate of 6%. What matrix can be used to show the total amount owed by each homeowner?

$$\begin{bmatrix} 221.60 & 132.96 & 332.40 \\ 443.21 & 664.81 & 886.41 \end{bmatrix}$$

To find the matrix that shows the total amount owed by each homeowner for 2 years, multiply the given matrix by 24, the number of months in the loan.

►Multiplying a matrix by a real number is called scalar multiplication. To multiply a matrix by a real number, *multiply each element of the matrix by that number.*

$$24\begin{bmatrix} 221.60 & 132.96 & 332.40 \\ 443.21 & 664.81 & 886.41 \end{bmatrix} = \begin{bmatrix} 24(221.60) & 24(132.96) & 24(332.40) \\ 24(443.21) & 24(664.81) & 24(886.41) \end{bmatrix}$$

$$= \begin{bmatrix} 5{,}318.40 & 3{,}191.04 & 7{,}977.60 \\ 10{,}637.04 & 15{,}955.44 & 21{,}273.84 \end{bmatrix}$$

So the total amount owed by each homeowner is shown

in the resulting matrix: $\begin{bmatrix} 5{,}318.40 & 3{,}191.04 & 7{,}977.60 \\ 10{,}637.04 & 15{,}955.44 & 21{,}273.84 \end{bmatrix}$.

►Multiplying two matrices uses both multiplication and addition. You can multiply two matrices only if *the rows of the first matrix have the same number of elements as the columns of the second matrix.*

Given: $A = \begin{bmatrix} -1 & 2 \\ 4 & 0 \end{bmatrix}$ and $B = \begin{bmatrix} 7 & -5 & 3 \\ 1 & 6 & 8 \end{bmatrix}$

Find AB.

$$AB = \begin{bmatrix} -1(7) + 2(1) & -1(-5) + 2(6) & -1(3) + 2(8) \\ 4(7) + 0(1) & 4(-5) + 0(6) & 4(3) + 0(8) \end{bmatrix}$$

$$= \begin{bmatrix} -7 + 2 & 5 + 12 & -3 + 16 \\ 28 + 0 & -20 + 0 & 12 + 0 \end{bmatrix}$$

$$= \begin{bmatrix} -5 & 17 & 13 \\ 28 & -20 & 12 \end{bmatrix}$$ ←Dimensions: A is 2 × 2, B is 2 × 3, so AB is 2 × 3.

_____ **Key Concept** _____

Multiplying Two Matrices

1. Multiply the elements of each row of the first matrix by the corresponding elements in each column of the second matrix.

2. Find the sum of each set of products; each sum then takes the corresponding position in the product matrix.

The product of an $m \times n$ matrix and an $n \times r$ matrix is an $m \times r$ matrix.

Example

1 Mia and Dana make jewelry to sell at boutique shops. This year, they have crafted bracelets made from onyx, coral, and silver beads. Their cost for each bead was $0.75 for onyx, $1.10 for coral, and $0.50 for silver. Mia used 125 onyx, 100 coral, and 150 silver beads. Dana used 175 onyx, 115 coral, and 200 silver beads. What was the total cost of the beads they used to make these bracelets?

- Set up matrix A to show how many beads of each type each partner used and matrix B to show the cost per bead for each type.

$$A = \begin{bmatrix} 125 & 100 & 150 \\ 175 & 115 & 200 \end{bmatrix} \quad B = \begin{bmatrix} 0.75 \\ 1.10 \\ 0.50 \end{bmatrix}$$

- Find the product matrix AB to determine each partner's costs for beads used.

$$AB = \begin{bmatrix} 125(0.75) + 100(1.10) + 150(0.50) \\ 175(0.75) + 115(1.10) + 200(0.50) \end{bmatrix} = \begin{bmatrix} 93.75 + 110 + 75 \\ 131.25 + 126.50 + 100 \end{bmatrix}$$

$$= \begin{bmatrix} 278.75 \\ 357.75 \end{bmatrix}$$

- Add the elements of AB to find the total cost of the beads used.
$278.75 + $357.75 = $636.50

So the total cost of the beads used to make the bracelets was $636.50.

Try These

Multiply each matrix by the real number.

1. $5\begin{bmatrix} -1 & 4 \\ 3 & 7 \\ 0 & -8 \end{bmatrix}$

2. $7\begin{bmatrix} 3 & -4 \\ 1 & 6 \\ -4 & 5 \end{bmatrix} - 2\begin{bmatrix} 4 & 5 \\ -1 & 3 \\ -2 & 8 \end{bmatrix}$

3. $2\begin{bmatrix} 4 & 7 \\ -3 & 5 \end{bmatrix} + \begin{bmatrix} 0 & -2 \\ 6 & 4 \end{bmatrix}$

Find the product matrix if it exists. If it does not exist, tell why not.

4. $\begin{bmatrix} 3 & -2 \\ 1 & 0 \end{bmatrix} \bullet \begin{bmatrix} 0 & -5 \\ 6 & 8 \end{bmatrix}$

5. $[4 \quad 3 \quad 1] \bullet \begin{bmatrix} 0 & -2 \\ 5 & 1 \\ -3 & 6 \end{bmatrix}$

6. $\begin{bmatrix} 7 & 1 & 2 \\ -3 & 5 & 8 \end{bmatrix} \bullet \begin{bmatrix} 6 & 4 \\ -2 & -8 \end{bmatrix}$

Use matrices to solve each problem.

7. John and Tim have collected money to build a clubhouse, which they will construct using both wood planks and plastic sheeting. For his work, John needs 6 planks and 8 square yards of sheeting. For his work, Tim needs 8 planks and 12 square yards of sheeting. A hardware store charges $8.75 per plank and $1.99 per square yard for the sheeting. A home supply store charges $7.95 per plank and $2.25 per square yard for the sheeting. Not including tax, at which store should the boys get their materials to get the better buy? How much money will they save?

8. **Discuss and Write** Explain how the conditions for multiplying matrices differ from those for adding matrices.

Go to PRACTICE BOOK **Lesson 1-12 for exercise sets.**

1-13

Technology:
Evaluate Numerical and Algebraic Expressions

Objective To evaluate numerical expressions involving the Order of Operations using a handheld • To evaluate algebraic expressions using a handheld

▶ You can use a handheld to evaluate numerical expressions.

Evaluate the expression $\dfrac{(5+3)^2 - 16}{2}$.

Step 1 Press 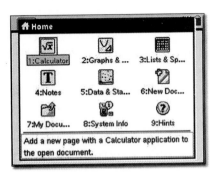. Then choose ① to select **Calculator**.

Step 2 Input *with* grouping symbols $((5+3)^2 - 16) \div 2$. Press **enter**.

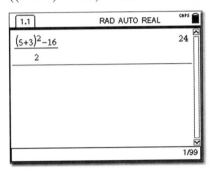

So the result is 24.

Evaluate the above expression *without* inputing grouping symbols.

Step 1 Input $5 + 3^2 - 16 \div 2$. Then press **enter**.

Notice that the answer changes to 6. The handheld follows the order of operations, so it will calculate 3^2 and $16 \div 2$ before finding the sum and difference. It is *important* to use grouping symbols when using a handheld to obtain the correct result.

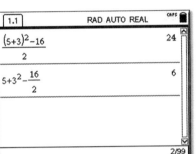

▶ You can also use a handheld to evaluate algebraic expressions.

A car travels at a constant speed of 45 miles per hour. How far will the car travel in 2.75 hours?

To find the distance the car will travel in t hours, multiply 45 by t.

Step 1 Press 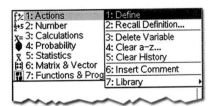. Then choose ① to select **Calculator**.

Step 2 Press **menu**. Select ① for **Actions**, and then choose ① for **Define**.

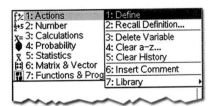

So the car will travel 123.75 miles in 2.75 hours.

Step 3 Input the equation $f(t) = 45t$. Press ⒡ ⓵ ⓣ ⓶ ⑤ ⓣ **enter**. Then input $f(2.75)$ and press **enter**.

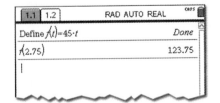

▶ You can use the *Lists and Spreadsheet Application* on your handheld to make a table of values for an algebraic expression.

Make a table to show the distance the car will travel in increments of 0.5 hours.

To complete this table be sure you have completed and retained steps 1 through 3 on page 30 in your handheld.

Step 4 Press ⌂. Then choose ③ to select **Lists and Spreadsheet Application**.

Step 5 Press menu. Select **Function Table**, then choose **Switch to Function Table**.

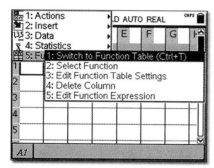

Step 6 Press enter to display the table.

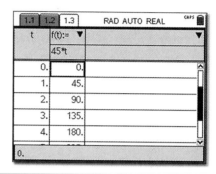

Step 7 Press menu. Select **Function Table**, then choose **Edit Function Table Settings**. Change **Table Step** to 0.5.

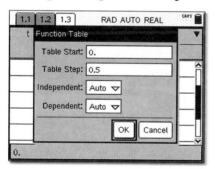

Step 8 Tab down to OK and press enter. The table will display the car's distance every 0.5 hour.

Try These

Use a handheld to evaluate the numerical expression.

1. $15 - 3(4 - 5)$

2. $12^2 + (22 - 16)^3$

3. $-2(14 + 2) + 8(12 - 6)$

4. $\dfrac{-(22 + 6)}{2^2}$

5. $\dfrac{(10 - 4)^3}{29 - 3^3}$

6. $\dfrac{8 + 3(4)^2}{5^2 - 6(3)}$

Use a handheld to evaluate the algebraic expression for the given value. Then make a table for the expression, starting at 0 and using increments of 0.25.

7. $-12x$ when $x = 2.5$

8. $22.6x$ when $x = 8$

9. $7x - 5$ when $x = 11$

10. $-9x + 6$ when $x = 5.7$

11. $42 - 10.5x$ when $x = -3$

12. $4(x - 14.2)$ when $x = -3$

13. Discuss and Write Compare the answer in Exercise 5 to what it would be if grouping symbols were not used. Explain why the answers are not the same.

See TI-Nspire™ Handbook on pages 415–422.

1-14

Technology:
Operations with Matrices

Objective To use a handheld to perform various operations with matrices

The top matrix at the right represents the numbers of short-sleeve shirts and long-sleeve shirts of different colors a store has in stock at the beginning of a one day sale. The bottom matrix represents the number of each type of shirt the store has left at the end of the sale. What matrix can be written to represent the numbers of each type of shirt sold?

$$\begin{array}{cccc} & \text{Red} & \text{Blue} & \text{Green} & \text{Yellow} \end{array}$$

$$\begin{array}{c} \text{short sleeve} \\ \text{long sleeve} \end{array} \begin{bmatrix} 25 & 18 & 32 & 19 \\ 40 & 22 & 28 & 15 \end{bmatrix}$$

$$\begin{array}{c} \text{short sleeve} \\ \text{long sleeve} \end{array} \begin{bmatrix} 15 & 4 & 21 & 8 \\ 32 & 16 & 19 & 11 \end{bmatrix}$$

▶ You can use a handheld to perform matrix subtraction.

To find the matrix representing the number of each type of shirt sold, find the difference of the two matrices.

$$\begin{bmatrix} 25 & 18 & 32 & 19 \\ 40 & 22 & 28 & 15 \end{bmatrix} - \begin{bmatrix} 15 & 4 & 21 & 8 \\ 32 & 16 & 19 & 11 \end{bmatrix}$$

> **Remember:** To add or subtract matrices, they *must* have equal dimensions.

Step 1 Press ⌂. Then choose **1** to select **Calculator**.

Step 2 Press ctrl ⊞ to bring up the matrix dialog box.

Step 3 Press ⚙ to choose the 3 by 3 matrix option.

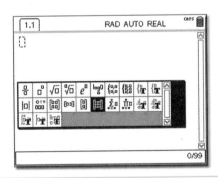

Step 4 Input 2 for *Number of rows* and 4 for *Number of columns*. Press tab to switch between fields.

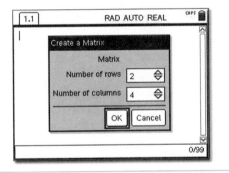

Step 5 Input the values of the first matrix, tabbing between each value.

Then press ⊟ to subtract.

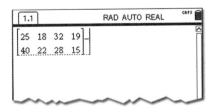

Step 6 Repeat Steps 2–4 and input the values of the second matrix.

Then press enter to find the difference.

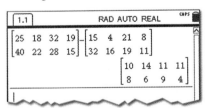

So $\begin{bmatrix} 10 & 14 & 11 & 11 \\ 8 & 6 & 9 & 4 \end{bmatrix}$ represents the numbers of each type of shirt sold.

▶ A handheld can also be used to perform matrix multiplication.

Multiply: $\begin{bmatrix} -3 & 2 & -1 \\ 4 & 0 & 5 \end{bmatrix} \cdot \begin{bmatrix} 1 & -2 \\ 2 & 4 \\ 0 & 1 \end{bmatrix}$

> **Remember:** The product of two matrices exists only if the number of columns of the first matrix is equal to the number of rows of the second.

Step 1 Press ⌂. Then choose ①to select **Calculator**.

Step 2 Press ctrl ⊠ to access the matrix dialog box. Choose the 3 by 3 matrix option.

Step 3 Input 2 for *Number of rows* and 3 for *Number of columns*. Press tab to switch between fields.

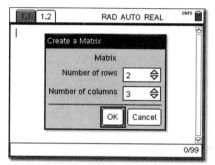

Step 4 Input the values of the first matrix, tabbing between each value.
Then press ⊠ to multiply.

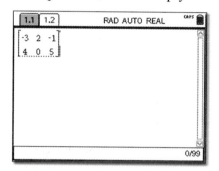

Step 5 Press ctrl ⊠ to access the matrix dialog box.

Step 6 Choose the 3 by 3 matrix option.

Step 7 Input 3 for *Number of rows* and 2 for *Number of columns*. Press tab to switch between fields.

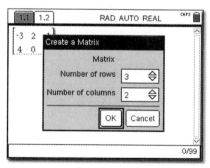

Step 8 Input the values of the second matrix, then press enter to find the product.

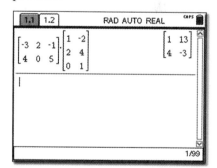

Try These

Use a handheld to perform the indicated operation.

1. $\begin{bmatrix} 3 & 3 \\ 7 & 1 \\ -2 & 4 \end{bmatrix} + \begin{bmatrix} 6 & -3 \\ -5 & 2 \\ 1 & 8 \end{bmatrix}$

2. $\begin{bmatrix} 0 & 4 \\ -1 & -2 \\ 5 & 3 \end{bmatrix} \cdot \begin{bmatrix} 15 & -7 & 12 \\ -5 & 6 & 9 \end{bmatrix}$

3. $\begin{bmatrix} 12 & 14 & -6 \\ -10 & 5 & 11 \\ 23 & -18 & 4 \end{bmatrix} - \begin{bmatrix} 3 & -19 & 2 \\ 16 & 15 & -7 \\ 22 & -4 & 6 \end{bmatrix}$

4. Discuss and Write Can you multiply the matrices in Exercise 1? Can you add the matrices in Exercise 2? Can you multiply the matrices in Exercise 3? Explain.

Go to PRACTICE BOOK **Lesson 1-14 for exercise sets.**

Problem-Solving Strategy:
Make a Drawing

Objective To solve problems using the strategy *Make a Drawing*

Problem 1: Wes and his brother Ted disagree about what color to paint their room. There are five cans of paint in the garage: 2 red, 2 blue, and 1 yellow. They decide that each of them will choose one can at random, and then the two colors will be combined. If mixing blue and yellow paint yields the color green, how many of the total two-color combinations will yield green?

Read **Read to understand what is being asked.**

List the facts and restate the question.

Facts: There are 2 red cans, 2 blue cans, and 1 yellow can.

Two brothers will mix the colors in two cans.

Mixing blue and yellow paint yields the color green.

Question: How many of the total two-color combinations will yield green?

Plan **Select a strategy.**

Use the strategy *Make a Drawing*. A tree diagram can help show all the possible paint mixtures.

Problem-Solving Strategies

1. Make a Drawing
2. Solve a Simpler Problem
3. Reason Logically
4. Consider Extreme Cases
5. Work Backward
6. Find a Pattern
7. Account for All Possibilities
8. Adopt a Different Point of View
9. Guess and Test
10. Organize Data

Solve **Apply the strategy.**

First, list all the possibilities for Wes's pick: R, R, B, B, and Y. (See the first row in the diagram below.) Next, as shown in the leftmost set of branches below, you can make branches for each of Ted's possible picks. For example, if Wes chooses red, then Ted can choose from one red can, two blue cans, and one yellow can. Finally, list the mixture color for each pair of cans. The diagram below shows what color results from each combination.

Wes	R				R				B				B				Y			
Ted	R	B	B	Y	R	B	B	Y	R	R	B	Y	R	R	B	Y	R	R	B	B
	r	p	p	o	r	p	p	o	p	p	b	g	p	p	b	g	o	o	g	g
	e	u	u	r	e	u	u	r	u	u	l	r	u	u	l	r	r	r	r	r
mixture	d	r	r	a	d	r	r	a	r	r	u	e	r	r	u	e	a	a	e	e
	p	p	p	n	p	p	p	n	p	p	e	e	p	p	e	e	n	n	e	e
	l	l	l	g	l	l	l	g	l	l	n	n	l	l	n	n	g	g	n	n
	e	e	e	e	e	e	e	e	e	e			e	e			e	e	e	e

Two-Color Combinations

blue and yellow ⟶ green
red and blue ⟶ purple
red and yellow ⟶ orange

According to the diagram there are 20 two-color combinations, and 4 of them are green. So 4 out of the 20 two-color combinations will yield green.

Check **Check to make sure your answer makes sense.**

There are 5 possibilities for the first can. For each first pick, there are 4 possibilities for the second, so there are 4(5), or 20, two-color combinations. Using B_1 and B_2 to represent the two blue cans, list all the combinations that give green: B_1Y, B_2Y, YB_1, YB_2. So 4 out of 20 two-color combinations will yield green, which is the same answer found above.

Problem 2: Along a line parallel to a straight stretch of highway, there are twelve equally spaced trees. A car on the highway passed these trees at a constant speed. It took the car 20 seconds to travel from the first tree to the fifth tree. How long did it take the car to travel from the fifth tree to the last tree?

Read ▶ **Read to understand what is being asked.**

List the facts and restate the question.

Facts: 12 trees are spaced equally along a straight line.

A car traveled at a constant speed along a road parallel to the trees.

It took the car 20 seconds to go from the first to the fifth tree.

Question: How long did it take the car to go from the fifth to the twelfth tree?

Plan ▶ **Select a strategy.**

Using the strategy *Make a Drawing* might reveal something significant about the problem.

Solve ▶ **Apply the strategy.**

- Draw 12 dots, as shown below, to represent the trees. The drawing reveals that passing 5 trees means traveling 4 *intervals* between the trees.

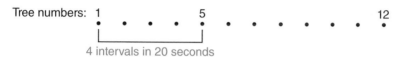

So it took the car 20 seconds to travel 4 intervals.

- The drawing above also shows that 4 intervals in 20 seconds is the same as 5 seconds per interval. How many intervals are between the fifth and twelfth trees?

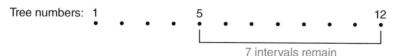

Since there are exactly 7 intervals between the 5th and 12th trees, the car will take 7 *times* 5 seconds, or 35 seconds, to travel from the fifth to the twelfth tree.

Check ▶ **Check to make sure your answer makes sense.**

You can look at the problem in a different way. The drawing below shows that the total distance from the fifth tree to the twelfth is $1\frac{3}{4}$ *times* the distance from the first tree to the fifth.

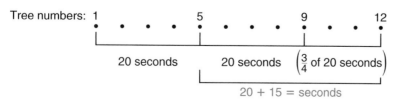

So the total time required is $\left(20 + \frac{3}{4} \cdot 20\right)$, or 35, seconds, which is the same answer as above.

Go to ▶ **PRACTICE BOOK Lesson 1-15 for exercise sets.**

Enrichment:
Modular Arithmetic

Objective To perform modular addition and multiplication

Adding with time is different from the addition you have come to know. For example, 10 o'clock + 5 hours ⟶ 3 o'clock, (*not* 15 o'clock). On a clock face, the hour hand starts at 10 and moves ahead by 5 hours, ending at 3.

10:00   3:00

Addition Modulo *m*

When you add on a clock, you are doing clock arithmetic, or modular arithmetic. Specifically, you are adding in what is called modulo 12, or "mod 12" for short.

Imagine a clock that has only an hour hand. When you add 12 hours to any time, the result is that time again (visually, the hour hand starts at that time and moves around the clock face one complete circle, ending back at the original time). For this reason, you use the number 0 instead of 12. So, mod 12 arithmetic involves *only* the set of integers $\{0, 1, 2, 3, 4, 5, 6, 7, 8, 9, 10, 11\}$.

► You can come up with a method for adding in mod 12 *without* using the clock face.

Find the following sums in mod 12, using the clock face at the right. Then find a pattern.

$$5 + 6 = 11 \qquad 9 + 11 = 8 \qquad 7 + 7 + 7 = 9$$
$$4 + 9 + 10 + 6 = 5 \qquad 1 + 5 + 7 + 8 = 9 \qquad 5 + 11 + 9 + 6 = 7$$

To find the sum in mod 12:

• Add using standard addition.

• Divide the result by 12. The remainder is the sum mod 12.

For example, $4 + 9 + 10 + 6 = 29$, and $29 \div 12 = 2\frac{5}{12} \longrightarrow 2 \text{ R } 5$

So $4 + 9 + 10 + 6 = 5 \pmod{12}$.

► Addition in other mods is similar to addition in mod 12.

Mod 5 addition uses *only* the five integers $\{0, 1, 2, 3, 4\}$.
To add, imagine moving around a clock face as the one at the right.
Add the following in mod 5 and find a pattern.

$$1 + 1 = 2 \qquad 4 + 3 = 2 \qquad 2 + 3 + 3 = 3$$
$$1 + 2 + 3 + 4 = 0 \qquad 4 + 4 + 3 + 3 = 4 \qquad 2 + 2 + 3 + 4 = 1$$

To find the sum in mod 5:

• Add using standard addition.

• Divide the result by 5. The remainder is the sum mod 5.

For example, $4 + 3 = 7$, and $7 \div 5 = 1\frac{2}{5} \longrightarrow 1 \text{ R } 2$

So $4 + 3 = 2 \pmod{5}$.

> **Key Concept**
>
> **Addition Modulo *m***
> • Add using standard addition.
> • Divide the result by *m*. The remainder is the sum mod *m*.

Properties of Modular Addition

At right is a mod-5 addition table. Notice the following properties:

- **Commutative Property**
  The table is symmetric about the blue diagonal.
  This shows that addition mod 5 is commutative.
  So $a + b = b + a$, for every a and b in the set $\{0, 1, 2, 3, 4\}$.

- **Additive Identity Property**
  The sum of any number and 0 is that number.
  That is, 0 is the additive identity.

- **Additive Inverse Property**
  Every row and column includes a 0. This shows that every
  number has an additive inverse. For every number a, there
  is a number b, such that $a + b = b + a = 0$. For example, the
  additive inverse of 2 is 3 because $2 + 3 = 3 + 2 = 0$.

+	0	1	2	3	4
0	0	1	2	3	4
1	1	2	3	4	0
2	2	3	4	0	1
3	3	4	0	1	2
4	4	0	1	2	3

Multiplication Modulo m

You can think of multiplication mod m as repeated addition.

$3 \cdot 4 \pmod 5 \longrightarrow 4 + 4 + 4 = 2 \pmod 5$

You can also multiply using standard multiplication, and then
divide the result by 5. The remainder is the product mod 5.

$3 \cdot 4 = 12$, and $12 \div 5 = 2\frac{2}{5} \longrightarrow 2 \text{ R } 2$

So $3 \cdot 4 = 2 \pmod 5$.

> ___ **Key Concept** ___
>
> **Multiplication Modulo m**
> - Multiply using standard multiplication.
> - Divide the result by m. The remainder
>   is the product mod m.

Properties of Modular Multiplication

At right is a mod-6 multiplication table. Notice the
following properties:

- **Commutative Property**
  The table is symmetric about the blue diagonal.
  This shows that multiplication mod 6 is commutative.
  So $ab = ba$ for every a and b in the set $\{0, 1, 2, 3, 4, 5\}$.

- **Multiplicative Identity Property**
  The product of any number and 1 is that number.
  That is, 1 is the multiplicative identity.

- **Multiplicative Inverse Property**
  Only the rows and columns for 1 and 5 contain a 1.
  This means that only 1 and 5 have multiplicative inverses.
  Each of these numbers is its own multiplicative inverse.
  That is, $1 \cdot 1 = 1$, and $5 \cdot 5 = 1$. (*Note:* Numbers that have
  multiplicative inverses depend on the mod.

•	0	1	2	3	4	5
0	0	0	0	0	0	0
1	0	1	2	3	4	5
2	0	2	4	0	2	4
3	0	3	0	3	0	3
4	0	4	2	0	4	2
5	0	5	4	3	2	1

Try These

Find the sum or product in the indicated mod.

1. $6 + 6 \pmod{12}$ **2.** $7 + 3 + 5 \pmod 9$ **3.** $4 \cdot 3 \pmod 5$ **4.** $2 \cdot 3 \cdot 3 \pmod 4$

5. Discuss and Write Make a mod-8 addition table and a mod-7 multiplication table. Explain
what properties of modular addition and modular multiplication these tables illustrate.

Go to PRACTICE BOOK pages 31–32 for exercise sets.

Test Prep: Multiple-Choice Questions
Strategy: Understand Distractors

The incorrect answer choices given for multiple-choice questions are called distractors. Distractors are answer choices that may seem reasonable and can distract you from selecting the correct answer. They are typically the results of common errors made when solving the problem. Even if the answer that you get when you work through the problem is one of the choices, it may not be the correct answer.

Look at the sample test item.

Read the whole test item, including the answer choices.
- Underline important words.

    What is the <u>product</u> of 1.2×10^{15} and 1.2×10^{10}?

    Product means "to multiply."

- Restate the question in your own words.

    Multiply: $(1.2 \times 10^{15})(1.2 \times 10^{10})$

Solve the problem.
- Apply appropriate properties and rules.

    $(1.2 \times 10^{15})(1.2 \times 10^{10})$

    $(1.2 \times 1.2)(10^{15} \times 10^{10})$ ←—Apply the Commutative and Associative Properties.

    1.44×10^{25} ←—Apply the Law of Exponents for Multiplication:
    $10^{15} \times 10^{10} = 10^{15 + 10} = 10^{25}$

Sample Test Item

What is the product of 1.2×10^{15} and 1.2×10^{10}?

A. 1.2×10^{25}
B. 1.2×10^{150}
C. 1.44×10^{25}
D. 1.44×10^{150}

Test-Taking Tips
- Underline important words.
- Restate the question.
- Apply appropriate rules, definitions, or properties.
- Analyze and eliminate answer choices.

Think
To multiply powers of the same base, keep the base and add the exponents.

Item Analysis

Choose the answer.
- Analyze and eliminate answer choices. Watch out for distractors.

    A. 1.2×10^{25} ←—This choice did not multiply 1.2×1.2. Eliminate this choice.

    B. 1.2×10^{150} ←—This choice did not multiply 1.2×1.2, *and* it multiplied the exponents. Eliminate this choice.

    (C.) 1.44×10^{25} ←—This is the correct choice!

    D. 1.44×10^{150} ←—This choice multiplied the exponents. Eliminate this choice.

Try These

Choose the correct answer. Explain how you eliminated answer choices.

1. Evaluate $\sqrt{x^2 + y^2} - 2(x - y^2)$
when $x = 4$ and $y = 3$.

    A. -21 **C.** 15

    B. -19 **D.** 17

2. Which of the following is equivalent to $\dfrac{3^3(5^{-2})}{3^{-6}(5^6)}$?

    F. $\dfrac{3^2}{5^3}$ **H.** $\dfrac{5^3}{3^2}$

    G. $\dfrac{3^9}{5^8}$ **J.** $\dfrac{5^8}{3^9}$

Go to   PRACTICE BOOK page 33 for exercise sets.

CHAPTER 2

Linear Equations

In This Chapter You Will:

- Distinguish between algebraic expressions and equations
- Solve equations by substitution, given replacement sets
- Write, model, solve, and check addition, subtraction, multiplication, and division equations
- Justify the steps of the solution process for addition, subtraction, multiplication, and division equations

- Solve equations that contain variable terms on both sides
- Recognize identities and contradictions
- Write and solve absolute-value equations
- Solve formulas and literal equations for particular variables
- Apply the strategy: *Solve a Simpler Problem*
- Look for new vocabulary words **highlighted** in each lesson

Do You Remember?

- To simplify numerical expressions, use the order of operations: grouping symbols, exponents, multiply or divide left to right, add or subtract left to right.

- Variables can be used to represent quantities.
- To simplify algebraic expressions, apply the properties of real numbers.

For Practice Exercises:

Go to PRACTICE BOOK, pp. 39–64

For Chapter Support: ONLINE

Go to www.progressinmathematics.com

- Skills Update Practice
- Practice Activities
- Audio Glossary
- Vocabulary Activities
- Technology Videos
- Enrichment Activities
- Electronic SourceBook

VIRTUAL MANIPULATIVES

Critical Thinking

While skating in the park, Ruth and Marsha play a math game called "What is the same as . . . ?" Ruth asks, "What is the same as $8\frac{1}{2}$ feet?" Marsha answers, "102 inches." Marsha asks, "What is the same as 8 times 3?" Ruth answers, "64 divided by 4." Marsha tells Ruth her answer is *not* "the same as." Is Marsha correct?

Open Sentences and Solution Sets

Objective To distinguish between open and closed number sentences • To determine whether a given number is a solution to a given equation • To solve equations by substitution, given replacement sets

A theater stage crew needs to fill a triangular gap in the play's set. The area of the space is 14 ft², the base is 7 ft, and the height is not given. What mathematical sentence can you use to determine the height of the space?

You can use the formula $A = \frac{1}{2}bh$ that relates the area of a triangle to the length of a base, b, and the corresponding height, h.

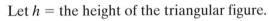

Let h = the height of the triangular figure.

area $= \frac{1}{2} \cdot$ base $\cdot$ height

$14 = \frac{1}{2} \cdot 7h$ ←—Substitute the known values.

The algebraic equation, $14 = \frac{1}{2} \cdot 7h$ shows that the algebraic expression $\frac{1}{2} \cdot 7h$ *is equal to* the numerical expression 14.

So the mathematical sentence for the area of the space is $14 = \frac{1}{2} \cdot 7h$.

__ Key Concept __

Equation

An equation is a statement that two mathematical expressions are equal.

► Equations can be either *open sentences* or *closed sentences*.
Open sentences contain variables that represent the unknown quantities and are neither true nor false.
Closed sentences contain no variables and are either true or false.

Open Sentence	Closed Sentence
$14 = \frac{1}{2} \cdot 7h$	$14 = \frac{1}{2} \cdot 7 \cdot 4$
	$14 = \frac{1}{2} \cdot 28$
	$14 = 14$ True

Think
This closed sentence is true because 4 *satisfies* the equation.

The number 4 is the **solution** to the equation. **Solution set:** {4}.

Examples

Determine whether the given value of the variable makes the open sentence *true* or *false*.

1 $5(m + 7) = 5m + 7$ when $m = 3$

$5(m + 7) = 5m + 7$

$5(3 + 7) \overset{?}{=} 5(3) + 7$

$5(10) \overset{?}{=} 15 + 7$

$50 = 22$ False

2 $3k^2 + 18 = 30$ when $k = -2$

$3k^2 + 18 = 30$

$3(-2)^2 + 18 \overset{?}{=} 30$

$3(4) + 18 \overset{?}{=} 30$

$12 + 18 \overset{?}{=} 30$

$30 = 30$ True

▶ To determine the solution set for an open sentence, given a replacement set, R, or domain set, you must substitute every element in the replacement set into the equation. That is, replace the variable with each element in that set.

> A *replacement set* is the set of elements that can be substituted for a variable.

Using the replacement set $\{-2, 0, 2\}$, find the solution set for the open sentence $|3c^2 - 1| = 11$.

Substitute each element of the replacement set into the equation. After replacing the variable c with these elements, evaluate the resulting closed sentences and determine if they are *true* or *false*.

$$|3(-2)^2 - 1| \stackrel{?}{=} 11$$
$$|3(4) - 1| \stackrel{?}{=} 11$$
$$|12 - 1| \stackrel{?}{=} 11$$
$$11 = 11 \text{ True}$$

$$|3(0)^2 - 1| \stackrel{?}{=} 11$$
$$|3(0) - 1| \stackrel{?}{=} 11$$
$$|0 - 1| \stackrel{?}{=} 11$$
$$1 = 11 \text{ False}$$

$$|3(2)^2 - 1| \stackrel{?}{=} 11$$
$$|3(4) - 1| \stackrel{?}{=} 11$$
$$|12 - 1| \stackrel{?}{=} 11$$
$$11 = 11 \text{ True}$$

So the solution set is $\{-2, 2\}$; this can be also written as $\{\pm 2\}$.

.Think...
Only the numbers from the replacement set that make the open sentence *true* will be in the solution set.

▶ It is possible that no element in a replacement set will make an open sentence true. If this is the case, then the solution set of the equation is the empty set, or null set, which is represented by the symbol $\varnothing$ or $\{\ \}$.

Using the replacement set $\{-1, 1, 2\}$, find the solution set for the open sentence $-4a^2 = (-4a)^2$.

$$-4(-1)^2 \stackrel{?}{=} [-4(-1)]^2$$
$$-4(1) \stackrel{?}{=} (4)^2$$
$$-4(1) \stackrel{?}{=} 16$$
$$-4 = 16 \text{ False}$$

$$-4(1)^2 \stackrel{?}{=} [-4(1)]^2$$
$$-4(1) \stackrel{?}{=} (-4)^2$$
$$-4(1) \stackrel{?}{=} 16$$
$$-4 = 16 \text{ False}$$

$$-4(2)^2 \stackrel{?}{=} [-4(2)]^2$$
$$-4(4) \stackrel{?}{=} (-8)^2$$
$$-4(4) \stackrel{?}{=} 64$$
$$-16 = 64 \text{ False}$$

So the solution set is $\varnothing$ or $\{\ \}$.

Try These

Identify each as an *open sentence*, a *true sentence*, a *false sentence*, or an *expression*.

1. $2^5 = 5^2$ **2.** $-7x^2$ **3.** $2x + 5 = 13$ **4.** $8 + 3(2) = 14$ **5.** $10 = \frac{1}{2}(8x)$

Using the replacement set $\{-2, -1, 1.2, 2, 4\}$, find the solution set for each.

6. $d + 5 = 9$ **7.** $8 = 3g - 4$ **8.** $2k - 3.6 = 0.2k$ **9.** $-b^2 + 11 = 1.5$ **10.** $n^2 = (-n)^2$

11. Discuss and Write Soup is on sale at $0.99 per can. The number of cans a customer can buy is limited to 5. Write an algebraic expression to model the cost of a number of cans of this soup. Tell what the variable represents, and write a domain set for that variable.

Go to   PRACTICE BOOK Lesson 2-1 for exercise sets.

Solve Addition and Subtraction Equations

Objective To solve and check addition equations using the Subtraction Property of Equality • To solve and check subtraction equations using the Addition Property of Equality • To justify the steps of the solution process for addition and subtraction equations

Sara has put aside some money to buy a new instrument case. She needs to save $4 more to make the purchase. If the case costs $15, how much has she saved?

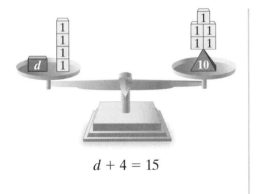

To find how much Sara has saved, write and solve an algebraic equation. First, define the variable. Then write two equivalent expressions.

Let d = the number of dollars Sara has saved.

$d + 4$ ◄— an expression for the number of dollars Sara has saved *plus* the $4-amount she will need

15 ◄— the expression showing the total cost

$d + 4 = 15$ ◄— an algebraic equation showing *equal expressions* for the total cost

► An equation that contains only the operation of addition such as $d + 4 = 15$, is called an *addition equation*. To solve the equation, find all the values of the variable that make the equation a *true* statement. The set containing all these values is the solution set.

To solve an addition equation, you can use the Subtraction Property of Equality.

To use this property, isolate the unknown term—that is, get the unknown term by itself. Then by using the inverse operation, subtraction, "undo" the addition operation in the given equation.

._____ **Key Concept** _____.

Subtraction Property of Equality
For real numbers a, b, and c,
if $a = b$, then $a - c = b - c$.

► An equation is like a balance. To keep the balance level, whatever you do to one side of the equation, you must do to the other so that you are forming *equations that have the same solution.* Such equations are called equivalent equations.

$d + 4 = 15$

$d + 4 - 4 = 15 - 4$ ◄—Use the Subtraction Property of Equality.

$d = 11$ ◄— equivalent equation

.**Think**..........
$d + 4 = 15$ and
$d = 11$ are
equivalent
equations.
....

So 11 is in the solution set of the equation $d + 4 = 15$.
Sara has saved $11.

▶To solve an equation, you may use *either* a vertical or a horizontal display.

Solve: $26.3 = y + 3.58$

Method 1 Solve vertically.

$$26.3 = y + 3.58$$
$$\underline{-\ 3.58 \qquad -\ 3.58} \quad \longleftarrow \text{Use the Subtraction Property of Equality. Subtract 3.58 to isolate } y.$$
$$22.72 = y$$

Method 2 Solve horizontally.

$$26.3 = y + 3.58$$
$$26.3 - 3.58 = y + 3.58 - 3.58 \quad \longleftarrow \text{Use the Subtraction Property of Equality. Subtract 3.58 to isolate } y.$$
$$22.72 = y$$

Always check a solution of an equation. Substitute each solution for the variable into the *original equation*.

Check: $26.3 = y + 3.58$

$$26.3 \overset{?}{=} 22.72 + 3.58 \quad \longleftarrow \text{Substitute 22.72 for } y; \text{ simplify.}$$

$$26.3 = 26.3 \quad \text{True}$$

Solution set: $\{22.72\}$

Examples

Solve each equation. Then check your solution.

1 **Solve:** $-9 = z - 4 + 16$

$$-9 = z - 4 + 16 \quad \longleftarrow \text{Identify like terms.}$$

$$-9 = z + 12 \quad \longleftarrow \text{Combine like terms.}$$

$$-9 - 12 = z + 12 - 12 \quad \longleftarrow \text{Use the Subtraction Property of Equality. Subtract 12 from both sides to isolate } z.$$

$$-21 = z \quad \longleftarrow \boxed{\text{solution}}$$

Check: $-9 = z - 4 + 16$

$$-9 \overset{?}{=} -21 - 4 + 16 \quad \longleftarrow \text{Substitute } -21 \text{ for } z; \text{ simplify.}$$

$$-9 = -9 \quad \text{True}$$

Solution set: $\{-21\}$

2 **Solve:** $m - 2\frac{3}{4} + 4 = -1\frac{1}{2}$

$$m - 2\frac{3}{4} + 4 = -1\frac{1}{2} \quad \longleftarrow \text{Identify like terms.}$$

$$m + 1\frac{1}{4} = -1\frac{1}{2} \quad \longleftarrow \text{Combine like terms.}$$

$$m + 1\frac{1}{4} - 1\frac{1}{4} = -1\frac{1}{2} - 1\frac{1}{4} \quad \longleftarrow \text{Use the Subtraction Property of Equality.}$$

$$m = -2\frac{3}{4} \quad \longleftarrow \boxed{\text{solution}}$$

Solution set: $\left\{-2\frac{3}{4}\right\}$

Check: $m - 2\frac{3}{4} + 4 = -1\frac{1}{2}$

$$-2\frac{3}{4} - 2\frac{3}{4} + 4 \overset{?}{=} -1\frac{1}{2}$$

$$-5\frac{1}{2} + 4 \overset{?}{=} -1\frac{1}{2}$$

$$-1\frac{1}{2} = -1\frac{1}{2} \quad \text{True}$$

Continue Lesson ➡

▶An equation that contains only the operation of subtraction, such as $w - 6.37 = -1.4$, is called a *subtraction equation*. To solve a subtraction equation, you can use the Addition Property of Equality.

Solve: $w - 6.37 = -1.4$

Method 1 Solve vertically.

$w - 6.37 = -1.4$

$\underline{\quad + 6.37 \quad + 6.37}$ ◄—Add 6.37 to isolate w.

$w \qquad = \quad 4.97$ ◄— solution

Check: $w - 6.37 = -1.4$

$4.97 - 6.37 \overset{?}{=} -1.4$ ◄—Substitute 4.97 for w.

$-1.4 = -1.4$ True

Solution set: {4.97}

Method 2 Solve horizontally.

$w - 6.37 = -1.4$

$w - 6.37 + 6.37 = -1.4 + 6.37$ ◄—Add 6.37 to isolate w.

$w = 4.97$ ◄— solution

Examples

1 **Solve:** $-9\frac{2}{5} + 4.3 = h - 3\frac{1}{2}$

$-9\frac{2}{5} + 4.3 = h - 3\frac{1}{2}$ ◄—Combine like terms.

$-9.4 + 4.3 = h - 3.5$ ◄— $-9\frac{2}{5} = 9.4$ and $3\frac{1}{2} = 3.5$

$-5.1 = h - 3.5$ ◄—Simplify.

$-5.1 + 3.5 = h - 3.5 + 3.5$ ◄—Use the Addition Property of Equality.

$-1.6 = h$ ◄— solution

Solution set: {−1.6}

Check: $-9\frac{2}{5} + 4.3 = h - 3\frac{1}{2}$

$-9.4 + 4.3 \overset{?}{=} -1.6 - 3.5$ ◄—Substitute; rename fractions as decimals.

$-5.1 = -5.1$ True

2 The difference between the ages of two brothers is 6 years. If the younger brother is 12 years old, how old is the other brother?

Let $x =$ the age of the older brother.
$x - 6 =$ the age of the younger brother

Solve: $x - 6 = 12$

$x - 6 + 6 = 12 + 6$ ◄—Use the Subtraction Property of Equality.

$x = 18$ ◄— solution

Check: Use the words of the problem. Does the solution make sense? If the older brother is 18, then the younger brother is $18 - 6 = 12$, which is the given value.

So the older brother is 18.

▶ You can use the Addition Property of Equality to solve an addition equation or a subtraction equation. Along with other familiar properties and definitions, you can justify the steps of the solution process.

Solve: $n + 2\frac{1}{2} = 7$. Write a justification for each step in the solution process.

$n + 2\frac{1}{2} + \left(-2\frac{1}{2}\right) = 7 + \left(-2\frac{1}{2}\right)$ ←—Use the Addition Property of Equality.

$n + \left[2\frac{1}{2} + \left(-2\frac{1}{2}\right)\right] = 7 + \left(-2\frac{1}{2}\right)$ ←—Use the Associative Property of Addition.

$n + 0 = 7 + \left(-2\frac{1}{2}\right)$ ←—Use the Additive Inverse Property.

$n = 7 + \left(-2\frac{1}{2}\right)$ ←—Use the Additive Identity Property.

$n = 4\frac{1}{2}$ ←— solution

Solution set: $\left\{4\frac{1}{2}\right\}$

Check: $n + 2\frac{1}{2} = 7$

$4\frac{1}{2} + 2\frac{1}{2} \stackrel{?}{=} 7$

$7 = 7$ True

Try These

Solve each equation. Check your solution.

1. $z - 19 = -28$

2. $h + \frac{1}{6} = 4\frac{1}{2} + 3$

3. $-8.7 = p - 16.4 + 6.2$

Write a justification for each step of the given solution process.

4. Solve: $w - 13 = -4$

  a. $w - 13 = -4$

  b. $w - 13 + 13 = -4 + 13$

  c. $w + (-13) + 13 = -4 + 13$

  d. $w + [(-13) + 13] = -4 + 13$

  e. $w + 0 = -4 + 13$

  f. $w = -4 + 13$

  g. $w = 9$

5. Solve: $-8 + p = -8$

  a. $-8 + p = -8$

  b. $-8 + 8 + p = -8 + 8$

  c. $[-8 + 8] + p = -8 + 8$

  d. $0 + p = -8 + 8$

  e. $p = -8 + 8$

  f. $p = 0$

Solve each equation. Write a justification for each step. Check your solution.

6. $b + 29 = -29$

7. $a - 19 = -25$

8. $-1 = d - 1 + 4.8$

9. Two angles are supplementary and the measure of one of these angles is 123°. Write and solve an equation that can be used to find the measure of the other angle. *Hint*: The sum of the measures of two supplementary angles is 180°.

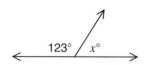

10. Discuss and Write When 15 is decreased by a number n, the result is -3. Write an equation that can be used to find n. Explain how to solve this equation. Show that your solution is correct.

Go to PRACTICE BOOK **Lesson 2-2 for exercise sets.**

Solve Multiplication and Division Equations

Objective To solve and check multiplication equations using the Division Property of Equality
• To solve and check division equations using the Multiplication Property of Equality • To justify the
steps of the solution process for multiplication and division equations

Raul's dad is helping to build props for a school play. He needs to cut a 2-foot-long wooden board into 4 short boards of equal length. What will be the measure of each short board?

► To find the measure of each short board, write and solve an equation. First, identify the variable. Then be sure that all measures are expressed with the same unit of measure.

Let x = the length of each of the short boards Raul's
    dad cuts, in inches.

$4x$ ◄— the expression for the total length of
    the short boards, in inches

2 ft = 2(12 in.) = 24 in. ◄— the expression for the length
    of the long board, in inches

$4x = 24$ ◄— an algebraic equation showing equal expressions
    for the length of the long board, in inches

Remember: 1 foot = 12 inches

____ **Key Concept** ____

Division Property of Equality
For real numbers, a, b, and c,
$c \neq 0$, if $a = b$, then $\dfrac{a}{c} = \dfrac{b}{c}$.

► An equation that contains only the operation of multiplication, such as $4x = 24$, is called a multiplication equation. To solve a multiplication equation, use the Division Property of Equality.

You can use a balance to visualize how a multiplication equation is solved.

$4x = 24$

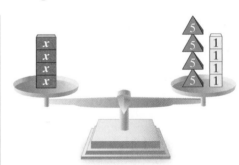

$\dfrac{4x}{4} = \dfrac{24}{4}$ ◄— Use the Division Property of Equality.

$x = 6$ ◄— equivalent equation

So the length of each short board that Raul's dad cuts is 6 inches.

► To solve algebraically a multiplication equation, isolate the unknown term by using division.

Solve: $-8.5 = 5y$

$\dfrac{-8.5}{5} = \dfrac{5y}{5}$ ◄— Use the Division Property of Equality.

$-1.7 = y$ ◄— solution

Solution set: $\{-1.7\}$

Check: $-8.5 = 5y$

$-8.5 \stackrel{?}{=} 5 \cdot 1.7$

$-8.5 = -8.5$ True

Example

1 **Solve:** $-5\frac{3}{8} = 2q$

$$\frac{-5\frac{3}{8}}{2} = \frac{2q}{2}$$ ←—Use the Division Property of Equality.

$$-\frac{43}{8} \div \frac{2}{1} = q$$ ←—Simplify.

$$-\frac{43}{8} \cdot \frac{1}{2} = q$$

$$-\frac{43}{16} = -2\frac{11}{16} = q$$ ←— $\boxed{\text{solution}}$

Solution set: $\left\{-2\frac{11}{16}\right\}$

Check: $-5\frac{3}{8} = 2q$

$$-\frac{43}{8} \overset{?}{=} 2\left(-2\frac{11}{16}\right)$$

$$-\frac{43}{8} \overset{?}{=} 2\left(-\frac{43}{16}\right)$$

$$-\frac{43}{8} = -\frac{43}{8} \text{ True}$$

▶ An equation that contains only the operation of division is called a **division equation**. To solve a division equation, use the **Multiplication Property of Equality**.

A box of paperback books is divided among 11 high school students. If each student receives 3 books, how many paperbacks were in the box?

To find how many paperbacks, write and solve a division equation.

Let $b =$ the number of paperback books in the box.

_____ **Key Concept** _____
Multiplication Property of Equality

For real numbers, a, b, and c, if $a = b$, *then* $ac = bc$.

number of paperbacks in a box	*divided by*	eleven	*equals*	number of paperbacks per child
b	$\div$	11	$=$	3 ←— $\boxed{\text{division equation}}$

Solve: $\dfrac{b}{11} = 3$ .Think..... $b \div 11 = \dfrac{b}{11}$

$$\frac{b}{11} \cdot 11 = 3 \cdot 11$$ ←—Use the Multiplication Property of Equality.

$$b = 33$$ ←— $\boxed{\text{solution}}$

Check: $\dfrac{b}{11} = 3$

$$\frac{33}{11} \overset{?}{=} 3$$

$$3 = 3 \text{ True}$$

So the box contained 33 paperbacks.

▶ In some equations, the coefficient of the unknown term will be a fraction. In such cases, multiply by the reciprocal of the coefficient to isolate the unknown term.

Remember: The *reciprocal* of a number is formed by interchanging the numerator and denominator.

Solve: $\dfrac{3}{7}z = 36$

$$\frac{7}{3} \cdot \frac{3}{7}z = \frac{7}{3} \cdot 36$$ ←—Multiply each side by the reciprocal of $\frac{3}{7}$.

$$z = \frac{7}{3} \cdot \overset{12}{36}$$ ←—Simplify.
$$\phantom{z = \frac{7}{3} \cdot 3}{\scriptstyle 1}$$

$$z = 84$$ ←— $\boxed{\text{solution}}$

Solution set: {84}

Check: $\dfrac{3}{7}z = 36$

$$\frac{3}{7}(84) \overset{?}{=} 36$$

$$36 = 36 \text{ True}$$

Continue Lesson ➡

Example

1 **Solve:** $\dfrac{2a}{3} = \dfrac{4}{9}$

.Think...........................

$\dfrac{2}{3}a = \dfrac{4}{9}$ | $\dfrac{2a}{3}$ is equivalent to $\dfrac{2}{3}a$.

$\dfrac{3}{2} \cdot \dfrac{2}{3}a = \dfrac{3}{2} \cdot \dfrac{4}{9}$ ← Use the Multiplication Property of Equality.

$a = \dfrac{\overset{1}{3}}{\underset{1}{2}} \cdot \dfrac{\overset{2}{4}}{\underset{3}{9}} = \dfrac{2}{3}$ ← Simplify.

$a = \dfrac{2}{3}$ ← $\boxed{\text{solution}}$

Solution set: $\left\{\dfrac{2}{3}\right\}$

Check: $\dfrac{2}{3}a = \dfrac{4}{9}$

$\dfrac{2}{3}\left(\dfrac{2}{3}\right) \overset{?}{=} \dfrac{4}{9}$

$\dfrac{4}{9} = \dfrac{4}{9}$ True

▶ You can use the Multiplication Property of Equality to solve a multiplication equation or a division equation. Along with other familiar properties and definitions, you can justify the steps of the solution process.

Solve: $6x = 72$. Write a justification for each step in the solution process.

$\dfrac{1}{6} \cdot 6x = \dfrac{1}{6} \cdot 72$ ← Use the Multiplication Property of Equality.

$\left(\dfrac{1}{6} \cdot 6\right) \cdot x = \dfrac{1}{6} \cdot 72$ ← Use the Associative Property of Multiplication.

$1 \cdot x = \dfrac{1}{6} \cdot 72$ ← Use the Multiplicative Inverse Property.

$x = \dfrac{1}{6} \cdot 72$ ← Use the Multiplicative Identity Property.

$x = 12$ ← $\boxed{\text{solution}}$

Solution set: {12}

Check: $6x = 72$

$6(12) \overset{?}{=} 72$

$72 = 72$ True

Examples

1 **Solve:** $\dfrac{k}{4} = 16$

$k \cdot \dfrac{1}{4} = 16$ ← Use the definition of division.

$k \cdot \dfrac{1}{4} \cdot 4 = 16 \cdot 4$ ← Use the Multiplication Property of Equality.

$k \cdot \left(\dfrac{1}{4} \cdot 4\right) = 16 \cdot 4$ ← Use the Associative Property of Multiplication.

$k \cdot 1 = 16 \cdot 4$ ← Use the Multiplicative Inverse Property.

$k = 16 \cdot 4$ ← Use the Multiplicative Identity Property.

$k = 64$ ← Simplify.

Solution set: {64}

Check: $\dfrac{k}{4} = 16$

$\dfrac{64}{4} \overset{?}{=} 16$

$16 = 16$ True

2 **Solve:** $11\frac{1}{4} + 3.75 = 5x$

$11\frac{1}{4} + 3.75 = 5x$ ←Identify like terms.

$15 = 5x$ ←Combine like terms.

$\dfrac{15}{5} = \dfrac{5 \cdot x}{5}$ ←Use the Division Property of Equality.

$3 = 1 \cdot x$ ←Simplify.

$3 = x$ ←Use the Multiplicative Identity Property.

Solution set: {3}

.**Think**......

$11\frac{1}{4} = 11.25$

Check: $11\frac{1}{4} + 3.75 = 5x$

$11\frac{1}{4} + 3.75 \overset{?}{=} 5(3)$

$15 = 15$ True

---

3 **Solve:** $19h = -114$

$\dfrac{19h}{19} = \dfrac{-114}{19}$ ←Use the Division Property of Equality.

$\dfrac{19h}{19 \cdot 1} = \dfrac{-114}{19}$ ←Use the Multiplicative Identity Property.

$\dfrac{19}{19} \cdot \dfrac{h}{1} = \dfrac{-114}{19}$ ←$\dfrac{ac}{bd} = \dfrac{a}{b} \cdot \dfrac{b}{d}$

$1 \cdot h = \dfrac{-114}{19}$ ←$\dfrac{a}{a} = 1; \dfrac{a}{1} = a$

$h = \dfrac{-114}{19}$ ←Use the Multiplicative Identity Property.

$h = -6$ ←Simplify.

Solution set: {−6}

Check: $19h = -114$

$19(-6) \overset{?}{=} -114$

$-114 = -114$ True

Try These

Solve each equation. Check your solution.

1. $-10.2 = 1.7j$

2. $-80 = \dfrac{h}{5}$

3. $2b = -7\frac{3}{4}$

4. $\dfrac{-4n}{5} = \dfrac{16}{25}$

Solve the equation. Write a justification for each step. Check your solution.

5. $27 = \dfrac{z}{9}$

6. $-216 = 72g$

7. $\dfrac{2}{5}z = 10$

8. $\dfrac{7}{2}m = 12.1 + 8.9$

Write and solve an equation.

9. The tallest player on a basketball team is $72\frac{3}{4}$ inches tall. If this is $1\frac{1}{4}$ times the height of the shortest player, what is the height of the shortest player?

10. The area of the triangle at the right is 156 in². If the base is 26 in. long, write and solve an equation that can be used to find the height h.

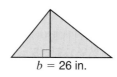

Hint: Area $\triangle = \frac{1}{2}bh$

$b = 26$ in.

11. **Discuss and Write** To solve the equation $\dfrac{x}{8} = 56$, Kyle divided 56 by 8 and said the solution is $x = 7$. Do you agree or disagree? Explain.

Go to PRACTICE BOOK Lesson 2-3 for exercise sets.

Solve Equations with Two Operations

Objective To solve and check a variety of equations with two operations

At a fair to promote recycling, a man used empty cans to make a costume. The number of cans he used was 5 more than twice the number of cans that had been in one collection bin. If there were 105 cans in the costume, how many cans were in the collection bin?

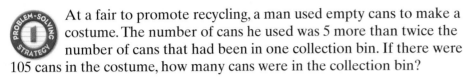

To find how many cans were in the bin, write and solve an equation.

Let x = the number of cans in the bin.

five	*more than*	twice the number of cans	*equals*	number of cans in the costume	
5	+	$2x$	=	105	← equation with two operations

▶ To solve an *equation with two operations*, isolate the variable by using inverse operations.

You can use a balance to visualize an equation with two operations and its solution.

Solve: $2x + 5 = 105$

> **Think**
> $5 + 2x = 105$ is equivalent to $2x + 5 = 105$.

$2x + 5 = 105$

$2x + 5 - 5 = 105 - 5$ ←Subtract 5 from both sides.

$\dfrac{2x}{2} = \dfrac{100}{2}$ ←Divide both sides by 2.

$x = 50$

So there were 50 cans in the collection bin.

Examples

1 **Solve:** $\dfrac{k}{3} - 0.5 = 4.5$

$\dfrac{k}{3} - 0.5 + 0.5 = 4.5 + 0.5$ ←Use the Addition Property of Equality.

$\dfrac{k}{3} = 5$ ←Simplify.

$3 \cdot \dfrac{k}{3} = 3 \cdot 5$ ←Use the Multiplication Property of Equality.

$k = 15$ ←Simplify.

Solution set: {15}

Check: $\dfrac{k}{3} - 0.5 = 4.5$

$\dfrac{15}{3} - 0.5 \stackrel{?}{=} 4.5$

$5 - 0.5 \stackrel{?}{=} 4.5$

$4.5 = 4.5$ True

2 **Solve:** $11 - b = 32$

$$11 - 1b = 32 \quad \longleftarrow \text{The coefficient of } b \text{ is 1.}$$

$$11 + (-1b) = 32 \quad \longleftarrow \text{Use the definition of subtraction.}$$

$$11 - 11 + (-1b) = 32 - 11 \quad \longleftarrow \text{Use the Subtraction Property of Equality.}$$

$$-1b = 21 \quad \longleftarrow \text{Simplify.}$$

$$\frac{-1b}{-1} = \frac{21}{-1} \quad \longleftarrow \text{Use the Division Property of Equality.}$$

$$b = -21 \quad \longleftarrow \text{Simplify.}$$

Solution set: $\{-21\}$

Check: $11 - b = 32$

$$11 - (-21) \stackrel{?}{=} 32$$

$$11 + 21 \stackrel{?}{=} 32$$

$$32 = 32 \quad \text{True}$$

▶ When an equation contains several fractions, you can either compute with fractions throughout, *or* you can transform the equation to an equivalent equation with integer coefficients.

Solve: $\frac{w}{18} - \frac{1}{9} = \frac{7}{9}$

Method 1 Compute with fractions.

$$\frac{w}{18} - \frac{1}{9} = \frac{7}{9}$$

$$\frac{w}{18} - \frac{1}{9} + \frac{1}{9} = \frac{7}{9} + \frac{1}{9} \quad \longleftarrow \text{Use the Addition Property of Equality.}$$

$$\frac{w}{18} = \frac{8}{9} \quad \longleftarrow \text{Simplify.}$$

$$18 \bullet \frac{w}{18} = 18 \bullet \frac{8}{9} \quad \longleftarrow \text{Use the Multiplication Property of Equality.}$$

$$w = \overset{2}{\cancel{18}} \bullet \frac{8}{\underset{1}{\cancel{9}}} = 16 \quad \longleftarrow \text{Simplify.}$$

Method 2 Use the LCD to transform the equation.

$$\frac{w}{18} - \frac{1}{9} = \frac{7}{9} \quad \longleftarrow \begin{array}{l} \text{Find the LCD of 9 and 18.} \\ \text{LCD = 18} \end{array}$$

$$18\left(\frac{w}{18} - \frac{1}{9}\right) = 18 \bullet \frac{7}{9} \quad \longleftarrow \begin{array}{l} \text{Multiply each side of the} \\ \text{equation by the LCD.} \end{array}$$

$$18 \bullet \frac{w}{18} - 18 \bullet \frac{1}{9} = 18 \bullet \frac{7}{9} \quad \longleftarrow \begin{array}{l} \text{Distribute 18 on the} \\ \text{left side.} \end{array}$$

$$w - 2 = 14 \quad \longleftarrow \text{Simplify.}$$

$$w - 2 + 2 = 14 + 2 \quad \longleftarrow \begin{array}{l} \text{Use the Addition} \\ \text{Property of Equality.} \end{array}$$

$$w = 16 \quad \longleftarrow \text{Simplify.}$$

Solution set: $\{16\}$

Check: $\frac{w}{18} - \frac{1}{9} = \frac{7}{9}$

$$\frac{16}{18} - \frac{1}{9} \stackrel{?}{=} \frac{7}{9}$$

$$\frac{8}{9} - \frac{1}{9} \stackrel{?}{=} \frac{7}{9}$$

$$\frac{7}{9} = \frac{7}{9} \quad \text{True}$$

Continue Lesson ➡

▶ If the unknown appears in more than one term, you will need to first combine like terms, then solve.

> **Remember:** *Like terms* have the same variable raised to the same power.

Examples

1 Solve: $2p - 7p - 1.98 = -35$

$2p - 7p - 1.98 = -35$ ◀—Identify like terms.

$-5p - 1.98 = -35$ ◀—Combine like terms.

$-5p - 1.98 + 1.98 = -35 + 1.98$ ◀—Use the Addition Property of Equality.

$-5p = -33.02$ ◀—Simplify.

$\dfrac{-5p}{-5} = \dfrac{-33.02}{-5}$ ◀—Use the Division Property of Equality.

$p = 6.604$ ◀—Simplify.

Check: $2p - 7p - 1.98 = -35$

$2(6.604) - 7(6.604) - 1.98 \overset{?}{=} -35$

$13.208 - 46.228 - 1.98 \overset{?}{=} -35$

$-33.02 - 1.98 \overset{?}{=} -35$

$-35 = -35$ True

Solution set: $\{6.604\}$

2 Solve: $7y - 1.8y + 4.3 = -8 + 7.1$

$7y - 1.8y + 4.3 = -8 + 7.1$ ◀—Identify like terms.

$5.2y + 4.3 = -0.9$ ◀—Combine like terms.

$5.2y + 4.3 - 4.3 = -0.9 - 4.3$ ◀—Use the Subtraction Property of Equality.

$5.2y = -5.2$ ◀—Simplify.

$\dfrac{5.2y}{5.2} = \dfrac{-5.2}{5.2}$ ◀—Use the Division Property of Equality.

$y = -1$ ◀—Simplify.

Check: $7y - 1.8y + 4.3 = -8 + 7.1$

$7(-1) - 1.8(-1) + 4.3 \overset{?}{=} -8 + 7.1$

$-7 + 1.8 + 4.3 \overset{?}{=} -8 + 7.1$

$-0.9 = -0.9$ True

Solution set: $\{-1\}$

3 There are three consecutive integers in counting order whose sum is 84. What are the integers?

Let $x, x + 1,$ and $x + 2$ represent the three consecutive integers.

Solve: $x + (x + 1) + (x + 2) = 84$

$x + x + 1 + x + 2 = 84$ ◀—Identify like terms.

$3x + 3 = 84$ ◀—Combine like terms.

$3x + 3 - 3 = 84 - 3$ ◀—Use the Subtraction Property of Equality.

$3x = 81$ ◀—Simplify.

$\dfrac{3x}{3} = \dfrac{81}{3}$ ◀—Use the Division Property of Equality.

$x = 27$ ◀—Simplify.

$x + 1 = 27 + 1 = 28$ ◀—
$x + 2 = 27 + 2 = 29$ ◀— ⎤ Find the other integers.

Check: $x + (x + 1) + (x + 2) = 84$

$27 + 28 + 29 \overset{?}{=} 84$

$84 = 84$ True

So the consecutive integers are 27, 28, and 29.

▶ You can use the Properties of Equality along with other familiar properties and definitions to justify the steps of a solution process when solving an equation involving more than one operation.

Solve: $7 - 0.8x - 11.7 + 0.1x = 2.3$

$(0.1x - 0.8x) + (7 - 11.7) = 2.3$ ←——Use the Commutative and Associative Properties to collect like terms.

$(0.1 - 0.8)x + (7 - 11.7) = 2.3$ ←——Use the Distributive Property on the x-terms.

$-0.7x + (-4.7) = 2.3$ ←——Simplify.

$-0.7x - 4.7 = 2.3$ ←——Use the definition of subtraction.

$-0.7x - 4.7 + 4.7 = 2.3 + 4.7$ ←——Use the Addition Property of Equality.

$-0.7x = 7$ ←——Simplify.

$\dfrac{1}{-0.7} \bullet -0.7x = \dfrac{1}{-0.7} \bullet 7$ ←——Use the Multiplication Property of Equality.

$\left(-0.7 \bullet \dfrac{1}{-0.7}\right)x = \dfrac{1}{-0.7} \bullet 7$ ←——Use the Associative Property of Multiplication.

$(1)x = \dfrac{1}{-0.7} \bullet 7$ ←——Use the Multiplicative Inverse Property.

$x = -10$

Check:

$7 - 0.8x - 11.7 + 0.1x = 2.3$

$7 - 0.8(-10) - 11.7 + 0.1(-10) \overset{?}{=} 2.3$

$7 + 8 - 11.7 - 1 \overset{?}{=} 2.3$

$2.3 = 2.3$ True

Try These

Solve each equation. Check your solution.

1. $121.3 = 6x - 42.5$

2. $\dfrac{2h}{3} - 4 = 14$

3. $12 - 0.5j = -13$

4. $\dfrac{z}{24} + \dfrac{1}{12} = \dfrac{5}{12}$

5. $-n + 8.4 = -9 + 7.7$

6. $2p + p + 4.3 = 8 + 2$

Solve each equation. Write a justification for each step. Check your solution.

7. $38m - 4 = 15$

8. $6y + 3 - 4y = 15$

9. $5 - 8t - 7 - t = 16$

Write and solve an equation for each problem.

10. There are three *consecutive even* integers in counting order whose sum is 102. Find these integers.

11. The measure of the larger acute angle of a right triangle is twice the measure of the smaller acute angle. Find each measure.

12. Discuss and Write Compare the process of solving an algebraic equation that contains two operations to the process of evaluating a numerical expression that contains two operations. Include specific examples.

Go to PRACTICE BOOK Lesson 2-4 for exercise sets.

Solve Multistep Equations

Objective To use the Distributive Property in equations with grouping symbols • To solve equations that contain variable terms on both sides • To recognize identities and contradictions • To state general principles for solving an equation in one variable

Nick, Joan, and Maya are selling handmade pottery pieces. So far, Joan has sold 10 more pottery pieces than Nick. Maya has sold twice as many pieces as Joan. If Maya has sold 40 pottery pieces, how many pieces has Nick sold?

► To find how many Nick has sold, write and solve an equation.

Let n = the number of pottery pieces Nick has sold.

$n + 10$ = the number of pottery pieces Joan has sold

twice as the number of pottery pieces Joan sold	*equals*	number of pottery pieces Maya has sold
$2(n + 10)$	$=$	40

40 ← equation with grouping symbols

► To solve an *equation with grouping symbols*, you can begin by using the Distributive Property.

Solve: $2(n + 10) = 40$

$$2(n + 10) = 40$$
$$2n + 2(10) = 40 \quad \longleftarrow \text{Use the Distributive Property.}$$
$$2n + 20 = 40 \quad \longleftarrow \text{Simplify.}$$
$$2n + 20 - 20 = 40 - 20 \quad \longleftarrow \text{Use the Subtraction Property of Equality.}$$
$$2n = 20 \quad \longleftarrow \text{Simplify.}$$
$$\frac{2n}{2} = \frac{20}{2} \quad \longleftarrow \text{Use the Division Property of Equality.}$$
$$n = 10 \quad \longleftarrow \boxed{\text{solution}}$$

Use the value for n to evaluate the other expressions.
Check with the words of the problem to verify the solution.

$$n = 10 \quad \longleftarrow \text{number of pottery pieces Nick has sold}$$
$$n + 10 = 10 + 10 = 20 \quad \longleftarrow \text{number of pottery pieces Joan has sold}$$
$$2(n + 10) = 2(10 + 10) = 2(20) = 40 \quad \longleftarrow \text{number of pottery pieces Maya has sold, which matches the given information}$$

Check: $2(n + 10) = 40$
$$2(10 + 10) \overset{?}{=} 40$$
$$2(20) \overset{?}{=} 40$$
$$40 = 40 \quad \text{True}$$

So Nick has sold 10 handmade pottery pieces.

Example

1 Sam framed a picture that is twice as long as it is wide. He used a 3-inch-wide mat around the picture. If Sam used 78 inches of wood to frame the picture, what are the dimensions of the picture?

Let w = the width of the picture, in inches;

$2w$ = the length of the picture, in inches;

$w + 6$ = the width of the frame, in inches; and

$2w + 6$ = the length of the frame, in inches.

Solve: $2(w + 6) + 2(2w + 6) = 78$ ◄——Use the perimeter formula: $P = 2\ell + 2w$

$2w + 12 + 4w + 12 = 78$ ◄——Use the Distributive Property twice, and identify like terms.

$6w + 24 = 78$ ◄——Combine like terms.

$6w + 24 - 24 = 78 - 24$ ◄——Use the Subtraction Property of Equality.

$6w = 54$ ◄——Simplify.

$\dfrac{6w}{6} = \dfrac{54}{6}$ ◄——Use the Division Property of Equality.

$w = 9$ ◄——Simplify.

$2w = 2(9) = 18$

Check: The dimensions of the frame are $w + 6 = 9 + 6 = 15$ and $2w + 6 = 18 + 6 = 24$.

The amount of framing is $2(15) + 2(24) = 30 + 48 = 78$.

So the dimensions of the picture are 9 inches by 18 inches.

► To solve an equation that has unknown terms on both sides, use inverse operations to write an equivalent equation with all of the unknown terms on one side.

Solve: $12z - 3 = 8z + 13$

$12z - 3 = 8z + 13$

> It is usually easier to collect the unknown terms on the side where the resulting coefficient will be positive.

$12z - 8z - 3 = 8z - 8z + 13$ ◄——Use the Subtraction Property of Equality.

$4z - 3 = 13$ ◄——Simplify.

$4z - 3 + 3 = 13 + 3$ ◄——Use the Addition Property of Equality.

$4z = 16$ ◄——Simplify.

$\dfrac{4z}{4} = \dfrac{16}{4}$ ◄——Use the Division Property of Equality.

$z = 4$ ◄——Simplify.

Solution set: $\{4\}$

Check: $12z - 3 = 8z + 13$

$12(4) - 3 \stackrel{?}{=} 8(4) + 13$

$48 - 3 \stackrel{?}{=} 32 + 13$

$45 = 45$ True

▶ Before collecting unknown terms, you may first need to simplify the equation.

Solve: $6v + v + 9 = 4 - 3v$

$6v + v + 9 = 4 - 3v$ ◀—Identify like terms.

$7v + 9 = 4 - 3v$ ◀—Combine like terms.

$7v + 3v + 9 = 4 - 3v + 3v$ ◀—Use the Addition Property of Equality.

$10v + 9 = 4$ ◀—Simplify.

$10v + 9 - 9 = 4 - 9$ ◀—Use the Subtraction Property of Equality.

$10v = -5$ ◀—Simplify.

$\dfrac{10v}{10} = \dfrac{-5}{10}$ ◀—Use the Division Property of Equality.

$v = -\dfrac{1}{2}$

Solution set: $\left\{-\dfrac{1}{2}\right\}$

Check: $6v + v + 9 = 4 - 3v$

$6\left(-\dfrac{1}{2}\right) + \left(-\dfrac{1}{2}\right) + 9 \overset{?}{=} 4 - 3\left(-\dfrac{1}{2}\right)$

$-3 + \left(-\dfrac{1}{2}\right) + 9 \overset{?}{=} 4 + \dfrac{3}{2}$

$-3\dfrac{1}{2} + 9 \overset{?}{=} 4 + 1\dfrac{1}{2}$

$5\dfrac{1}{2} = 5\dfrac{1}{2}$ True

Example

1 **Solve:** $2(3m - 1) = 2m + 2$

$2(3m - 1) = 2m + 2$

$2(3m) + 2(-1) = 2m + 2$ ◀—Use the Distributive Property.

$6m - 2 = 2m + 2$ ◀—Simplify.

$6m - 2m - 2 = 2m - 2m + 2$ ◀—Use the Subtraction Property of Equality.

$4m - 2 = 2$ ◀—Simplify.

$4m - 2 + 2 = 2 + 2$ ◀—Use the Addition Property of Equality.

$4m = 4$ ◀—Simplify.

$\dfrac{4m}{4} = \dfrac{4}{4}$ ◀—Use the Division Property of Equality.

$m = 1$

Solution set: $\{1\}$

Check: $2(3m - 1) = 2m + 2$

$2(3 \bullet 1 - 1) \overset{?}{=} 2 \bullet 1 + 2$

$2(3 - 1) \overset{?}{=} 2 + 2$

$2(3 - 1) \overset{?}{=} 4$

$2(2) \overset{?}{=} 4$

$4 = 4$ True

▶ Sometimes, equations may have infinitely many solutions or no solutions. When a solution process ends in a *true numerical statement*, the original equation is called an **identity**, and its solution set is all the real numbers.

Solve: $k + 3 + 7k = 5 + 8k - 2$

$k + 3 + 7k = 5 + 8k - 2$ ◀—Identify like terms.

$8k + 3 = 3 + 8k$ ◀—Combine like terms.

$8k - 8k + 3 = 3 + 8k - 8k$ ◀—Use the Subtraction Property of Equality.

$3 = 3$ ◀—*true* numerical statement

Think $k + 3 + 7k = 5 + 8k - 2$ is an identity.

Solution set: $\{k | k \text{ is any real number}\}$.

▶ When a solution process ends in a *false numerical statement*, the original equation is a contradiction, and its solution set is the null set.

Solve: $-3y + 7 + 5y = -11 + 2y$

$-3y + 7 + 5y = -11 + 2y$ ◀—Identify like terms.

$2y + 7 = -11 + 2y$ ◀—Combine like terms.

$2y - 2y + 7 = -11 + 2y - 2y$ ◀—Use the Subtraction Property of Equality.

$7 = -11$ ◀—*false* numerical statement

Think..
$-3y + 7 + 5y = -11 + 2y$ is a contradiction.

Solution set: $\varnothing$

Principles for Solving Equations in One Variable

1. Remove grouping symbols by applying the Distributive Property.

2. Simplify the expressions on each side by combining like terms that are on the same side of the equation.

3. Use the Addition and/or Subtraction Property of Equality to position all of the unknown terms on one side and the numbers without unknown terms on the other side.

4. Simplify the expressions on each side of the equal sign.

5. Use the Multiplication and/or Division Property of Equality to isolate the unknown term and solve the equation.

6. Check the result in the original equation. Work each side separately.

7. State the solution set.
   If the steps above lead to a *true* numerical statement, the solution set is {real numbers}.
   If the steps above lead to a *false* numerical statement, the solution set is $\varnothing$.

Try These

Solve each equation. Check your solution.

1. $\frac{1}{7}(35 + 7x) = 4$

2. $12 = 7 - (p + 4)$

3. $\frac{1}{2}(4j - 6) + \frac{2}{3}(3j) = 1$

4. $6n - 3 = 10n + 17$

5. $7(0.1d - 1) = d + 2$

6. $2g + g - 7 = 1 + 3g$

7. $t + 1 + 5t = 3 - 2 + t$

8. $-5r - 1 + 4r = -1 - r$

Write and solve an equation for each problem.

9. Nick drew a rectangle that is 4 times as long as it is wide. Stacey increased each dimension of Nick's rectangle by 5 inches. If the perimeter of Stacey's rectangle is 60 inches, what are the dimensions of Nick's rectangle?

10. Claire's cousin is now 3 times as old as Claire. In 10 years, her cousin will be twice as old as Claire. How old is Claire now?

11. Derek drew a square and an equilateral triangle that are equal in perimeter. If a side of the equilateral triangle is 1 inch longer than a side of the square, what is the area of the square?

12. **Discuss and Write** Ms. Kinney wrote the equation $4x + 16 = 80$ on the board and asked her class to find the value of $x + 4$. Penny said she would solve the given equation for x and then use that value to find $x + 4$. The class agreed that Penny's method is correct. Explain how you can find the value of $x + 4$ without first solving for x.

Go to PRACTICE BOOK Lesson 2-5 for exercise sets.

Solve Absolute-Value Equations

Objective To write and solve absolute-value equations

The late night news reported that today's temperature varied 18 degrees from the midmorning reading of 42°. What were the day's possible maximum and minimum temperatures?

To find the maximum and minimum temperatures, write and solve an equation.

Let t = the day's temperature.

Since it is not given which temperature (the day's or midmorning temperature) is higher, you can represent the difference between the temperatures by an *absolute-value expression*.

Remember: The *absolute value* of a number is always nonnegative, it is the number's distance from 0 on the number line.

the day's temperature	*minus*	midmorning's temperature	*equals*	positive difference
$\lvert t$	$-$	$42 \rvert$	$=$	18 ← absolute-value equation

.**Think**....................
: There are two points on the number line
: that are 18 units away from 0: 18 and -18

Key Concept

Solving Absolute-Value Equations
> Case 1: $\lvert x \rvert = a \longrightarrow x = a$ when x is nonnegative,
> *or* Case 2: $\lvert x \rvert = a \longrightarrow x = -a$ when x is negative.

► To solve an *absolute-value equation*, apply the definition of absolute value to establish two cases. Solve each case.

Case 1: The expression within the absolute-value symbols is *positive*.

Solve: $t - 42 = 18$

$t - 42 + 42 = 18 + 42$

$t = 60$

Check: $\lvert 60 - 42 \rvert \overset{?}{=} 18 \longrightarrow \lvert -18 \rvert \overset{?}{=} 18$

$18 = 18$ True

Case 2: The expression within the absolute-value symbols is *negative*.

Solve: $t - 42 = -18$

$t - 42 + 42 = -18 + 42$

$t = 24$

Check: $\lvert 24 - 42 \rvert \overset{?}{=} 18 \longrightarrow \lvert -18 \rvert \overset{?}{=} 18$

$18 = 18$ True

So the maximum possible temperature was 60°, and the minimum possible temperature was 24°.

Examples

1 Solve: $2\lvert x + 9 \rvert = 14$ | Isolate the absolute-value expression on one side of the equation.

$\dfrac{2\lvert x + 9 \rvert}{2} = \dfrac{14}{2}$ ← Use the Division Property of Equality.

$\lvert x + 9 \rvert = 7$

$x + 9 = 7 \qquad$ or $\qquad x + 9 = -7$

$x + 9 - 9 = 7 - 9 \mid x + 9 - 9 = -7 - 9$

$x = -2 \qquad\qquad x = -16$

Check: $2\lvert x + 9 \rvert = 14$

$2\lvert -2 + 9 \rvert \overset{?}{=} 14 \quad$ or $\quad 2\lvert -16 + 9 \rvert \overset{?}{=} 14$

$2\lvert 7 \rvert \overset{?}{=} 14 \qquad\qquad 2\lvert -7 \rvert \overset{?}{=} 14$

$2(7) \overset{?}{=} 14 \qquad\qquad 2(7) \overset{?}{=} 14$

$14 = 14$ True $\qquad\qquad 14 = 14$ True

Solution set: $\{-16, -2\}$

2 **Solve:** $3|y - 2| - 4 = 11$

$3|y - 2| - 4 + 4 = 11 + 4$ ◄—Use the Addition Property of Equality.

$3|y - 2| = 15$ ◄—Simplify.

$\dfrac{3|y - 2|}{3} = \dfrac{15}{3}$ ◄—Use the Division Property of Equality.

$|y - 2| = 5$ ◄—Simplify.

$y - 2 = 5$ or $y - 2 = -5$

$y - 2 + 2 = 5 + 2$ | $y - 2 + 2 = -5 + 2$

$y = 7$ | $y = -3$

Solution set: $\{-3, 7\}$

Check: $3|y - 2| - 4 = 11$

$3|7 - 2| - 4 \overset{?}{=} 11$ or $3|-3 - 2| - 4 \overset{?}{=} 11$

$3|5| - 4 \overset{?}{=} 11$ $3|-5| - 4 \overset{?}{=} 11$

$3(5) - 4 \overset{?}{=} 11$ $3(5) - 4 \overset{?}{=} 11$

$15 - 4 \overset{?}{=} 11$ $15 - 4 \overset{?}{=} 11$

$11 = 11$ True $11 = 11$ True

► Not all absolute-value equations have two solutions.

- If an absolute-value expression equals 0, there is only *one solution*.

$|x - 8| + 20 = 20$

$|x - 8| + 20 - 20 = 20 - 20$

$|x - 8| = 0$

$x - 8 = 0$ ◄—With 0, there is only one case.

$x - 8 + 8 = 0 + 8$

$x = 8$

Solution set: $\{8\}$

- If an absolute-value expression corresponds to a negative value, there are *no solutions*.

$|y + 2| + 7 = 1$

$|y + 2| + 7 - 7 = 1 - 7$

$|y + 2| = -6$ ◄—Absolute value cannot be negative.

Solution set: $\varnothing$

Try These

Find the solution set for each equation. Check your result.

1. $|y| + 17 = 17$　　　**2.** $-|14n + 2| = -7$　　　**3.** $|m + 2| + 5 = 5$　　　**4.** $8|p - 5| - 4 = 20$

Write and solve an equation for each problem. Check your solution.

5. A poll reported the approval rating of the CEO of a corporation to be 62%. If the poll is accurate within 2.8%, what are the maximum and minimum approval ratings for the CEO?

6. Discuss and Write As shown in the diagram at the right, a 30-unit-long line segment is divided into two sections. Explain how to find possible values. Verify that your solution is correct.

├────30────┤

├───┼────┤
$2|y - 3|$ $3|y - 3|$

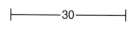**Go to**   PRACTICE BOOK Lesson 2-6 for exercise sets.

Formulas and Literal Equations

Objective To solve formulas for particular variables • To solve literal equations for particular variables

Finish times are recorded for the runners of a race. If Connor won his 200-meter race in 41.5 seconds, what was his average speed?

You can determine Connor's average speed by using a *formula* that relates distance, rate of speed, and time.

▶ A formula is an equation that states a rule for a relationship among particular quantities.

To determine Connor's average speed, use the formula $d = rt$, where d represents distance, r represents rate of speed, and t represents time.

$$d = rt$$
$$200 = r \bullet 41.5 \quad \longleftarrow \text{Substitute 200 for } d \text{ and 41.5 for } t.$$
$$\frac{200}{41.5} = \frac{r \bullet 41.5}{41.5} \quad \longleftarrow \text{Use the Division Property of Equality.}$$
$$4.8 \approx r \quad \longleftarrow \text{Round to the nearest tenth.}$$

So Connor's average speed was about 4.8 meters per second.

▶ To *solve for a variable* in a given formula, isolate that variable. Identify the operations on that variable, and use inverse operations to undo them.

If you wanted to know the average speed of the other runners in that race, it would be efficient to first "rearrange" (transform) the formula to isolate the variable r. This is called *solving for a variable*.

$$d = rt$$
$$\frac{d}{t} = \frac{rt}{t} \quad \longrightarrow \quad \frac{d}{t} = r$$

Example

1 $F = \frac{9}{5}C + 32$ is a formula for temperature in degrees Fahrenheit, F, in terms of temperature in degrees Celsius, C. Solve for C.

$$F = \frac{9}{5}C + 32$$

$$F - 32 = \frac{9}{5}C + 32 - 32 \quad \longleftarrow \text{Use the Subtraction Property of Equality.}$$

$$F - 32 = \frac{9}{5}C \quad \longleftarrow \text{Simplify.}$$

$$\frac{5}{9}(F - 32) = \frac{5}{9} \bullet \frac{9}{5}C \quad \longleftarrow \text{Use the Multiplication Property of Equality.}$$

$$\frac{5}{9}(F - 32) = C \quad \longleftarrow \boxed{\text{solution of the formula for } C}$$

▶ A formula is a type of <u>literal equation</u>, which is an equation with two or more variables. In a given literal equation, you can solve for any one of the variables in terms of the others.

Examples

1 Solve for d: $3(d + m) = 8$

$3d + 3m = 8$ ◀—Use the Distributive Property.

$3d + 3m - 3m = 8 - 3m$ ◀—Use the Subtraction Property of Equality.

$3d = 8 - 3m$ ◀—Simplify.

$\dfrac{3d}{3} = \dfrac{8 - 3m}{3}$ ◀—Use the Division Property of Equality.

$d = \dfrac{8 - 3m}{3}$ ◀—Simplify.

or $d = \dfrac{8}{3} - m$

2 Solve for z: $12z - a = 3z + 7a$

$12z - 3z - a = 3z - 3z + 7a$ ◀—Use the Subtraction Property of Equality.

$9z - a = 7a$ ◀—Combine the like z-terms.

$9z - a + a = 7a + a$ ◀—Use the Addition Property of Equality.

$9z = 8a$ ◀—Combine the like a-terms.

$\dfrac{9z}{9} = \dfrac{8a}{9}$ ◀—Use the Division Property of Equality.

$z = \dfrac{8a}{9}$ ◀—Simplify.

Try These

Solve for the indicated variable.

1. Solve for x:

$y = mx + b$

2. Solve for h:

$V = \dfrac{1}{3}\pi r^2 h$

3. Solve for x:

$y - y_1 = m(x - x_1)$

4. Solve for y:

$7y + 2h = 3y + 5h$

5. Solve for m:

$q = \dfrac{m - 10x}{w}$

6. Solve for b_1:

$A = \dfrac{1}{2}h(b_1 + b_2)$

Use the given formula to find the indicated quantity.

7. Shoe sizes and foot length are related by the formula $S = 3F - 24$, where S represents the shoe size and F represents the length of the foot, in inches. How long is the foot of a person who wears a size $7\frac{1}{2}$ shoe?

8. The formula $V = \pi r^2 h$ can be used to find the volume, V, of a right circular cylinder with radius r and height h. What is the volume of the cylinder shown at the right?

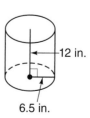

12 in.

6.5 in.

9. The formula $S = 2\pi rh + 2\pi r^2$ can be used to find the surface area, S, of a right circular cylinder with radius r and height h. What is the surface area of the cylinder shown at the right?

10. Discuss and Write Albert Einstein's famous formula, $E = mc^2$, relates energy, E, to mass, m, and the speed of light, c. Explain how you would solve this formula for c.

Go to PRACTICE BOOK Lesson 2-7 for exercise sets.

2-8

Technology:
Solve Linear and Literal Equations

Objective To use a handheld to solve linear and literal equations

Quinn has 3 more than twice the number of DVDs that Karole has. If Quinn has 21 DVDs, how many does Karole have?

To find out how many DVDs Karole has, first write an equation to represent the situation and then solve by graphing.
Let x = the number of DVDs Karole has *and* y = the number of DVDs Quinn has.

$$y = 2x + 3$$

► You can use a handheld to make a graph to solve an equation representing a problem situation.

Step 1 Press ⌂. Then choose ② to select **Graphs & Geometry**.

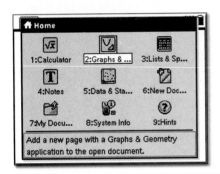

Step 2 Input the equation $2x + 3$. Then press ≈enter to graph.

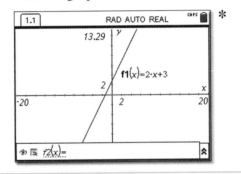

Step 3 Press menu. Select **Trace**, then choose **Graph Trace**.

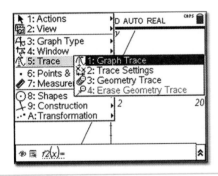

Step 4 Press menu. Select **Trace**, then choose **Trace Settings**. Change **Trace Step** to 1, then press tab ≈enter.

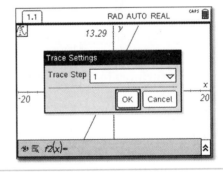

Step 5 Press ◯ to move the trace along the line until the y-coordinate of the graph equals the number of DVDs Quinn has, which is 21. The x-value is the number of DVDs Karole has.

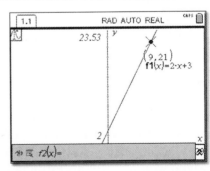

So Karole has 9 DVDs if Quinn has 21.

＊ Window setting adjusted to fit graph

▶ You can also use a handheld to make a graph to solve a literal equation.

The formula $C = \frac{5}{9}(F - 32)$ relates the temperature in °F to the temperature in °C. Find the temperature in °F if it is −10°C.

Step 1 Press 🏠. Then choose ② to select **Using Graphs & Geometry**.

Step 2 Input the formula $(5 \div 9)(x - 32)$. Then press ≈enter to graph the equation.

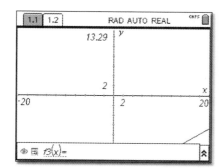

Step 3 Change the window size. Press menu. Select **Window**, then choose **Window Settings**. Change **XMin** and **YMin** to −50 and **XMax** and **YMax** to 100. Then press ≈enter.

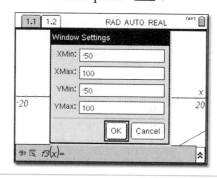

Step 4 Press menu. Select **Trace**, then choose **Graph Trace**.

Step 5 Press menu. Select **Trace**, then choose **Trace Settings**. Change **Trace Step** to 2. Then press tab ≈enter.

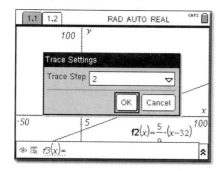

Step 6 Press ▷ to move the trace along the line until the y-coordinate of the graph equals −10.

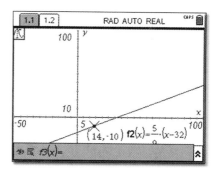

The x-value is the temperature in degrees Fahrenheit. So −10°C is equivalent to 14°F.

Try These

Use a handheld. Make a graph to solve the equation for the given value.

1. $y = 4x + 3$
when $y = 15$

2. $y = 3x - 1$
when $y = -10$

3. $y - \frac{1}{2}x = 7$
when $y = 4$

4. Discuss and Write Barry's age is 2 less than three times his sister Suzie's age. Explain how to use a handheld to make a graph to find Suzie's age when Barry is 16 years old. When Barry is 16, how old is Suzie?

Go to PRACTICE BOOK **Lesson 2-8 for exercise sets.**

Problem-Solving Strategy:
Solve a Simpler Problem

Objective To solve problems using the strategy *Solve a Simpler Problem*

Problem I: For two distinct real numbers x and y, where x is not equal to $-y$, is the product $(x - y)(y - x)(x + y)(y + x)$ positive or negative?

Read ▶ **Read to understand what is being asked.**

List the facts and restate the question.

Facts: Two *different* real numbers x and y are involved.

x is not equal to $-y$.

Question: Four different numbers are created by adding and subtracting the two given real numbers in different orders. Then the four new numbers are multiplied. Is the product positive or negative?

Plan ▶ **Select a strategy.**

When a problem involves relationships among variables, trying out specific values for the variables can be a straightforward way to see what relationships exist.

You can apply the strategy *Solve a Simpler Problem*. It will be easiest to use numbers that make the computation simple, such as two integers.

Problem-Solving Strategies
1. Make a Drawing
2. Solve a Simpler Problem
3. Reason Logically
4. Consider Extreme Cases
5. Work Backward
6. Find a Pattern
7. Account for All Possibilities
8. Adopt a Different Point of View
9. Guess and Test
10. Organize Data

Solve ▶ **Apply the strategy.**

Try $x = 5$ and $y = 3$.
$(5 - 3)(3 - 5)(5 + 3)(3 + 5) = (2)(-2)(8)(8)$,
which is negative.

Try another pair of numbers with *different characteristics*.

Two negative numbers might be a good choice. Let $x = -2$ and $y = -5$.
$[-2 - (-5)][-5 - (-2)][-2 + (-5)][-5 + (-2)] = (3)(-3)(-7)(-7)$,
which is negative.

Notice that no matter what numbers are chosen for x and y, the two differences will just be opposites of each other. Therefore, their product will be negative. The two sums are equal numbers, so their product will be positive. Therefore, the product of the four numbers will be a positive *times* a negative, which will always be negative.

Check ▶ **Check to make sure your answer makes sense.**

Are there any cases where the relationship would *not* hold? If x and y were equal or if x and $-y$ were equal, the product would be 0; but the problem excludes these cases.

Would the same answer hold true if x and y are fractions or irrational numbers?

Yes, because the rules for the signs in a product hold for all real numbers, not only for integers.

Problem 2: The sum of the interior-angle measures of all 10-sided polygons is the same. What is this sum?

Read | **Read to understand what is being asked.**

List the facts and restate the question.

Facts: The sum of the interior-angle measures is the same for all 10-sided polygons.

Question: What is the sum of the interior-angle measures of a 10-sided polygon?

Plan | **Select a strategy.**

Because the shape of the polygon does *not* matter, use the strategy *Solve a Simpler Problem*. Draw a polygon for which finding the angle sum is easy.

Solve | **Apply the strategy.**

Draw a 10-sided polygon like the one below, in which adjacent sides are perpendicular. Each interior angle is either a right angle or a reflex angle. The measures of each reflex angle is 360° − 90°, or 270°. Specifically, there are seven 90° angles and three 270° angles.

> A *reflex angle* is an angle greater than 180° and less than 360°.

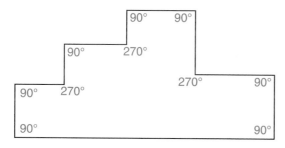

The angle sum is 7(90°) + 3(270°), or 1440°.

So the sum of the angle measures of any 10-sided polygon is 1440°.

Check | **Check to make sure your answer makes sense.**

Solve the problem a different way.

Draw a 10-sided polygon, as shown below. By drawing all the diagonals from one vertex, you can divide the 10-sided polygon into 8 triangles.

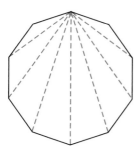

Since the sum of the angle measures of a triangle is 180°, the sum of the angle measures for the polygon is 8(180°), or 1440°. This agrees with the answer above.

Go to PRACTICE BOOK Lesson 2-9 for exercise sets.

Enrichment:
Diophantine Equations

Objective To solve linear Diophantine equations in two variables

Coach Miyamoto bought sandwiches for players on the tennis team and their families. He bought only veggie sandwiches, which cost $3 each, and turkey sandwiches, which cost $4 each. He bought at least one sandwich of each type and spent a total of $80. How many sandwiches of each type could he have bought? Find all the possibilities.

To find how many sandwiches, write and solve an equation.

Let x = the number of veggie sandwiches the coach bought, and
y = the number of turkey sandwiches he bought.

dollars spent on veggie sandwiches	plus	dollars spent on turkey sandwiches	equals	total dollars spent on sandwiches
$3x$	$+$	$4y$	$=$	80

A solution of the above equation is a pair of values (x, y) that satisfies the equation. Note that only positive integer values of x and y make sense.

▶ Equations of the form $ax + by = c$ where a, b, and c are integers and have only integer solutions for x and y, such as $3x + 4y = 80$, are called Diophantine equations, named after Diophantus of Alexandria, the third-century mathematician who studied them.

To find the solutions of a Diophantine equation, such as $3x + 4y = 80$:

- First, solve for one variable in terms of the other.

$$3x + 4y = 80$$

$$3x - 3x + 4y = 80 - 3x \quad \longleftarrow \text{Apply the Subtraction Property of Equality.}$$

$$4y = 80 - 3x \quad \longleftarrow \text{Simplify.}$$

$$\frac{4y}{4} = \frac{80}{4} - \frac{3x}{4} \quad \longleftarrow \text{Apply the Division Property of Equality.}$$

$$y = 20 - \frac{3}{4}x \quad \longleftarrow \text{Simplify.}$$

The quantity y, which equals $20 - \frac{3}{4}x$, will be an integer only when $\frac{3}{4}x$ is an integer, and only when x is a multiple of 4 will $\frac{3}{4}x$ be an integer. Note that 0 is not a possible value for x, since the coach bought at least one veggie sandwich.

- Then make a table, like the one at the right, showing all the possibilities for values of x and y.

  Note that the next multiple of 4 after 24 is 28, and when x is 28, y is -1, which does not make sense as the corresponding number for turkey sandwiches.

  So the table includes all the possible combinations of numbers of veggie and turkey sandwiches that Coach Miyamoto could have bought.

x (veggie)	y (turkey)
4	17
8	14
12	11
16	8
20	5
24	2

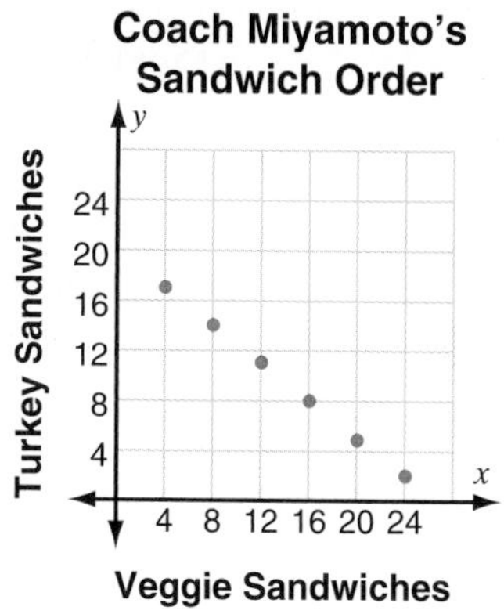

▶ You can show the solutions of a Diophantine equation, such as $3x + 4y = 80$, on a coordinate graph, as shown at the right.

Each point represents one possible (veggie, turkey) sandwich combination. Notice that the points fall on a line, and, because the values are positive integers, all the points are in the first quadrant.

▶ Not all equations of the form $ax + by = c$, where a, b, and c are integers, have integer solutions. Such an equation will have integer solutions *only if* the greatest common factor of a and b is also a factor of c. If an equation of this form *does* have an integer solution, then it has an *infinite number* of integer solutions.

Consider the equation $12x + 10y = 15$. The GCF of 12 and 10 is 2. Because 2 is *not* a factor 15, this equation has no integer solution.

Coach Miyamoto's Sandwich Order

Turkey Sandwiches

Veggie Sandwiches

▶ Although it is easy to determine whether $ax + by = c$ has integer solutions, it is not always easy to find solutions. You can try guessing and testing, or you can see if it helps to solve for one variable in terms of another.

Consider the equation $6x + 4y = 10$. The GCF of 6 and 4 is 2. Because 2 is a factor of 10, this equation has an infinite number of integer solutions. Note that $(1, 1)$ is a solution of the equation. To find other solutions, solve for y in terms of x.

$6x - 6x + 4y = 10 - 6x$ ◀——Apply the Subtraction Property of Equality.

$4y = 10 - 6x$ ◀——Simplify.

$\dfrac{4y}{4} = \dfrac{10y - 6x}{4}$ ◀——Apply the Division Property of Equality.

$y = \dfrac{5 - 3x}{2}$ ◀——Simplify.

Note that y is an integer only when $(5 - 3x)$ is divisible by 2; that is, when $(5 - 3x)$ is even. This will happen whenever $-3x$ is odd, which will happen whenever x is odd.

For example, let $x = -5$. Then $y = \dfrac{5 - 3(-5)}{2} = 10$. So $(-5, 10)$ is a solution.

Check: $6x + 4y = 10 \longrightarrow 6(-5) + 4(10) \overset{?}{=} 10$

$-30 + 40 \overset{?}{=} 10$

$10 = 10$ True

Try These

Tell whether each equation has integer solutions. If it does, find one solution—that is, one (x, y) pair that satisfies the equation.

1. $2x + 3y = 11$

2. $-6x + 8y = 21$

3. $3x + 12y = -9$

Solve for positive values of x and y.

4. $8x + 6y = 20$

5. $7x + 3y = 10$

6. $10x + 8y = 36$

7. Discuss and Write Rachel went to a film museum. At the souvenir shop, she bought only DVDs that cost $14 each and advertisement posters that cost $7 each. (These prices include sales tax.) The cashier told her that the total cost was exactly $100. Is this possible? Explain how you know.

Go to PRACTICE BOOK **pages 57–58 for exercise sets.**

Test Prep: Short-Answer Questions
Strategy: Show All Your Work

To respond to short-answer questions completely, show all the steps you take to reach a solution, and *explain your thinking*. You can receive partial credit for the explanation and steps you use even if your final answer is not correct.

Look at the sample test item.

Read the test item for a general idea of the problem.

- Reread the test item carefully. Clarify the meaning of the text.

    What information is needed to find the total cost?

- Explain your thinking by writing a verbal model that describes the short-answer problem.

total cost	equals	cost for 300 minutes	plus	cost per additional minutes	times	number of additional minutes

- Use this verbal model to show how you can *write* and *solve* an equation to find the total number of minutes Marcus used.

Sample Test Item

A phone company charges $30 a month for up to 300 minutes of talk time, plus $0.50 for each additional minute used. One month, Marcus received a bill for $55. How many minutes did he use altogether? ***Show your work.***

Test-Taking Tips

- Reread the test item.
- Use the Test-Prep strategy.
- Apply appropriate rules, definitions, properties, or strategies.
- Analyze your answers.

Solve the problem.

- Apply appropriate rules, properties, and strategies. Translate the verbal model, then solve.

    total cost = (cost for 300 minutes) + (cost per additional minute)(number of additional minutes)

$$55 = 30 + 0.5m \quad \longleftarrow \text{Substitute the known values. Use } m \text{ for the unknown additional minutes.}$$

$$25 = 0.5m \quad \longleftarrow \text{Use the Subtraction Property of Equality.}$$

$$50 = m \quad \longleftarrow \text{Use the Division Property of Equality.}$$

To find the total number of minutes used, *add* the number of additional minutes to 300.

$$50 + 300 = 350$$

Answer: Marcus used 350 minutes.

Item Analysis

Check your work. Make sure you show all your work.

- Analyze your answer. Does it make sense?

    Substitute 50 for m in the equation: $55 \stackrel{?}{=} 30 + 0.5(50)$

    $$55 = 55 \quad \text{True}$$

Try These

Solve. Show your work and explain your thinking.

1. The length of a whiteboard is 3 times its height. Its perimeter is 40 feet. What are the length and height of the whiteboard? ***Show your work.***

2. Robert can paint a 6 ft-by-5 ft rectangular wall using a half a gallon of paint. How many gallons of paint will he need to cover a 10 ft-by-12 ft wall? ***Show your work.***

Go to   PRACTICE BOOK page 59 for exercise sets.

Linear Inequalities

CHAPTER 3

In This Chapter You Will:

- Translate mathematical sentences that use the symbols <, ≤, >, ≥, or ≠ to compare two expressions
- Graph inequalities on a number line
- Write the solution set of an inequality in both set-builder and interval notation
- Connect verbal, numeric, symbolic, and graphic representations of inequalities
- Solve addition, subtraction, multiplication, and division inequalities
- Solve one-step, multistep, compound, and absolute-value inequalities
- Graph the solution sets of inequalities
- Apply the strategy: *Reason Logically*
- Look for new vocabulary words **highlighted** in each lesson

Do You Remember?

- An equation is a statement that two mathematical expressions are equal.
- Numerical equations are either true or false. Algebraic equations are usually neither true nor false.
- Set notation can be used to represent the solution of an equation.
- A two-step equation requires the use of two inverse operations to isolate the variable.

For Practice Exercises:

 Go to **PRACTICE BOOK, pp. 65–88**

For Chapter Support: ONLINE

 Go to **www.progressinmathematics.com**

- Skills Update Practice
- Practice Activities
- Audio Glossary
- Vocabulary Activities
- Technology Videos
- Enrichment Activities
- Electronic SourceBook

 VIRTUAL MANIPULATIVES

Critical Thinking

Selwyn received grades of 84%, 92%, and 86% on his first three science tests. If all the tests are weighted equally, what possible grades on the fourth test would give Selwyn a final average of at least 90%?

Write and Graph Inequalities

Objective To translate a word sentence into an inequality and vice versa • To identify equivalent symbolic forms for representing the solution sets of inequalities • To connect symbolic and graphic representations of inequalities

The Rockville School wants to donate at least $1500 to a relief fund. The student council decides to raise the money through a student car wash. The cost for customers will be $12 per car. What algebraic sentence can be written to represent the number of cars that will be needed in order to raise at least the intended dollar amount?

To represent the number of cars as an algebraic sentence, translate the word sentences into an inequality.

▶ An inequality is a statement that compares two expressions or quantities that may not be equal. It uses one or more comparison symbols.

To write an inequality:

• Look for the key words associated with inequality symbols.

• Associate the remaining word phrases with symbols, and use a variable to represent the unknown quantity.

Algebraic Word Sentence	Comparison Symbol
a is less than b.	$a < b$
a is greater than b.	$a > b$
a is less than or equal to b. *a is at most b.*	$a \le b$
a is greater than or equal to b. *a is at least b.*	$a \ge b$
a is not equal to b.	$a \ne b$

cost per car	times	number of cars washed	*is at least*	intended dollar amount
↓	↓	↓	↓	↓
12	•	c	$\ge$	1500

So $12c \ge 1500$ is an inequality that represents the number of cars that will have to be washed in order to raise at least 1500.

This inequality can also be written as $1500 \le 12c$.

> If you *reverse* the order of the expressions in the inequality, you must *reverse* the inequality symbol.

▶ Since an inequality may have too many solutions to list, you can use a graph on a number line to show all the solutions.

Graph: $\{a \mid a \ge -5\}$

> **Think**
> Graph all real numbers (*not just integers*) greater than or equal to −5

To graph $a \ge -5$, place a *dot* at −5 on the number line, and then shade the number line to the right of −5. The dot denotes that −5 *is* a solution of $a \ge -5$.

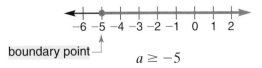

boundary point ⌐

$a \ge -5$

Graph: $6.5 > m$

> **Think**
> $m < 6.5$; graph all real numbers less than 6.5

To graph $m < 6.5$, place a *circle* at 6.5 on the number line, and then shade the number line to the left of 6.5. The circle denotes that 6.5 is *not* a solution of $6.5 > m$.

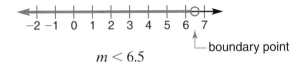

└ boundary point

$m < 6.5$

▶ **Interval notation** shows the endpoints of a solution set. All the real numbers between these endpoints are in the interval.

Set-Builder Notation   Interval Notation

$$\{x \mid x > 10\} \quad \text{or} \quad (10, \infty)$$

Read both as: x is greater than 10.
10 is *not included* in the solution set.

When using interval notation to represent a solution set, the symbol:

( ) means *not included* or *open*.
[ ] means *included* or *closed*.
  ∞ means that the interval continues endlessly in the positive direction.
  $-\infty$ means that the interval continues endlessly in the negative direction.

Set-Builder Notation	Interval Notation	Graph
$\{x \mid x \geq -3\}$	Closed at Left, Nonending at Right: $[-3, \infty)$	
$\{x \mid x \leq 1\}$	Nonending at Left, Closed at Right: $(-\infty, 1]$	

▶ You can also write a solution set to an inequality to represent a given graph and then describe a situation for it.

Graph	Symbolic Notation	Words
	$t \geq -2$ $\{t \mid t \geq -2\}$ $[-2, \infty)$ ← −2 is included in the interval, which continues without end in the positive direction.	The recorded temperature *is no less than* −2°C.
	$x \leq 175$ $\{x \mid x \leq 175\}$ $(-\infty, 175]$ ← 175 is included in the interval, which continues without end in the negative direction.	The interval includes all real numbers that *are no more than* 175.

Try These

Define a variable, and write an inequality for each word sentence.

1. Jamie's arcade game score is more than 1200 points.

2. Miss Jones said each student's class party expense is to be a maximum of $15.

3. The temperature of Al's mixture in chemistry lab did not exceed 72°F.

4. The carpeted area of the school library is less than 82 ft².

Rewrite each solution set in a different symbolic notation. Then graph each solution set.

5. $h < 4$ 6. $\{x \mid x > 16\}$ 7. $w \leq 190.5$ 8. $(-\infty, \infty)$ 9. $[80, \infty)$

10. **Discuss and Write** The Transitive Property of Equality states that if $a = b$ and $b = c$, then $a = c$. Do you think there is a Transitive Property of Inequality using the symbol >? Give examples to justify your answer. Include negative integers.

Go to   PRACTICE BOOK Lesson 3-1 for exercise sets.

Solve Inequalities Using Addition or Subtraction

Objective To solve one-step inequalities using the Addition and Subtraction Properties of Inequality • To graph the solution sets of addition and subtraction inequalities

The J. Bank High School auditorium has a maximum seating capacity. The senior class is planning its commencement exercises and determines that no more than 445 invitations can be distributed, excluding those for students and faculty. If there are 155 students and faculty, what is the maximum seating capacity of the school auditorium?

▶ To find the maximum seating capacity of the school auditorium, write and solve a subtraction inequality.

Let s = the seating capacity.

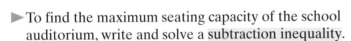

maximum seating capacity	minus	students and faculty	is *no more than*	distributed invitations for seats	
↓	↓	↓	↓	↓	
s	$-$	155	$\leq$	445	◀— subtraction inequality

▶ To solve a subtraction inequality, use the Addition Property of Inequality. Solve a subtraction inequality *the same way* you solve a subtraction equation.

Solve: $s - 155 \leq 445$

$s - 155 + 155 \leq 445 + 155$ ◀—Use the Addition Property of Inequality.

$s \leq 600$

The school auditorium has a maximum seating capacity of 600, which means it can seat up to 600 people.

_____ **Key Concept** _____

Addition Property of Inequality

If a, b, and c are real numbers and $a > b$, then $a + c > b + c$.

These statements are also true if $>$ is replaced by $<$, $\leq$, or $\geq$.

▶ You can graph and check the solution set after solving an inequality.

Solve: $n - 26 > -12$

$n - 26 + 26 > -12 + 26$ ◀—Use the Addition Property of Inequality.

$n > 14$

Remember that $n > 14$ can also be written as $\{n \mid n > 14\}$ or $(14, \infty)$.

Graph: $n > 14$

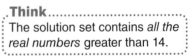

Think

The solution set contains *all the real numbers* greater than 14.

Check: According to the graph, 20 is in the solution set, and 10 is *not*.

Try $n = 20$.

$n - 26 > -12$

$20 - 26 \overset{?}{>} -12$ ◀—Substitute 20 for n.

$-6 > -12$ True

Try $n = 10$.

$n - 26 > -12$

$10 - 26 \overset{?}{>} -12$ ◀—Substitute 10 for n.

$-16 > -12$ False

Always check using the original inequality.

▶ To solve an **addition inequality**, use the **Subtraction Property of Inequality**.
Solve an addition inequality *the same way* you solve an addition equation.

Solve: $10 - 7x + 8x \geq 8$

$10 + (-7x) + 8x \geq 8$ ◀—Identify like terms.

$10 + x \geq 8$ ◀—Simplify; combine like terms.

$10 - 10 + x \geq 8 - 10$ ◀— Use the Subtraction Property
of Inequality.

$x \geq -2$

Key Concept

Subtraction Property of Inequality

If a, b, and c are real numbers and
$a > b$, then $a - c > b - c$.

These statements are also true
if $>$ is replaced by $<$, $\leq$, or $\geq$.

Graph: $\{x \mid x \geq -2\}$ or $[-2, \infty)$

$-4\ -3\ -2\ -1\ \ 0\ \ 1\ \ 2\ \ 3\ \ 4$

Check: According to the graph, 0 is in the solution set, and -4 is *not*.

Try $x = 0$.

$10 - 7x + 8x \geq 8$

$10 - 7(0) + 8(0) \overset{?}{\geq} 8$

$10 \overset{?}{\geq} 8$

$10 \geq 8$ True

Try $x = -4$.

$10 - 7x + 8x \geq 8$

$10 - 7(-4) + 8(-4) \overset{?}{\geq} 8$

$10 + 28 - 32 \overset{?}{\geq} 8$

$6 \geq 8$ False

Example

1 **Solve:** $9 < 1 + 6m - 5m + 2$

$9 < 1 + 6m + (-5m) + 2$ ◀—Identify like
terms.

$9 < m + 3$ ◀—Simplify; combine
like terms.

$9 - 3 < m + 3 - 3$ ◀—Use the Subtraction
Property of Inequality.

$6 < m$

Check: According to the graph,
7 is in the solution set, and 2 is *not*.

Try $m = 7$.

$9 < 1 + 6m - 5m + 2$

$9 \overset{?}{<} 1 + 6(7) - 5(7) + 2$

$9 \overset{?}{<} 1 + 42 - 35 + 2$

$9 < 10$ True

Try $m = 2$.

$9 < 1 + 6m - 5m + 2$

$9 \overset{?}{<} 1 + 6(2) - 5(2) + 2$

$9 \overset{?}{<} 1 + 12 - 10 + 2$

$9 < 5$ False

Graph: $\{m \mid m > 6\}$ or $(6, \infty)$

$4\ \ 5\ \ 6\ \ 7\ \ 8\ \ 9\ \ 10\ 11\ 12$

Remember:
$6 < m$ is equivalent to $m > 6$.

Try These

Solve each inequality. Then graph and check the solution.

1. $c - 114 \leq 99$

2. $-7 + h > 5$

3. $-13.1 < 6x - 16.7 - 5x$

4. $-8 + 11 \leq 7 + k$

5. Discuss and Write Explain how the Addition and Subtraction Properties of Inequality
are like the Addition and Subtraction Properties of Equality. Use examples to support
your statements.

Go to PRACTICE BOOK **Lesson 3-2 for exercise sets.**

Solve Inequalities Using Multiplication or Division

Objective To solve one-step inequalities using the Multiplication or the Division Properties of Inequality • To graph the solution sets of multiplication and division inequalities

The senior class is going on a field trip. The school buses hold 52 passengers, and there are at least 235 teachers and students going on the trip. What is the minimum number of buses needed?

To find the number of buses the school will need, write and solve a multiplication inequality.

Let b = the number of buses.

number of passengers for one bus	*times*	number of buses	*is at least*	total number of teachers & students	
52	•	b	$\geq$	235	← multiplication inequality

▶ To solve a multiplication inequality, use the Division Property of Inequality.

Solve: $52b \geq 235$

$\dfrac{52b}{52} \geq \dfrac{235}{52}$ ←—Use the Division Property of Inequality.

$b \geq 4.52$ ←—Since the answer represents buses, it will need to be the next greater whole number.

$b \geq 5$

The answer to the problem is 5. However, the solution set to the inequality contains *all the integers* greater than or equal to 5.

The school will need at least 5 buses.

> _____ **Key Concept** _____
>
> **Division Property of Inequality**
>
> If a, b, and c are real numbers, c is positive, and $a < b$, then $a \div c < b \div c$.
>
> If a, b, and c are real numbers, c is negative, and $a < b$, then $a \div c > b \div c$.
>
> Similar statements can be written for $a > b$, $a \leq b$, and $a \geq b$.

▶ When you divide both sides of an inequality by a *negative* number, you must *reverse* the inequality symbol to get a true statement.

Solve: $-7.30n > 365$

$\dfrac{-7.30n}{-7.30} < \dfrac{365}{-7.30}$ ←—Divide by a negative number; reverse the inequality symbol.

$n < -50$ ←—Simplify.

$\{n \mid n < -50\}$ or $(-\infty, -50)$ ←—solution set

Graph:

```
 ←—+——+——+——+——+——⊕——+——+——+——→
 -100 -90 -80 -70 -60 -50 -40 -30 -20
```

Think
The solution set contains *all real numbers* less than −50.

Check: According to the graph, −60 is in the solution set, and −30 is *not*.

Try $n = -60$.

$-7.30n > 365$

$-7.30(-60) \overset{?}{>} 365$ ←—Substitute −60 for n.

$438 > 365$ True

> **Remember:** Check using the original inequality.

Try $n = -30$.

$-7.30(-30) \overset{?}{>} 365$ ←—Substitute −30 for n.

$219 > 365$ False

▶ To solve a **division inequality**, use the **Multiplication Property of Inequality**.

Solve the inequality. Then graph and check the solution set.

Solve: $\frac{x}{12} \geq 15$ ←—division inequality

$\frac{x}{12} \cdot 12 \geq 15 \cdot 12$ ←—Use the Multiplication Property of Inequality.

$x \geq 180$

Graph: $\{x \mid x \geq 180\}$ or $[180, \infty)$

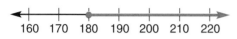

Check: According to the graph, 204 is in the solution set, and 132 is *not*.

Try $x = 204$.

$\frac{x}{12} \geq 15$

$\frac{204}{12} \overset{?}{\geq} 15$ Substitute 204 for x.

$17 \geq 15$ True

Try $x = 132$.

$\frac{x}{12} \geq 15$

$\frac{132}{12} \overset{?}{\geq} 15$ Substitute 132 for x.

$11 \geq 15$ False

> **Key Concept**
>
> **Multiplication Property of Inequality**
>
> If a, b, and c are real numbers, c is positive, and $a < b$, then $ac < bc$.
>
> If a, b, and c are real numbers, c is negative, and $a < b$, then $ac > bc$.
>
> Similar statements can be written for $a > b$, $a \leq b$, and $a \geq b$.

▶ When you multiply both sides of an inequality by a *negative* number, you must *reverse* the inequality symbol to get a true statement.

Solve the inequality. Then graph and check the solution set.

Solve: $-y - \frac{1}{5}y < 30$

$-y + -\frac{1}{5}y < 30$ ←—Identify like terms.

$-\frac{6}{5}y < 30$ ←—Simplify; combine like terms.

$\left(-\frac{5}{6}\right)\left(-\frac{6}{5}y\right) > 30\left(-\frac{5}{6}\right)$ ←—Multiply by a negative number; reverse the inequality symbol.

$y > -25$

Graph: $\{y \mid y > -25\}$ or $(-25, \infty)$

Check: According to the graph, 0 is in the solution set, and -40 is *not*.

$-y - \frac{1}{5}y < 30$

$0 - \frac{1}{5}(0) \overset{?}{<} 30$

$0 < 30$ True

$-y - \frac{1}{5}y < 30$

$-(-40) - \frac{1}{5}(-40) \overset{?}{<} 30$

$48 < 30$ False

Try These

Solve each inequality. Then graph and check the solution set.

1. $4k < 24$
2. $-1 \geq \frac{-x}{11}$
3. $-12x + 4x < -4$
4. $-20 < -8z - 2z$
5. $\frac{3}{5} < \frac{r}{-5}$

6. Monica's new car averages 23 miles per gallon of gasoline. What is the greatest number of gallons of gasoline she will need if she travels no more than 500 miles?

7. **Discuss and Write** Explain, using a number line or model, why it is necessary to reverse the inequality symbol when multiplying and dividing by a negative number.

Go to **PRACTICE BOOK Lesson 3-3 for exercise sets.**

Solve Multistep Inequalities

Objective To solve and graph multistep inequalities

Sally wants to cater a party, but she needs to spend less than $800. If the caterer charges $350 to set up the event and $12.50 per person, how many guests can Sally invite?

To find all the possible different numbers of guests Sally can invite, write and solve a multistep inequality.

▶ A multistep inequality involves more than one operation. To solve a multistep inequality, isolate the variable by using the properties of inequality or the inverse of each operation.

Let g = the number of guests.

per person charge *times* number of guests	*plus*	set-up fee	*is less than*	spending limit	
↓	↓	↓	↓	↓	
$12.50g$	$+$	350	$<$	800	◀— multistep inequality

Solve: $12.50g + 350 < 800$

$12.50g + 350 - 350 < 800 - 350$ ◀— Use the Subtraction Property of Inequality.

$$12.50g < 450$$

$$\frac{12.50g}{12.50} < \frac{450}{12.50}$$ ◀— Use the Division Property of Inequality.

$$g < 36$$

Graph: $\{g \mid g < 36\}$

```
←——+——+——+——+——+——⊕——+——+——→
   31  32  33  34  35  36  37  38
```

Check: According to the graph, 30 is in the solution set, and 40 is *not*.

Try $g = 30$.

$12.50g + 350 < 800$

$12.50(30) + 350 \overset{?}{<} 800$ ◀— Substitute 30 for g.

$375 + 350 \overset{?}{<} 800$

$725 < 800$ True

> **Remember:** Check by substitution using the original inequality.

Try $g = 40$.

$12.50g + 350 < 800$

$12.50(40) + 350 \overset{?}{<} 800$ ◀— Substitute 40 for g.

$500 + 350 \overset{?}{<} 800$

$850 < 800$ False

So if the party is catered, Sally will invite fewer than 36 guests.

Example

Solve the inequality. Then graph and check the solution set.

1 **Solve:** $5 + 10 \geq \frac{1}{5}c + 20 - \frac{2}{5}c$

$5 + 10 \geq \frac{1}{5}c + 20 + \left(-\frac{2}{5}c\right)$ ◄— Identify like terms.

$15 \geq -\frac{1}{5}c + 20$ ◄— Simplify; combine like terms.

$15 - 20 \geq -\frac{1}{5}c + 20 - 20$ ◄— Use the Subtraction Property of Inequality.

$-5 \geq -\frac{c}{5}$ ◄— $-\frac{1}{5}c = -\frac{c}{5}$

$-5 \bullet -5 \leq -\frac{c}{5} \bullet -5$ ◄— Use the Multiplication Property of Inequality.

$25 \leq c$ ◄— Simplify.

$c \geq 25$

Graph: $\{c \mid c \geq 25\}$ or $[25, \infty)$

Check: According to the graph, 30 is in the solution set.

Try $c = 30$.

$5 + 10 \geq \frac{1}{5}c + 20 - \frac{2}{5}c$

$5 + 10 \stackrel{?}{\geq} \frac{1}{5}(30) + 20 - \frac{2}{5}(30)$ ◄— Substitute.

$15 \stackrel{?}{\geq} 6 + 20 - 12$

$15 \geq 14$ True

▶ You can use the Distributive Property to help solve inequalities that contain grouping symbols.

Solve: $3(2y + 1) - 2 \leq 31$

$3(2y + 1) - 2 \leq 31$ ◄— Use the Distributive Property.

$6y + 3 + -2 \leq 31$ ◄— Identify and combine like terms.

$6y + 1 \leq 31$

$6y - 1 + 1 \leq 31 - 1$ ◄— Use the Subtraction Property of Inequality.

$6y \leq 30$

$\frac{6y}{6} \leq \frac{30y}{6}$ ◄— Use the Division Property of Inequality.

$y \leq 5$

Graph: $\{y \mid y \leq 5\}$ or $(-\infty, 5]$

Check: According to the graph, 0 is in the solution set, and 10 is *not*.

Try $y = 0$.

$3(2y + 1) - 2 \leq 31$

$3(2 \bullet 0 + 1) - 2 \stackrel{?}{\leq} 31$ ◄— Substitute.

$3(0 + 1) - 2 \stackrel{?}{\leq} 31$

$3(1) - 2 \stackrel{?}{\leq} 31$

$1 \leq 31$ True

> **Remember:** Follow the Order of Operations.

Try $y = 10$.

$3(2y + 1) - 2 \leq 31$

$3(2 \bullet 10 + 1) - 2 \stackrel{?}{\leq} 31$ ◄— Substitute.

$3(20 + 1) - 2 \stackrel{?}{\leq} 31$

$3(21) - 2 \stackrel{?}{\leq} 31$

$61 \leq 31$ False

Continue Lesson ➡

▶Sometimes you can also solve a multistep inequality by simplifying its terms using division.

Solve: $4(-2n + 8) > -16$

$\dfrac{4(-2n + 8)}{4} > \dfrac{-16}{4}$ ◀—Since -16 is divisible by 4, divide both sides by 4.

$-2n + 8 > -4$ ◀—Simplify.

$-2n + 8 - 8 > -4 - 8$ ◀—Use the Subtraction Property of Inequality.

$-2n > -12$

$\dfrac{-2n}{-2} < \dfrac{-12}{-2}$ ◀—Use the Division Property of Inequality.

$n < 6$

Check: According to the graph, 1 is in the solution set.

Try $n = 1$.

$4(-2n + 8) > -16$

$4(-2 \bullet 1 + 8) \overset{?}{>} -16$ ◀—Substitute.

$4(-2 + 8) \overset{?}{>} -16$

$4(6) \overset{?}{>} -16$

$24 > -16$ True

Graph: $\{n \mid n < 6\}$ or $(-\infty, 6)$

▶Sometimes it is easier to work with integers in an inequality than with fractions or decimals. To create an equivalent inequality with coefficients that are integers, *multiply each term* of an inequality with fractions by the LCD. If the inequality includes decimals, *multiply each term* of the inequality by a power of 10.

Solve the inequality. Then graph and check the solution set.

Solve: $-\dfrac{x}{3} + \dfrac{1}{4} \leq \dfrac{1}{6}$

$12\left(-\dfrac{x}{3} + \dfrac{1}{4}\right) \leq 12\left(\dfrac{1}{6}\right)$ ◀—The LCD of the fractions is 12. Multiply both sides by 12.

$12\left(-\dfrac{x}{3}\right) + 12\left(\dfrac{1}{4}\right) \leq 12\left(\dfrac{1}{6}\right)$ ◀—Use the Distributive Property.

$-4x + 3 \leq 2$

$-4x + 3 - 3 \leq 2 - 3$ ◀—Use the Subtraction Property of Inequality.

$-4x \leq -1$

$\dfrac{-4x}{-4} \geq \dfrac{-1}{-4}$ ◀—Use the Division Property of Inequality.

$x \geq \dfrac{1}{4}$

Check: According to the graph, 3 is in the solution set.

Try $x = 3$.

$-\dfrac{x}{3} + \dfrac{1}{4} \leq \dfrac{1}{6}$

$-\dfrac{3}{3} + \dfrac{1}{4} \overset{?}{\leq} \dfrac{1}{6}$ ◀—Substitute.

$-1 + \dfrac{1}{4} \overset{?}{\leq} \dfrac{1}{6}$

$-\dfrac{3}{4} \leq \dfrac{1}{6}$ True

Graph: $\left\{x \mid x \geq \dfrac{1}{4}\right\}$ or $\left[\dfrac{1}{4}, \infty\right)$

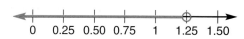
Example

1 **Solve:** $-0.3 + 4.4h < 5.2$

$$10(-0.3 + 4.4h) < 10(5.2)$$ ◂—Multiply both sides by 10 to create an equivalent inequality with integers.

$$10(-0.3) + 10(4.4h) < 10(5.2)$$ ◂—Use the Distributive Property.

$$-3 + 44h < 52$$ ◂—Simplify.

$$-3 + 3 + 44h < 52 + 3$$ ◂—Use the Addition Property of Inequality.

$$44h < 55$$ ◂—Simplify.

$$\frac{44h}{44} < \frac{55}{44}$$ ◂—Use the Division Property of Inequality.

$$h < \frac{5}{4}$$ ◂—Simplify.

$$h < 1.25$$ ◂—$\frac{5}{4} = 1\frac{1}{4} = 1.25$

Graph: $\{h \,|\, h < 1.25\}$ or $(-\infty, 1.25)$

| | | | | | ⊕ | |
|0|0.25|0.50|0.75|1|1.25|1.50|

Check: According to the graph, 0 is in the solution set.

Try $h = 0$.

$$-0.3 + 4.4h < 5.2$$

$$-0.3 + 4.4(0) \overset{?}{<} 5.2$$ ◂—Substitute.

$$-0.3 + 0 \overset{?}{<} 5.2$$

$$-0.3 < 5.2 \text{ True}$$

▸ Solving inequalities with variables on both sides is similar to solving equations with variables on both sides.

PROBLEM-SOLVING STRATEGY 2

Solve: $\frac{3x}{8} - 2 < \frac{5x}{8}$

$$\frac{3x}{8} - \frac{3x}{8} - 2 < \frac{5x}{8} - \frac{3x}{8}$$ ◂—Use the Subtraction Property of Inequality.

$$-2 < \frac{2x}{8}$$

$$\frac{8}{2} \cdot -2 < \frac{2x}{8} \cdot \frac{8}{2}$$ ◂—Use the Multiplication Property of Inequality.

$$-8 < x$$

$$x > -8$$

Check: According to the graph, 0 is in the solution set.

Try $x = 0$.

$$\frac{3x}{8} - 2 < \frac{5x}{8}$$

$$\frac{3}{8}(0) - 2 \overset{?}{<} \frac{5}{8}(0)$$ ◂—Substitute.

$$-2 < 0 \text{ True}$$

Graph: $\{x \,|\, x > -8\}$ or $(-8, \infty)$

| ⊕ | | | | | | | | | |
|−9|−8|−7|−6|−5|−4|−3|−2|−1|0|1|

Try These

Solve each inequality. Then graph and check the solution set.

1. $9y + 12 < -12$
2. $15 > -2m - 5$
3. $10 \leq -7 - 4h - 2$
4. $2(d + 5) + 8d \geq 4$

5. $3x - (7x - 11) > 9$
6. $\frac{2}{3} + \frac{1}{4}c \geq \frac{3}{4}$
7. $1 - 0.4r \leq 3.4 - 0.6r$
8. $-2k + 8 < \frac{2k}{3}$

9. **Discuss and Write** Mark solved the inequality $-2x + 7 < 13$ and got the solution $x > -3$, but Jane got $-3 < x$. Who is correct? Explain your response.

Go to **PRACTICE BOOK Lesson 3-4 for exercise sets.**

Solve Compound Inequalities

Objective To write and solve compound inequalities involving AND • To write and solve compound inequalities involving OR

Every day, the caretaker at the university's biology lab checks the water quality in the lab's aquarium. The ideal pH level recommended for freshwater aquariums is between 6.5 and 7.5. How can the caretaker make a graph to show all the possible values of the pH?

To make a graph that shows all the possible values of the pH, first write the range as a compound inequality or as two simple inequalities joined by the word AND. Then graph the inequality.

► A compound inequality joined by the word AND is called a conjunction. Solutions that satisfy *both* parts of the compound inequality are the solution to the conjunction.

Let p = the pH between 6.5 and 7.5.
Then $p > 6.5$ AND $p < 7.5$. ◄──| compound inequality |

► To graph a compound inequality joined by AND:

• Draw and label a number line that includes the boundary points. The boundary points are the points where you start the graph—that is, 6.5 and 7.5.

• Graph the first inequality: $p > 6.5$

• On the same number line, graph the second inequality: $p < 7.5$

• Identify the region where the two graphs overlap. This is the graph of the solution set. The *intersection* satisfies *both* inequalities.

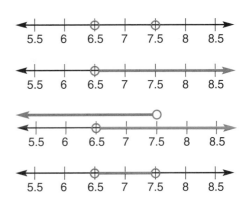

The solution set of the compound inequality is: $\{p \mid 6.5 < p < 7.5\}$.

So the graph represents the pH range between 6.5 and 7.5, not including either endpoint.

► The table below illustrates some graphs, symbols, and words that represent a compound inequality joined by the conjunction AND.

Key Concept

Shortened Form of a Compound Inequality Joined by *And*

If a, b, and c are real numbers, $a < b$ and $b < c$, then $a < b < c$.

This statement is also true if $<$ is replaced by $\leq$, $>$, or $\geq$.

Graph	Symbolic Notation	Words
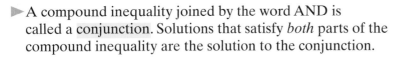 −3 −2 −1 0 1 2 3 4 5 6	$x > -2$ AND $x < 5$ $\{x \mid -2 < x < 5\}$ ◄──set-builder notation $(-2, 5)$ ◄──interval notation	All real numbers greater than −2 AND less than 5
−3 −2 −1 0 1 2 3 4 5 6	$x \geq -2$ AND $x < 5$ $\{x \mid -2 \leq x < 5\}$ $[-2, 5)$	All real numbers greater than or equal to −2 AND less than 5

▶ You can solve compound inequalities that are *conjunctions* algebraically and then represent the solution sets graphically or by using symbolic notation.

.Think...................

Solve: $2 \le x + 6 \le 8$ | Use the Properties of Inequality.

$2 \le x + 6 \text{ AND } x + 6 \le 8$ ←Rewrite the inequality using AND.

$\underline{-6 \qquad -6} \qquad \underline{-6 \quad -6}$ ←Solve each simple inequality using the Subtraction Property of Inequality.

$-4 \le x \qquad \text{AND} \qquad x \le 2$

$-4 \le x \le 2$

Graph:

- Graph the first inequality: $x \ge -4$

- Graph the second inequality: $x \le 2$

- Identify the region where the two graphs intersect. This is the graph of the solution set.

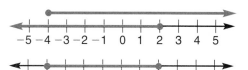

Check: Choose a test point to verify the solution set. Try 0.

$2 \le x + 6 \le 8$

$2 \overset{?}{\le} 0 + 6 \overset{?}{\le} 8$ ←Substitute 0 for x.

$2 \le 6 \le 8$ True

> Choose a value from the solution set that is *between* −4 and 2, *including both* endpoints. Try 0 as a test point.

So the solution set to the compound inequality is $\{x \mid -4 \le x \le 2\}$.
Alternatively, you can write $[-4, 2]$.

Example

1 Solve and check the compound inequality. Graph the solution set.

Solve: $-7 \le 2x - 1 < 3$

$-7 \le 2x - 1 \text{ AND } 2x - 1 < 3$ ←Rewrite the inequality using AND.

$\underline{+1 \qquad +1} \qquad \underline{+1 + 1}$ ←Use the Addition Property of Inequality.

$-6 \le 2x \qquad \qquad 2x < 4$

$\dfrac{-6}{2} \le \dfrac{2x}{2} \qquad \qquad \dfrac{2x}{2} < \dfrac{4}{2}$ ←Use the Division Property of Inequality.

$-3 \le x \qquad \text{AND} \qquad x < 2$

Check: Choose a test point. Try −1 to verify the solution set.

$-7 \le 2x - 1 < 3$

$-7 \overset{?}{\le} 2(-1) - 1 \overset{?}{<} 3$

$-7 \overset{?}{\le} -2 - 1 \overset{?}{<} 3$

$-7 \le -3 < 3$ True

Graph:

- Graph the first inequality: $x \ge -3$

- Graph the second inequality: $x < 2$

- Identify the region where the two graphs intersect. This is the graph of the solution set.

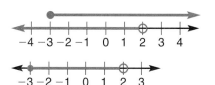

So the solution set to the compound inequality is $\{x \mid -3 \le x < 2\}$.
Alternatively, you can write $[-3, 2)$.

Continue Lesson ➡

▶ Two simple inequalities may also be joined by the word OR. This type of compound inequality is called a **disjunction**. Solutions that satisfy at least one part of this type of compound inequality are the solution to the disjunction.

Graph: $n \le -2$ OR $n > 3$

Graph all numbers that are either *less than or equal to* -2 OR *greater than* 3.

▶ To graph a compound inequality joined by OR:

- Draw and label a number line that includes the boundary points.

- Graph the first inequality: $n \le -2$

- On the same number line, graph the second inequality: $n > 3$

- Identify the *union* of the two graphs. This is the graph of the solution set. The union satisfies *both* inequalities.

So the solution set for the graph is $\{n \mid n \le -2$ or $n > 3\}$. Alternatively, you can write $(-\infty, -2] \cup (3, \infty)$.

> **Remember:**
> $\cup$ means union.

▶ You can solve compound inequalities that are *disjunctions* algebraically and then show the solution sets graphically or by using symbolic notation.

Solve and check the compound inequality. Then graph the solution set.

> .Think.....................................
> Use the Properties of Inequality.

Solve: $-5 + a > 2$ OR $-5 + a < -3$

$$-5 + a > 2 \text{ OR } -5 + a < -3$$
$$\underline{+5 \qquad +5 \qquad +5 \qquad +5} \leftarrow \text{Solve each simple inequality using the}$$
$$a > 7 \text{ OR} \qquad a < 2 \qquad \text{Addition Property of Inequality.}$$

Graph:

- The graph identifies the solutions of the compound inequality.

- Identify the union of the two graphs. This is the graph of the solution set.

Check: Choose test points to verify the solution set.

$-5 + a > 2$ OR $-5 + a < -3$

Try 8.   Try 1.

$-5 + 8 \overset{?}{>} 2$ $-5 + 1 \overset{?}{<} -3$

$\quad 3 > 2$ True $\quad -4 < -3$ True

> .Think.................................
> Choose a value from the solution set, which is $a > 7$ OR $a < 2$.

So the solution set to the compound inequality is $\{a \mid a < 2$ or $a > 7\}$. Alternatively, you can write $(-\infty, 2) \cup (7, \infty)$.

Example

1 Solve and check the compound inequality. Graph the solution set.

Solve: $-4c \geq 8$ OR $6c > 24$

$$-4c \geq 8 \qquad \text{OR} \qquad 6c > 24$$

$$\frac{-4c}{-4} \leq \frac{8}{-4} \qquad \frac{6c}{6} > \frac{24}{6} \qquad \longleftarrow \text{Use the Division Property of Inequality.}$$

$$c \leq -2 \quad \text{OR} \quad c > 4$$

Check: Choose test points. Try -3 and 6 to verify the solution set.

$$-4c \geq 8 \qquad \text{OR} \qquad 6c > 24$$

$$-4(-3) \overset{?}{\geq} 8 \qquad 6(6) \overset{?}{>} 24$$

$$12 \geq 8 \;\text{True} \qquad 36 > 24 \;\text{True}$$

Graph:

- The graph identifies the solutions of the compound inequality.

- Identify the union of the two graphs. This is the graph of the solution set.

So the solution set to the compound inequality is $\{c \,|\, c \leq -2 \text{ or } c > 4\}$.
Alternatively, you can write $(-\infty, -2] \cup (4, \infty)$.

▶You can write a compound inequality from a graph.

- First, identify the boundary points of the graph. Determine whether they are *included* or *excluded* in the solution set.

- Then use the inequality symbol that corresponds to the direction of the arrow.

Write a compound inequality shown by each graph.

The shaded region on the graph includes -3 and is *between* the values -3 and 4, not including 4. Thus, the compound inequality is a *conjunction*, which involves AND.

So the inequality is $\{x \,|\, -3 \leq x < 4\}$.
Alternatively, you can write interval notation: $[-3, 4)$.

The shaded regions on the graph are *not between* two values.
Thus, the compound inequality is a *disjunction*, which involves OR.

So the inequality is $\{x \,|\, x \leq 0 \text{ or } x \geq 6\}$.
Alternatively, you can write interval notation: $(-\infty, 0] \cup [6, \infty)$.

Try These

Solve and check each compound inequality. Then graph the solutions.

1. $-4 < x + 1 < 6$

2. $-1 \leq -3z + 2 \leq 5$

3. $4r - 1 < 7$ AND $4r + 8 > 8$

4. $y + 3 > 13$ OR $y + 3 < -4$

5. $-4m + 6 < 18$ OR $-4m + 6 > 42$

6. $\frac{3x}{4} < 9$ AND $4x + 8 > 8$

7. Discuss and Write What are the similarities and differences for the graphs of the compound inequalities $x > -1$ OR $x \leq -4$ and $-4 < x \leq -1$?

Go to PRACTICE BOOK **Lesson 3-5 for exercise sets.**

Solve Absolute-Value Inequalities

Objective To solve inequalities involving absolute-value expressions

▶ Inequalities that contain an absolute-value expression can be written as a compound inequality.

> **Remember:** The absolute value of any real number, x, is the distance from zero to x on a number line.

When $a > 0$:

$|x| = a \longrightarrow$ means that x is a units from 0.

$\quad x = a$ OR $x = -a$

$|x| < a \longrightarrow$ means that x is less than a units from 0.

$\quad x > -a$ AND $x < a$

The above is also true for $\leq$.

$|x| > a \longrightarrow$ means that x is greater than a units from 0.

$\quad x < -a$ OR $x > a$

The above is also true for $\geq$.

▶ To solve an absolute-value inequality involving the "is less than" symbol, rewrite the inequality as a conjunction, and solve.

Solve: $|x| + 4 < 14$ ◀—Isolate the absolute-value expression.

$|x| + 4 - 4 < 14 - 4$ ◀—Use the Subtraction Property of Inequality.

$\qquad |x| < 10$

Rewrite this statement as a *conjunction*.

$x > -10$ AND $x < 10$ ◀—x is *between* -10 and 10.

Graph: $\{x | -10 < x < 10\}$; also written as $(-10, 10)$

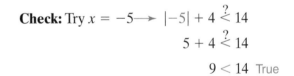

_____ **Key Concept** _____

Principles for Solving an Absolute-Value Inequality

1. Isolate the absolute-value expression.

2. Write the statement as a compound inequality.

3. Solve the two simple inequalities.

4. Graph the solution set and check.

Check: Try $x = -5 \longrightarrow |-5| + 4 \overset{?}{<} 14$

$\qquad 5 + 4 \overset{?}{<} 14$

$\qquad 9 < 14$ True

Example

1 **Solve:** $|r + 7| - 2.5 \leq 11$

$\qquad |r + 7| - 2.5 \leq 11$

$|r + 7| - 2.5 + 2.5 \leq 11 + 2.5$

$\qquad |r + 7| \leq 13.5$

$r + 7 \geq -13.5$ AND $r + 7 \leq 13.5$

$\quad \underline{-7 \qquad -7} \qquad \underline{-7 \quad -7}$

$\quad r \geq -20.05$ AND $\quad r \leq 6.5$

Graph: $\{r | -20.5 \leq r \leq 6.5\}$; also written as $[-20.5, 6.5]$

Check: Try $r = 0.$ ⟶ $|0 + 7| - 2.5 \overset{?}{\leq} 11$

$\qquad |7| - 2.5 \overset{?}{\leq} 11$

$\qquad 4.5 \leq 11$ True

▶To solve an absolute-value inequality involving the "is greater than" symbol, rewrite the inequality as a disjunction, and solve.

Solve: $|x| - 3 > 5$ ◀—Isolate the absolute-value expression.

$|x| - 3 + 3 > 5 + 3$ ◀—Use the Addition Property of Inequality.

$|x| > 8$

Rewrite this statement as a *disjunction*.

$x < -8 \text{ OR } x > 8$ ◀—x is either less than -8 OR greater than 8.

Graph: $\{x \mid x < -8 \text{ or } x > 8\}$; also written as $(-\infty, -8) \cup (8, \infty)$

Check: Try $x = -10$ ⟶ $|-10| - 3 \overset{?}{>} 5$

$10 - 3 \overset{?}{>} 5$

$7 > 5$ True

Example

1 **Solve:** $2|c - 1| + 14 \geq 26$ ◀—Isolate the absolute-value expression.

$2|c - 1| + 14 - 14 \geq 26 - 14$ ◀—Use the Subtraction Property of Inequality.

$\dfrac{2|c - 1|}{2} \geq \dfrac{12}{2}$ ◀—Use the Division Property of Inequality.

$|c - 1| \geq 6$ ◀—Rewrite this statement as a *disjunction*.

$c - 1 \leq -6 \text{ OR } c - 1 \geq 6$

$\underline{+1 \quad +1 \qquad +1 +1}$ ◀—Use the Addition Property of Inequality.

$c \leq -5 \quad \text{OR} \quad c \geq 7$ ◀—c is either less than or equal to -5 OR greater than or equal to 7.

Graph: $\{c \mid c \leq -5 \text{ OR } c \geq 7\}$; also written as $(-\infty, -5] \text{ OR } [7, \infty)$

Check: Try $r = -8$.

$2|-8 - 1| + 14 \overset{?}{\geq} 26$

$2|-9| + 14 \overset{?}{\geq} 26$

$2(9) + 14 \overset{?}{\geq} 26$

$32 \geq 26$ True

Try These

Solve each inequality. Then graph and check the solution set.

1. $|m| - 16 < 4$ **2.** $16|d| \geq 4$ **3.** $|x + 11| - 4 \leq 9$ **4.** $\dfrac{4}{5}|d| > 3$

5. $|y + 6| - 2\frac{1}{4} \geq 1\frac{3}{4}$ **6.** $|2x| - 1 < 11$ **7.** $-2 + |3b - 5| > 8$ **8.** $2.4 + |g - 1| \geq 1.5$

9. Discuss and Write Explain the similarities and differences between solving an inequality that contains an absolute-value expression and one that does not. Use specific examples to support your reasoning.

Go to **PRACTICE BOOK Lesson 3-6 for exercise sets.**

3-7

Technology:
Solve Linear Inequalities

Objective To use a handheld to solve linear inequalities

▶ Some handhelds allow you to solve linear inequalities. You can use the **Solve** command on a handheld to determine the solution set.

Solve the inequality $x - 12 < 2x + 6$ using a handheld.

Step 1 Press ⌂ . Then choose **1** to select **Calculator**.

Step 2 Press (menu). Select **Algebra**, then choose **Solve**.

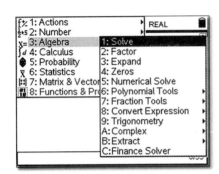

Step 3 Input $x - 12 < 2x + 6$ *and* then ⊙ x.

Press (enter). The x parameter means to solve the inequality for x.

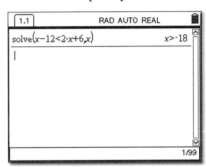

To verify that the solution set satisfies the inequality without using a handheld, graph the solution set and choose test points.

$$x > -18$$

◄—+——+——⊕——+——+——+——►
−20 −19 −18 −17 −16 −15

Try $x = -20$. $x - 12 < 2x + 6$

$$-20 - 12 \overset{?}{<} 2(-20) + 6$$

$$-32 < -34 \text{ False}$$

Try $x = -15$. $x - 12 < 2x + 6$

$$-15 - 12 \overset{?}{<} 2(-15) + 6$$

$$-27 < -24 \text{ True}$$

Represent the solution set from the handheld in set-builder and interval notation. Solution set: $\{x \mid x > -18\}$, or $(-18, \infty)$.

• Solve the inequality $3x + 4 \leq x + 12$ using a handheld. Verify the solution, then represent the solution set in set-builder and interval notation.

Step 1 Press (menu). Select **Algebra**, then choose **Solve**.

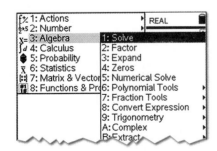

Step 2 Input $3x + 4 \leq x + 12, x$. Then press (enter). Use (ctrl) ⊙ for the inequality symbol $\leq$.

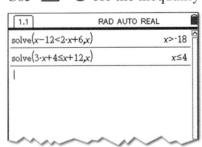

The solution set is $x \leq 4$.

Verify the solution set without using a handheld.

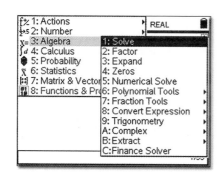

Try $x = 5$.

$3x + 4 \leq x + 12$

$3(5) + 4 \overset{?}{\leq} 5 + 12$

$19 \leq 17$ False

Try $x = 2$.

$3x + 4 \leq x + 12$

$3(2) + 4 \overset{?}{\leq} 2 + 12$

$10 \leq 14$ True

Solution set: $\{x \mid x \leq 4\}$, or $(-\infty, 4]$

Example

1 Solve the inequality $-6x + 3 \geq 2x + 27$ using a handheld. Verify the solution, then represent the solution set in set-builder and interval notation.

Step 1 Press ⬚menu. Select **Algebra**, then choose **Solve**.

Step 2 Input $-6x + 3 \geq 2x + 27, x$. Then press ⬚enter. Use ⬚ctrl ⬚> for the inequality symbol $\geq$.

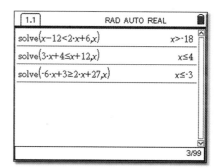

Verify the solution set without using the handheld.

Try $x = 0$.

$-6x + 3 \geq 2x + 27$

$-6(0) + 3 \overset{?}{\geq} 2(0) + 27$

$3 \geq 27$ False

Try $x = -5$.

$-6x + 3 \geq 2x + 27$

$-6(-5) + 3 \overset{?}{\geq} 2(-5) + 27$

$33 \geq 17$ True

Solution set: $\{x \mid x \leq -3\}$, or $(-\infty, -3]$.

Try These

Use a handheld to solve each inequality. Verify the solution set, then represent your answer in set-builder and interval notation.

1. $7x + 15 > 2x$

2. $5x - 2 \leq 3x + 2$

3. $x - 3 < 15 - 2x$

4. $2x + 7 > 4x + 11$

5. $6 - x > 6x - 1$

6. $3x + 4 \leq 5x + 12$

7. Discuss and Write Write two inequalities that have the same solution. Verify your answer using a handheld.

Problem-Solving Strategy:
 **③ Reason Logically**

Objective **To solve problems using the strategy *Reason Logically***

Problem 1: Is there a two-digit whole number with the property that, when the digits are reversed, the resulting number is twice the original number?

Read ▸ **Read to understand what is being asked.**

List the facts and restate the question.

Facts: The digits of a two-digit number can be reversed to form another two-digit number.

Question: Is there a two-digit number for which the number that results from reversing the digits is twice the original number?

Plan ▸ **Select a strategy.**

You could examine all two-digit numbers. However, that could take some time. It might be easier to use the strategy *Reason Logically*.

Problem-Solving Strategies

1. Make a Drawing
2. Solve a Simpler Problem
3. Reason Logically
4. Consider Extreme Cases
5. Work Backward
6. Find a Pattern
7. Account for All Possibilities
8. Adopt a Different Point of View
9. Guess and Test
10. Organize Data

Solve ▸ **Apply the strategy.**

• Since the "reversed" number must be *double* the original, then it must be *a multiple of 2*. Its units digit must be 0, 2, 4, 6, or 8. But it cannot be 0 because that would mean the tens digit of the original number is 0, which is not possible for a two-digit number. So the original number has to have a tens digit of 2, 4, 6, or 8.

• Since the "reversed" number is *twice* the original, then the units digit of the original number must be *twice* the tens digit. The only numbers that satisfy both these criteria are 24 and 48. Neither of these numbers has a "reverse" that is twice the original.

Therefore, there is no two-digit whole number with the property that, when the digits are reversed, the resulting number is twice the original number.

Check ▸ **Check to make sure your answer makes sense.**

You can also look at this problem algebraically. Suppose such a number exists. If t is the tens digit and u is the units digit, then the value of the number is $(10t + u)$. If you reverse the digits so u becomes the tens digit and t becomes the units digit, the value of the new number is $(10u + t)$.

If the new number is twice the original, then $(10u + t) = 2(10t + u)$. Solve for t in terms of u, as shown to the right.

Note that the tens digit, t, of the original number t is $\frac{8}{19}$ *times* the units digit u. But there is no digit u between 0 and 9, for which $\frac{8}{19}u$ is a digit between 1 and 9

$$
\begin{aligned}
(10u + t) &= 2(10t + u) \\
10u + t &= 20t + 2u \quad \longleftarrow \text{Apply the Distributive Property.} \\
8u + t &= 20t \quad \longleftarrow \text{Subtract } 2u \text{ from both sides.} \\
8u &= 19t \quad \longleftarrow \text{Subtract } t \text{ from both sides.} \\
\frac{8}{19}u &= t \quad \longleftarrow \text{Divide both sides by 19.}
\end{aligned}
$$

between 1 and 9. Therefore, there is no two-digit number for which you can reverse the digits to get a new number twice the original.

Problem 2: If you follow the steps given in the example in the table below, the result will be divisible by 9 no matter what number you start with. Explain why this is true.

Steps	Example
1. Start with a four-digit whole number.	4783
2. Multiply the number by 3.	3(4783) = 14,349
3. Add each digit of the result to the result.	14,349 + 1 + 4 + 3 + 4 + 9 = 14,370
4. Multiply the new number by 3.	3(14,370) = 43,110
5. Add each digit of the result to the result.	43,110 + 4 + 3 + 1 + 1 + 0 = 43,119

Read ▶ **Read to understand what is being asked.**

List the facts and restate the question.

Facts: You begin with any four-digit number. You triple the number, add each digit of the result to the result, triple the new number, and then add each digit of the result to the result.

Question: Why is the final number divisible by 9 no matter what the initial number is?

Plan ▶ **Select a strategy.**

Try using the strategy *Reason Logically*, using some basic divisibility rules.

Solve ▶ **Apply the strategy.**

- Let n represent the original number in Step 1.
- In Step 2, when you triple the number, n, the result is $3n$. Because $3n$ is divisible by 3, you know that the *sum of its digits*, s, is divisible by 3. Then $s = 3m$, where m is a whole number.
- In Step 3, when you add the sum of the digits of $3m$ to $3n$, the result is $3n + 3m$, or $3(n + m)$.
- In Step 4, when you triple the number, $3(n + m)$, the result is $3 \cdot 3(n + m)$, or $9(n + m)$.

  Let $k = n + m$. Since n and m are whole numbers, then k is a whole number and $9(n + m) = 9k$. Since $9k$ is divisible by 9, the *sum of its digits*, S, must be divisible by 9. Then $S = 9M$, where M is a whole number.
- In Step 5, the result is $9k + 9M$, or $9(k + M)$, which is divisible by 9.

> **Remember:**
> A number is divisible by 3 *if and only if* the sum of its digits is divisible by 3.
>
> A number is divisible by 9 *if and only if* the sum of its digits is divisible by 9.

Check ▶ **Check to make sure your answer makes sense.**

Read back through the solution. Make sure each step follows logically from the one before. Start with a couple of different four-digit numbers and use a handheld to verify that the steps in the solution are true for that specific number. For example:

- Start with 5156 and triple it. The result:15,468. Verify that it is divisible by 3.
- Add each digit of 15,468 to 15,468. (15,468 + 1 + 5 + 4 + 6 + 8 = 15,492). Verify that 15,492 is divisible by 3.
- Multiply 15,492 by 3. The result is 46,476. Verify that 46,476, is divisible by 9.
- Add each digit of 46,476 to 46,476. Verify that the result is divisible by 9.

Go to PRACTICE BOOK Lesson 3-8 for exercise sets.

Enrichment:
The Triangle Inequality Theorem

Objective To determine when three given lengths can be side lengths of a triangle • To determine the range of possible lengths for a side of a triangle given the lengths of the other two sides

When Can Three Lengths Form a Triangle?

Can any three lengths be side lengths of a triangle?
Try this experiment.

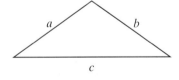

• Use four straws with these lengths: 2 inches, 3 inches, 4 inches, and 6 inches. Take three straws at a time and try to arrange them to form a triangle.

• Record the combinations of lengths that make a triangle and the combinations that do not.

• Write down anything interesting you discover.

You should have found that, for some combinations of lengths, such as 2 inches, 3 inches, and 6 inches., you could *not* form a triangle. If you join the 2-inch and 3-inch straws, the "unjoined" endpoints will not reach the ends of the 6-inch straw, as shown in the figures below.

 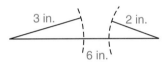

This experiment illustrates the Triangle Inequality Theorem.

For any triangle, the sum of the lengths of any two sides is greater than the length of the third side.

If *a*, *b*, and *c* are the side lengths of a triangle, as shown in the figure at the right, then the following inequalities must be true because of the Triangle Inequality Theorem.

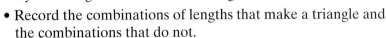

$$a + b > c \qquad a + c > b \qquad b + c > a$$

▶ To determine if three given lengths can be side lengths of a triangle, apply the Triangle Inequality Theorem by adding any two lengths and comparing their sum with the third length. The sum must be *greater than* the third length.

• Is it possible for a triangle to have side lengths of 45 ft, 31 ft, and 24 ft? Explain your answer.

Verify that all three inequalities are true.

Is 45 + 31 > 24? Yes; 76 > 24

Is 45 + 24 > 31? Yes; 69 > 31

Is 31 + 24 > 45? Yes; 55 > 45

All three inequalities are true, so the lengths can be side lengths of a triangle.

• Is it possible for a triangle to have side lengths of 52 yd, 98 yd, and 38 yd? Explain your answer.

Verify that all three inequalities are true.

Is 52 + 98 > 38? Yes; 150 > 38

Is 52 + 38 > 98? No; 90 < 98

Is 98 + 38 > 52? Yes; 136 > 52

One of the three inequalities is *not* true, so the three lengths *cannot* be side lengths of a triangle.

Find the Range of Lengths for the Third Side of a Triangle

Suppose you know that the lengths of two sides of a triangle are 6.3 cm and 8.8 cm. What are the possible lengths for the third side?

To find the possible lengths, write and solve the three inequalities relating the side lengths by using the Triangle Inequality Theorem.

Let x = the unknown side length.

$6.3 + 8.8 > x$	$x + 6.3 > 8.8$	$x + 8.8 > 6.3$
$15.1 > x$	$x + 6.3 - 6.3 > 8.8 - 6.3$	$x + 8.8 - 8.8 > 6.3 - 8.8$
	$x > 2.5$	$x > -2.5$

The solution to the first inequality shows that x is less than 15.1 cm.
The solution to the second inequality shows that x must be greater than 2.5 cm.
The solution to the third inequality does not give any new information.
It is already known that x is greater than 2.5, so it must also be greater
than -2.5 (and, of course, it must be a positive number).

So the missing side length must be between 2.5 cm and 15.1 cm *or* 2.5 cm $< x <$ 15.1 cm.

Using the Theorem When Side Lengths Are Algebraic Expressions

Suppose the side lengths of a triangle are $3x$, $x + 11$, and $x - 1$.
What are the possible values of x?

To find the possible values, use the Triangle Inequality Theorem to write
three inequalities relating the side lengths and solve each one for x.

$3x + x + 11 > x - 1$	$x + 11 + x - 1 > 3x$	$3x + x - 1 > x + 11$
$4x - x + 11 > x - x - 1$	$2x - 2x + 10 > 3x - 2x$	$4x - x - 1 > x - x + 11$
$3x + 11 > -1$	$10 > x$	$3x - 1 > 11$
$3x + 11 - 11 > -1 - 11$		$3x - 1 + 1 > 11 + 1$
$3x > -12$		$3x > 12$
$3x \div 3 > -12 \div 3$		$3x \div 3 > 12 \div 3$
$x > -4$		$x > 4$

Combining the three solutions: $4 < x < 10$

Try These

Determine whether it is possible for a triangle to have the given side lengths. Explain.

1. 5 in., 5 in., 10 in. **2.** 64 ft, 45 ft, 37 ft **3.** 21 yd, 13 yd, 39 yd

Solve.

4. The side lengths of a triangle are $5x$, $2x + 7$, and $4x - 3$. Find the possible values of x.

5. Use the inequality $a + b > c$, where a, b, and c are the sides of a triangle.
If you add c to both sides of the inequality, what can you say about the
length of any side of a triangle and the triangle's perimeter?

6. Discuss and Write Jerry lives 7 miles from Ben. Ben lives 4 miles from Rob.
Jerry says he lives exactly 2 miles from Rob. Is this possible? Explain.

Test Prep: Multiple-Choice Questions
Strategy: Apply Mathematical Reasoning

When answering or solving a multiple-choice question, *justify your steps*. This will help you make sure that you do not miss any steps as you work through the problem. State the appropriate rules, definitions, or properties to be sure that your process is reasonable.

Look at the sample test item.

Read the whole test item, including the answer choices.

Identify the information you need to solve the problem.

• Underline important words.

Find the <u>solution set</u> of $-3x + 7 \leq 28$.

The *solution set* consists of the values that make the inequality a true statement.

• Restate the question in your own words.

Find the values of x that make $-3x + 7 \leq 28$ true.

Solve the problem.

• Justify your steps to be sure that your process is correct.

• Apply appropriate rules and properties.

$$-3x + 7 \leq 28$$

$$-3x + 7 - 7 \leq 28 - 7 \quad \longleftarrow \text{Use the Subtraction Property of Inequality.}$$

$$-3x \leq 21 \quad \longleftarrow \text{Simplify.}$$

$$-3x \div -3 \geq 21 \div -3 \quad \longleftarrow \text{Use the Division Property of Inequality.}$$

$$x \geq -7 \quad \longleftarrow \text{Simplify.}$$

Test-Taking Tips

• Underline important words.

• Restate the question.

• Use the Test-Prep strategy.

• Apply appropriate rules, definitions, properties, or strategies.

• Analyze and eliminate answer choices.

Remember: Reverse the inequality symbol when multiplying or dividing both sides of an inequality by a negative number.

Item Analysis

• Analyze and eliminate answer choices. Watch out for distractors.

A. $\{x \,|\, x \leq -7\}$ $\longleftarrow$ The inequality symbol was not reversed when dividing by -3. Eliminate this choice.

B. $\{x \,|\, x \leq 7\}$ $\longleftarrow$ The negative sign was ignored when dividing. Eliminate this choice.

C. $\{x \,|\, x \geq -7\}$ $\longleftarrow$ This is the correct choice!

D. $\{x \,|\, x \geq 7\}$ $\longleftarrow$ The inequality symbol was reversed, but the negative sign was ignored. Eliminate this choice.

Try These

Choose the correct answer. Explain how you eliminated answer choices.

1. Solve $|x + 3| - 6 > 9$.

    A. $-18 < x < 12$ **C.** $x < -18$ or $x > 12$

    B. $-12 < x < 18$ **D.** $x < -12$ or $x > 18$

2. Solve $-3 \leq 2x + 5 \leq 21$.

    F. $-4 \leq x \leq 8$ **H.** $x \leq -4$ or $x \geq 8$

    G. $-8 \leq x \leq 4$ **J.** $x \leq -8$ or $x \geq 4$

Go to **PRACTICE BOOK** page 83 for exercise sets.

Relations and Functions

CHAPTER 4

In This Chapter You Will:

- Recognize and define the domain and range of relations, given different representations
- Identify and define functions
- Apply the vertical-line test to graphs
- Write function rules and make function tables
- Identify dependent and independent variables in problem situations

- Recognize and extend arithmetic and geometric sequences
- Write a function rule for an arithmetic sequence
- Write a recursive formula for a geometric sequence
- Solve problems using a variety of strategies
- Look for new vocabulary words **highlighted** in each lesson

Do You Remember?

- A coordinate plane, or grid, is formed by the intersection of a horizontal number line called the *x*-axis and a vertical number line called the *y*-axis.
- The origin is the point of intersection of the two axes.
    - A quadrant is one of four sections into which the coordinate plane is divided.
    - The solution(s) of an equation or an inequality is the value(s) of the variable that makes the equation or inequality true.

For Practice Exercises:

Go to **PRACTICE BOOK, pp. 89–108**

For Chapter Support: ONLINE

Go to **www.progressinmathematics.com**

- Skills Update Practice
- Practice Activities
- Audio Glossary
- Vocabulary Activities

- Technology Videos
- Enrichment Activities
- Electronic SourceBook

VIRTUAL MANIPULATIVES

Critical Thinking

Jack is installing brick patios. Each square foot of patio is patterned as shown at the right. What expression or rule can Jack write to find the number of bricks he will need for each rectangular patio he installs if he knows the length (ℓ) and the width (w) of the patio?

Introduction to Relations

Objective To define relation, domain, and range • To represent relations with rules, tables, mapping diagrams, or graphs • To identify the domain and range of a relation

Ira is playing a computer game in which he has to swap adjacent pieces of the same colored shape to make groups of 3 or more. If he makes a group of 3, he earns 6 points. A group of 4 earns 8 points, a group of 5 earns 10 points, and a group of 6 earns 12 points. How can the relationship between the number of shapes in the group and the number of points earned be represented?

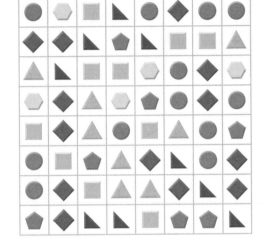

You can use a set of ordered pairs of numbers to show the relationship between the number of shapes in the group and the corresponding number of points earned.

$$\{(3,6), (4,8), (5,10), (6,12)\}$$

In an ordered pair, it is important to note which element is the first of the pair and which is the second. The ordered pair $(3,6)$ is not the same as the ordered pair $(6,3)$.

▶ A relationship that is represented by a set of ordered pairs is called a **relation**. The **domain** of a relation is the set of all *first* elements of the ordered pairs. The **range** of a relation is the set of all *second* elements of the ordered pairs.

For Ira's game relation, the domain is $\{3, 4, 5, 6\}$, and the range is $\{6, 8, 10, 12\}$.

▶ The set of ordered pairs in a relation may be represented by a rule, a table, a **mapping diagram**, or a graph.

Express Ira's game relation as a *rule*, as a *table*, as a *mapping diagram*, and as a *graph*.

Rule

If (x, y) represents an ordered pair in Ira's game relation, then a rule for that relation is:

$$y = 2x$$

The *x*-value is the **input value**.

The *y*-value is the **output value**.

Table

Ira's Game Relation	
Group (*x*)	Points (*y*)
3	6	← 6 = 2(3)
4	8	← 8 = 2(4)
5	10	← 10 = 2(5)
6	12	← 12 = 2(6)

Mapping Diagram

Ira's Game Relation

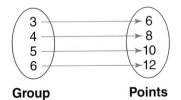

Graph

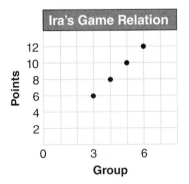

Examples

Write the domain and range of each relation.

1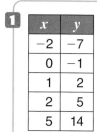

x	y
−2	−7
0	−1
1	2
2	5
5	14

Ordered Pairs: $(-2, -7)$, $(0, -1), (1, 2) (2, 5), (5, 14)$

Domain (D) = $\{-2, 0, 1, 2, 5\}$

Range (R) = $\{-7, -1, 2, 5, 14\}$

2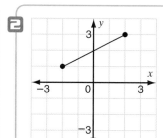

There are infinitely many ordered pairs in this relation.

Domain (D) = $\{x | -2 \le x \le 2\}$

Range (R) = $\{y | 1 \le y \le 3\}$

3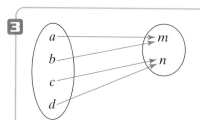

Ordered Pairs: $(a, m), (b, m)$, $(c, n), (d, n)$

Domain (D) = $\{a, b, c, d\}$

Range (R) = $\{m, n\}$

▶ You can determine the ordered pairs in a relation specified by a rule.

A relation, T, is represented by the rule $y = -4x - 1$.

a. Does the ordered pair $(1, -3)$ belong to the relation represented by the rule? Explain.

$$y = -4x - 1$$
$$-3 \overset{?}{=} -4(1) - 1 \quad \longleftarrow \text{Substitute 1 for } x \text{ and } -3 \text{ for } y.$$
$$-3 = -5 \quad \text{False}$$

No, the ordered pair $(1, -3)$ is not in T.

b. If $(2, k)$ belongs to the relation, find k.

$$y = -4x - 1$$
$$k = -4(2) - 1 \quad \longleftarrow \text{Substitute 2 for } x \text{ and } k \text{ for } y.$$
$$k = -9$$

For the relation, an input value of 2 results in an output value of -9.

Try These

Write the domain and range of each relation.

1.

x	y
−6	−2.5
−4	−1.5
−2	−0.5
0	0.5
2	1.5

2.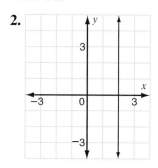

3.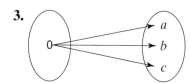

4. Does the ordered pair $(-7, 7)$ belong to the relation $y = -|x|$? Explain.

5. Find the value of h if the ordered pair $(h, 0)$ belongs to the relation $y = -3x + 4$.

6. Discuss and Write Describe a verbal situation using a relation. Create a rule and a mapping diagram to represent the situation you wrote about.

Introduction to Functions

Objective To define a function • To identify relations as functions, given different representations • To apply the vertical-line test to graphs • To use function notation

Mike is planning to plant vegetables in a rectangular section of his garden. To protect the vegetables from foraging deer, Mike intends to fence in the section. If the length of the vegetable garden is to be 40 feet, how much fencing will Mike need?

To find the amount of fencing needed, you can use the formula for the perimeter of a rectangle, $P = 2\ell + 2w$.

▶ The formula for the perimeter of a rectangle gives the relationship between the perimeter and the dimensions of the rectangle.

Since the length of the rectangular section is given, the perimeter will depend upon the width he chooses.

$P = 2\ell + 2w \longrightarrow P = 2(40) + 2w$ ◀ Substitute the given length into the Perimeter Formula.

$$P = 80 + 2w$$

To record some possibilities for the perimeter relation, use a table.

• The rule for this relation is $P = 80 + 2w$.

• The ordered pairs are of the form (w, P).

• The domain for this relation, the possible values for w, is limited to positive real numbers.

• The range for this relation, the possible values for P, is also limited to positive real numbers.

w	$80 + 2w$	P	(w, P)
10	$80 + 2(10)$	100	(10, 100)
25	$80 + 2(25)$	130	(25, 130)
37.5	$80 + 2(37.5)$	155	(37.5, 155)
40	$80 + 2(40)$	160	(40, 160)

So Mike might need 100 ft, 130 ft, 155 ft, or 160 ft of fencing depending on the width of the garden.

In this relation, when you input a positive real number for the value of w, there is *exactly one output value* for P. Such a relation is called a function.

_____ **Key Concept** _____

Function

A *function* is a special type of relation that pairs each domain value with exactly one range value.

Example

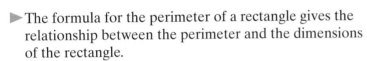

Write the domain and range for the relation and tell whether the relation is a function.

1

x	y
−2	16
−1	1
0	0
1	1
2	16

Think
The table represents a set of ordered pairs (x, y).

Domain = $\{-2, -1, 0, 1, 2\}$

Range = $\{0, 1, 16\}$

The set of ordered pairs in this table does represent a function because every domain value is paired with exactly one range value.

► To determine if a set of ordered pairs is a function, check if no first element can be paired with more than one second element. It does not matter if some second elements are repeated.

Determine whether each relation is a function. Explain.

- $(0, 7), (1, 7), (2, 9), (3, 16)$ ◄— No domain value has more than one range value.

  These ordered pairs define a function.

- $(0, 7), (0, 9), (2, 9), (3, 16)$ ◄— The domain value 0 has more than one range value.

  These ordered pairs *do not* define a function.

> **Remember:**
> The *domain* of a relation is the set of all *first* elements of the ordered pairs.
> The *range* of a relation is the set of all *second* elements of the ordered pairs.

► To determine if a relation represented by a mapping diagram is a function, use the arrows to find the pairing for each domain value.

Determine whether each relation is a function. Explain.

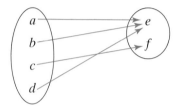

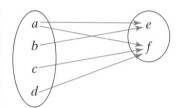

There is only one arrow leading away from each domain value. So each domain value is paired with exactly one range value. This mapping diagram represents a relation that is a function.

There is more than one arrow leading away from domain value *a*. So not every domain value is paired with exactly one range value. This mapping diagram represents a relation that is not a function.

► To determine if a relation represented by a graph is a function, use the vertical-line test. When any vertical line intersects a graph:

- at exactly one point, the graph represents a function.
- at more than one point, the graph does not represent function.

Which of these graphs represent a function? Explain your answer.

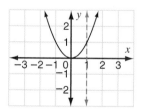

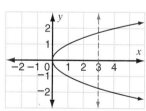

Each vertical line drawn through the graph intersects the graph at exactly one point. This graph represents a relation that is a function.

A vertical line drawn through the graph intersects the graph at more than one point. This graph represents a relation that is not a function.

Continue Lesson ➡

Determine whether each represents a function. Explain.

1

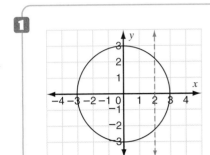

.Think..
Use the vertical-line test on the graph.
....

Domain = $\{x \mid -3 \le x \le 3\}$ There are infinitely
many ordered pairs

Range = $\{y \mid -3 \le y \le 3\}$ on this graph.

This graph represents a relation that is not a function because at least one vertical line will intersect the graph at more than one point.

2

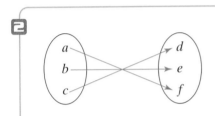

.Think..
Is there more than one arrow going out
from any domain value?
....

Ordered Pairs: (a, f), (b, e), (c, d)

Domain = $\{a, b, c\}$

Range = $\{d, e, f\}$

This mapping diagram represents a relation that is a function because each domain value is paired with exactly one range value.

▶ A **function rule** is an equation that describes a function. Sometimes the equation is written using **function notation**.

To write a rule in function notation, you use the symbol $f(x)$ in place of y.

You read $f(x)$ as "f of x."

Function notation allows you to see the input value, x. The table at the right shows the names or symbols used with a function.

domain	range
input	output
x	$f(x)$
x	y
independent variable	dependent variable

> Function Rule: $y = 4x$ ◀—This equation describes a relationship between y and x.
> It allows you to find ordered pairs that satisfy this relation.

> Function Notation: $f(x) = 4x$ ◀—The symbol $f(x)$ (read "f of x") replaces y.
> It shows that x represents the *input values*.

> $f(3) = 4(3)$ ◀—The symbol $f(3)$ (read "f of 3")
> specifies an input value for x.

> $= 12$ ◀—the corresponding *output value*

So the ordered pair $(3, 12)$ satisfies the function rule $f(x) = 4x$. Inputting other values for the variable x will determine other ordered pairs that satisfy this function rule.

▶ To distinguish among different functions of the same variable, different letters are used in the function notation. For example, if x is the independent variable, you may see $f(x)$, $g(x)$, and $h(x)$.

If $f(x) = 5x + 7$ and $g(x) = x^2 - 12$, find $f(-4) + g(3)$.

• Substitute -4 for x in $f(x)$.	• Substitute 3 for x in $g(x)$.	• Determine the required sum.
$f(x) = 5x + 7$	$g(x) = x^2 - 12$	$f(-4) + g(3)$
$f(-4) = 5(-4) + 7$	$g(3) = 3^2 - 12$	$-13 + (-3)$
$\quad = -20 + 7 = -13$	$\quad = 9 - 12 = -3$	-16

Examples

Evaluate each function. Write the ordered pair to show the correspondence.

1 $f(x) = 3x - 4$, for $f(-4)$

$f(-4) = 3(-4) - 4$

$\quad = -12 - 4 = -16$

So the ordered pair is $(-4, -16)$.

2 $f(x) = -x^2$, for $f(6)$

$f(6) = -6^2$

$\quad = -36$

So the ordered pair is $(6, -36)$.

3 If $f(x) = 3x + 6$ and $h(x) = (x + 1)^2$, find $2[f(-3) + h(1.5)]$.

• Substitute -3 for x in $f(x)$.	• Substitute 1.5 for x in $h(x)$.	• Determine the required product.
$f(x) = 3x + 6$	$h(x) = (x - 1)^2$	$2[f(-3) + h(1.5)]$
$f(-3) = 3(-3) + 6$	$h(1.5) = (1.5 - 1)^2$	$2[-3 + 0.25]$
$\quad = -9 + 6 = -3$	$\quad = (0.5)^2 = 0.25$	$2[-2.75]$
		-5.5

Try These

Write the domain and range for the relation and tell whether the relation is a function.

1.

x	y
-2	2
-1	1
0	0
1	1
2	2

2.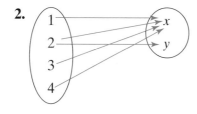

3.

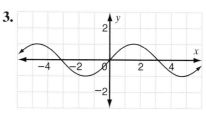

Evaluate the expression, given $f(x) = 3x + 4$, $g(x) = x^2 - 4x + 1$, and $h(x) = \sqrt{x}$.

4. $f(-2) + g(5)$ **5.** $f(1.5) + g(-2) - h(9)$ **6.** $2[f(4) + g(8)]$ **7.** $\dfrac{f(5) + g(0)}{h(25)}$

8. Discuss and Write Hal said that the relation $\{(-8, 16), (-6, 16), (-6, 12)\}$ is not a function because 16 appears twice in the ordered pairs. Do you agree with Hal's reasoning? Is this relation a function? Explain.

Go to ▶ PRACTICE BOOK Lesson 4-2 for exercise sets.

Write Function Rules

Objective To write function rules • To make function tables

Michael is going on a 2-week vacation. Since he cannot bring his dog on the trip, he decides to hire a dog sitter. A local pet shop charges $3 per hour for home dog-sitting services plus a basic 2-week fee of $50. How can Michael determine the total cost of the dog-sitting services?

To determine the total cost of the dog-sitting services, write a function rule or an equation.

- Write a relationship for the total cost. Notice that there are two components: the basic fee and the hourly charges. Since the basic fee is constant, the total cost then depends on the number of hours spent carrying out the selected services.

Let c = the total cost. ←—the dependent variable

Let h = the number of hours of service. ←—the independent variable

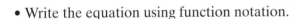

total cost	equals	basic fee	plus	hourly charges
↓	↓	↓	↓	↓
c	$=$	50	$+$	$3h$

- Write the equation using function notation.

Since h is the independent variable, c is a function of h.

$c(h) = 50 + 3h$ ←—[function rule]   **Remember:** Read $c(h)$ as "c of h."

So Michael can input different values of h into the function rule to determine the total costs of the dog-sitting services.

Suppose Michael needs dog-sitting services for 28 hours over a 2-week period. What is the total cost of the services?

$$c(h) = 50 + 3h \longrightarrow c(28) = 50 + 3 \bullet 28$$
$$= 50 + 84$$
$$= 134$$

So the 2-week cost for 28 hours of dog-sitting services is $134.

▶ To show solutions of a function, such as $c(h) = 50 + 3h$, you can make a function table. Choose several values for the input, h. Then substitute each value into the function to find the corresponding output, c.

[function table]

h	$c(h) = 50 + 3h$	Relation (hours, cost)
10	$c(10) = 50 + 3 \bullet 10 = 80$	(10, 80)
20	$c(20) = 50 + 3 \bullet 20 = 110$	(20, 110)
30	$c(30) = 50 + 3 \bullet 30 = 140$	(30, 140)

...Think....................
The ordered pair (10, 80) stands for "$80 for 10 hours of service."

▶ Given a function table, you can write a function rule that describes the relationship by looking for a pattern.

Write a rule that expresses a relationship between the given x- and y-values.

.Think...
Since the y-values are greater than the x-values, test patterns using addition or multiplication.

x	y
-2	2
-1	3
0	4
1	5

Test Addition
$-2 + 4 = 2$ True
$-1 + 4 = 3$ True
$0 + 4 = 4$ True
$1 + 4 = 5$ True

Test Multiplication
$-2(-1) = 2$ True
$-1(-1) = 3$ False
There is no need to continue the test.

So a rule that relates the given x- and y-values is $y = x + 4$, or $f(x) = x + 4$.

You can find other ordered pairs that satisfy the function rule $f(x) = x + 4$ by using different input values for x.

Examples

What equation or function rule can be written to represent the relationship between x and $f(x)$?

1

Input (x)	Output $f(x)$	
-1	1.5	$\leftarrow -1 + 2.5 = 1.5$
0	2.5	$\leftarrow 0 + 2.5 = 2.5$
1	3.5	$\leftarrow 1 + 2.5 = 3.5$
2	4.5	$\leftarrow 2 + 2.5 = 4.5$
3	5.5	$\leftarrow 3 + 2.5 = 5.5$
4	6.5	$\leftarrow 4 + 2.5 = 6.5$

Each $f(x)$ value is 2.5 greater than each x value. The function rule is $f(x) = x + 2.5$.

2

Input (x)	Output $f(x)$	
0	5	$\leftarrow 5(0) + 5 = 5$
1	10	$\leftarrow 5(1) + 5 = 10$
2	15	$\leftarrow 5(2) + 5 = 15$
3	20	$\leftarrow 5(3) + 5 = 20$

Each $f(x)$ value is five more than five times the x value. The function rule is $f(x) = 5x + 5$.

Try These

Write a function rule for the situation. Use function notation.

1. The total distance, d, traveled after h hours at a constant rate of 55 miles per hour

2. The perimeter, p, of an equilateral triangle when you know the length, s, of a side

3. Janet has joined a gym. By contract, she pays a one-time membership fee of $100 and $60 per month for as long as she remains a member.

Make a function table using integers from -2 to 2 as input values for each function.

4. $f(x) = 2x - 7$

5. $c(m) = 20 + 3.5m$

6. $d(t) = 6t + 55$

7. **Discuss and Write** Mr. Higgins asked his class to write a function rule for the values shown in the table at the right. Harriet's answer is $y = |x| + 5$. Pat's answer is $y = |x + 5|$. Who is correct? Justify your answer.

x	5	0	-6	-10
y	10	5	1	5

Go to PRACTICE BOOK Lesson 4-3 for exercise sets.

Arithmetic Sequences

Objective To recognize and extend arithmetic sequences • To find an indicated term of an arithmetic sequence • To write a function rule for an arithmetic sequence

Marisol is an accomplished skydiver. Suppose in today's freefall jump, Marisol fell 16 feet in the first second, 48 feet in the next second, 80 feet in the third second, and 112 feet in the fourth second. If Marisol continued to fall at this rate, how many feet would she fall in the fifth second?

To find how many feet she would fall in the fifth second, look for a pattern that occurred during the first four seconds.

▶ To look for a pattern, organize the data by using a table or by using a graph.

• Use a Table

Time (seconds)	1	2	3	4	5
Distance (feet)	16	48	80	112	?

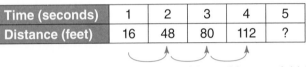

$+ 32$ $+ 32$ $+ 32$ ◀—Add 32 to get the next term in the pattern.

According to the pattern, you can find the number of feet Marisol fell in the fifth second by adding 32 to the number of feet she fell in the fourth second. So in the fifth second, she fell $112 + 32$, or 144, feet.

• Use a Graph

When the information about Marisol's jump is shown on a graph, the points appear to fall on a straight line.

Applying the vertical-line test to this graph shows that this relation is a function.

You can find the number of feet Marisol fell during the fifth second and sixth second by continuing the pattern:
$16, 48, 80, 112, 112 + 32 = 144, 144 + 32 = 176, \ldots$

> **Remember:** An ellipsis (three dots) indicates that a pattern continues.

▶ An ordered set of elements that follows a pattern is called a sequence. A sequence, such as 16, 48, 80, 112, which has a first term and a last term, is called a finite sequence. A sequence such as 16, 48, 80, 112, ..., in which there is another term after each term of the sequence, is called an infinite sequence.

In the sequence whose terms are $a_1, a_2, a_3, \ldots, a_{n-1}, a_n \ldots, a_1$ represents the first term, a_3 represents the third term, and a_n represents the *n*th term of the sequence. The term before the *n*th term is represented by a_{n-1}. The subscript in a term represents the place of the term in the sequence.

A sequence in which each term after the first is found by *adding* a nonzero constant (called the common difference, *d*) to the previous term is called an arithmetic sequence.

The sequence 16, 48, 80, 112, ... is an arithmetic sequence, and the constant difference is 32.

Examples

Determine if each sequence is an arithmetic sequence.
If the sequence is arithmetic, find the next term.

1 $2, 3, 5, 8, \ldots$

.....Think.....................
Test for a common difference.
....

2nd term $-$ 1st term $= 3 - 2 = 1$ ⎤ The differences
are not the same.
3rd term $-$ 2nd term $= 5 - 3 = 2$ ⎦

So $2, 3, 5, 8, \ldots$ is *not* an arithmetic sequence.

2 $42, 19, -4, -27, \ldots$

2nd term $-$ 1st term $= 19 - 42 = -23$

3rd term $-$ 2nd term $= -4 - 19 = -23$

4th term $-$ 3rd term $= -27 - (-4) = -23$

There is a common difference, $d = -23$.

So $42, 19, -4, -27, \ldots$ is an arithmetic
sequence. The next term is $-27 + (-23)$,
or -50.

▶ Each term of an arithmetic sequence can be related to the first term, a_1,
and the common difference, d. The sequence may be written as follows:

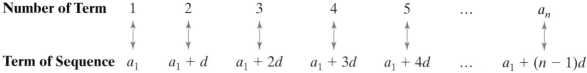

Number of Term	1	2	3	4	5	$\ldots$	a_n
Term of Sequence	a_1	$a_1 + d$	$a_1 + 2d$	$a_1 + 3d$	$a_1 + 4d$	$\ldots$	$a_1 + (n-1)d$

In general, the nth term of an arithmetic
sequence is the sum of the first term, a_1,
and $(n - 1)$ common differences, that is,
$a_n = a_1 + (n - 1)d$.

_____ **Key Concept** _____

Formula for the nth Term of an Arithmetic Sequence

$a_n = a_1 + (n - 1)d$ where a_n is the nth term, a_1 is
the first term, n is the number of terms, and d $(d \neq 0)$
is the common difference.

Find a_{10} of $-0.2, -0.8, -1.4, -2, \ldots$

- Find d by subtracting the first term from the second term.

$$d = a_2 - a_1 = -0.8 - (-0.2) = -0.6$$

- Use the formula to find the nth term of an arithmetic sequence.

$$a_n = a_1 + (n - 1)d$$

$$a_{10} = -0.2 + (10 - 1)(-0.6) \quad \leftarrow \text{Substitute 10 for } n, -0.2 \text{ for } a_1, \text{ and } -0.6 \text{ for } d.$$

$$= -0.2 + 9(-0.6) = -0.2 + (-5.4) \quad \leftarrow \text{Simplify.}$$

$$= -5.6$$

Examples

1 Find a_{16} of $1, \frac{2}{3}, \frac{1}{3}, 0, \ldots$

$$d = a_2 - a_1 = \frac{2}{3} - 1 = -\frac{1}{3} \quad \leftarrow \text{Find } d \text{ by subtracting the first term from the second term.}$$

$$a_{16} = 1 + (16 - 1)\left(-\frac{1}{3}\right) \quad \leftarrow \text{Substitute 16 for } n, 1 \text{ for } a_1, \text{ and } -\frac{1}{3} \text{ for } d \text{ in } a_n = a_1 + (n - 1)d.$$

$$= 1 + 15\left(-\frac{1}{3}\right) = 1 + (-5) \quad \leftarrow \text{Simplify.}$$

$$= -4$$

Continue Lesson ➡

2 The odometer on a motorcycle read 50,500 at the end of a day. Every day thereafter, the motorcycle is driven 35 miles. What is the odometer reading 40 days later?

Since the odometer reading will *increase* by 35 miles per day, this situation can be represented using an arithmetic sequence with $a_1 = 50{,}500$, $d = 35$, and the odometer reading 40 days later as a_{41}.

$a_n = a_1 + (n - 1)d$ ◄—Write the rule to find the nth term.

$a_{41} = 50{,}500 + (41 - 1)(35)$ ◄—Substitute the given values.

$\qquad = 50{,}500 + (40)(35) = 50{,}500 + 1400$ ◄—Simplify.

$\qquad = 51{,}900$

So the motorcycle's odometer will read 51,900 miles 40 days later.

▶ By writing an algebraic expression for the nth term of a sequence, you are writing a function rule for the sequence.

Write a function rule for the nth term of the arithmetic sequence: $2, 5, 8, 11, \ldots$

Make a table to help identify a relationship between the number of the term, n, and the value of the term, a_n, of the sequence.

.Think..
$d = a_2 - a_1 = 5 - 2 = 3$
....

Term Number, n	Value of Term, a_n	$a_n = a_1 + (n - 1)d$
1	2	$a_1 = 2$
2	5	$a_2 = 2 + (2 - 1)3 = 2 + 1 \cdot 3 = 5$
3	8	$a_3 = 2 + (3 - 1)3 = 2 + 2 \cdot 3 = 8$
4	11	$a_4 = 2 + (4 - 1)3 = 2 + 3 \cdot 3 = 11$
$\vdots$	$\vdots$	$\vdots$
n	a_n	$a_n = 2 + (n - 1)3$ $\quad = 2 + 3n - 3$ ◄—Simplify. $\quad = 3n - 1$

Each term, after the first, is 2 *plus* 3 *times* 1 *less than* the term number, n.

Function rule: $a_n = 3n - 1$

Example

1 Write a function rule for the nth of the arithmetic sequence: $-50, -25, 0, 25, 50, \ldots$

$d = a_2 - a_1 = -25 - (-50) = 25$ ◄—Find d by subtracting the first term from the second term.

$a_n = -50 + (n - 1)(25)$ ◄—Substitute -50 for a_1, and 25 for d in $a_n = a_1 + (n - 1)d$.

$\qquad = -50 + 25n - 25$ ◄—Simplify.

$\qquad = 25n - 75$

Function rule: $a_n = 25n - 75$

Try These

Determine if each sequence is an arithmetic sequence.
Use a pattern to write the next four terms.

1. $2, -5, -12, -19, \ldots$

2. $1, 2, 4, 7, \ldots$

3. $t + 8, 3t + 5, 5t + 2, 7t - 1, \ldots$

4. $0.1, 0.01, 0.001, 0.0001, \ldots$

5. $\frac{1}{2}, \frac{3}{2}, \frac{5}{2}, \frac{7}{2}, \ldots$

6. $\frac{1}{2}, \frac{1}{3}, \frac{1}{4}, \frac{1}{5}, \ldots$

Find the indicated term of each arithmetic sequence.

7. a_{13} for $7, 4, 1, -2, \ldots$

8. a_{20} for $-19, -15, -11, -7, \ldots$

9. a_{100} for $0.25, 0.5, 0.75, 1, \ldots$

Write a function rule for the *n*th term of each arithmetic sequence.

10. $2, 4, 6, 8, \ldots$

11. $4, 7, 10, 13, \ldots$

12. $3, 8, 13, 18, \ldots$

13. Mr. and Mrs. Tomkins started a college fund for their son Marcus when he was in the first grade. They began the fund with $2500, and each year, they increased their contribution to the fund by $500. What was their contribution to the fund when Marcus was a senior in high school?

14. Discuss and Write Josie has written an arithmetic sequence. In her sequence, the third term is 12 and the ninth term is -12. What is the first term of Josie's sequence? Explain your reasoning.

 PRACTICE BOOK Lesson 4-4 for exercise sets.

Acceleration: Use Arithmetic Series to Represent Triangular Numbers

Numbers that can be represented by dots arranged in the shapes of certain geometric figures are named for the shapes they form.

The following dot patterns are representations of the first four *triangular numbers*.

1st	**2nd**	**3rd**	**4th**

$1, 2$ $1, 2, 3$ $1, 2, 3, 4$ ◄── arithmetic sequence

1 $1 + 2 = 3$ $1 + 2 + 3 = 6$ $1 + 2 + 3 + 4 = 10$ ◄── arithmetic series

Notice that each triangular number after the first can be written as the *sum* of the terms of a finite arithmetic sequence, called an arithmetic series.

Follow the pattern above. What is the fifth triangular number? 15

What is the tenth triangular number? 55
Explain how you arrived at your answer.

$1, 2, 3, 4, 5, 6, 7, 8, 9, 10$ ◄── arithmetic sequence

$1 + 2 + 3 + 4 + 5 + 6 + 7 + 8 + 9 + 10 = 55$ ◄── arithmetic series

Geometric Sequences

Objective To recognize and extend geometric sequences • To find an indicated term of a geometric sequence • To write a recursive formula for a geometric sequence

Some students are measuring the progress of a bouncing ball. In one experiment, the ball is dropped from a height of 16 feet to the floor below. After the first bounce, the ball rebounds to a height of 4 feet above the floor; after the second bounce, it rebounds to a height of 1 foot; and after the third bounce, it rebounds to a height of $\frac{1}{4}$ foot. If the ball continues to bounce and rebound at this rate, what will be the height of the ball after the fourth bounce?

To find the height after the fourth bounce, look for a pattern that occurs during the first three bounces.

▶ To look for a pattern, organize the data by using a table or by using a graph.

• Use a Table

Bounce Number	0	1	2	3	4
Height (feet)	16	4	1	$\frac{1}{4}$	?

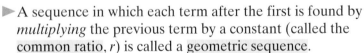

$\div 4 \quad \div 4 \quad \div 4$

Divide by 4 $\left(\text{or multiply by } \frac{1}{4}\right)$ to get the next number.

According to the pattern, you can find the height of the ball after the fourth bounce by dividing its height after the third bounce by 4. So after the fourth bounce, the height of the ball is $\frac{1}{4} \div 4 = \frac{1}{4} \cdot \frac{1}{4} = \frac{1}{16}$ foot.

• Use a Graph

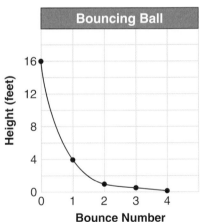

Bouncing Ball

When the information about the bouncing ball is shown on a graph, the points appear to fall on a curve.

Applying the vertical-line test to this graph shows that this relation is a function.

You can find the height of the ball after the fifth bounce by continuing the pattern: $16, 4, 1, \frac{1}{4}, \frac{1}{16}, \frac{1}{16} \div 4 = \frac{1}{16} \cdot \frac{1}{4} = \frac{1}{64}, \cdots$

▶ A sequence in which each term after the first is found by *multiplying* the previous term by a constant (called the common ratio, r) is called a geometric sequence.

In the sequence, $16, 4, 1, \frac{1}{4}, \frac{1}{16}, \frac{1}{64}$:

$4 = 16 \cdot \frac{1}{4} \qquad \frac{1}{4} = 1 \cdot \frac{1}{4} \qquad \frac{1}{64} = \frac{1}{16} \cdot \frac{1}{4}$

$1 = 4 \cdot \frac{1}{4} \qquad \frac{1}{16} = \frac{1}{4} \cdot \frac{1}{4}$

Note that the constant $\frac{1}{4}$ may be found by dividing any term by its preceding term.

$\frac{4}{16} = \frac{1}{4} \qquad \frac{\frac{1}{4}}{1} = \frac{1}{4} \qquad \frac{\frac{1}{16}}{\frac{1}{4}} = \frac{1}{16} \cdot \frac{4}{1} = \frac{1}{4} \qquad \frac{\frac{1}{64}}{\frac{1}{16}} = \frac{1}{64} \cdot \frac{16}{1} = \frac{1}{4}$

Examples

Determine if each sequence is a geometric sequence. If the sequence is geometric, find the next term.

> **Think**
> Test for a common ratio.

1 $-\frac{1}{4}, \frac{1}{2}, -1, 2, \ldots$

$\dfrac{a_2}{a_1} = \dfrac{\frac{1}{2}}{-\frac{1}{4}} = \dfrac{1}{2}\left(-\dfrac{\overset{2}{\cancel{4}}}{\underset{1}{1}}\right) = -2$ $\quad\Big|\quad$ $\dfrac{a_3}{a_2} = \dfrac{-1}{\frac{1}{2}} = -\dfrac{1}{1} \cdot \dfrac{2}{1} = -2$ $\quad\Big|\quad$ $\dfrac{a_4}{a_3} = \dfrac{2}{-1} = -2$ $\longleftarrow$ There is a common ratio, $r = -2$.

So the sequence $-\frac{1}{4}, \frac{1}{2}, -1, 2, \ldots$ is a geometric sequence.

The next term is $2(-2) = -4$.

2 $10, 3\frac{1}{3}, 1\frac{1}{9}, \frac{10}{27}, \ldots$

$10, \dfrac{10}{3}, \dfrac{10}{9}, \dfrac{10}{27}, \ldots$ $\longleftarrow$ Rewrite mixed numbers as improper fractions.

$\dfrac{a_2}{a_1} = \dfrac{\frac{10}{3}}{10} = \dfrac{\overset{1}{\cancel{10}}}{3} \cdot \dfrac{1}{\underset{1}{\cancel{10}}} = \dfrac{1}{3}$ $\quad\Big|\quad$ $\dfrac{a_3}{a_2} = \dfrac{\frac{10}{9}}{\frac{10}{3}} = \dfrac{\overset{1}{\cancel{10}}}{\underset{3}{\cancel{9}}} \cdot \dfrac{\overset{1}{\cancel{3}}}{\underset{1}{\cancel{10}}} = \dfrac{1}{3}$ $\quad\Big|\quad$ $\dfrac{a_4}{a_3} = \dfrac{\frac{10}{27}}{\frac{10}{9}} = \dfrac{\overset{1}{\cancel{10}}}{\underset{3}{\cancel{27}}} \cdot \dfrac{\overset{1}{\cancel{9}}}{\underset{1}{\cancel{10}}} = \dfrac{1}{3}$ $\longleftarrow$ There is a common ratio, $r = \frac{1}{3}$.

So $10, 3\frac{1}{3}, 1\frac{1}{9}, \frac{10}{27}, \ldots$ is a geometric sequence.

The next term is $\frac{10}{27}\left(\frac{1}{3}\right) = \frac{10}{81}$.

▶ Each term of a geometric sequence can be related to the first term, a_1, and the common ratio, r. The sequence may be written as follows:

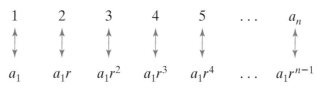

Number of Term	1	2	3	4	5	. . .	a_n
Term of Sequence	a_1	a_1r	a_1r^2	a_1r^3	a_1r^4	. . .	a_1r^{n-1}

In general, the nth term of a geometric sequence is the product of the first term, a_1, and the common ratio, r, raised to the $(n-1)$ power, that is, $a_n = a_1r^{n-1}$.

> **Key Concept**
> **Formula for the nth term of a Geometric Sequence**
> $a_n = a_1r^{n-1}$, where a_n is the nth term, a_1 is the first term, n is the number of terms, and $r(r \neq 0, 1)$ is the common ratio.

Find a_9 of $2, 20. 200, 2000, \ldots$

• Find r by dividing the second term by the first term.

$r = \dfrac{a_2}{a_1} = \dfrac{20}{2} = 10$

• Use the formula to find the nth term of a geometric sequence.

$a_n = a_1r^{n-1}$

$a_9 = 2 \bullet 10^{9-1}$ $\longleftarrow$ Substitute 9 for n, 2 for a_1, and 10 for r.

$= 2 \bullet 10^8$

$= 2 \bullet 100,000,000$ $\longleftarrow$ Simplify.

$= 200,000,000$

Continue Lesson ➡

1 What is the 10th term of the geometric sequence given that the first term is -128, and the common ratio is 0.5?

$a_n = a_1 \quad r^{n-1}$ ←—Write the rule to find the nth term.

$a_{10} = -128 \quad (0.5)^{10-1}$ ←—Substitute 10 for n, -128 for a_1, and 0.5 for r.

$a_{10} = -0.25$ ←—Simplify.

2 Find a_7 of $-8, 4, -2, 1, \ldots$.

$r = \dfrac{a_2}{a_1} = \dfrac{4}{-8} = -\dfrac{1}{2}$ ←—Find r by dividing the second term by the first term.

$a_7 = -8 \cdot \left(-\dfrac{1}{2}\right)^{7-1}$ ←—Substitute 7 for n, -8 for a_1, and $-\dfrac{1}{2}$ for r in $a_n = a_1 r^{n-1}$.

$= -8 \cdot \left(-\dfrac{1}{2}\right)^{6} = -8 \cdot \dfrac{1}{64}$ ←—Simplify.

$= -\dfrac{8}{64} = -\dfrac{1}{8}$

▶ You can also use a <u>recursive formula</u> to find the nth term, a_n, of a geometric sequence by using the preceding term, a_{n-1}, and the common ratio, r. A recursive formula is a rule for calculating a new term of a sequence from the term preceding it.

In general, in a geometric sequence, if r represents the common ratio and a_{n-1} and a_n represent two consecutive terms, then $r = \dfrac{a_n}{a_{n-1}}$. This will lead to the recursive formula for the nth term, a_n.

$r \cdot a_{n-1} = \dfrac{a_n}{a_{n-1}} \cdot a_{n-1}$ ←—Use the Multiplication Property of Equality.

$= \dfrac{a_n}{a_{n-1}}^{1} \cdot a_{n-1}^{1}$ ←—Divide out common factors.

$= a_n$ ←—Simplify.

_____ **Key Concept** _____

Recursive Formula for the nth Term of a Geometric Sequence

$a_n = ra_{n-1}$, where a_n is the nth term, n is the number of terms, and $r(r \neq 0, 1)$ is the common ratio.

Write a recursive formula for the nth term of the sequence: $8, -28, 98, -343, \ldots$

$r = \dfrac{a_n}{a_1} = \dfrac{-28}{8} = -\dfrac{7}{2}$ ←—Find r, by dividing the second term by the first term.

$a_n = -\dfrac{7}{2}a_{n-1}$ ←—Substitute -3 for r in $a_n = ra_{n-1}$.

Example

1 Write a recursive formula for the nth term of the geometric sequence:

$\dfrac{1}{4}, -\dfrac{3}{4}, \dfrac{9}{4}, -\dfrac{27}{4}, \ldots$

$r = \dfrac{a_2}{a_1} = \dfrac{-\dfrac{3}{4}}{\dfrac{1}{4}} = \dfrac{-3}{4} \cdot \dfrac{4}{1} = -3$ ←—Find r, by dividing the second term by the first term.

$a_n = -3a_{n-1}$ ←—Substitute -3 for r in $a_n = ra_{n-1}$.

Try These

**Determine whether each sequence could be *geometric*, *arithmetic*, or *neither*.
Then find the next four terms using a pattern.**

1. $456, 45.6, 4.56, 0.456, \ldots$

2. $3^3, 3^{-3}, 3^3, 3^{-3}, \ldots$

3. $0.07, 0.08, 0.09, 0.10, \ldots$

4. $\dfrac{3}{4}, \dfrac{1}{2}, \dfrac{1}{3}, \dfrac{2}{9}, \ldots$

5. $\dfrac{3}{2}, \dfrac{5}{2}, \dfrac{7}{2}, \dfrac{9}{2}, \ldots$

6. $\dfrac{1}{4}, \dfrac{1}{9}, \dfrac{1}{16}, \dfrac{1}{25}, \ldots$

Find the indicated term of each geometric sequence.

7. a_8 for $1, -5, 25, -125, \ldots$

8. a_7 for $3, 0.6, 0.12, 0.024, \ldots$

9. a_9 for $x, 2x, 4x, 8x, \ldots$

Write a recursive formula for the *n*th term of each geometric sequence.

10. $0.3, 1.2, 4.8, 19.2, \ldots$

11. $-\dfrac{2}{81}, \dfrac{2}{27}, -\dfrac{2}{9}, \dfrac{2}{3}, \ldots$

12. $y^{-4}, y^{-2}, 1, y^2, \ldots$

13. Hilda bought a car for $17,500. Her car depreciated 25% in value each year. What was Hilda's car worth 3 years after she bought it?

14. Discuss and Write Barry has written a geometric sequence. In his sequence, the third term is $\dfrac{3}{2}$, and the seventh term is $\dfrac{3}{32}$. What is the first term of Barry's sequence? Explain your reasoning.

Go to PRACTICE BOOK **Lesson 4-5 for exercise sets.**

Acceleration: Geometric Sequences of Fractals

A fractal is a fragmented geometric shape that is subdivided in parts, each of which is similar to the entire shape. Waclaw Sierpinksi, a Polish mathematician, created fractals using a triangle. The figures below show the first four steps in making Sierpinksi's Triangle.

Step 1

Step 2

Step 3

Step 4

To create each step, connect the midpoints of the sides of the shaded triangles at the previous step and remove the middle triangles.

Look at the number of shaded triangles at each stage. What fraction of each step is shaded?

	Step 1	Step 2	Step 3	Step 4
Number of shaded triangles →	1	3	9	27
Fraction shaded →	1	$\dfrac{3}{4}$	$\dfrac{9}{16}$	$\dfrac{27}{64}$

Notice that $1, \dfrac{3}{4}, \dfrac{9}{16}, \dfrac{27}{64}$ is a geometric sequence with a common ratio, $\dfrac{3}{4}$.

Write a recursive formula for the *n*th term of the geometric sequence. $a_n = \dfrac{3}{4}a_{n-1}$

What fraction of Step 5 is shaded? $\dfrac{81}{256}$

Explain how you arrived at your answer. $a_5 = \dfrac{3}{4} \cdot \dfrac{27}{64} = \dfrac{81}{256}$

Problem Solving: Review of Strategies

Objective To solve problems by using a variety of strategies

Problem: Over the five days (Monday–Friday) of a technology expo, Jerry sold 100 copies of his software program. Each day he sold five more copies than he sold the day before. How many copies did Jerry sell each day?

Read to understand what is being asked.

List the facts and restate the question.

Facts: Jerry sold 100 copies of his program over five consecutive days. Each day, he sold 5 more copies than on the previous day.

Question: How many copies did Jerry sell on each of Monday, Tuesday, Wednesday, Thursday, and Friday?

Select a strategy.

You can try using the strategy *Reason Logically*. Or, you can attempt to *Solve a Simpler Problem*.

Apply the strategy.

▶ **Method 1: Reason Logically**

Jerry sold an average of $\frac{100}{5}$, or 20, copies per day.

Think of the average as the number he would have sold each day *if* he had sold the *same number* each day.

- Start by envisioning that Jerry, as shown in the table below, had sold the same number of copies each day.

Day	Monday	Tuesday	Wednesday	Thursday	Friday
Copies Sold	20	20	20	20	20

- "Redistribute," as shown in the table below, the copies to meet the problem criteria—that is, so the number of copies increases by 5 each day. First, take 5 copies from Tuesday and add them to Thursday. Then take 10 copies from Monday and add them to Friday.

Day	Monday	Tuesday	Wednesday	Thursday	Friday
Copies Sold	20 − 10	20 − 5	20	20 + 5	20 + 10

The table below shows the total number of copies is still 100 and the number of copies increases by 5 each day.

Day	Monday	Tuesday	Wednesday	Thursday	Friday
Copies Sold	10	15	20	25	30

So Jerry sold 10 copies on Monday, 15 on Tuesday, 20 on Wednesday, 25 on Thursday, and 30 on Friday.

Problem-Solving Strategies
1. Make a Drawing
2. Solve a Simpler Problem
3. Reason Logically
4. Consider Extreme Cases
5. Work Backward
6. Find a Pattern
7. Account for All Possibilities
8. Adopt a Different Point of View
9. Guess and Test
10. Organize Data

▶ **Method 2: Solve a Simpler Problem**

Start by considering an easier problem. Ignore the fact that 100 copies were sold. That is, consider only the fact that 5 more copies were sold each day.

- Begin with *any* first day sale. For example, assume that Jerry sold no copies on Monday. Then you get the following:

Monday:	0 copies
Tuesday:	5 copies
Wednesday:	10 copies
Thursday:	15 copies
Friday:	20 copies

  This accounts for $0 + 5 + 10 + 15 + 20$, or 50 copies.

- Now, bring back into play the fact that 100 copies were sold. You must include 50 more copies. Because 50 *divided by* 5 is 10, simply add 10 sales to each day to get:

Monday:	10 copies
Tuesday:	15 copies
Wednesday:	20 copies
Thursday:	25 copies
Friday:	30 copies

- Consider this question:
  What would have happened if you had started with a number other than 0 for the first day's sales?

  Suppose you had picked 3 instead. Then for each day, Jerry would have the following sales:

Monday:	3 copies
Tuesday:	8 copies
Wednesday:	13 copies
Thursday:	18 copies
Friday:	23 copies

  This accounts for 65 copies. You would need to add 35 more copies. Since 35 *divided by* 5 is 7, add 7 copies to each day's sales to get 10, 15, 20, 25, 30.

  So Jerry sold 10 copies on Monday, 15 on Tuesday, 20 on Wednesday, 25 on Thursday, and 30 on Friday.

Check to make sure your answer makes sense.

- Is the total number of copies sold 100? $10 + 15 + 20 + 25 + 30 \overset{?}{=} 100$

  $$100 = 100 \checkmark$$

- Do the number of copies sold increase by 5 each day?

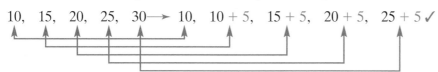

$$10, \quad 15, \quad 20, \quad 25, \quad 30 \longrightarrow 10, \quad 10 + 5, \quad 15 + 5, \quad 20 + 5, \quad 25 + 5 \checkmark$$

Go to **PRACTICE BOOK Lesson 4-6 for exercise sets.**

Enrichment:
Step Functions

Objective To define step functions, the least-integer function, and the greatest-integer function • To examine real-life situations that can be modeled by step functions

At ACME Delivery Service, the cost to ship a package depends on its weight. The graph at the right shows the costs for two-day delivery.

Examine the graph and note that the shipping costs change as weights of the package change.

- The cost to ship packages weighing up to 1 pound is $2.
- For packages weighing more than 1 pound, but not more than 2 pounds, the cost jumps by $0.50 to $2.50.
- For packages weighing more than 2 pounds, but not more than 3 pounds, the cost jumps by $0.50 again to $3.00.
- This pattern of "jumps" continues for subsequent 1-pound intervals.

2-Day Shipping Costs

The relationship between weight of a package and its shipping cost is an example of a step function, which is a least-integer function, or a ceiling function. The name, step function, comes from the fact that the graph resembles a series of steps.

►Another type of a step function is the greatest-integer function, or floor function. The greatest-integer function is usually denoted $f(x) = \lfloor x \rfloor$ or $f(x) = [x]$. For any number x, $\lfloor x \rfloor$ is the greatest integer less than or equal to x.

To find $\lfloor x \rfloor$, if x is not an integer, round x *down* to the preceding integer.

$\lfloor 11.8 \rfloor = 11$ ◄——11 is the greatest integer less than 11.8.

$\lfloor -1.5 \rfloor = -2$ ◄——−2 is the greatest integer less than −1.5.

$\lfloor 3\frac{1}{6} \rfloor = 3$ ◄——3 is the greatest integer less than $3\frac{1}{6}$.

$\lfloor -5\frac{5}{6} \rfloor = -6$ ◄——−6 is the greatest integer less than $-5\frac{5}{6}$.

►The table on the left below shows the value of $\lfloor x \rfloor$ for several values of x. At the right below is a graph of the greatest integer function $f(x) = \lfloor x \rfloor$, for x values −4 to 4.

x	$\lfloor x \rfloor$	$f(x)$
$-38\frac{3}{4}$	$\lfloor -38\frac{3}{4} \rfloor$	−39
−15.111	$\lfloor -15.111 \rfloor$	−16
0.019	$\lfloor 0.019 \rfloor$	0
π	$\lfloor \pi \rfloor$	3
51	$\lfloor 51 \rfloor$	51

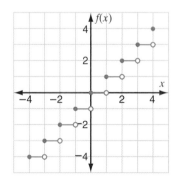

▶ You can use a handheld to graph the greatest-integer function.

1 Press 🏠 **2** to select **Graphs & Geometry**. Change the window size. Press menu **4** to select **Window**.

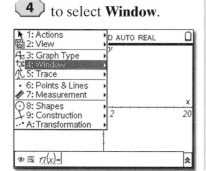

2 Press **1** to select **Window Settings**. Change **XMin** and **YMin** to −5 and **XMax** and **YMax** to 5.

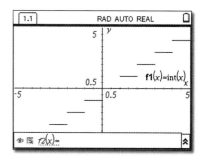

3 Press enter. Use the small green letters to type "int," and then type (x). Press enter.

Compare each example below to the graph of $f(x) = \lfloor x \rfloor$.
Use your handheld to graph and explore their differences.

Function: $f(x) = \lfloor x \rfloor + 3$

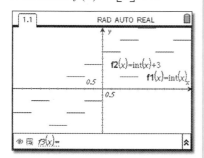

The graph shifted up 3 units.

Function: $f(x) = \lfloor x - 2 \rfloor$

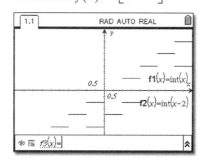

The graph shifted right 2 units.

Function: $f(x) = \lfloor 0.5x \rfloor$

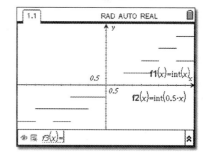

The graph has "steps" twice as long.

▶ Many real-life situations can be modeled by step functions.

Ana displays her baseball cards in plastic sheets. Each sheet holds 6 cards. The relationship between the number of cards and the number of sheets is a step function. Only whole numbers make sense for both variables, so the graph is made up of discrete points.

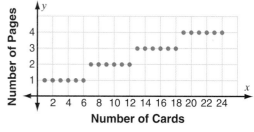

Baseball-Card Binder

Try These

Solve.

1. $\lfloor 53.19 \rfloor$ **2.** $\lfloor -9.758 \rfloor$ **3.** $\lfloor 0.89 \rfloor$ **4.** $\left\lfloor 7\frac{11}{12} \right\rfloor$ **5.** $\left\lfloor -23\frac{2}{7} \right\rfloor$

6. For $f(x) = \lceil x \rceil$, the value of $\lceil x \rceil$ is the least integer that is greater than or equal to x. Make a graph of $f(x) = \lceil x \rceil$ for x values from −5 to 5.

7. Discuss and Write How does the ceiling function $f(x) = \lceil x \rceil$ compare to the floor function $f(x) = \lfloor x + 1 \rfloor$? Explain.

Go to PRACTICE BOOK **pages 101–102 for exercise sets.**

Test Prep: Gridded-Response Questions
Strategy: Apply Mathematical Reasoning

Information needed to answer a question may be given in the text of the question, in diagrams, or in tables. To solve such problems, *look for relationships* expressed in the given information. Use mathematical reasoning to help you understand the written and visual cues.

Some tests include free-response questions whose answers go on a gridded-response answer sheet. First, print your answers on the grid, and then fill in corresponding bubbles to match those answers.

Look at the sample test item.

Reread the test item carefully. Draw conclusions based on written or visual cues.

- Underline important words.

  What is the eighth term in the <u>pattern</u>?

  A *pattern* is a regularity that helps you predict the next term.

- Restate the question in your own words.

  If you extend the pattern, what will the 8th term be?

Solve the problem.

- Apply appropriate rules. Look for a pattern.

  $-3.9 - (-6.2) = 2.3; -1.6 - (-3.9) = 2.3; \ldots$

  Each term is 2.3 greater than the previous term. Extend the pattern by adding 2.3 until you get to the eighth term.

  $+2.3 +2.3 +2.3$

  $-6.2, -3.9, -1.6, 0.7, 3, 5.3, \ 7.6, \ 9.9$

Item Analysis

Check your work.

- Analyze your answer. Does it make sense?

  The list is an arithmetic sequence with constant difference 2.3. Write a rule and evaluate for $n = 8$.

  $a_n = a_1 + (n - 1)d$

  $a_n = -6.2 + (n - 1)2.3$

  $a_8 = -6.2 + (8 - 1)2.3 = 9.9$

Sample Test Item

What is the eighth term in the pattern?

$-6.2, -3.9, -1.6, 0.7, 3, \ldots$

Test-Taking Tips

- Underline important words.
- Restate the question.
- Apply appropriate rules, definitions, properties, or strategies.
- Analyze your answer.

Record your answer on the grid.

- Print your answer in the answer boxes. Print only one number or symbol in each answer box.
- Fill in one bubble for every answer box you have written in. Do not fill in a bubble under a blank answer box.

Try These

Solve. Justify your steps. Grid your response.

1. The table shows a linear relationship between the cost of peppers and their weight in pounds. How much will 35 pounds of peppers cost in dollars?

Weight (pounds)	0.25	0.5	1	1.5
Cost	$0.70	$1.40	$2.80	$4.20

Go to **PRACTICE BOOK page 103 for exercise sets.**

Linear Functions

CHAPTER 5

In This Chapter You Will:

- Identify linear functions and graphs
- Relate a constant rate of change to the slope of a line
- Find slopes of lines and identify possible values for slope
- Identify, interpret, write, and graph direct variation
- Write a linear equation and graph a line in slope-intercept form
- Write and graph linear equations using point-slope form
- Understand the relationship of the slopes of parallel and perpendicular lines
- Write equations of lines given their relationship to other lines
- Graph a linear inequality in two variables
- Apply the strategy: *Consider Extreme Cases*
- Look for new vocabulary words **highlighted** in each lesson

Do You Remember?

- A function is a special type of relation that pairs each domain value with exactly one range value. A function rule is an equation that describes a function.
- A ratio is a way of comparing two numbers, a and b, by division.
- Parallel lines are lines in the same plane that do not intersect.
- Two lines are perpendicular if they intersect and form right angles.
  - $\overleftrightarrow{AB}$ and $\overleftrightarrow{BA}$ are symbols for the line that contains points A and B.

For Practice Exercises:

 PRACTICE BOOK, pp. 109–140

For Chapter Support: (ONLINE)

 www.progressinmathematics.com

- Skills Update Practice
- Practice Activities
- Audio Glossary
- Vocabulary Activities
- Technology Videos
- Enrichment Activities
- Electronic SourceBook

 VIRTUAL MANIPULATIVES

Critical Thinking

A limited edition electric guitar signed by a famous guitarist sold for $550 in 2005. By 2009, that same guitar sold for $800 through an online auction. Assuming that the value of the guitar increases at a constant rate, what would be its predicted value in 2014?

Update your skills. See page 407 XI.

5-1 Identify Linear Functions and Their Graphs

Objective To identify linear functions and their graphs • To relate a constant rate of change to the slope of a line • To find slopes of lines • To identify possible values for slope

Monica is traveling by train across America. The train is moving at a constant speed of 60 miles per hour. Monica can determine the number of miles she will travel every 5 hours by using a pattern. What pattern can Monica use?

To find the pattern, make a table of ordered pairs, and analyze the relationship between the x- and y-coordinates.

Let x = the number of hours traveled.
Let y = the distance traveled.

Time Traveled (hours)	Distance Traveled (miles)	Ordered Pairs (x, y)
5	300	(5, 300)
10	600	(10, 600)
15	900	(15, 900)
20	1200	(20, 1200)

Think
5(60) = 300
10(60) = 600
15(60) = 900
20(60) = 1200

A constant change of $+5$ in x corresponds to a constant change of $+300$ in y.

This constant rate of change can be written as a ratio, $\dfrac{\text{change in } y}{\text{change in } x} = \dfrac{300}{5}$.

So there is a pattern for the ordered pairs—namely, as the domain value increases by 5, the corresponding range value increases by 300.

▶ A constant rate of change represents a linear function. A linear function is a function whose graph is a nonvertical line.

To determine if a given set of ordered pairs or relation represents a linear function, find whether there is a constant rate of change, *or* graph the ordered pairs on a coordinate plane to determine if a nonvertical line is formed.

Tell whether the set of ordered pairs represents a linear function.

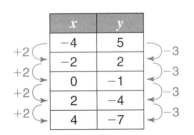

Method 1 Find the rate of change.

Find the change in x and the corresponding change in y.

$$\frac{\text{change in } y}{\text{change in } x} = -\frac{3}{2}$$

Since the ratio of change is constant, the ordered pairs represent a linear function.

Method 2 Plot the points on a coordinate plane.

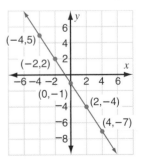

Since the graph is a nonvertical line, the ordered pairs represent a linear function.

▶ First degree equations in two variables are linear functions. Not all functions are linear.

Tell whether the given function is a linear function.
$f(x) = x^2 - 3$

To determine if a given function is linear:

- Make a function table, choosing at least three consecutive values for x.
- Use substitution to find corresponding values of $f(x)$.
- Find the rate of change, *or* plot the points on a coordinate plane.

Make a function table.

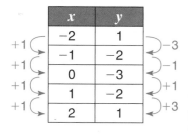

x	y
−2	1
−1	−2
0	−3
1	−2
2	1

Method 1 Find the rate of change.

- Find the change in x and the corresponding change in y.

$\dfrac{\text{change in } y}{\text{change in } x}$ is *not* constant.

Since the rate of change is *not* constant, the function does not represent a linear function.

Method 2 Plot the points on a coordinate plane.

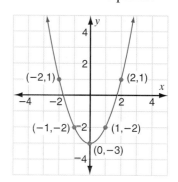

Since the graph is not a straight line, the function does not represent a linear function.

Example

1 Does $y = 7$ represent a linear function?

Make a function table.

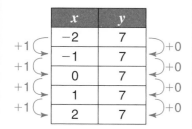

x	y
−2	7
−1	7
0	7
1	7
2	7

Method 1 Find the rate of change.

- Find the change in x and the corresponding change in y.

$\dfrac{\text{change in } y}{\text{change in } x} = \dfrac{0}{1}$, or 0

Since the rate of change is constant, $y = 7$ represents a linear function.

Method 2 Plot the points on a coordinate plane.

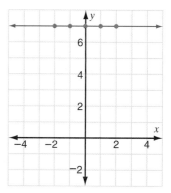

Since the graph is a horizontal line, $y = 7$ represents a linear function.

Continue Lesson ➡

► Look at the line at the right. Notice that it has a specified steepness and slants or inclines from left to right. The constant ratio of the change in y to the corresponding change in x is called the **slope** (m) of the line.

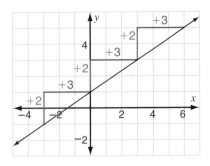

To find the slope, begin at one point on the line, and count vertically to a second point on the line to find the change in y. Then count horizontally to the second point on the line to find the change in x. It does *not* matter what point you start with.

$$\text{slope}(m) = \frac{\text{change in } y}{\text{change in } x} = \frac{\text{vertical change}}{\text{horizontal change}} = \frac{\text{rise}}{\text{run}}$$

The line slants up from left to right. For every vertical change of $+2$, the horizontal change is $+3$. The slope of the line is $\frac{2}{3}$.

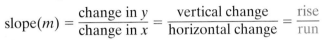

Find the slope of each line.

1
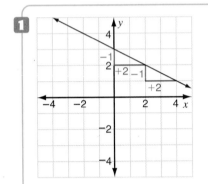

The line slants down from left to right. For every vertical change of -1, the horizontal change is $+2$.

The slope is $\frac{-1}{2}$ or $-\frac{1}{2}$.

2
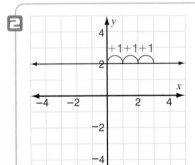

The line is horizontal. The vertical change is 0 for every horizontal change of $+1$.

The slope is $\frac{0}{1}$ or 0.

3
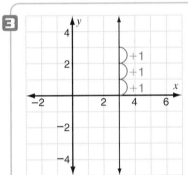

The line is vertical. For every vertical change of $+1$, the horizontal change is 0.

The slope is undefined.

► The slope of a line can be positive, negative, zero, or undefined.

Positive Slope	**Negative Slope**	**Zero Slope**	**Undefined Slope**

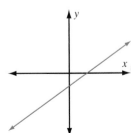 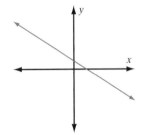 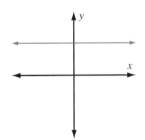 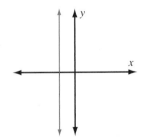

The line slants up from left to right.	The line slants down from left to right.	The line is horizontal. All the y-values are the same.	The line is vertical. All the x-values are the same.

▶ You can also find the slope of a line using a formula if you know the coordinates of any two different points on the line.

Key Concept

Slope Formula

For two different points, (x_1, y_1) and (x_2, y_2), on a line:

slope $(m) = \dfrac{\text{vertical change}}{\text{horizontal change}} = \dfrac{y_2 - y_1}{x_2 - x_1}$, where $x_2 - x_1 \neq 0$.

Find the slope of the line that contains $(0, 3)$ and $(1, -2)$. Describe the line.

$\dfrac{y_2 - y_1}{x_2 - x_1} = \dfrac{-2 - 3}{1 - 0} = \dfrac{-5}{1} = -5$ ◀— Substitute (0, 3) and (1, −2) into the formula, and simplify.

The slope is -5. Since the slope is negative, the line slants down from left to right.

Examples

Find the slope of the line that contains the given points. Describe the line.

1 $(3, 1)$ and $(-1, -7)$

$\dfrac{y_2 - y_1}{x_2 - x_1} = \dfrac{-7 - 1}{-1 - 3} = \dfrac{-8}{-4} = 2$

The slope is 2.
The line slants up from left to right.

2 $(6, 5)$ and $(6, -8)$

$\dfrac{y_2 - y_1}{x_2 - x_1} = \dfrac{-8 - 5}{6 - 6} = \dfrac{-13}{0}$

The slope is undefined.
The line is vertical.

3 $(3, -1)$ and $(-3, 7)$

$\dfrac{y_2 - y_1}{x_2 - x_1} = \dfrac{7 - (-1)}{-3 - 3} = \dfrac{8}{-6} = -\dfrac{4}{3}$

The slope is $-\dfrac{4}{3}$.

The line slants down from left to right.

Try These

Tell whether each relation represents a linear function. Explain *why* or *why not*. If the relation represents a linear function, find its slope.

1.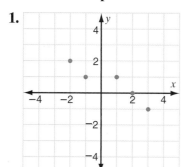

2.

x	y
−2	5
0	4
2	3
4	2
6	1

3. $y = -2x + 4$

Find the slope of the line that contains the given points. Describe the line.

4. $(3, 5)$ and $(-1, -1)$

5. $\left(-7, \dfrac{1}{3}\right)$ and $\left(9, \dfrac{1}{3}\right)$

6. $(-2, 6)$ and $(0, -2)$

7. **Discuss and Write** Are all equations linear functions? Give examples to support your answer.

Go to PRACTICE BOOK Lesson 5-1 for exercise sets.

Direct Variation

Objective To identify and interpret direct variation • To write and graph direct variation

The table below and the graph at the right show how long it took Pablo to read each of the first three chapters of his history book. Is there a mathematical relationship between the number of pages in a chapter and the time it took Pablo to read them?

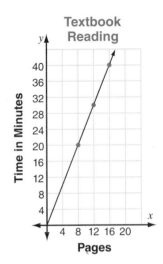

Textbook Reading

Chapter	Pages (x)	Time in Minutes (y)
One	8	20
Two	16	40
Three	12	30

As the number of pages in a chapter increases, the amount of time it takes Pablo to read the chapter changes by a constant factor. The time, y, varies *directly* with the number of pages in the chapter, x. This relationship is called a direct variation.

▶ A direct variation is a linear function that can be written in the form $y = kx$, where k is a nonzero constant called the constant of variation.

constant of variation: $k = \dfrac{y}{x} = \dfrac{20}{8} = \dfrac{40}{16} = \dfrac{30}{12} = \dfrac{5}{2}$

Substituting $\frac{5}{2}$ for k in the equation $y = kx$ gives $y = \frac{5}{2}x$.

So the relationship between the number of pages, x, and the time it took Pablo to read them, y, is $y = \frac{5}{2}x$.

▶ For every direct variation:

• The graph is a straight line that passes through the origin.

• The constant of variation is the slope of the line.

Not *all* linear equations represent direct variations. If a linear equation cannot be written in the form of $y = kx$, then the function is not a direct variation.

Key Concept

Direct Variation

A direct variation is a linear function in which for each ordered pair, (x, y), $y = kx$ or $k = \dfrac{y}{x}$, $k \neq 0$.

Examples

Tell whether each relation represents a direct variation. If so, give the constant of variation.

1

x	y
-3	6
-2	4
1	-2

Method 1 Find the constant of variation, $\frac{y}{x}$, for each ordered pair.

$k = \dfrac{y}{x} = \dfrac{6}{-3} = \dfrac{4}{-2} = \dfrac{-2}{1} = -2$

Yes, the ordered pairs represent a direct variation because $\frac{y}{x} = -2$ for each ordered pair. y varies directly with x.

Method 2 Write an equation.

$y = -2x$ ◀— Each value for y is equal to -2 times the corresponding value for x.

Yes, the ordered pairs represent a direct variation because they can be written in the form $y = kx$, where $k = -2$.

2 $3y = 2x + 6$ ◄—Solve the equation for y.

$\dfrac{3y}{3} = \dfrac{2x + 6}{3}$ ◄—Use the Division Property of Equality.

$y = \dfrac{2}{3}x + 2$

The equation is not a direct variation because it cannot be written in the form $y = kx$.

3 $y - x = 0$ ◄—Solve the equation for y.

$y - x + x = 0 + x$ ◄—Use the Addition Property of Equality.

$y = x$

The equation is a direct variation because it can be written in the form $y = kx$. The constant of variation is 1.

▶ You can write and solve direct variation equations.

The value of y varies directly with x, and $y = 9$ when $x = 6$. Find x when $y = 6$.

First find k. Then write an equation and solve for x.

$k = \dfrac{y}{x} = \dfrac{9}{6} = \dfrac{3}{2}$ ◄—Find the constant of variation.

$y = \dfrac{3}{2}x$ ◄—Write the equation, substituting $\dfrac{3}{2}$ for k.

$6 = \dfrac{3}{2}x$ ◄—Substitute 6 for y.

$\dfrac{2}{\cancel{3}}(\cancel{6}) = \dfrac{\cancel{2}}{\cancel{3}}\left(\dfrac{\cancel{3}}{\cancel{2}}x\right)$ ◄—Use the Multiplication Property of Equality.

$4 = x$

Try These

Explain whether each relation represents a direct variation. If so, state the constant of variation.

1.

x	y
1	−2
−2	−4
4	8

2.

x	y
4	6
6	9
10	15

3. $2y + x = 0$

4. $y - 2 = -3x$

Solve.

5. The value of y varies directly with x, and $y = 7.2$ when $x = 1.6$. Find y when $x = 2.4$.

6. The amount of dog food Bowser eats varies directly with the number of days he is fed. If he eats 0.75 pounds in 2 days, how long will it take him to finish a 30-pound bag? (*Hint:* Let x = number of days and y = amount of food.)

7. Discuss and Write Every direct variation is a linear function, but not every linear function is a direct variation. Explain.

Equations in Slope-Intercept Form

Objective To graph a line using slope-intercept form • To write a linear equation in slope-intercept form

Mei lives in the city and does not own a car. She pays a $20 monthly fee to Urban Car Rental plus $15 per hour each time she uses one of its cars. You can write an equation to represent Mei's monthly cost.

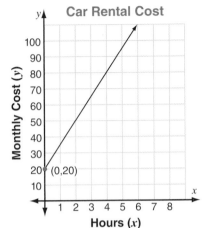

Car Rental Cost

Let x = the number of hours Mei rents a car.
Let y = total monthly cost.

Total monthly cost = cost *per* hour + monthly fee

$$y = 15 \cdot x + 20$$

The monthly cost increases $15 for every 1 hour Mei rents a car.

The constant rate, or *slope*, of this line is $\frac{15}{1}$, or 15.

Notice that the line crosses, or intersects, the y-axis at the point $(0, 20)$. The y-coordinate of the point where the graph crosses the y-axis is the y-intercept. The y-intercept of this line is 20.

The equation that describes this relationship, $y = 15x + 20$, is in slope-intercept form. When an equation is written in slope-intercept form, $y = mx + b$, the slope, m, is the coefficient of x, and the y-intercept, b, is the constant.

Key Concept

Slope-Intercept Form of a Linear Equation
The slope-intercept form of a linear equation is
$$y = mx + b,$$
where m is the *slope* of the line and b is the *y*-intercept.

▶ The slope-intercept form, $y = mx + b$, allows you to quickly identify the slope and y-intercept and to graph the line.

Given the equation $y = -\frac{1}{2}x - 1$, identify the slope and y-intercept. Then graph the line.

1 Identify and plot the y-intercept.
$$y = -\frac{1}{2}x - 1$$

.......**Think**.......................
The x-coordinate for the
y-intercept is always 0.
....

y intercept is -1, which is the point $(0, -1)$.

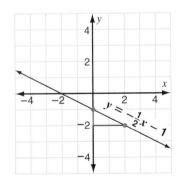

2 Use the slope to plot another point on the line.
$$\text{slope} = \frac{-1}{2} = \frac{\text{vertical change}}{\text{horizontal change}}$$

From $(0, -1)$, count 1 unit down and 2 units to the right to plot another point. Plot the point $(2, -2)$.

3 Draw the line through the two points.

Examples

For each equation, identify the slope and y-intercept, and graph the line.

1 $y = \frac{5}{3}x$

$y = \frac{5}{3}x + 0$

Slope $(m) = \frac{5}{3}$, and

y-intercept $(b) = 0$, so the line contains $(0, 0)$.

$m = \frac{5}{3}; b = 0$

- Plot the y-intercept $(0, 0)$.
- Use the slope to plot another point.

  $\text{slope} = \frac{\text{rise}}{\text{run}} = \frac{5}{3}$

  From $(0, 0)$, count 5 units up and 3 units to the right to plot another point. Plot the point $(3, 5)$.
- Draw the line through the two points.

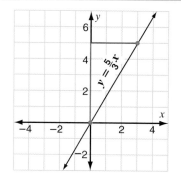

2 $y = -5$

$y = 0 + (-5)$

$y = -5$

Slope $(m) = 0$, and y-intercept $(b) = -5$, so the line contains $(0, -5)$.

$m = 0; b = -5$

- Plot the y-intercept $(0, -5)$.
- Use the slope to plot another point.

  $\text{slope} = 0 = \frac{\text{rise}}{\text{run}} = \frac{0}{1}$

  From $(0, -5)$, count 0 units up and 1 unit to the right to plot another point. Plot the point $(1, -5)$.
- Draw the line through the two points.

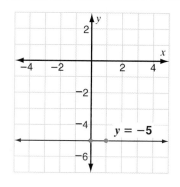

▶ Linear equations are *not always* given in slope-intercept form. In this case to find the slope and y-intercept, rewrite the equation by solving for y.

 Identify the slope and y-intercept of the line $2y + 2x = 5$. Then graph the line.

Write the equation in the form $y = mx + b$ by solving for y.

$2y + 2x = 5$

$2y + 2x - 2x = -2x + 5$ ◄— Use the Subtraction Property of Equality.

$2y = -2x + 5$

$\dfrac{2y}{2} = \dfrac{-2x + 5}{2}$ ◄— Use the Division Property of Equality.

$y = -1x + \frac{5}{2}$

$m = -1; b = \frac{5}{2}$

- Plot the y-intercept, $\left(0, \frac{5}{2}\right)$.
- Use the slope to plot another point.

  $\text{Slope} = \frac{\text{rise}}{\text{run}} = \frac{-1}{1} = -1$

  From $\left(0, \frac{5}{2}\right)$, count 1 unit down and 1 unit to the right to plot another point. Plot the point $\left(1, 1\frac{1}{2}\right)$.
- Draw a line through the two points.

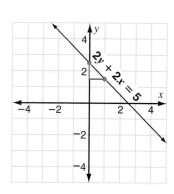

Continue Lesson ➡

► Given the slope and y-intercept, you can write an equation of a line.

Write an equation of the line in slope-intercept form for the line with slope -2 and y-intercept -5.

$y = mx + b$ ◄—Use the slope-intercept form.

$y = -2x + (-5)$ ◄—Substitute the given values in the slope-intercept form.

$y = -2x - 5$ ◄—Simplify.

The equation is $y = -2x - 5$.

Examples

Write an equation of the line in slope-intercept form.

1 slope $= 0$; y-intercept $= -3$

$y = mx + b$ ◄—Use the slope-intercept form.
$y = 0(x) + (-3)$ ◄—Substitute the given values.
$y = -3$ ◄—Simplify.

So the equation is $y = -3$.

2 slope $= -\dfrac{8}{5}$; y-intercept $= 12$

$y = mx + b$ ◄—Use the slope-intercept form.
$y = -\dfrac{8}{5}x + 12$ ◄—Substitute the given values.

So the equation is $y = -\dfrac{8}{5}x + 12$.

► You can write an equation of a line in slope-intercept form, given the graph of a line.

Write the slope-intercept form of the equation of the line shown.

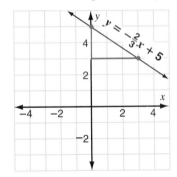

$y = mx + b$ ◄—Use the slope-intercept form.

$b = 5$ ◄—The line crosses the y-axis at $y = 5$.

$m = \dfrac{-2}{3}$ ◄—The line moves down 2 units for every 3 units it moves to the right.

$y = -\dfrac{2}{3}x + 5$ ◄—Substitute 5 for b and $\dfrac{-2}{3}$ for m.

So the equation of the line is $y = -\dfrac{2}{3}x + 5$.

Example

Write the slope-intercept form of the equation of the line shown.

1

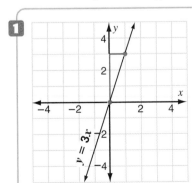

$y = mx + b$ ◄—Use the slope-intercept form.

$b = 0$ ◄—The line crosses the y-axis at $y = 0$.

$m = \dfrac{3}{1}$ ◄—The line moves up 3 units for every 1 unit it moves to the right.

$y = 3x + 0$ ◄—Substitute 3 for m and 0 for b.

$y = 3x$ ◄—Simplify.

So the equation of the line is $y = 3x$.

▶ You can also write an equation of a line in slope-intercept form, given the slope *and* any point on the line.

Write an equation of the line in slope-intercept form with slope $-\frac{5}{4}$ that contains $(-8, 0)$.

Method 1 Use the slope formula.

$$m = \frac{y_2 - y_1}{x_2 - x_1}$$

$$\frac{-5}{4} = \frac{y - 0}{x - (-8)} \leftarrow\text{Substitute the given values.}$$

$$-5(x + 8) = 4(y) \leftarrow\text{Simplify, and apply the Cross-Products Rule.}$$

$$-5x - 40 = 4y \leftarrow\text{Apply the Distributive Property.}$$

$$\frac{-5x - 40}{4} = \frac{4y}{4} \leftarrow\text{Use the Division Property of Equality.}$$

$$\frac{-5x}{4} - \frac{40}{4} = y$$

$$y = -\frac{5}{4}x - 10 \leftarrow\text{Simplify.}$$

Method 2 Use the slope-intercept form.

$$y = mx + b$$

$$0 = -\frac{5}{4}(-8) + b \leftarrow\text{Substitute the given values.}$$

$$0 = 10 + b \leftarrow\text{Simplify.}$$

$$-10 = b \leftarrow\text{Use the Subtraction Property of Equality to solve for } b.$$

$$y = -\frac{5}{4}x - 10 \leftarrow\text{Substitute } -\frac{5}{4} \text{ for } m \text{ and } -10 \text{ for } b \text{ in } y = mx + b.$$

Try These

Identify the slope and *y*-intercept of the line whose equation is given. Graph the line.

1. $y = x + 7$ **2.** $3y = 8x - 6$ **3.** $2x - 3y = 5$

Write an equation of the line in slope-intercept form with the given slope and *y*-intercept.

4. slope: $\frac{6}{5}$; *y*-intercept: -8 **5.** slope: -0.8; *y*-intercept: $\frac{4}{7}$ **6.** slope: 0; *y*-intercept: 3.8

Write an equation of each line in slope-intercept form.

7.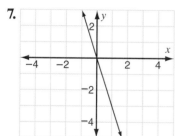

8.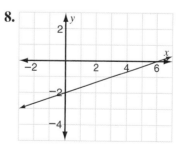

Write an equation of the line in slope-intercept form with the given slope and containing the given point.

9. $m = -2$; $(-3.5, 7)$ **10.** $m = \frac{3}{4}$; $(6, -2)$

11. Discuss and Write Can two different lines have the same *y*-intercept? Explain. Provide examples to support your answer.

Go to ▶ PRACTICE BOOK **Lesson 5-3 for exercise sets.**

Equations in Point-Slope Form

Objective To write and graph linear equations using point-slope form

Zach operates a tech support business. He charged one customer $45 for $1\frac{1}{2}$ hours of work and a second customer $85.00 for $3\frac{1}{2}$ hours of work. The graph shows the relationship between Zach's fee (y) and how long he works (x). What equation describes this graph?

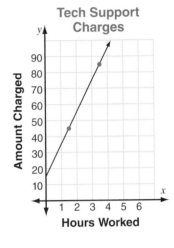

Tech Support Charges

Find the slope of the line using the points $\left(1\frac{1}{2}, 45\right)$ and $\left(3\frac{1}{2}, 85\right)$.

$$m = \frac{y_2 - y_1}{x_2 - x_1} = \frac{85 - 45}{3\frac{1}{2} - 1\frac{1}{2}} = \frac{40}{2} = 20$$

Suppose (x, y) is another point on the line. The slope of the line through $\left(1\frac{1}{2}, 45\right)$ and (x, y) must also be 20.

Therefore, $\dfrac{y - 45}{x - 1\frac{1}{2}} = \dfrac{20}{1}$. ←—Use the slope formula.

$$y - 45 = 20\left(x - 1\frac{1}{2}\right) \quad \text{←—Apply the Cross-Products Rule.}$$

So the equation $y - 45 = 20\left(x - 1\frac{1}{2}\right)$ describes the graph.

This form of a linear equation is called the **point-slope form**: $y - y_1 = m(x - x_1)$.

_____ **Key Concept** _____

Point-Slope Form of a Linear Equation

The equation of a nonvertical line with slope m and through point (x_1, y_1) is $y - y_1 = m(x - x_1)$.

▶ When you know the slope of a line and a point that the line contains, use the point-slope form to write an equation of a line.

Write the point-slope form of a line with slope -2 that passes through $(2, -1.5)$. Then graph the line.

$y - y_1 = m(x - x_1)$ ←—Use the point-slope form.

$y - (-1.5) = -2(x - 2)$ ←—Substitute the given values.

$y + 1.5 = -2(x - 2)$ ←—Simplify.

The point-slope form of the equation is $y + 1.5 = -2(x - 2)$.

• Plot: $(2, -1.5)$

• Use the slope to locate another point on the line.

• Draw the line.

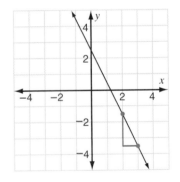

Example

Write the point-slope form of a line with the given slope that contains the given point. Then graph the line.

1 slope: $\frac{2}{3}$; point: $(-2, -1)$

$y - y_1 = m(x - x_1)$ ←—Use the point-slope form.

$y - (-1) = \frac{2}{3}[x - (-2)]$ ←—Substitute the given values.

$y + 1 = \frac{2}{3}(x + 2)$ ←—Simplify.

The point-slope form of the equation is $y + 1 = \frac{2}{3}(x + 2)$.

• Plot: $(-2, -1)$

• Use the slope to locate another point on the line.

• Draw the line.

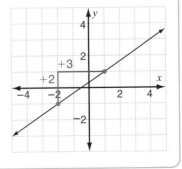

▶ You can also use the point-slope form to write the equation of a line when you know two points on the line.

- Find the slope using both points.

- Substitute the slope and the coordinates of one of the points into the formula $y - y_1 = m(x - x_1)$.

- Simplify if necessary.

Write an equation of a line in point-slope form passing through the points.

$(-1, 5)$ and $(3, -5)$.

$m = \dfrac{-5 - 5}{3 - (-1)} = \dfrac{-10}{4} = \dfrac{-5}{2}$ ◀—Find the slope.

$y - y_1 = m(x - x_1)$ ◀—Use the point-slope form.

Let $(-1, 5) = (x_1, y_1)$ ◀—Choose one of the points.

$y - 5 = -\dfrac{5}{2}[x - (-1)]$ ◀—Substitute 5 for y_1, $-\dfrac{5}{2}$ for m, and -1 for x_1.

$y - 5 = -\dfrac{5}{2}(x + 1)$ ◀—Simplify.

So an equation of the line in point-slope form is $y - 5 = -\dfrac{5}{2}(x + 1)$.

Example

1 Given points $(5, -9)$ and $(-7, -9)$, write an equation of a line in point-slope form.

$m = \dfrac{-9 - (-9)}{-7 - 5} = \dfrac{0}{-12} = 0$ ◀—Find the slope.

$y - y_1 = m(x - x_1)$ ◀—Use the point-slope form.

Let $(5, -9) = (x_1, y_1)$ ◀—Choose one of the points.

$y - (-9) = 0(x - 5)$ ◀—Substitute -9 for y_1, 0 for m, and 5 for x_1.

$\quad y + 9 = 0(x - 5)$ ◀—Simplify.

$\quad y + 9 = 0$

So an equation of the line in point-slope form is $y + 9 = 0$.

Try These

Write an equation of a line in point-slope form. Then graph the line.

1. slope: $-\dfrac{3}{5}$; point: $(0, -6)$

2. slope: 6; point: $(-2.5, 0.5)$

3. $(-3, 0)$ and $(0, -3)$

4. $(-1, 5)$ and $(3, -1)$

5. Discuss and Write Explain how to write an equation of a line in point-slope form when given two points on the line.

Go to PRACTICE BOOK Lesson 5-4 for exercise sets.

Change the Form of a Linear Equation

Objective To rewrite a linear equation using a different form • To determine whether a given point is on a line

Brian started a new fitness program with a goal of burning 1200 calories a week running and bicycling. If 1 minute of running burns 8 calories and 1 minute of bicycling burns 6 calories, what equation can be written to determine the length of time Brian should participate in each activity to burn 1200 calories?

To write an equation for Brian's new fitness program, let x = minutes spent running *and* y = minutes spent bicycling.

calories burned in running	plus	calories burned in bicycling	equals	total calories burned
$8x$	$+$	$6y$	$=$	1200

So the equation $8x + 6y = 1200$ can be written to describe the situation. This relation is an example of what is called a linear equation in standard form.

_____ **Key Concept** _____

Standard Form of a Linear Equation

The standard form of a linear equation is $Ax + By = C$, where A, B, and C are real numbers, and A and B are not both zero.

▶ The standard form of a linear equation allows you to quickly find the x- and y-intercepts of the line. The x-coordinate of the point where the graph crosses the x-axis is the x-intercept.

Find the x- and y-intercepts of the equation $8x + 6y = 1200$.

To find the x-intercept, substitute 0 for y, and solve for x.

$8x + 6(0) = 1200$ ←Substitute 0 for y.

$\dfrac{8x}{8} = \dfrac{1200}{8}$ ←Use the Division Property of Equality.

$x = 150$ ←x-intercept

So the x-intercept is 150, which is the point $(150, 0)$ where the line crosses the x-axis.

To find the y-intercept, substitute 0 for x, and solve for y.

$8(0) + 6y = 1200$ ←Substitute 0 for x.

$\dfrac{6y}{6} = \dfrac{1200}{6}$ ←Use the Division Property of Equality.

$y = 200$ ←y-intercept

So the y-intercept is 200, which is the point $(0, 200)$ where the line crosses the y-axis.

▶ You can graph the equation by plotting the intercepts and drawing a line through them.

The x-intercept is 150. Plot $(150, 0)$.
If Brian just runs, he needs to run for 150 minutes to burn 1200 calories.

The y-intercept is 200. Plot $(0, 200)$.
If Brian just bicycles, he needs to bicycle for 200 minutes to burn 1200 calories.

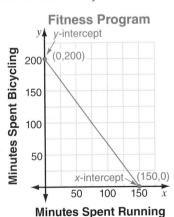

►When a linear equation is written in standard form, A or B can be zero, but *not* both. If either A or B is zero, the line is horizontal or vertical.

Examples

1 Graph: $x = -3$

$x + 0y = -3$ ◄——Write in standard form.

The x-intercept is -3. There is no y-intercept. For every y-value, $x = -3$.

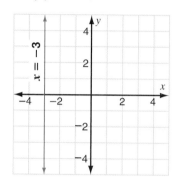

2 Graph: $y = 3$

$0x + y = 3$ ◄——Write in standard form.

The y-intercept is 3. There is no x-intercept. For every x-value, $y = 3$.

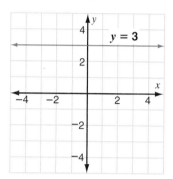

►You can transform linear equations from one form to another. You can write a linear equation in slope-intercept, point-slope, and standard forms.

Equation Form	Example	When to Use
$y = mx + b$ m = the slope of the line b = the y-intercept	$y = -\frac{2}{3}x + 4$	Use when you know the slope and the y-intercept.
$y - y_1 = m(x - x_1)$ m = slope (x_1, y_1) = *any* point on the line	$y - 6 = -\frac{2}{3}(x + 3)$	Use when you know a point and the slope or when you are only given two points.
$Ax + By = C$ A, B, and C are real numbers, and A and B are not both zero.	$2x + 3y = 12$	Use to quickly find the x- and y-intercepts.

Examples

1 Rewrite $y = -\frac{1}{2}x + 5$ in standard form.

$2(y) = 2\left(-\frac{1}{2}x + 5\right)$ ◄——Use the Multiplication Property of Equality to re-write the equation without fractions.

$2y = -x + 10$ ◄——Apply the Distributive Property.

$2y + x = -x + x + 10$ ◄——Use the Addition Property of Equality.

$x + 2y = 10$ ◄——Apply the Commutative Property.

$x + 2y = 10$ *is equivalent to* the equation $y = -\frac{1}{2}x + 5$.

So $y = -\frac{1}{2}x + 5$ in standard form is $x + 2y = 10$.

Continue Lesson ➡

Rewrite in the indicated form.

2 $5x + 2y = 20$; slope-intercept form

$5x - 5x + 2y = -5x + 20$ ←—Use the Subtraction Property of Equality.

$2y = -5x + 20$

$\dfrac{2y}{2} = \dfrac{-5x + 20}{2}$ ←—Use the Division Property of Equality.

$y = -\dfrac{5}{2}x + 10$

$y = -\dfrac{5}{2}x + 10$ is the slope-intercept form of $5x + 2y = 20$.

3 $y - 5 = -\dfrac{5}{6}(x + 12)$; slope-intercept form

$y - 5 = -\dfrac{5}{6}x - 10$ ←—Apply the Distributive Property.

$y - 5 + 5 = -\dfrac{5}{6}x - 10 + 5$ ←—Use the Addition Property of Equality.

$y = -\dfrac{5}{6}x - 5$

$y = -\dfrac{5}{6}x - 5$ is the slope-intercept form of $y - 5 = -\dfrac{5}{6}(x + 12)$.

▶ All the points on the graph of a linear equation are solutions of the equation. Each point on the line is an ordered pair that makes the equation true.

To determine if a point is on the graph of a line, substitute its coordinates into the equation of the line. If the result is a true statement, the point is on the line.

• Is the point $(-6, -5)$ on the graph of $4x - 3y = -9$?

$4(-6) - 3(-5) = -9$ ←—Substitute the coordinates of the point for x and y.

$-24 + 15 \overset{?}{=} -9$ ←—Simplify.

$-9 = -9$ True

So the point $(-6, -5)$ is on the graph of $4x - 3y = -9$.

• Is the point $(-3, 0)$ on the graph of $4x - 3y = -9$?

$4(-3) - 3(0) = -9$ ←—Substitute the coordinates of the point for x and y.

$-12 - 0 \overset{?}{=} -9$ ←—Simplify.

$-12 = -9$ False

So the point $(-3, 0)$ is *not* on the graph of $4x - 3y = -9$.

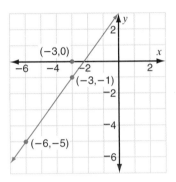

Examples

Tell if the given point is on the given line.

1 $\left(\dfrac{1}{4}, -\dfrac{3}{2}\right)$; $y = -4x - \dfrac{1}{2}$

$-\dfrac{3}{2} = -4\left(\dfrac{1}{4}\right) - \dfrac{1}{2}$ ←—Substitute $\dfrac{1}{4}$ for x and $-\dfrac{3}{2}$ for y.

$-\dfrac{3}{2} \overset{?}{=} -1 - \dfrac{1}{2}$

$-\dfrac{3}{2} = -\dfrac{3}{2}$ True

The point $\left(\dfrac{1}{4}, -\dfrac{3}{2}\right)$ is on the line $y = -4x - \dfrac{1}{2}$.

2 $(-0.8, 3.2)$; $y + 3.2 = -2(x - 2.4)$

$3.2 + 3.2 = -2(-0.8 - 2.4)$ ←—Substitute -0.8 for x and 3.2 for y.

$6.4 \overset{?}{=} -2(-3.2)$

$6.4 = 6.4$ True

The point $(-0.8, 3.2)$ is on the line $y + 3.2 = -2(x - 2.4)$.

▶ You can determine the coordinates of a point on a line if you know one coordinate of the point and the equation of the line.

Find the value of y so that the given point lies on the given line.

$(-4, y); y = -\frac{3}{2}x - 7$

$y = -\frac{3}{2}(-4) - 7$ ←—Use substitution.

$y = 6 - 7$ ←—Simplify.

$y = -1$

.Think.....................................
Substitute the given coordinate
into the equation, and then solve
for the unknown coordinate.
....

The point $(-4, -1)$ lies on the line $y = -\frac{3}{2}x - 7$.

Example

Find the value of x so that the given point lies on the given line.

1 $\left(x, -\frac{2}{3}\right); 4x + 6y = -5$

$4x + 6\left(-\frac{2}{3}\right) = -5$ ←—Use substitution.

$4x - 4 = -5$ ←—Simplify.

$4x - 4 + 4 = -5 + 4$ ←—Use the Addition Property of Equality.

$\frac{4x}{4} = -\frac{1}{4}$ ←—Use the Division Property of Equality.

$x = -\frac{1}{4}$

The point $\left(-\frac{1}{4}, -\frac{2}{3}\right)$ lies on the line $4x + 6y = -5$.

Try These

Find the x- and y-intercepts of each line. Then graph the line.

1. $6x - 9y = -3$

2. $\frac{2}{3}x - \frac{1}{4}y = -6$

3. $12x - 9y = -18$

Tell whether the graph is a horizontal or vertical line.

4. $4x = 8$

5. $-5y = 3$

6. $\frac{1}{2}y = -8$

Write the equation in the form indicated.

7. $y - 3 = \frac{1}{3}(x - 5)$; slope-intercept form

8. $y = -\frac{2}{5}x + 1$; standard form

Tell if the given point is on the given line.

9. $(0.5, -2.5); 6x - 4y = -7$

10. $\left(\frac{3}{4}, -\frac{2}{3}\right); y = -\frac{4}{3}x + \frac{1}{3}$

Find the value of x or y so that the given point lies on the given line.

11. $(-1.25, y); y = 4x + 5$

12. $\left(x, \frac{1}{6}\right); x + 2y = 1$

13. Discuss and Write Are $y - 3 = 2(x + 2)$ and $y + 1 = 2(x + 4)$ equivalent equations for the same line? Explain.

Go to ▶ **PRACTICE BOOK Lesson 5-5 for exercise sets.**

Parallel and Perpendicular Lines

Objective To determine if two lines are parallel or perpendicular using slope
• To write an equation of a line that is parallel or perpendicular to a given line

The lines shown in the graph(s) at the right are parallel. They are in the same plane but have no point in common. Notice that they have the same slope but cross the y-axis at different points.

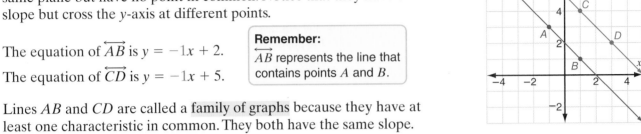

The equation of $\overleftrightarrow{AB}$ is $y = -1x + 2$.

The equation of $\overleftrightarrow{CD}$ is $y = -1x + 5$.

> **Remember:**
> $\overleftrightarrow{AB}$ represents the line that contains points A and B.

Lines AB and CD are called a family of graphs because they have at least one characteristic in common. They both have the same slope.

▶ To determine whether lines are parallel:

- Write each equation in slope-intercept form.
- Compare the slopes of the lines. If the slopes are the same and the y-intercepts are different, the lines are parallel.

Are the graphs of $y = -\frac{1}{2}x + 1$ and $x + 2y = 6$ parallel? Explain.

_____ **Key Concept** _____

Parallel Lines
- If two different nonvertical lines have the same slope, then they are parallel.
- If two different nonvertical lines are parallel, then they have the same slope.
- Any two different vertical lines are parallel.

Write $x + 2y = 6$ in slope-intercept form.

Compare it with $y = -\frac{1}{2}x + 1$.

$x - x + 2y = -x + 6$ ◀— Use the Subtraction Property of Equality.

$\dfrac{2y}{2} = \dfrac{-x + 6}{2}$ ◀— Use the Division Property of Equality.

$y = -\frac{1}{2}x + 3$

The slope of $y = -\frac{1}{2}x + 3$ is $-\frac{1}{2}$. The slope of $y = -\frac{1}{2}x + 1$ is $-\frac{1}{2}$.

The lines are parallel. They have the same slope and different y-intercepts.

Examples

1 Determine whether the lines are parallel.

The equation of $\overleftrightarrow{EF}$ is $6x - 2y = 4$. The equation of $\overleftrightarrow{GH}$ is $y = -3x + 8$.

Write $\overleftrightarrow{EF}$ in slope-intercept form. Compare it with $\overleftrightarrow{GH}$.

$6x - 6x - 2y = -6x + 4$ ◀— Use the Subtraction Property of Equality.

$\dfrac{-2y}{-2} = \dfrac{-6x + 4}{-2}$ ◀— Use the Division Property of Equality.

$y = 3x - 2$

So the slope of $\overleftrightarrow{EF}$ is 3 and the slope of $\overleftrightarrow{GH}$ is -3.

$\overleftrightarrow{EF}$ and $\overleftrightarrow{GH}$ are not parallel lines because they do not have the same slope.

2 Determine whether the lines are parallel.

Given $J(-4, -2)$, $K(-4, 1)$, $L(2, -1)$, and $M(2, 5)$, is $\overleftrightarrow{JK} \parallel \overleftrightarrow{LM}$?

Remember:
$\parallel$ is the symbol for "is parallel to."

Find the slope of $\overleftrightarrow{JK}$. ◄—J is $(-4, -2)$; K is $(-4, 1)$.

$\dfrac{1 - (-2)}{-4 - (-4)} = \dfrac{3}{0}$ ◄——Substitute the coordinates into the slope formula, and simplify.

The slope of $\overleftrightarrow{JK}$ is *undefined*.
$\overleftrightarrow{JK}$ is a vertical line.

Find the slope of $\overleftrightarrow{LM}$. ◄—L is $(2, -1)$; M is $(2, 5)$.

$\dfrac{5 - (-1)}{2 - 2} = \dfrac{6}{0}$ ◄——Substitute the coordinates into the slope formula, and simplify.

The slope of $\overleftrightarrow{LM}$ is *undefined*.
$\overleftrightarrow{LM}$ is a vertical line.

Because $\overleftrightarrow{JK}$ and $\overleftrightarrow{LM}$ are two different vertical lines, $\overleftrightarrow{JK} \parallel \overleftrightarrow{LM}$.

► Since the slopes of parallel lines are the *same*, you can use this fact to write the equation of a line parallel to a given line.

- Find the slope of the given line.
- Substitute that information into *either* the slope-intercept form or the point-slope form of a linear equation to write the equation of a parallel line.

Write an equation of a line parallel to the graph of $2x - y = 3$ with y-intercept of -5.

$2x - y = 3$ ◄—Solve for y to find the slope of the given line.

$2x - 2x - y = -2x + 3$ ◄—Use the Subtraction Property of Equality.

$\dfrac{-y}{-1} = \dfrac{-2x + 3}{-1}$ ◄—Use the Division Property of Equality.

$y = 2x - 3$

The slope is 2 and the y-intercept of the parallel line is -5.

$y = mx + b$ ◄—Use the slope-intercept form.

$y = 2x - 5$ ◄—Substitute the given values.

Think
Since the y-intercept is given, substitute the given information into the slope-intercept form.

So the graph of $y = 2x - 5$ is parallel to the graph of $2x - y = 3$.

Example

1 Write an equation of a line parallel to the graph of $y = -\frac{1}{3}x + 2$ and passing through the point $(3, 2)$.

$y = -\frac{1}{3}x + 2$

The slope is $-\frac{1}{3}$.

$y - y_1 = m(x - x_1)$ ◄—Use the point-slope form.

$y - 2 = -\frac{1}{3}(x - 3)$ ◄—Substitute the given values.

$y - 2 + 2 = -\frac{1}{3}x + 1 + 2$ ◄—Simplify; use the Addition Property of Equality.

$y = -\frac{1}{3}x + 3$

Think
Since a point is given, substitute the given information into the point-slope form.

So the graph of $y = -\frac{1}{3}x + 3$ is parallel to the graph of $y = -\frac{1}{3}x + 2$.

Continue Lesson ➡

▶ The lines shown in the graph at the right are perpendicular *because* they intersect to form right angles. The slopes of perpendicular lines are negative reciprocals of each other and their product is -1.

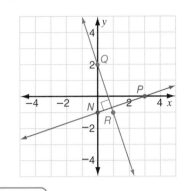

The equation of $\overleftrightarrow{NP}$ is $y = \frac{1}{3}x - 1$. Its slope is $\frac{1}{3}$.

The equation of $\overleftrightarrow{QR}$ is $y = -3x + 2$. Its slope is -3.

The product of the slopes is $\frac{1}{3}(-3) = -1$.

So $\overleftrightarrow{NP}$ is perpendicular to $\overleftrightarrow{QR}$.

---- **Key Concept** ----

> **Perpendicular Lines**
> • If the product of the slopes of two lines is -1, then the lines are perpendicular.
> • If two lines are perpendicular and neither one is vertical, the product of their slopes is -1.
> • Vertical lines are perpendicular to horizontal lines.

▶ To determine whether lines are perpendicular:

• Find the slope of each line that is given.

• Compare the slopes of the lines. If the slopes are negative reciprocals, the lines are perpendicular.

Are the graphs of $y = \frac{4}{3}x - 1$ and $3x + 4y = -8$ perpendicular?

Write $3x + 4y = -8$ in slope-intercept form. Compare it with $y = \frac{4}{3}x - 1$.

$3x - 3x + 4y = -3x - 8$ ◀— Use the Subtraction Property of Equality.

$\dfrac{4y}{4} = \dfrac{-3x - 8}{4}$ ◀— Use the Division Property of Equality.

$y = -\dfrac{3}{4}x - 2$

The slope of $y = -\frac{3}{4}x - 2$ is $-\frac{3}{4}$. The slope of $y = \frac{4}{3}x - 1$ is $\frac{4}{3}$.

$\left(-\frac{3}{4}\right)\left(\frac{4}{3}\right) = -1$, so the slopes are negative reciprocals, and the lines are perpendicular.

Examples

1 Determine if the given lines are perpendicular.

$\overleftrightarrow{ST}$ is $y = 5x - 1$; $\overleftrightarrow{UV}$ is $10x + 2y = 12$.
Is $\overleftrightarrow{ST} \perp \overleftrightarrow{UV}$?

Remember:
$\perp$ is the symbol for "is perpendicular to."

Write $\overleftrightarrow{UV}$ in slope-intercept form. Compare it to $\overleftrightarrow{ST}$.

$10x + 2y = 12$

$10x - 10x + 2y = -10x + 12$ ◀—Use the Subtraction Property of Equality.

$\dfrac{-2y}{2} = \dfrac{-10x + 12}{2}$ ◀—Use the Division Property of Equality.

$y = -5x + 6$

The slope of $\overleftrightarrow{UV}$ is -5. The slope of $\overleftrightarrow{ST}$ is 5. $(-5)(5) \neq -1$
The slopes are not negative reciprocals, so the lines are not perpendicular.

2 $l_1 \perp l_2$. If the slope of l_1 is 4 and the slope of l_2 is $\frac{x - 6}{16}$, find the value of x.

Since $l_1 \perp l_2$, the slope of l_2 is $-\frac{1}{4}$, the negative reciprocal of 4, the slope of l_1.

Solve: $\frac{x - 6}{16} = -\frac{1}{4}$ ←—Write an equation to solve for x.

$4(x - 6) = -16$ ←—Apply the Cross-Products Rule.

$4x - 24 = -16$ ←—Apply the Distributive Property.

$4x - 24 + 24 = -16 + 24$ ←—Use the Addition Property of Equality.

$4x \div 4 = 8 \div 4$ ←—Use the Division Property of Equality.

$x = 2$

Check: $\frac{x - 6}{16} = -\frac{1}{4}$

$\frac{2 - 6}{16} \overset{?}{=} -\frac{1}{4}$

$\frac{-4}{16} \overset{?}{=} -\frac{1}{4}$

$-\frac{1}{4} = -\frac{1}{4}$ True

▶There are many lines perpendicular to a given line. For each of them you can write an equation using the negative reciprocal of the slope of the given line.

- Use the slope-intercept form of the given line to find its slope. Find its negative reciprocal for the slope of the perpendicular line.

- Use this slope and the other information about the perpendicular line to write the equation.

Write an equation, in slope-intercept form, of the line that is perpendicular to the graph of $y = x + 2$ and that passes through the point $(-1, -4)$.

$y = 1x + 2$ ←—Identify the slope: 1

The slope of the perpendicular line is -1. ←—Find the negative reciprocal of 1.

$y - y_1 = m(x - x_1)$ ←—Use the point-slope form.

$y - (-4) = -1[x - (-1)]$ ←—Substitute the given values.

$y + 4 = -x - 1$ ←—Simplify; then apply the Distributive Property.

$y + 4 - 4 = -x - 1 - 4$ ←—Use the Addition Property of Equality.

$y = -x - 5$ ←—Simplify.

So the equation of the perpendicular line is $y = -x - 5$.

Try These

Tell whether the pair of lines is *parallel*, *perpendicular*, or *neither*.

1. $y = -\frac{5}{2}x + 7$ and $2x - 5y = 6$

2. Line 1 passes through $(0, 6)$ and $(-5, -1)$; line 2 passes through $(-1, 6)$ and $(4, -1)$.

Find an equation of a line in slope-intercept form.

3. parallel to $3x + 3y = -2$ with a y-intercept of 5

4. perpendicular to $y = -2x + 2$ and containing $(2, 1)$

5. Discuss and Write Can two parallel lines have the same y-intercept? Can two perpendicular lines have the same y-intercept? Explain.

Go to PRACTICE BOOK **Lesson 5-6 for exercise sets.**

Graph a Linear Inequality in the Coordinate Plane

Objective To graph a linear inequality in two variables

The number sentence $y \geq -x + 4$ is a linear inequality in two variables. Its graph is shown at the right. The related equation, $y = -x + 4$, separates the coordinate plane into three sets of points: the points *on* the line, the points *above* the line, and the points *below* the line. The regions above and below the line are called half-planes. The line is the boundary of each half-plane.

A solution to a linear inequality in two variables is any ordered pair that makes the inequality true. To identify specific solutions, substitute any ordered pair located in the identified region or on the boundary line into the original linear inequality.

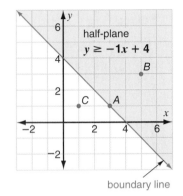

boundary line

Point A $(3, 1)$	Point B $(5, 3)$	Point C $(1, 1)$
$1 \geq = -(3) + 4$	$3 \geq = -(5) + 4$	$1 \geq = -(1) + 4$
$1 \geq 1$ True	$3 \geq -1$ True	$1 \geq 3$ False

According to this graph, point A, $(3, 1)$, and point B, $(5, 3)$, are solutions of $y \geq -1x + 4$. Notice that point C, $(1, 1)$, does *not* lie either in the shaded area or on the boundary line, and, therefore, it cannot be a solution of the inequality.

▶ To graph the solutions of a linear inequality:

- Write the inequality in slope-intercept form.

- Graph the boundary line by replacing the inequality sign with an equal sign. If the inequality is $\leq$ or $\geq$, the boundary is a *solid line*, which shows that the points on the line are included in the solution region. However, if the inequality is $<$ or $>$, the boundary is a *dashed line*, which shows that the points on the line are *not* part of the solution region.

- Shade the appropriate half-plane.

- Choose test points on the line, below the line, and above the line to verify that the shaded area represents the solution.

Solve: $2x + 3y \leq 9$ ◀— Solve for y and write in slope-intercept form.

$$3y \leq -2x + 9$$

$$y \leq -\frac{2}{3}x + 3$$

Graph: $y = -\frac{2}{3}x + 3$ ◀— Use a solid boundary line for $\leq$.

Shade the half-plane *below* the line.

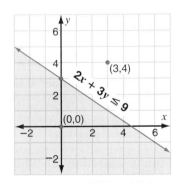

Check: Check by choosing test points.

$3 \overset{?}{\leq} -\frac{2}{3}(0) + 3$	$0 \overset{?}{\leq} -\frac{2}{3}(0) + 3$	$4 \overset{?}{\leq} -\frac{2}{3}(3) + 3$
$3 \leq 3$ True	$0 \leq 3$ True	$4 \leq 1$ False

So the y-values in the solution include those that are both *equal to* and *less than* $-\frac{2}{3}x + 3$. Shade the half-plane that is *below* the line.

Examples

Graph each inequality.

1 $4x - 2y < -1$

Solve: $-2y < -4x - 1$ ←—Use the Subtraction Property of Inequality.

$y > 2x + \frac{1}{2}$ ←—Use the Division Property of Inequality.

Remember: Reverse the inequality symbol when dividing by a negative number.

Graph: $y = 2x + \frac{1}{2}$ ←—Use a dashed line for $>$.

Shade the half-plane *above* the line.

Check: Choose test points.

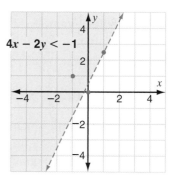

Point: $(0,0)$	Point: $\left(1, 2\frac{1}{2}\right)$	Point: $(-1, 1)$
$0 \overset{?}{>} 2(0) + \frac{1}{2}$	$2\frac{1}{2} \overset{?}{>} 2(1) + \frac{1}{2}$	$1 \overset{?}{>} 2(-1) + \frac{1}{2}$
$0 > \frac{1}{2}$ False	$2\frac{1}{2} > 2\frac{1}{2}$ False	$1 > -2\frac{1}{2}$ True

Since the statement is false, the half-plane containing $(0,0)$ should *not* be shaded.

2 $x < 1$

Graph: $x = 1$ ←—Use a dashed line for $<$.

Shade the half-plane to the *left* of the line.

Check: Choose test points.

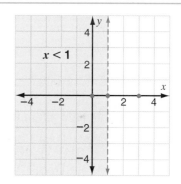

Point: $(0,0)$	Point: $(1,0)$	Point: $(3,0)$
$0 < 1$ True	$1 < 1$ False	$3 < 1$ False

Since the statement is true, the half-plane containing $(0,0)$ should be shaded.

Try These

Determine whether or not the ordered pair is a solution of the linear inequality.

1. $y > x + 3; (1, 4)$ **2.** $3y \geq -9; (-5, 2)$ **3.** $2x - y \leq 6; (4, -2)$ **4.** $3x + 2y < 9; \left(\frac{1}{2}, \frac{7}{2}\right)$

Write the equation of the boundary line in slope-intercept form.
Describe each line as *dashed* or *solid*.

5. $2y - x \leq 6$ **6.** $6x + 3y > 9$ **7.** $3x - y < 4$ **8.** $-2x + y \geq 0$

Graph each linear inequality.

9. $x + y > 5$ **10.** $2y \leq 5$ **11.** $3x \geq y$ **12.** $-3x - 6 > 0$

13. Discuss and Write Lee has $220 to spend on shirts at $22 each and pants at $38 each. What inequality represents the possible number of shirts and pants that he can buy? Find at least three possible solutions. Can the solutions include negative numbers?

Go to PRACTICE BOOK Lesson 5-7 for exercise sets.

5-8

Absolute-Value Functions

Objective To graph the basic absolute-value function and identify its characteristics
• To investigate the graphs of absolute-value functions using a handheld device

A function rule that contains an absolute-value expression is called an **absolute-value function**. The graphs of absolute-value functions are not linear, although they are related to linear functions.

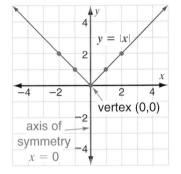

► To graph the absolute-value function $y = |x|$, make a function table, and graph the points.

x	−2	−1	0	1	2
$y = |x|$	2	1	0	1	2

The graph is V-shaped and is separated into two congruent parts by a line, called the **axis of symmetry**. The left and right parts are the graphs of $y = -x$ for $y \le 0$ and $y = x$ for $y \ge 0$, respectively. The point in which the two parts meet is called the **vertex**.

An absolute-value graph shows:

• the vertex
• the axis of symmetry
• the x- and y-intercepts
• the domain
• the range

An absolute-value graph is a *function* because for every x-value, there is only one y-value.

The absolute-value graph above shows:

• The vertex is $(0, 0)$.
• The axis of symmetry is the y-axis ($x = 0$).
• The x- and y-intercepts are both 0.
• The domain (x-values) is the set of all real numbers.
• The range (y-values) is $y \ge 0$.

The graph of $y = |x|$ is a function because for every x-value, there is only one y-value.

► There are other absolute-value functions whose graphs are V-shaped. The graphs of these functions can *open up* or *down*.

Graph: $y = -|x|$
Identify the vertex, axis of symmetry, x- and y-intercepts, domain, and range. Tell whether the graph opens up or down.

Make a function table. Choose positive, negative, and zero values for x. Then graph.

x	$y = -|x|$
−2	−2
−1	−1
0	0
1	−1
2	−2

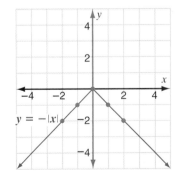

The absolute-value graph at the left shows the following:

• The vertex is $(0, 0)$.
• The axis of symmetry is $x = 0$.
• The x-intercept is 0.
• The y-intercept is 0.
• The domain is all real numbers.
• The range is $y \le 0$.
• The graph opens down.

Notice when $y = |x|$, the graph of the absolute-value function opens up, and when $y = -|x|$, the graph of the absolute-value function opens down.

Example

1 Graph: $y = |x| - 2$
Choose positive, negative, and zero values for x. Then graph.

x	$y = |x| - 2$
-2	0
-1	-1
0	-2
1	-1
2	0

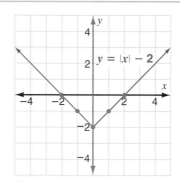

The absolute-value graph at the left shows the following:
- The vertex is $(0, -2)$.
- The axis of symmetry is $x = 0$.
- The x-intercepts are $-2, 2$.
- The y-intercept is -2.
- The domain is all real numbers.
- The range is $y \geq -2$.
- The graph opens up.

▶ You can graph various absolute-value functions such as $f(x) = |x|$, $f(x) = |x + c|$, and $f(x) = |x - c|$, on the same coordinate plane using a handheld. This device can make exploring each graph's unique and similar characteristics easier.

Graph $y = |x|$, $y = |x + 2|$, and $y = |x - 2|$ on the same coordinate plane using a handheld device.

To enter the equations, press 🏠, select **2**:
Graphs and Geometry, and then input each function
separately into $f_1(x)$, $f_2(x)$, and $f_3(x)$.

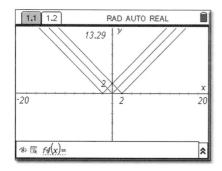

	$y = |x|$	$y = |x + 2|$	$y = |x - 2|$
vertex	$(0, 0)$	$(-2, 0)$	$(2, 0)$
axis of symmetry	$x = 0$	$x = -2$	$x = 2$
x-intercept(s)	0	-2	2
y-intercept	0	2	2
domain	all real numbers		
range	$y \geq 0$	$y \geq 0$	$y \geq 0$

Notice that when c is 0, the axis of symmetry is $x = 0$;
when c is $+2$, the axis of symmetry is $x = -2$; and
when c is -2, the axis of symmetry is $x = 2$.

Try These

Identify the vertex by graphing the absolute-value function.

1. $y = |x - 1|$ **2.** $y = |x| - 1$ **3.** $y = |x + 1|$ **4.** $y = |x| + 1$

Graph the absolute-value function. Identify the vertex, axis of symmetry, x- and y-intercepts, domain, and range. Tell whether the graph opens up or down.

5. $y = -|x + 3|$ **6.** $y = |x - 2| + 1$ **7.** $y = -|x| - 2$

8. Discuss and Write Use a handheld to graph $y = |x|$, $y = |\frac{1}{2}x|$, and
$y = |5x|$. What is the same and what is different about the graphs?
Describe how changing the coefficient of x affects the graph.

Go to   **PRACTICE BOOK Lesson 5-8 for exercise sets.**

5-9

Technology:
Graph Linear Functions and Inequalities

Objective To use a handheld to graph linear functions and inequalities

Diego burns 7.5 calories per minute playing tennis. Write and graph a function representing the number of calories Diego burns after x minutes of playing tennis.

An equation in two variables can be written to represent the total calories burned playing tennis in x minutes.

$y = 7.5x$ ◄— Total calories burned = 7.5 *times* minutes playing.

► You can use a handheld to graph the linear function.

Step 1 Press ⌂. Then choose **2** to select **Graphs & Geometry**.

Step 2 Use $f1(x)$ for y. Input 7.5x. Then press **enter** to graph the equation.

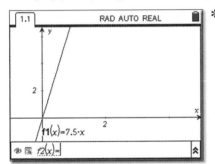

The graph of the function shown on the handheld represents the number of calories Diego can burn in x minutes. Note that *only* the first quadrant or the positive values of the linear function can correspond to time and calories burned.

► Sometimes before you can graph an equation using a handheld, you need to solve the equation for y.

Graph the equation: $-x = 2y - 3$ using a handheld.

Solve the equation for y.

$$-x = 2y - 3$$

$$-x + 3 = 2y - 3 + 3 \quad ◄— \text{Use the Addition Property of Equality.}$$

$$-x + 3 = 2y$$

$$-\frac{1}{2}x + \frac{3}{2} = y \quad ◄— \text{Use the Division Property of Equality.}$$

Step 1 Press ⌂. Then choose **2** to select **Graphs & Geometry**.

Step 2 Use $f2(x)$ for y. Input $-\frac{1}{2}x + \frac{3}{2}$. Then press **enter** to graph the equation.

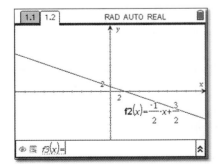

* Window setting adjusted to fit graph

You can also use a handheld to graph linear inequalities.

Graph the inequality $-4y + 7 < 9$ using a handheld.

Solve the inequality for y.

$$-4y + 7 < 9$$

$$-4y + 7 - 7 < 9 - 7 \quad \leftarrow \text{Use the Subtraction Property of Inequality.}$$

$$-4y < 2$$

$$\frac{-4y}{-4} > \frac{2}{-4} \quad \leftarrow \text{Use the Division Property of Inequality.}$$

$$y > -0.5$$

Remember: Reverse the inequality symbol when multiplying or dividing by a negative number.

Step 1 Press ⌂. Then choose ②
to select **Graphs & Geometry**.

Step 2 Use ⟵ᶜˡᵉᵃʳ to delete the equal sign.
Then input ▷ -0.5. Press enter≈ to graph
the inequality. Since an inequality is
not a function, $f3(x)$ changes to y.

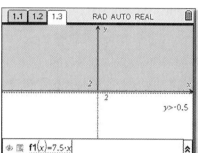

Example

1 Graph the inequality $2y + 6 \geq x - 2$ using a handheld.

Solve the inequality for y.

$$2y + 6 \geq x - 2$$

$$2y + 6 - 6 \geq x - 2 - 6 \quad \leftarrow \text{Use the Subtraction Property of Inequality.}$$

$$2y \geq x - 8 \quad \leftarrow \text{Simplify.}$$

$$\frac{2y}{2} \geq \frac{x - 8}{2} \quad \leftarrow \text{Use the Division Property of Inequality.}$$

$$y \geq \frac{1}{2}x - 4 \quad \leftarrow \text{Simplify.}$$

Step 1 Press ⌂. Then choose ②
to select **Graphs & Geometry**.

Step 2 Use ⟵ᶜˡᵉᵃʳ to delete the equal sign.
Input $\geq \frac{1}{2}x - 4$. Press ᶜᵗʳˡ ▷
for the $\geq$ symbol. Then press enter≈
to graph the inequality.

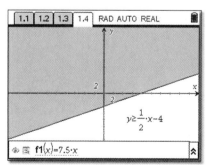

Try These

Use a handheld to graph the linear function or inequality.

1. $y = 2x + 3$

2. $y + 6 = -x - 4$

3. $-3y - 4 = 9x + 7$

4. $y \leq 3x - 9$

5. $y + 6 \geq x - 2$

6. $-4y + 10 > 2x - 3$

7. Discuss and Write How would the graph $y > 5x - 6$ change if the inequality
symbol was $\geq$? or $<$? or $\leq$? Use a handheld to check your answers.

Go to PRACTICE BOOK **Lesson 5-9 for exercise sets.**

5-10 Technology:
Families of Lines

Objective To use a handheld to explore families of linear functions

Families of functions are functions that have similar characteristics, for example, the same slope or the same y-intercept.

▶ You can use a handheld to see how the value of the y-intercept, b, affects the graph of $y = mx + b$.

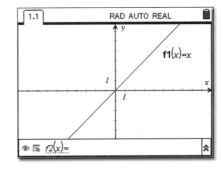

Step 1 Press 🏠 2 to select **Graphs & Geometry**.

Step 2 Type x, then press **enter** to graph the line.

The most basic of a family of functions is called the **parent function**. The parent linear function is $y = x$.

Step 3 Input $x + 4$, then press **enter**.

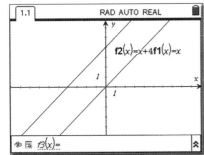

Step 4 Input $x + 7$, then press **enter**.

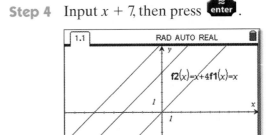

Step 5 Input $x - 4$, then press **enter**.

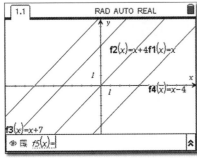

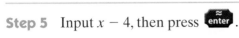

Step 6 Input $x - 7$, then press **enter**.

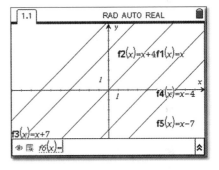

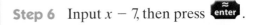

Note that the value of b shifts the graph *up* or *down*. If b is positive, such as in $x + 4$, then the graph is shifted *up*. If b is negative, such as in $x - 4$, the graph is shifted *down*. The lines are *all* parallel because they all have a slope of $+1$.

Predict how the graphs of the functions $y = 5x$, $y = 5x + 4$, $y = 5x + 8$, $y = 5x - 3$, and $y = 5x - 6$ will be *similar* to each other and how they will be *different*. Then use your handheld to verify the prediction.

The equations have the form $y = mx + b$. They have the *same slope* $+5$, therefore the lines will be parallel.

So the graph of $y = 5x + 4$ and $y = 5x + 8$ will be shifted *up* from $y = 5x$ and the graphs of $y = 5x - 3$ and $y = 5x - 6$ will be shifted *down*.

▶ You can also use a handheld to see how the value of the slope, m, affects the graph of $y = mx + b$.

Graph the equations $y = x$, $y = 3x$, $y = 0.5x$, $y = -4x$, and $y = -0.25x$. How does the value of m affect the graph?

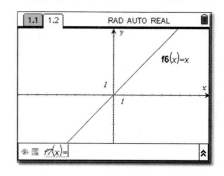

Step 1 Press 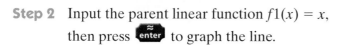.

Then choose ②
to select **Graphs & Geometry**.

Step 2 Input the parent linear function $f1(x) = x$,
then press **enter** to graph the line.

Step 3 Input $3x$, then press **enter**.

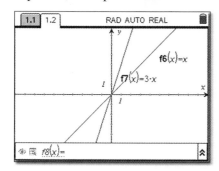

Step 4 Input $0.5x$, then press **enter**.

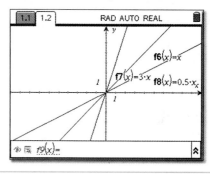

Step 5 Input $-4x$, then press **enter**.

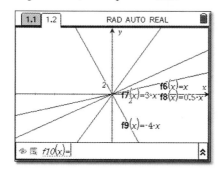

Step 6 Input $-0.25x$, then press **enter**.

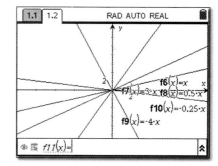

Note that the value of m changes the *steepness* of the graph. If m is positive, then the graph has a *positive slope*. If m is negative, the graph has a *negative slope*. The greater the absolute value of m, the greater the steepness of the line.

Try These

Predict how the graphs of the functions will compare. Use a handheld to verify your prediction.

1. $y = -7x$, $y = -7x + 4$, $y = -7x + 6$, $y = -7x - 3$, and $y = -7x - 8$

2. $y = x$, $y = 3x$, $y = 0.5x$, $y = -6x$, and $y = -0.75x$

3. **Discuss and Write** Explain how the graphs of the equations $y = 4x + 1$ and $y = -4x + 1$ will be similar and how they will be different.
   Explain how the graphs of the equations $y = 2x - 4$ and $y = 2x + 5$ will be similar and how they will be different.

Go to PRACTICE BOOK **Lesson 5-10 for exercise sets.**

Problem-Solving Strategy:
Consider Extreme Cases

Objective To solve problems using the strategy *Consider Extreme Cases*

Problem I: He-Ping claims that if the length of one segment is the average of the lengths of two other segments, then the three segments can be arranged to form the sides of a triangle. Is He-Ping correct?

 Read ▶ **Read to understand what is being asked.**

List the facts and restate the question.

Facts: You have three lines segments. The length of one segment is the average of the lengths of the other two.

Question: Is it *always* possible to make a triangle with those segments as sides?

> **Remember:** The sum of the lengths of any two sides of a triangle must be greater than the length of the third side.

Plan ▶ **Select a strategy.**

It is easy to think of particular cases where it *is* possible to make a triangle. For example, 4 is the average of 3 and 5, and you can make a triangle as shown below, with side lengths 3 cm, 4 cm, and 5 cm.

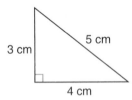

It might be useful to try the strategy *Consider Extreme Cases* to look for a case where making a triangle is *not* possible.

Problem-Solving Strategies

1. Make a Drawing
2. Solve a Simpler Problem
3. Reason Logically
4. **Consider Extreme Cases**
5. Work Backward
6. Find a Pattern
7. Account for All Possibilities
8. Adopt a Different Point of View
9. Guess and Test
10. Organize Data

Solve ▶ **Apply the strategy.**

Consider a case where one segment is very long relative to another.

Suppose two of the segments have lengths of 1 cm and 39 cm, and the length of the third segment is 20 cm, which is the average of these lengths. As the diagram below shows, there is no way to make a triangle with these side lengths because 1 cm + 20 cm < 39 cm.

```
           39 cm
1 cm_____
        \                   /
          \              /
            \         /
              \    /  20 cm
```

So He-Ping is incorrect. If the length of one segment is the average of the lengths of the other two, then it may not be possible to form a triangle.

Check ▶ **Check to make sure your answer makes sense.**

The example in the solution is clearly a counterexample. One counterexample is all that is needed to show that a statement is not true.

Problem 2: In the figure at the right (a regular hexagon), the six labeled angles have the same measure. What is the measure of one of them?

Read **Read to understand what is being asked.**

List the facts and restate the question.

Facts: A regular hexagon is constructed in such a way that the six angles numbered 1 through 6 have exactly the same measure.

Question: What is the measure of each of the labeled angles?

Plan **Select a strategy.**

As shown in the figures below, if you reduce the original figure (as with a copying machine), and only the side lengths change, the angle measures stay the same. Use the strategy *Consider Extreme Cases* and consider what happens as the figure is reduced to a point.

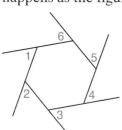

original   50% reduction

Solve **Apply the strategy.**

The series of figures at the right shows the original figure reduced to a smaller and smaller size.

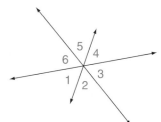

Consider the *extreme case*, in which the figure, as shown at the right, is simply a point.

The diagram shows that the six labeled angles combine to subtend exactly one full circle. So the sum of their measures must be 360°. The angles are all the same size, so each one must have a measure of (360° ÷ 6), or 60°.

Check **Check to make sure your answer makes sense.**

Look at the problem a different way.

Notice that each interior angle of the hexagon is the supplement of one of the labeled angles. Since all the labeled angles have the same measure, all the interior angles must also have the same measure.

The sum of the interior angle measures of a hexagon is (6 − 2) • 180°, or 720°. So each interior angle has measure (720° ÷ 6), or 120°.

Since each interior angle is the supplement of a labeled angle, then the measure of a labeled angle is (180 − 120)°, or 60°. This agrees with the answer above.

Remember: The sum of the interior angles in a polygon with *n* sides is (*n* − 2) • 180°.

Go to **PRACTICE BOOK Lesson 5-11 for exercise sets.**

Enrichment:
Slope in Coordinate Geometry

Objective **To apply slope in coordinate geometry**

Showing That a Quadrilateral Is a Parallelogram

Quadrilateral $ABCD$, shown at the right, has vertices $A(4, 3)$, $B(3, -2)$, $C\left(-2, -4\frac{1}{2}\right)$, and $D\left(-1, \frac{1}{2}\right)$. Use coordinate geometry to show that quadrilateral $ABCD$ is a parallelogram.

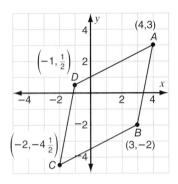

Since parallel lines have equal slopes, use the slope formula to show that the opposite sides have equal slopes. Recall that a parallelogram is a quadrilateral with two pairs of parallel sides. To prove that quadrilateral $ABCD$ is a parallelogram, you need to show that $\overline{AB} \parallel \overline{DC}$ and $\overline{DA} \parallel \overline{CB}$.

$$m_{\overline{AB}} = \frac{3 - (-2)}{4 - 3} = \frac{5}{1} = 5 \qquad m_{\overline{DC}} = \frac{\frac{1}{2} - \left(-4\frac{1}{2}\right)}{-1 - (-2)} = \frac{5}{1} = 5$$

$$m_{\overline{DA}} = \frac{3 - \frac{1}{2}}{4 - (-1)} = \frac{2\frac{1}{2}}{5} = \frac{1}{2} \qquad m_{\overline{CB}} = \frac{-2 - \left(-4\frac{1}{2}\right)}{3 - (-2)} = \frac{2\frac{1}{2}}{5} = \frac{1}{2}$$

Because $\overline{AB}$ and $\overline{DC}$ have the same slope, 5, they are parallel.

Because $\overline{DA}$ and $\overline{CB}$ have the same slope, $\frac{1}{2}$, they are also parallel.

So quadrilateral $ABCD$ is a parallelogram since both pairs of opposite sides are parallel.

> **Remember:**
> For two different points (x_1, y_1) and (x_2, y_2) on a line,
> slope $(m) = \dfrac{(y_2 - y_1)}{(x_2 - x_1)}$.

Showing That a Triangle Is a Right Triangle

$\triangle LMN$, shown at the right, has vertices $L(-6, 1)$, $M(-2, 2)$, and $N(-\frac{1}{2}, -4)$. Use coordinate geometry to show that $\triangle LMN$ is a right triangle.

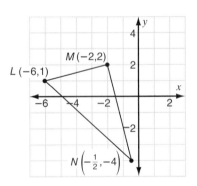

Recall that a right triangle has two sides that are perpendicular, which form a right angle. To prove that $\triangle LMN$ is a right triangle, you need to find the slopes of $\overline{LM}$ and $\overline{NM}$, the sides that appear to form a right angle, to show that they are perpendicular. The slopes of perpendicular lines are negative reciprocals.

$$m_{\overline{LM}} = \frac{2 - 1}{-2 - (-6)} = \frac{1}{4} \qquad m_{\overline{NM}} = \frac{2 - (-4)}{-2 - \left(-\frac{1}{2}\right)} = \frac{6}{-1\frac{1}{2}} = -4$$

The slopes of $\overline{LM}$ and $\overline{NM}$, $\frac{1}{4}$ and -4, are negative reciprocals, so those sides are perpendicular and form a right angle.

So $\triangle LMN$ is a right triangle.

Proving a Geometry Theorem

A well-known geometry theorem states that the segment joining the midpoints of two sides of a triangle is parallel to the third side. Use coordinate geometry to prove this theorem.

Consider $\triangle STU$ at the right, with vertices $S(-4, -2)$, $T(0, 4)$, and $U(2, -6)$. Prove that the segment connecting the midpoints of $\overline{TS}$ and $\overline{TU}$ is parallel to $\overline{SU}$.

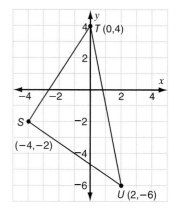

• First, find the midpoints of $\overline{TS}$ and $\overline{TU}$ by using the Midpoint Formula.

> **Key Concept**
>
> **Midpoint Formula**
>
> The midpoint of a line segment with endpoints (x_1, y_1) and (x_2, y_2) is $\left(\dfrac{x_1 + x_2}{2}, \dfrac{y_1 + y_2}{2}\right)$.

Midpoint of $\overline{TS}$: $M_1 = \left(\dfrac{0 + (-4)}{2}, \dfrac{4 + (-2)}{2}\right) = (-2, 1)$

Midpoint of $\overline{TU}$: $M_2 = \left(\dfrac{0 + 2}{2}, \dfrac{4 + (-6)}{2}\right) = (1, -1)$

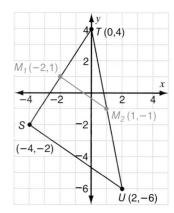

• Next, show that $\overline{M_1 M_2}$ is parallel to $\overline{SU}$ by finding their slopes.

$m_{\overline{M_1 M_2}} = \dfrac{-1 - 1}{1 - (-2)} = -\dfrac{2}{3}$

$m_{\overline{SU}} = \dfrac{-6 - (-2)}{2 - (-4)} = \dfrac{-4}{6} = -\dfrac{2}{3}$

$\overline{M_1 M_2}$ and $\overline{SU}$ have the same slope, $-\dfrac{2}{3}$, so $\overline{M_1 M_2} \parallel \overline{SU}$.

Try These

Use coordinate geometry to solve.

1. A rectangle is a parallelogram with four right angles. Show that quadrilateral $LMNP$ at the right is a rectangle.

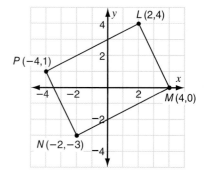

2. Refer to $\triangle STU$ above. Show that the segment joining the midpoints of $\overline{US}$ and $\overline{UT}$ is parallel to $\overline{ST}$.

3. The points $A(-2, 1)$, $B(2, 5)$, $C(6, -1)$, and $D(4, -7)$ form a quadrilateral. The points $W, X, Y,$ and Z are the midpoints of sides $\overline{AB}, \overline{BC}, \overline{CD},$ and $\overline{AD}$, respectively. Prove that quadrilateral $WXYZ$ is a parallelogram.

4. **Discuss and Write** Give the coordinates of the vertices of a right triangle that does *not* have a vertical or horizontal leg. Explain how you know the triangle is a right triangle using coordinate geometry.

Test Prep: Multiple-Choice Questions
Strategy: Understand Distractors

The information given in a multiple-choice question can sometimes be used to answer several related but different questions. The provided distractors often answer other questions that could have been asked. Be sure to read every test item carefully and *answer the question asked*.

Look at the sample test item.

Read the whole test item, including the answer choices, to determine the type of answer required.

- Underline important words.

  What is the <u>slope-intercept form</u> of the equation of the line?

  An equation in *slope-intercept form* is $y = mx + b$.

- Restate the question in your own words.

  Write an equation in the form $y = mx + b$.

Solve the problem.

- Be sure to answer the question asked.
- Apply appropriate rules and properties.

  Use the point-slope form to write an equation of the line. Then solve for y to write the equation in slope-intercept form.

  $y - (-1) = 2(x - 3)$ ←—Substitute the given values into the point-slope form $y - y_1 = m(x - x_1)$.

  $y + 1 = 2x - 6$ ←—Simplify.

  $y = 2x - 7$ ←—Use the Subtraction Property of Equality.

> ## Sample Test Item
>
> A line passes through the point $(3, -1)$ and has a slope of 2. What is the slope-intercept form of the equation of the line?
>
> **A.** $y = 2x - 7$ **C.** $y + 1 = 2(x - 3)$
>
> **B.** $y = 2x + 7$ **D.** $2x + y = -7$

Test-Taking Tips

- Underline important words.
- Restate the question.
- Use the Test-Prep strategy.
- Apply appropriate rules, definitions, properties, or strategies.
- Analyze and eliminate answer choices.

Item Analysis

Choose the answer.

- Analyze and eliminate answer choices. Watch out for distractors.

  Ⓐ $y = 2x - 7$ ←—This is the correct choice!

  B. $y = 2x + 7$ ←—Point-slope form was not simplified correctly. Eliminate this choice.

  C. $y + 1 = 2(x - 3)$ ←—This equation is in point-slope form. Eliminate this choice.

  D. $2x + y = -7$ ←—This equation is in standard form. Eliminate this choice.

Try These

Choose the correct answer. Explain how you eliminated answer choices.

1. What is the x-intercept of the graph of $y + 3x = 15$?

   A. -3 **C.** 5

   B. 3   **D.** 15

2. The graph of which equation is perpendicular to the graph of $y = -8x + 7$?

   F. $y = -8x - 7$ **H.** $y = 8x - 7$

   G. $y = -\frac{1}{8}x + 7$ **J.** $y = \frac{1}{8}x + 7$

Go to PRACTICE BOOK page 135 for exercise sets.

Systems of Linear Equations and Inequalities

CHAPTER 6

In This Chapter You Will:

- Solve systems of linear equations in two variables graphically
- Solve systems of linear equations in two variables algebraically by substitution
- Solve systems of linear equations in two variables algebraically by using addition or subtraction to eliminate one variable
- Solve systems of linear equations in two variables using equivalent systems
- Solve a variety of verbal problems using systems of linear equations in two variables
- Graph and solve systems of linear inequalities in two variables
- Apply the strategy: *Work Backward*
- Look for new vocabulary words **highlighted** in each lesson

Do You Remember?

- The graph of a linear equation is a line. Every point on the line is a solution.
- To solve an equation that has unknown terms on both sides, transform it using the Properties of Equality to write an equivalent equation with all the unknown terms on one side.
- The solution set of an inequality in two variables is the set of all ordered pairs that make the inequality true.

For Practice Exercises:

 PRACTICE BOOK, pp. 141–168

For Chapter Support: ONLINE

 www.progressinmathematics.com

- Skills Update Practice
- Practice Activities
- Audio Glossary
- Vocabulary Activities
- Technology Videos
- Enrichment Activities
- Electronic SourceBook

 VIRTUAL MANIPULATIVES

Critical Thinking

At her store, Ms. Harrison has 12 pounds of pasta worth 70 cents a pound. She wants to mix it with pasta worth 45 cents a pound so that the total mixture can be sold for 55 cents a pound without any gain or loss. How much of the 45-cent pasta must she use?

Solve Systems of Linear Equations Graphically

Objective To solve systems of linear equations in two variables graphically

Max challenges his brother Eru to a race on the way to football practice. He gives Eru a 20-yard head start. If Max runs 6 yards per second and Eru runs 4 yards per second, how long will it take Max to catch up to Eru?

To find how long it would take Max to catch up to Eru, write and solve two equations that represent the situation.

▶ A set of two or more equations that have variables in common is a **system of linear equations** or **simultaneous equations**.

Let y = the distance (in yards).
Let x = time (in seconds).

.....Think.....................
: distance = rate • time :
....

$$\begin{cases} y = 6x & \longleftarrow \text{Max's position at time } x \\ y = 4x + 20 & \longleftarrow \text{Eru's position at time } x \end{cases}$$

▶ A **solution of a system of equations** is a set of values for the variables that make each equation in the system true.

To find a solution, you can use a graph. A graph can tell you what *appears* to be the solution, or the point that both lines have in common. This point is called the *point of intersection*.

Graph each of the equations on the same coordinate plane by making a function table, or by using the slope and y-intercept for each equation. Locate the point where the lines intersect to find the solution of the system.

Method 1 Make a function table for each equation.

$y = 6x$

x	y
0	0
5	30
8	48

$y = 4x + 20$

x	y
0	20
5	40
8	52

Method 2 Use the slope and y-intercept.

$y = 6x$ ⟵ slope $= \frac{6}{1}$, y-intercept $= 0$

$y = 4x + 20$ ⟵ slope $= \frac{4}{1}$, y-intercept $= 20$

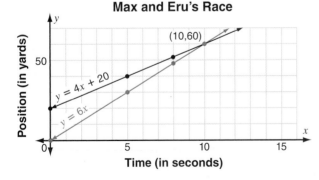

Max and Eru's Race

Position (in yards) / Time (in seconds)

Check: Substitute the values for the variables into each equation, and verify that the solution, $(10, 60)$, satisfies *both* equations.

$$y = 6x \qquad\qquad y = 4x + 20$$
$$60 \overset{?}{=} 6(10) \qquad 60 \overset{?}{=} 4(10) + 20$$
$$60 = 60 \text{ True} \qquad 60 = 60 \text{ True}$$

The lines appear to intersect at $(10, 60)$.

So it will take Max 10 seconds to catch up to Eru.

Example

1 Solve the system by graphing: $\begin{cases} 5x + 2y = 6 \\ x = 2 \end{cases}$

Use the slope and y-intercept to graph each equation. Then locate the point of intersection.

Graph: $5x + 2y = 6$ ←—Solve for y to write the equation in slope-intercept form.

$$5x - 5x + 2y = 6 - 5x$$

$$\frac{2y}{2} = \frac{6 - 5x}{2}$$

$$y = \frac{6}{2} - \frac{5x}{2}$$

$$y = 3 - \frac{5}{2}x$$

$$y = -\frac{5}{2}x + 3$$ ←—The slope is $-\frac{5}{2}$, and the y-intercept is 3.

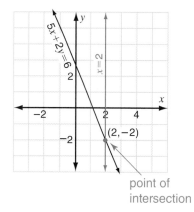

point of intersection

Graph: $x = 2$ ←—This is a vertical line.

$(2, -2)$ ←—This is the point where the two lines appear to intersect.

Check: Substitute the solution into each of the original equations.

$$5x + 2y = 6 \qquad\qquad x = 2$$
$$5(2) + 2(-2) \overset{?}{=} 6 \qquad 2 = 2 \text{ True}$$
$$10 - 4 \overset{?}{=} 6$$
$$6 = 6 \text{ True}$$

So the solution of the system of equations is $(2, -2)$.

▶ A system of equations can have no solution. This occurs when two lines do *not* intersect, or are parallel.

Solve the system by graphing: $\begin{cases} x + y = 4 \\ y = -x - 2 \end{cases}$

Use the slope and y-intercept to graph each equation. Then locate the point of intersection.

Graph: $x + y = 4$ ←—Solve for y.

$$y = -x + 4$$ ←—The slope is -1, and the y-intercept is 4.

Graph: $y = -x - 2$ ←—The slope is -1, and the y-intercept is -2.

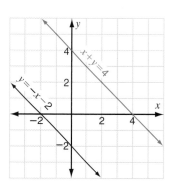

The lines have the same slope and different y-intercepts. They are parallel lines and do not intersect. There is no ordered pair that makes both of the equations true. The system has *no solution*.

Continue Lesson ➡

▶ A system of equations can also have infinitely many solutions.

Solve the system by graphing: $\begin{cases} x + 2y = 2 \\ -3x - 6y = -6 \end{cases}$

Use the slope and *y*-intercept to graph each equation. Then locate the point of intersection.

Graph: $x + 2y = 2$ ◄——Solve for *y* to write the equation in slope-intercept form.

$$y = -\frac{1}{2}x + 1$$ ◄——The slope is $-\frac{1}{2}$, and the *y*-intercept is 1.

Graph: $-3x - 6y = -6$ ◄——Solve for *y*.

$$y = -\frac{1}{2}x + 1$$ ◄——The slope is $-\frac{1}{2}$, and the *y*-intercept is 1.

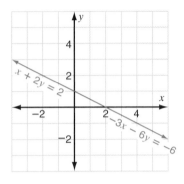

The graphs coincide. The equations are equivalent; they describe the same line. Every point *on the line* is a solution of both equations. There are infinitely many solutions for this system of equations.

Example

1 Solve the system by graphing: $\begin{cases} 6x - 10y = -20 \\ -\frac{3}{5}x = 2 - y \end{cases}$

Use the slope and *y*-intercept to graph each equation. Then locate the point of intersection.

Graph: $6x - 10y = -20$ ◄——Solve for *y*.

$$y = \frac{3}{5}x + 2$$ ◄——The slope is $\frac{3}{5}$, and the *y*-intercept is 2.

Graph: $-\frac{3}{5}x = 2 - y$ ◄——Solve for *y*.

$$y = \frac{3}{5}x + 2$$ ◄——The slope is $\frac{3}{5}$, and the *y*-intercept is 2.

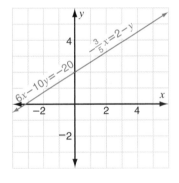

The graphs *coincide*. There are infinitely many solutions for the system.

▶ The terms *consistent, inconsistent, independent,* and *dependent* are used to describe systems of equations.

- If there is at least one solution for a system of equations, the system is consistent.

- If there are no solutions, the system is inconsistent.

- If a system of equations describes two different lines that intersect, the system is independent.

- If both equations describe the same line, the system is dependent.

The chart below summarizes the three types of systems of equations.

Systems of Equations		
Graphs of the Equations	**Number of Solutions**	**Description of System**
parallel lines	none	inconsistent
intersecting lines	exactly one	consistent and independent
same line	infinitely many	consistent and dependent

Try These

Graph each system of equations. Find the number of solutions, and then describe the system.

1. $\begin{cases} 6x - 4y = -36 \\ 9x - 54 = 6y \end{cases}$

2. $\begin{cases} 2x + 3y = 2 \\ y = -x + 2 \end{cases}$

3. $\begin{cases} 2y - 10 = -\frac{5}{2}x \\ 15x - 60 = -12y \end{cases}$

4. $\begin{cases} 2x - y = -8 \\ y = 4 \end{cases}$

5. Nasim wants to compare the membership costs of two gyms. Gym I requires a $120 membership fee and then charges $20 each month. Gym II has no membership fee but charges $30 a month. In what month will the cost be the same?

6. **Discuss and Write** How can you determine whether two lines will intersect without graphing the lines? Explain.

Go to **PRACTICE BOOK Lesson 6-1 for exercise sets.**

Solve Systems of Linear Equations by Substitution

Objective To solve systems of linear equations in two variables algebraically by substitution

The length of a rectangle is 2 cm more than 3 times its width. If the perimeter of the rectangle is 28 cm, find its dimensions.

To find the dimensions of the rectangle, write and solve a system of linear equations.

Let x = width of the rectangle.
Let y = length of the rectangle.

$$\begin{cases} y = 3x + 2 \quad \longleftarrow \text{The length } (y) \text{ is 2 cm } \textit{more than } 3 \textit{ times } \text{its width.} \\ 2x + 2y = 28 \quad \longleftarrow \text{The perimeter is 28 cm.} \end{cases}$$

▶ One way to find an exact solution to a system of linear equations is to use substitution. To use this method, solve one of the equations for one of the variables and then substitute the expression for the variable into the second expression.

Solve: $\begin{cases} y = 3x + 2 \\ 2x + 2y = 28 \end{cases}$

Substitute: $3x + 2$ for y into the second equation.

$$2x + 2y = 28$$
$$2x + 2(3x + 2) = 28 \quad \longleftarrow \text{Substitute } 3x + 2 \text{ for } y.$$
$$2x + 6x + 4 = 28 \quad \longleftarrow \text{Apply the Distributive Property.}$$
$$8x + 4 = 28 \quad \longleftarrow \text{Combine like terms.}$$
$$8x + 4 - 4 = 28 - 4 \quad \longleftarrow \text{Use the Subtraction Property of Equality.}$$
$$8x = 24$$
$$8x \div 8 = 24 \div 8 \quad \longleftarrow \text{Use the Division Property of Equality.}$$
$$x = 3$$

To find the corresponding y-value, substitute 3 for x into one of the equations, then solve.

$$y = 3x + 2$$
$$y = 3(3) + 2 \quad \longleftarrow \text{Substitute 3 for } x.$$
$$y = 11$$

Check: Substitute 3 for x and 11 for y into the original equations.

$y = 3x + 2$	$2x + 2y = 28$
$11 \overset{?}{=} 3(3) + 2$	$2(3) + 2(11) \overset{?}{=} 28$
$11 = 11$ True	$6 + 22 \overset{?}{=} 28$
	$28 = 28$ True

So the length of the rectangle is 11 cm, and the width is 3 cm.

▶Sometimes you need to transform one of the equations to solve for one of the variables. The equation that is easier to solve is the one with a variable that has a coefficient of 1.

Solve: $\begin{cases} x + 4y = 7 \\ 2x - 2y = 9 \end{cases}$

$x + 4y - 4y = 7 - 4y$ ◀——Use the Subtraction Property of Equality.

$\qquad x = 7 - 4y$

Substitute: Replace $7 - 4y$ for x in the second equation, and solve for y. To find the corresponding x-value, substitute the value you determine for y into one of the equations.

$2x - 2y = 9$

$2(7 - 4y) - 2y = 9$ ◀——Substitute $7 - 4y$ for x.

$14 - 8y - 2y = 9$ ◀——Use the Distributive Property.

$14 - 10y = 9$ ◀——Combine like terms.

$14 - 14 - 10y = 9 - 14$ ◀——Use the Subtraction Property of Equality.

$\dfrac{-10y}{-10} = \dfrac{-5}{-10}$ ◀——Use the Division Property of Equality.

$y = \dfrac{1}{2}$

$x + 4\left(\dfrac{1}{2}\right) = 7$ ◀——Substitute $\dfrac{1}{2}$ for y.

$x + 2 = 7$

$x + 2 - 2 = 7 - 2$ ◀——Use the Subtraction Property of Equality.

$x = 5$

Check: Substitute 5 for x and $\dfrac{1}{2}$ for y into *both* equations.

$x + 4y = 7$

$5 + 4\left(\dfrac{1}{2}\right) \overset{?}{=} 7$

$5 + 2 \overset{?}{=} 7$

$7 = 7$ True

$2x - 2y = 9$

$2(5) - 2\left(\dfrac{1}{2}\right) \overset{?}{=} 9$

$10 - 1 \overset{?}{=} 9$

$9 = 9$ True

Solution: $\left(5, \dfrac{1}{2}\right)$ ◀——Write the solution as an ordered pair.

Try These

Solve each system of equations by using the substitution method.

1. $\begin{cases} x + 2y = 14 \\ 3x + 5y = 40 \end{cases}$

2. $\begin{cases} 3x - 6y = 0 \\ 2x - 2y = 1 \end{cases}$

3. $\begin{cases} 3x + 2y = -12 \\ 0.2x - 0.4y = -1.4 \end{cases}$

4. A box containing 3 dictionaries and 8 atlases weighs 35 pounds. Each dictionary weighs twice as much as an atlas. How much does each type of book weigh?

5. Discuss and Write If you were asked to solve $\begin{cases} 2x + 4y = -6 \\ 3x - y = 5 \end{cases}$ using substitution, which equation would you choose to solve for x or y? Explain.

Solve Systems of Linear Equations by Elimination

Objective To solve systems of linear equations in two variables algebraically by using addition or subtraction to eliminate one variable

Tanisha pays $49 for one pair of jeans and two shirts. The next day, she returns the two shirts for store credit, buys two more pairs of the same jeans, and pays an additional $26. What is the cost of one pair of jeans? What is the cost of one shirt?

To find the cost of one pair of jeans and one shirt, write and solve a system of linear equations.

Let j = the cost of a pair of jeans.
Let s = the cost of a shirt.

$$\begin{cases} j + 2s = 49 & \longleftarrow \text{The cost of 1 pair of jeans and 2 shirts is \$49.} \\ 2j - 2s = 26 & \longleftarrow \text{The cost of 2 pairs of jeans less a credit for} \\ & \text{2 shirts is \$26.} \end{cases}$$

▶ Another way to solve a system of equations is by eliminating one variable by using addition or subtraction. When the coefficients of the same variable are *opposites*, you can *add* the two equations to eliminate one variable.

1 Add the equations.

$$\begin{array}{l} j + 2s = 49 \\ \underline{2j - 2s = 26} \\ 3j \phantom{{}+ 2s} = 75 \end{array}$$
┌ $+2s$ and $-2s$ are opposites.
└ Use the Addition Property of Equality.

$$\frac{3j}{3} = \frac{75}{3} \quad \longleftarrow \text{Use the Division Property of Equality.}$$

$$j = 25$$

___ **Key Concept** ___

Addition Property of Equality:
For all numbers a, b, c, and d,
if $a = b$ and $c = d$, then $a + c = b + d$.

2 Substitute the value of the variable into one of the original equations. Solve for the other variable.

$$25 + 2s = 49 \quad \longleftarrow \text{Solve for } s \text{ by substituting 25 for } j.$$
$$25 - 25 + 2s = 49 - 25 \quad \longleftarrow \text{Use the Subtraction Property of Equality.}$$
$$2s = 24$$
$$\frac{2s}{2} = \frac{24}{2} \quad \longleftarrow \text{Use the Division Property of Equality.}$$
$$s = 12$$

3 Check the answer by substituting the values of j and s into *both* equations.

$$\begin{array}{rl} j + 2s & = 49 \\ 25 + 2(12) & \overset{?}{=} 49 \\ 25 + 24 & \overset{?}{=} 49 \\ 49 & = 49 \ \text{True} \end{array} \qquad \begin{array}{rl} 2j - 2s & = 26 \\ 2(25) - 2(12) & \overset{?}{=} 26 \\ 50 - 24 & \overset{?}{=} 26 \\ 26 & = 26 \ \text{True} \end{array}$$

So one pair of jeans costs $25, and one shirt costs $12.

▶ If the coefficients of one of the variables are *the same* rather than opposites, you can *subtract* the systems of equations to eliminate one of the variables.

Steven usually walks or bikes when he wants to go somewhere. Last week, he walked for 2.5 hours and biked for 5 hours, traveling a total of 55 miles. This week, he walked for 2.5 hours and biked for 2 hours, traveling a total of 28 miles. Assume his walking and riding speeds are the same each week. What is his rate of speed while walking? While biking?

Let w = the rate at which Steven walks.

Let b = the rate at which Steven bikes.

> **Remember:**
> rate • time = distance

$$\begin{cases} 2.5w + 5b = 55 & \leftarrow\text{last week's distance} \\ 2.5w + 2b = 28 & \leftarrow\text{this week's distance} \end{cases}$$

1 Subtract the equations.

$$\begin{array}{r} 2.5w + 5b = 55 \\ \underline{-2.5w - 2b = -28} \quad \leftarrow\text{To subtract, add the opposite of each term.} \\ 3b = 27 \end{array}$$

$3b \div 3 = 27 \div 3 \quad \leftarrow$Use the Division Property of Equality.

$b = 9$

2 Substitute and solve for the other variable.

$2.5w + 2b = 28$

$2.5w + 2(9) = 28 \quad \leftarrow$Substitute 9 for b.

$2.5w + 18 = 28$

$2.5w + 18 - 18 = 28 - 18 \quad \leftarrow$Use the Subtraction Property of Equality.

$2.5w \div 2.5 = 10 \div 2.5 \quad \leftarrow$Use the Division Property of Equality.

$w = 4$

3 Check by substituting the values of both variables into *both* equations.

$2.5w + 5b = 55$ | $2.5w + 2b = 28$
$2.5(4) + 5(9) \stackrel{?}{=} 55$ | $2.5(4) + 2(9) \stackrel{?}{=} 28$
$10 + 45 \stackrel{?}{=} 55$ | $10 + 18 \stackrel{?}{=} 28$
$55 = 55$ True | $28 = 28$ True

So Steven walks 4 mph and bikes 9 mph.

Try These

Solve each system of equations by addition or subtraction.

1. $\begin{cases} x - y = 5 \\ 3x - y = 7 \end{cases}$

2. $\begin{cases} 3a + 2b = 0 \\ -4a + 2b = 7 \end{cases}$

3. $\begin{cases} 3r + 2s = -\frac{1}{2} \\ -2r - 2s = \frac{1}{6} \end{cases}$

4. $\begin{cases} 2x - 0.8 = -y \\ 2y + 1.4 = 2x \end{cases}$

5. Discuss and Write Explain how to solve a system of equations using elimination. Give an example of how to use subtraction.

Go to ▶ **PRACTICE BOOK Lesson 6-3 for exercise sets.**

Solve Equivalent Systems of Linear Equations

Objective To solve systems of linear equations in two variables using equivalent systems

Sometimes a system of linear equations cannot immediately be solved using the elimination method by addition or subtraction. You may need to make an equivalent system, a system that has the same solution set, by multiplication.

Consider the system:

$$\begin{cases} 2x + y = 2 \\ 5x - 3y = 27 \end{cases}$$

Think..
Adding or subtracting the equations will *not* eliminate a variable.

▶ To solve the system, multiply one or both equations by a constant so that the coefficients of one of the variables are opposites.

- First, multiply the first equation by 3.

$$3(2x + y = 2) \longrightarrow 6x + 3y = 6$$

Think ....
Multiply the first equation by 3 so that when added to the second equation, the *y* terms are eliminated.

So the systems $\begin{cases} 2x + y = 2 \\ 5x - 3y = 27 \end{cases}$ and $\begin{cases} 6x + 3y = 6 \\ 5x - 3y = 27 \end{cases}$ are equivalent and will have the *same solution set*.

- Then solve this system by elimination, since the coefficients of *y* are now opposites.

$$\begin{array}{r} 6x + 3y = 6 \\ 5x - 3y = 27 \\ \hline 11x \quad\ = 33 \end{array}$$ ← Eliminate the *y* variable. Use the Addition Property of Equality.

$$\frac{11x}{11} = \frac{33}{11}$$ ← Use the Division Property of Equality.

$$x = 3$$

- Now, solve for *y*.

$$2(3) + y = 2$$ ← Solve for *y* by substituting 3 for *x*.
$$6 + y = 2$$
$$6 - 6 + y = 2 - 6$$ ← Use the Subtraction Property of Equality.
$$y = -4$$

Check: Substitute $(3, 4)$ into the original equations.

$$
\begin{array}{c|c}
2x - y = 2 & 5x - 3y = 27 \\
2(3) - 4 \overset{?}{=} 2 & 5(3) - 3(-4) \overset{?}{=} 27 \\
6 - 4 \overset{?}{=} 2 & 15 + 12 \overset{?}{=} 27 \\
2 = 2 \text{ True} & 27 = 27 \text{ True}
\end{array}
$$

So the solution for the system is $(3, -4)$.

▶ You can use a graph to test that the solution is reasonable. Look at the graph at the right. The solution of the equivalent systems by elimination is the same as the solution by graphing.

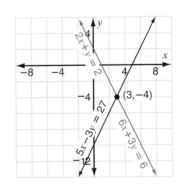

▶ Sometimes both of the equations must be multiplied by a nonzero number to get an equivalent system with opposite coefficients for one variable.

Solve $\begin{cases} 6x - 4y = 14 \\ 9x + 5y = -1 \end{cases}$

.........**Think**...

The LCM of 6 and 9 is 18.
The LCM of 4 and 5 is 20.

The coefficients of y have opposite signs, so one way to find the solutions is to multiply the first equation by 5 and the second equation by 4.
....

$5(6x - 4y = 14)$ ◀—Use the Multiplication Property of Equality
$4(9x + 5y = -1)$ to get an equivalent system with opposite coefficients for one of the variables.

$30x - 20y = 70$ ◀—Eliminate the y variable.
$36x + 20y = -4$ Since the coefficients of y are opposites, the system can now be solved by elimination.

$30x - 20y = 70$
$\underline{36x + 20y = -4}$

$66x \qquad = 66$ ◀—Use the Addition Property of Equality to combine equations.

$66x \div 66 = 66 \div 66$ ◀—Use the Division Property of Equality.

$x = 1$

$6(1) - 4y = 14$ ◀—Solve for y by substituting 1 for x.

$6 - 6 - 4y = 14 - 6$ ◀—Use the Subtraction Property of Equality.

$-4y \div (-4) = 8 \div (-4)$ ◀—Use the Division Property of Equality.

$y = -2$

Check: Substitute the solution in the original equations.

$6x - 4y = 14$	$9x + 5y = -1$
$6(1) - 4(-2) \overset{?}{=} 14$	$9(1) + 5(-2) \overset{?}{=} -1$
$6 + 8 \overset{?}{=} 14$	$9 - 10 \overset{?}{=} -1$
$14 = 14$ True	$-1 = -1$ True

So the solution for the system is $(1, -2)$.

Try These

Solve each system of equations by using substitution or elimination.

1. $\begin{cases} 3x + 6y = 3 \\ 4x = 8y - 5 \end{cases}$

2. $\begin{cases} 4a - 2b = 10 \\ 3a + 5b = -18\frac{1}{2} \end{cases}$

3. $\begin{cases} 5x = y + 8 \\ -x + 2y = -7 \end{cases}$

4. $\begin{cases} 2x - 3y = 0 \\ 3x - 2y = 1 \end{cases}$

5. Discuss and Write How would you solve the following system: $\begin{cases} 3x + 2y = 7 \\ 2y - 1 = 5x \end{cases}$?

Would you use the substitution or the elimination method? Show how you would set up the system, and explain why you chose that method.

Go to PRACTICE BOOK Lesson 6-4 for exercise sets.

Apply Systems of Linear Equations

Objective To solve a variety of verbal problems using systems of linear equations in two variables

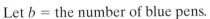

Alan bought 5 pens, some blue pens for $0.70 each and some red pens for $.65 each. If he received $1.65 change from $5.00, how many red pens did he buy?

Let b = the number of blue pens.
Let r = the number of red pens.

$$\begin{cases} 0.70b + 0.65r = 3.35 \leftarrow \text{The total cost was } \$5.00 - \$1.65, \text{ or } \$3.35. \\ b + r = 5 \leftarrow \text{Alan bought a total of 5 pens.} \end{cases}$$

$$100(0.70b + 0.65r) = 100(3.35) \leftarrow \text{Multiply by 100 so that the coefficients of the variables are whole numbers.}$$

$$70b + 65r = 335$$

Since the second equation, $b + r = 5$, is easily solved for b or r, substitution is a convenient way to solve this system.

- Solve the second equation for b.

$$b + r = 5$$
$$b + r - r = 5 - r \leftarrow \text{Use the}$$
$$b = 5 - r \quad \text{Subtraction Property of Equality.}$$

- Substitute the value for b into the other equation.

$$70b + 65r = 335$$
$$70(5 - r) + 65r = 335 \leftarrow \text{Apply the Distributive Property.}$$
$$350 - 70r + 65r = 335 \leftarrow \text{Combine like terms.}$$
$$350 - 5r = 335 \leftarrow \text{Use the Subtraction Property of Equality.}$$
$$-5r = -15 \leftarrow \text{Use the Division Property of Equality.}$$
$$r = 3$$

So Alan bought 3 red pens.

Examples

1 Two river towns are 60 miles apart. A boat can cover the 60 miles in 4 hours when traveling with the current. Traveling against the current, the boat takes 6 hours. What is the speed of the current? the speed of the boat?

Let b = the speed of the boat.
Let c = speed of the current.

$$\begin{cases} 4b + 4c = 60 \\ 6b - 6c = 60 \end{cases}$$

	Rate (mph)	•	Time (hrs)	=	distance
With the current	$b + c$	•	4	=	60
Against the current	$b - c$	•	6	=	60

- You can use elimination to solve this system by multiplying the first equation by 3 and the second equation by 2.

$$3(4b + 4c = 60) \longrightarrow 12b + 12c = 180$$
$$2(6b - 6c = 60) \longrightarrow \underline{12b - 12c = 120}$$
$$24b \qquad = 300$$
$$b = 12.5$$

The speed of the boat is 12.5 miles per hour.

- Substitute the value of b into either original equation.

$$4(12.5) + 4c = 60$$
$$50 + 4c = 60$$
$$4c = 10$$
$$c = 2.5$$

The speed of the current is 2.5 mph.

2 How much pure bleach and how much of a 20% bleach solution must be mixed to get 4 liters of a 30% bleach solution?

Let x = the number of liters of 20% bleach solution.
Let y = the number of liters of pure bleach.

	20% solution	+	pure bleach	=	30% solution
Amount of solution (L)	x	+	y	=	4
Amount of bleach (L)	0.20x	+	y	=	0.30(4)

$$\begin{cases} x + y = 4 \\ 0.20x + y = 1.20 \end{cases}$$

One way to solve this system is by subtraction.

$$\begin{array}{rcl} x + y = 4 & \longrightarrow & x + y = 4 \\ -(0.20x + y = 1.20) & \longrightarrow & -0.20x - y = -1.20 \\ \hline & & 0.80x = 2.80 \\ & & x = 3.5 \end{array}$$

Substitute the value of x into either one of the original equations.

$x + y = 4$

$3.5 + y = 4$

$y = 0.5$

So for a 30% bleach solution, mix 3.5 liters of a 20% bleach solution and 0.5 liter of pure bleach.

Try These

Solve each problem by writing and solving a system of linear equations.

1. Brianna has $3.30 in dimes and quarters. The number of dimes she has is 3 fewer than twice the number of quarters. How many of each coin does she have?

2. In 5 years, Nick will be $\frac{3}{4}$ as old as his cousin. Three years ago, he was half as old as his cousin. How old are Nick and his cousin now?

3. Alma invested a total of $4000. She put one in certificates of deposit that paid 5% annual interest and the rest in a money market account that paid 7% annual interest. The interest for 1 year totaled $248. How much money did she invest in each type of account?

4. Todd charges twice as much for tutoring as he does for baby-sitting. One week, he earned $105 for tutoring 4 hours and for baby-sitting 6 hours. How much does he charge for each activity?

5. Discuss and Write The following problem can be solved using one equation in one variable or a system of linear equations.

The length of a rectangle is twice the width. Its perimeter is 30 centimeters. Find the length and width.

Show how to set up and solve the problem using each method. Discuss the advantages of each one.

Graph Systems of Linear Inequalities

Objective To graph and solve systems of linear inequalities in two variables

A system of linear inequalities is a set of two or more linear inequalities with the same variables. A graph of the system shows all of its solutions. A solution makes each inequality in the system true.

Solve by graphing: $\begin{cases} x + y > 10 \\ x + 3y \le 24 \end{cases}$

► To solve a system of inequalities by graphing:

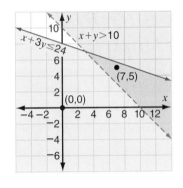

- Graph the first inequality.

  Remember: The graph of a linear inequality is a shaded half-plane.

  $x + y > 10$

  $y > -x + 10$ ◄—Solve the inequality for y.
  $m = -1, b = 10$

  The solution lies *above* the boundary line $y = -x + 10$.

- Graph the second inequality.

  $x + 3y \le 24$

  $y \le -\frac{1}{3}x + 8$ ◄—Solve the inequality for y.
  $m = -\frac{1}{3}, b = 8$

  The solution *includes* the boundary line $y = -\frac{1}{3}x + 8$ and all points *below* the boundary line.

The coordinates of the points in the pink region make the inequality $x + y > 10$ true. The coordinates of the points in the blue region *and* on the blue line makes the inequality $x + 3y \le 24$ true. The coordinates of the points in the region where the graphs of the two inequalities *intersect* (the purple region and part of the blue line) make *both* inequalities true and are solutions to the system.

According to the graph, $(7, 5)$ appears to be an ordered pair in the solution set for this system, and $(0, 0)$ is not.

- Check the solution. Substitute the points above into *both* inequalities.

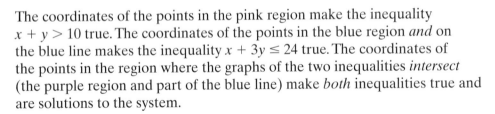

Ordered Pair	$x + y > 10$	$x + 3y \le 24$	Solution
$(7, 5)$	$7 + 5 \overset{?}{>} 10$ $12 > 10$ True	$7 + 3(5) \overset{?}{\le} 24$ $7 + 15 \overset{?}{\le} 24$ $22 \le 24$ True	$(7, 5)$ is a solution to the system because it *satisfies* both inequalities.
$(0, 0)$	$0 + 0 \overset{?}{>} 10$ $0 > 10$ False	$0 + 3(0) \overset{?}{\le} 24$ $0 + 0 \overset{?}{\le} 24$ $0 \le 24$ True	$(0, 0)$ is a not a solution to the system because it does *not satisfy* both inequalities.

1 Solve by graphing: $\begin{cases} x + y \leq 3 \\ 2x - y < 3 \end{cases}$

Name two ordered pairs that are solutions and two that are not.

- Graph the first inequality.

  $x + y \leq 3$

  $\qquad y \leq -x + 3$ ←—Solve the inequality for y.

  $\qquad\qquad m = -1, b = 3$

  The solution *includes* the boundary line $y = -x + 3$ and all points *below* the boundary line.

- Graph the second inequality.

  $2x - y < 3$

  $\qquad y > 2x - 3$ ←—Solve the inequality for y.

  $\qquad\qquad m = 2, b = -3$

> **Remember:** Reverse the direction of the inequality symbol when multiplying by a negative number.

The solution lies *above* the boundary line $y = 2x - 3$.

The solution of the system of inequalities consists of the coordinates of all the ordered pairs in the area where the shaded regions *intersect*.

$(-4, -2)$ and $(0, 3)$ are some examples of points that are solutions.
$(4, 2)$ and $(0, -3)$ are some examples of points that are *not* solutions.

► Systems of linear equations that involve parallel lines are inconsistent. They do not contain a solution. This is *not* always true in a system of *linear inequalities*.

Examples

Graph the system of linear inequalities. Describe the solution sets.

1 $\begin{cases} y < -\frac{3}{2}x + 2 \\ y \geq -\frac{3}{2}x - 2 \end{cases}$

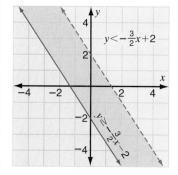

The solutions are all the points in the region *between* the parallel lines and *on the solid line.*

2 $\begin{cases} y > -\frac{3}{2}x + 2 \\ y < -\frac{3}{2}x - 2 \end{cases}$

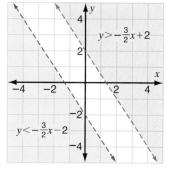

The graphs of the two linear inequalities *do not overlap* or *intersect.* The system has *no solution.*

3 $\begin{cases} y > -\frac{3}{2}x + 2 \\ y > -\frac{3}{2}x - 2 \end{cases}$

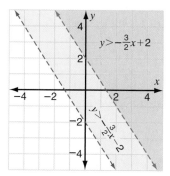

The solutions of the system are the same as those of $y > -\frac{3}{2}x + 2.$

Continue Lesson ➡

▶ You can use systems of linear inequalities to solve verbal problems. You should consider whether fractions or negative numbers make sense as possible solutions.

For her birthday, Djana received a $75 gift card to an online bookstore. She wants to buy at least 6 books. If all books at this store cost either $8 or $5, write a system of inequalities that describe the situation. Then graph the system to show all possible solutions.

Let x = number of $8 books and y = number of $5 books.

Djana wants to buy *at least* 6 books.
$$x + y \geq 6$$

Djana can spend *no more than* $75.
$$8x + 5y \leq 75$$

Solve by graphing: $\begin{cases} x + y \geq 6 \\ 8x + 5y \leq 75 \end{cases}$

- Graph: $x + y \geq 6$
$$y \geq -x + 6 \quad \longleftarrow \text{Solve the inequality for } y.$$
$$m = -1, b = 6$$

The solution includes the boundary line $y = -x + 6$ *and* all the points above the line.

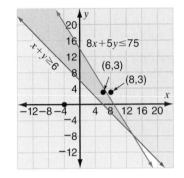

- Graph: $8x + 5y \leq 75$
$$y \leq -\frac{8}{5}x + 15 \quad \longleftarrow \text{Solve the inequality for } y.$$
$$m = -\frac{8}{5}, b = 15$$

The solution *includes* the boundary line $y = -\frac{8}{5}x + 15$ *and* all the points *below* the line.

The solution of the system of inequalities consists of the coordinates of all the ordered pairs in the area where the shaded regions overlap (the purple region) and the ordered pairs on the part of the lines $y = -x + 6$ and $y = -\frac{8}{5}x + 15$ that are boundaries of the purple region.

- Check the solution.

In the context of the problem, the only reasonable solutions are those in Quadrant I. Since Djana cannot buy a negative or fractional number of books, the domain and range for this situation include *only positive integers*.

One solution is the ordered pair $(6, 3)$. Djana could buy 6 books that cost $8 each and 3 books that cost $5 each. This solution *satisfies both conditions*, because Djana would buy at least 6 books and spend no more than $75.

$$x + y \geq 6$$
$$6 + 3 \overset{?}{\geq} 6$$
$$9 \geq 6 \text{ True}$$

$$8x + 5y \leq 75$$
$$8(6) + 5(3) \overset{?}{\leq} 75$$
$$63 \leq 75 \text{ True}$$

The ordered pair $(8, 3)$ is *not* a solution. If Djana bought 8 books that cost $8 each and 3 books that cost $5 each, she would spend $79, and $79 is more than $75.

$$x + y \geq 6$$
$$8 + 3 \overset{?}{\geq} 6$$
$$11 \geq 6 \text{ True}$$

$$8x + 5y \leq 75$$
$$8(8) + 5(3) \overset{?}{\leq} 75$$
$$79 \leq 75 \text{ False}$$

Example

1 Sylvia's profit on her handmade jewelry is $8 on a pair of earrings and $12 on a necklace. She has the materials to make at most 20 pairs of earrings and 16 necklaces. From these, Sylvia wants to make a profit of at least $240. Write a system of inequalities to represent the situation. Graph the system to show possible solutions.

Let x = the number of pairs of earrings.
Let y = the number of necklaces.

$$\begin{cases} 8x + 12y \geq 240 & \text{(earrings profit + necklace profit \textit{is at least} \$240)} \\ x \leq 20 & \text{\textit{at most} 20 pairs of earrings} \\ y \leq 16 & \text{\textit{at most} 16 necklaces} \end{cases}$$

• Graph the first inequality.
$8x + 12y \geq 240$

$y \geq -\dfrac{2}{3}x + 20$ ←—Solve the inequality for y. Use a solid line, and shade the region above the line.

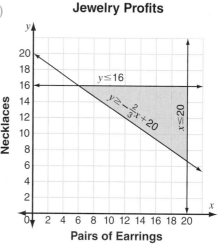

Jewelry Profits

• Graph the next two inequalities.

$x \leq 20$ ←—The boundary line is a solid vertical line. Shade to the left of the line.

$y \leq 16$ ←—The boundary line is a solid horizontal line. Shade below the line.

All possible combinations of earrings and necklaces that meet her requirements are represented by ordered pairs within the triangular region where the three inequalities intersect.

Two of the many possible combinations that meet Sylvia's requirements are:

(12, 14); 12 pairs of earrings, 14 necklaces
(20, 16); 20 pairs of earrings, 16 necklaces

..Think..........
Only use combinations with whole-number coordinates. It would not make sense to sell a part of a necklace or earring.

Try These

Graph each system of inequalities.
Tell if the given ordered pair is a solution of the system.

1. $\begin{cases} y \geq 3x \\ x + y \leq -2 \end{cases}$
$(0, -5)$

2. $\begin{cases} x + 2y \leq 10 \\ 2x - y < 3 \end{cases}$
$(4, -1)$

3. $\begin{cases} -7 > x + y \\ 3x \geq -3y + 12 \end{cases}$
$(-2, -2)$

Graph to show all possible solutions to the problem.
Then name 3 ordered pairs that are solutions.

4. The Band Boosters hope to make at least $400 at a fundraiser. They have 40 date books to sell at a profit of $8 each, and 50 calendars to sell at a profit of $5 each. How many of each could they sell to make at least $400?

5. Discuss and Write Explain why the solutions to Exercise 4 have to be positive integers.

Go to **PRACTICE BOOK Lesson 6-6 for exercise sets.**

6-7

Technology:
Graph Systems of Equations

Objective To use a handheld to graph a system of linear equations

Two numbers have a sum of 14 and a difference of 4. What are the numbers?

Write a system of equations to represent the situation. Let x and y represent the numbers.

$$\begin{cases} x + y = 14 \\ x - y = 4 \end{cases}$$

Solve each equation for y.

$x + y = 14$ $x - y = 4$

$\quad y = -x + 14$ ←—Use the Subtraction $\quad y = x - 4$ ←—Use the Subtraction and
$\qquad\qquad\qquad$ Property of Equality $\qquad\qquad\qquad$ Division Properties of Equality

▶ You can use a handheld to graph and solve a system of linear equations.

Step 1 Press 🏠. Then choose ② to select **Graphs & Geometry**.

Step 2 Input $-x + 14$, then press **enter**.

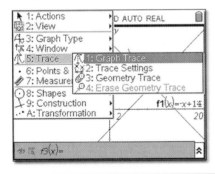

Step 3 Input $x - 4$, then press **enter**.

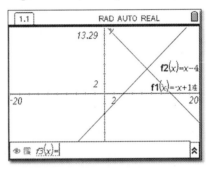

Step 4 Press **menu**. Select **Trace**, then choose **Graph Trace**.

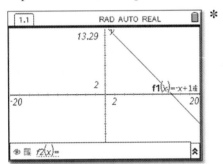

Step 5 Press **menu**. Select **Trace**, then choose **Trace Settings**. Change **Trace Step** to 1.

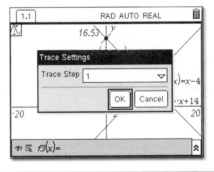

Step 6 Press ▶ to move the trace along the line to the intersection of the two linear equations.

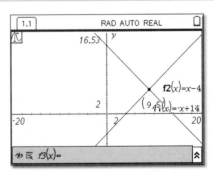

The lines intersect at (9, 5).
So the two numbers are 9 and 5.

✻ Window setting adjusted to fit graph

Example

1 Use a handheld to solve the system of linear equations: $\begin{cases} y = 2x - 3 \\ y = 5x + 6 \end{cases}$

Step 1 Press ⌂. Then choose **2** to select **Graphs & Geometry**.

Step 2 Input $2x - 3$, then press ≈enter to graph the first equation.

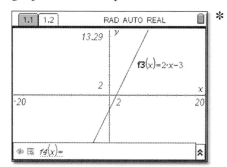

Step 3 Input $5x + 6$, then press ≈enter to graph the linear equation.

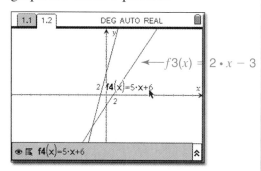

Step 4 Press menu. Select **Trace**, then press **1** to select **Graph Trace**.

Step 5 Press menu. Select **Trace**, then choose **Trace Settings**. Change **Trace Step** to 1.

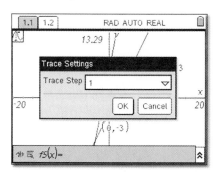

Step 6 Press ◐ to move the trace along the line to the intersection of the two linear equations.

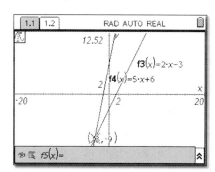

The lines intersect at $(-3, -9)$, so the solution is $(-3, -9)$.

Try These

Use a handheld to solve the system of linear equations. Check your solutions.

1. $\begin{cases} y = 3x + 4 \\ y = 5x + 8 \end{cases}$

2. $\begin{cases} y = 6 - x \\ y = 2x - 6 \end{cases}$

3. $\begin{cases} y = -2x + 7 \\ y = 3 - 6x \end{cases}$

4. $\begin{cases} x + 2y = 13 \\ 2x - 3y = -9 \end{cases}$

5. $\begin{cases} -4x + 7y = -19 \\ 5x + 4y = 11 \end{cases}$

6. $\begin{cases} 5x - 3y = 15 \\ -5x + 8y = -65 \end{cases}$

7. Discuss and Write The sum of two numbers is 0. Their difference is 16. Explain how to use a handheld to find the two numbers.

✳ Window setting adjusted to fit graph

Go to ▶ **PRACTICE BOOK Lesson 6-7 for exercise sets.**

6-8

Technology:
Graph Systems of Inequalities

Objective To use a handheld to graph a system of linear inequalities

▶You can use a graph to solve a system of linear inequalities.

Use a handheld to graph the system: $\begin{cases} x + y < 9 \\ 2x + y \geq 14 \end{cases}$

First, solve each inequality for y.

$x + y < 9$ $2x + y \geq 14$

     $y < -x + 9$ ◀—Use the Subtraction $y \geq -2x + 14$ ◀—Use the Subtraction
                  Property of Inequality.   Property of Inequality.

Step 1 Press 🏠. Then choose **2** to select **Graphs & Geometry**.

Step 2 Use the ⬅ **clear** key to delete the equals sign. Input $< -x + 9$, then press **enter** ≈ to graph the inequality.

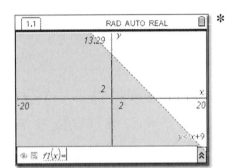

Step 3 Use the ⬅ **clear** key to delete the equals sign. Input $\geq -2x + 14$, then press **enter** ≈ to graph the inequality. Use **ctrl** > to enter the inequality symbol.

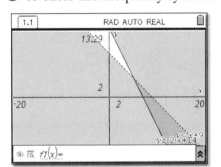

The solution to the system of inequalities is the shaded region where the two graphs overlap.

▶You can use the **Trace** command to name two points that are part of a system's solution set.

Step 4 Press menu. Select **Trace**, and then choose **Graph Trace**.

Step 5 Press 🔽 to select both lines. Then press ▶ to move along the lines. Choose a test point that is part of the solution set. $(8, 0)$ is one point.

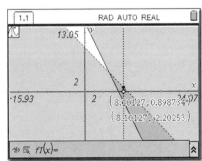

Step 6 Continue to press ▶ to choose another test point. The point $(9, -1)$ is also in the solution set.

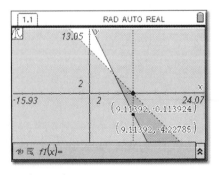

So two points that *appear* to be part of the solution are $(8, 0)$ and $(9, -1)$.

                                    ✱ Window setting adjusted to fit graph

▶ Since you cannot verify a solution set to a system using a graph, you can use the chosen test points to check the solution algebraically.

Try: $(8, 0)$

$$x + y < 9 \qquad 2x + y \geq 14$$
$$8 + 0 \overset{?}{<} 9 \qquad 2(8) + 0 \overset{?}{\geq} 14$$
$$8 < 9 \checkmark \qquad 16 \geq 14 \checkmark$$

Try: $(9, -1)$

$$x + y < 9 \qquad 2x + y \geq 14$$
$$9 + -1 \overset{?}{<} 9 \qquad 2(9) + -1 \overset{?}{\geq} 14$$
$$8 < 9 \checkmark \qquad 17 \geq 14 \checkmark$$

So $(8, 0)$ and $(9, -1)$ are part of the solution set for the inequality.

Example

1 Use a handheld to graph the system. $\begin{cases} y \leq 3x - 2 \\ y > -2x + 6 \end{cases}$

Step 1 Press 🏠. Then choose **2** to select **Graphs & Geometry**.

Step 2 Use the ⬅ clear key to delete the equals sign. Input $\leq 3x - 2$. Use **ctrl** ◁ to enter the inequality symbol. Press **enter** ≈ to graph the first inequality.

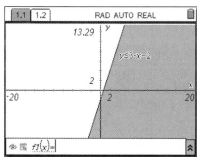

Step 3 Use the ⬅ clear key to delete the equals sign. Input $> -2x + 6$, then press **enter** ≈ to graph the second inequality.

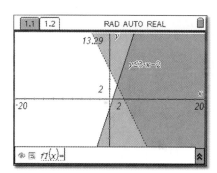

Looking at the graph, the points $(5, 0)$ and $(6, 0)$ *appear* to be part of the solution set. Choose test points and check the solution set.

Try: $(5, 0)$

$$y \leq 3x - 2 \qquad y > -2x + 6$$
$$0 \overset{?}{\leq} 3(5) - 2 \qquad 0 \overset{?}{>} -2(5) + 6$$
$$0 \leq 13 \checkmark \qquad 0 > -4 \checkmark$$

Try: $(6, 0)$

$$y \leq 3x - 2 \qquad y > -2x + 6$$
$$0 \overset{?}{\leq} 3(6) - 2 \qquad 0 \overset{?}{>} -2(6) + 6$$
$$0 \leq 16 \checkmark \qquad 0 > -6 \checkmark$$

Try These

Use a handheld to graph the system. Then name two points that are part of the solution set.

1. $\begin{cases} y > 5x \\ y \geq 5x - 4 \end{cases}$

2. $\begin{cases} -4x + y > 8 \\ x + 4y > 8 \end{cases}$

3. $\begin{cases} x - 3y < 15 \\ -6x - 8y \leq -12 \end{cases}$

4. Discuss and Write Graph the system $\begin{cases} y \geq 5x + 3 \\ y < 5x - 4 \end{cases}$ using a handheld. Describe and explain the result.

Go to PRACTICE BOOK **Lesson 6-8 for exercise sets.**

Problem-Solving Strategy:

Work Backward

Objective To solve problems using the strategy *Work Backward*

Problem I: Four college roommates—Ari, Ben, Joe, and Ty—baked oatmeal chews for their holiday trips home. The next morning, Ari woke up first and grabbed $\frac{1}{4}$ of the chews before he left. Ben then took $\frac{1}{4}$ of the chews that remained. Then Joe and Ty each took $\frac{1}{4}$ of the remaining chews in turn when leaving the dorm. If 81 chews still remained, how many had the roommates baked?

Read **Read to understand what is being asked.**

List the facts and restate the question.

Facts: Four college roommates baked oatmeal chews. One at a time, each took $\frac{1}{4}$ of the chews that remained.
After everyone had taken oatmeal chews, 81 remained.

Question: How many oatmeal chews had the roommates baked?

Plan **Select a strategy**

By using the strategy *Work Backward*, you can start from the amount that remains after everyone had taken oatmeal chews and figure out how much the roommates had baked.

Problem-Solving Strategies
1. Make a Drawing
2. Solve a Simpler Problem
3. Reason Logically
4. Consider Extreme Cases
5. Work Backward
6. Find a Pattern
7. Account for All Possibilities
8. Adopt a Different Point of View
9. Guess and Test
10. Organize Data

Solve **Apply the strategy.**

• There were 81 oatmeal chews left after Ty took his $\frac{1}{4}$.
If t is the number of chews Ty found when he woke up, then $\frac{3}{4}t = 81$. Multiplying both sides by $\frac{4}{3}$ gives $t = 108$. There were 108 oatmeal chews when Ty got to them.

• If j is the number of chews Joe found when he woke up, then $\frac{3}{4}j = 108$. Multiplying both sides by $\frac{4}{3}$ gives $j = 144$. There were 144 oatmeal chews when Joe got to them.

• If b is the number of chews Ben found, then $\frac{3}{4}b = 144$. Multiplying both sides by $\frac{4}{3}$ gives $b = 192$. There were 192 oatmeal chews when Ben got to them.

• Finally, if a is the number of chews Ari found when he woke up, then $\frac{3}{4}a = 192$. Multiplying both sides by $\frac{4}{3}$ gives $a = 256$. So Ari found 256 chews.

So the roommates baked 256 oatmeal chews.

Check **Check to make sure your answer makes sense.**

Assume the roommates baked 256 oatmeal chews and re-enact the scenario.
Ari took $\frac{1}{4}$ of 256, or 64, oatmeal chews. So (256 − 64), or 192, chews remained.
Ben took $\frac{1}{4}$ of 192, or 48, oatmeal chews. So (192 − 48), or 144, chews remained.
Joe took $\frac{1}{4}$ of 144, or 36, oatmeal chews. So (144 − 36), or 108, chews remained.
Ty took $\frac{1}{4}$ of 108, or 27, oatmeal chews. So (108 − 27), or 81, chews remained.

The answer checks.

Problem 2: At dawn on the morning of July 1, Ruben is adrift on a raft 22 miles from shore. He can paddle 7 miles each day, but drifts back 2 miles each night while asleep. On what date will Ruben finally reach shore?

Read ▸ **Read to understand what is being asked.**

List the facts and restate the question.

Facts: Ruben has 22 miles to go.

He can advance 7 miles each day, but will lose 2 miles each night.

Question: How many days will it take for Ruben to advance 22 miles?

Plan ▸ **Select a strategy.**

Sometimes a problem can often be more easily solved by starting with the solution or destination, and then working backward toward the problem, filling in all necessary steps along the way. To accomplish this, you can use the strategy *Work Backward*.

Solve ▸ **Apply the strategy.**

Once Ruben gets within 7 miles of land, he can reach the shore in a day without losing 2 miles at night.

So "put aside" 7 of the 22 miles for the final days paddle. This leaves $(22 - 7)$, or 15, miles to consider.

Ruben's "net gain" each day is 5 miles (forward 7 miles and backward 2 miles). So he can cover $(3 \bullet 5)$, or 15, miles in exactly 3 days.

Therefore, Ruben can reach shore in $3 + 1$, or 4, days, which would be on the evening of July 4.

Check ▸ **Check to make sure your answer makes sense.**

As a check, run forward through the scenario.

July 1: Ruben wakes up 22 miles from shore; advances 7 miles; loses 2 miles. He gains only $(7 - 2)$, or 5, miles.

July 2: Ruben wakes up $(22 - 5)$, or 17, miles from shore; advances 7 miles; loses 2 miles. He gains another $(7 - 2)$, or 5, miles.

July 3: Ruben wakes up $(17 - 5)$, or 12, miles from shore; advances 7 miles; loses 2 miles. He gains another $(7 - 2)$, or 5, miles.

Ruben has gained a total of $(3 \bullet 5)$, or 15, miles in 3 days. He has $(22 - 15)$, or 7, miles to go.

July 4: Ruben wakes up 7 miles from shore; advances 7 miles during the day and reaches shore.

The answer checks.

Enrichment:
Use Cramer's Rule to Solve Systems of Linear Equations

Objective To solve systems of linear equations in two variables using Cramer's Rule

You have solved systems of linear equations in two variables graphically and by using substitution and elimination. Another method involves a technique known as Cramer's Rule. This method was developed by the Swiss mathematician Gabriel Cramer (1704–1752) in 1750. Cramer, who received his doctorate degree at age 18, is known for his early acceleration in mathematics.

Gabriel Cramer

▶ Cramer's Rule is a formula that solves a system of linear equations by using determinants to find the values of the variables. A *determinant* is a real number obtained by evaluating a square array of numbers (a matrix) by a specific rule.

The determinant of a 2-by-2 matrix $\begin{bmatrix} a & b \\ c & d \end{bmatrix}$, denoted by $\begin{vmatrix} a & b \\ c & d \end{vmatrix}$, is

defined as $\begin{vmatrix} a & b \\ c & d \end{vmatrix} = ad - bc$. Notice that the symbol for a matrix is

enclosed in brackets, whereas the symbol for a determinant is a pair of vertical lines similar to the absolute-value symbol.

Evaluate each determinate.

- $\begin{vmatrix} 3 & 2 \\ 4 & 6 \end{vmatrix} = (3 \cdot 6) - (4 \cdot 2)$
  $= 18 - 8$
  $= 10$

- $\begin{vmatrix} -5 & -1 \\ 8 & 2 \end{vmatrix} = (-5 \cdot 2) - (8)(-1)$
  $= -10 + 8$
  $= -2$

▶ The solution of the system $\begin{cases} ax + by = e \\ cx + dy = f \end{cases}$ is $x = \dfrac{\begin{vmatrix} e & b \\ f & d \end{vmatrix}}{\begin{vmatrix} a & b \\ c & d \end{vmatrix}}$ and $y = \dfrac{\begin{vmatrix} a & e \\ c & f \end{vmatrix}}{\begin{vmatrix} a & b \\ c & d \end{vmatrix}}$.

Note that the denominator of the values of x and y is the determinant made up of the coefficients of the equations, $\begin{vmatrix} a & b \\ c & d \end{vmatrix}$. The numerator of the value of x has the column of the coefficients of x replaced by the column of constants. The numerator of the value of y is the same as the denominator, and has the column of coefficients of y replaced by the column of constants.

Use Cramer's Rule to solve the system $\begin{cases} 2x + y = 8 \\ 4x - 3y = 6 \end{cases}$.

$x = \dfrac{\begin{vmatrix} 8 & 1 \\ 6 & -3 \end{vmatrix}}{\begin{vmatrix} 2 & 1 \\ 4 & -3 \end{vmatrix}} = \dfrac{(8)(-3) - (6 \cdot 1)}{(2)(-3) - (4 \cdot 1)}$

$= \dfrac{-24 - 6}{-6 - 4} = \dfrac{-30}{-10}$

$= 3$

$y = \dfrac{\begin{vmatrix} 2 & 8 \\ 4 & 6 \end{vmatrix}}{\begin{vmatrix} 2 & 1 \\ 4 & -3 \end{vmatrix}} = \dfrac{(2 \cdot 6) - (4 \cdot 8)}{(2)(-3) - (4 \cdot 1)}$

$= \dfrac{12 - 32}{-6 - 4} = \dfrac{-20}{-10}$

$= 2$

So the solution of the system is $x = 3$ and $y = 2$.

To apply Cramer's Rule, the system of equations must be in standard form.

Use Cramer's Rule to solve the system $\begin{cases} 2x = y - 5 \\ 2y = 6x + 5 \end{cases}$.

• First, rewrite the system in standard form.

$$\begin{cases} 2x = y - 5 \\ 2y = 6x + 5 \end{cases} \longrightarrow \begin{cases} 2x - y = -5 \\ -6x + 2y = 5 \end{cases}$$

• Then apply Cramer's Rule.

$$x = \frac{\begin{vmatrix} -5 & -1 \\ 5 & 2 \end{vmatrix}}{\begin{vmatrix} 2 & -1 \\ -6 & 2 \end{vmatrix}} = \frac{(-5 \bullet 2) - (5)(-1)}{(2 \bullet 2) - (-6)(-1)}$$

$$= \frac{-10 + 5}{4 - 6} = \frac{-5}{-2}$$

$$= \frac{5}{2}$$

$$y = \frac{\begin{vmatrix} 2 & -5 \\ -6 & 5 \end{vmatrix}}{\begin{vmatrix} 2 & -1 \\ -6 & 2 \end{vmatrix}} = \frac{(2 \bullet 5) - (-6)(-5)}{(2 \bullet 2) - (-6)(-1)}$$

$$= \frac{10 - 30}{4 - 6} = \frac{-20}{-2}$$

$$= 10$$

So the solution of the system is $x = \frac{5}{2}$ and $y = 10$.

▶ When using Cramer's Rule to solve a system of linear equations that is a dependent system, both numerator and denominator have their determinant equal to zero.

Use Cramer's Rule to show that the system $\begin{cases} 2x + 3y = 4 \\ -4x - 6y = -8 \end{cases}$ is dependent.

$$x = \frac{\begin{vmatrix} 4 & 3 \\ -8 & -6 \end{vmatrix}}{\begin{vmatrix} 2 & 3 \\ -4 & -6 \end{vmatrix}} = \frac{(4)(-6) - (-8)(3)}{(2)(-6) - (-4)(3)}$$

$$= \frac{-24 + 24}{-12 + 12} = \frac{0}{0}$$

$$y = \frac{\begin{vmatrix} 2 & 4 \\ -4 & -8 \end{vmatrix}}{\begin{vmatrix} 2 & 3 \\ -4 & -6 \end{vmatrix}} = \frac{(2)(-8) - (-4)(4)}{(2)(-6) - (-4)(3)}$$

$$= \frac{-16 + 16}{-12 + 12} = \frac{0}{0}$$

So the system is dependent and has infinitely many solutions.

Try These

Evaluate each determinant.

1. $\begin{vmatrix} 3 & -2 \\ 4 & 5 \end{vmatrix}$

2. $\begin{vmatrix} 8 & -1 \\ -3 & 0 \end{vmatrix}$

3. $\begin{vmatrix} -3 & -4 \\ -2 & -1 \end{vmatrix}$

Solve each system of equation using Cramer's Rule.

4. $\begin{cases} 4x + y = -3 \\ 3x + 2y = 4 \end{cases}$

5. $\begin{cases} 2x = 3y + 9 \\ 5y = 2x - 11 \end{cases}$

6. $\begin{cases} y = 3x - 4 \\ y = -3x - 4 \end{cases}$

7. Discuss and Write Explain how Cramer's Rule is used to solve $\begin{cases} 5x + 3y = 9 \\ -5x - 3y = 12 \end{cases}$.

Describe the system.

Go to PRACTICE BOOK pages 161–162 for exercise sets.

Test Prep: Extended-Response Questions
Strategy: Answer All Parts

Extended-response questions often include multipart questions and require you to complete several steps for each part. *Show or describe your steps* to help organize your thoughts and to demonstrate your understanding. Use complete sentences to explain your reasoning.

Look at the sample test item.

Read the test item for a general idea of the problem.

- Reread the test item carefully. Identify and summarize the information you will need to solve the problem.
- Determine the steps you will need to answer each part.

    The system will consist of one equation for the total number of coins and one equation for the total value of the coins.

Solve the problem.

- Apply appropriate rules and properties.

Sample Test Item

Emmanuel has 43 coins consisting of n nickels and d dimes. The total value of the coins is \$3.05.

Part A Write a system of equations to find the number of nickels and dimes Emmanuel has.

Part B How many dimes does Emmanuel have?

Test-Taking Tips

- Reread the test item.
- Use the Test-Prep strategy.
- Apply appropriate rules, definitions, properties, or strategies.
- Analyze your answers.

Part A

1 Write an equation for the total number of coins.

nickels + dimes = total number of coins

$$n + d = 43$$

2 Write an equation for the total value of the coins.

value of nickels + value of dimes = total value

$$0.05n + 0.10d = 3.05$$

Answer: $\begin{cases} n + d = 43 \\ 0.05n + 0.10d = 3.05 \end{cases}$

Part B
Solve the system of equations.

1 Solve the first equation for n.

$$n + d = 43$$
$$n = 43 - d \leftarrow \text{Use the Subtraction Property of Equality.}$$

2 Substitute for n in the other equation. Solve.

$$0.05(43 - d) + 0.10d = 3.05$$
$$2.15 - 0.05d + 0.10d = 3.05 \leftarrow \text{Apply the Distributive Property.}$$
$$2.15 + 0.05d = 3.05$$
$$0.05d = 0.9$$
$$d = 18$$

Answer: Emmanuel has 18 dimes.

Item Analysis

Check your work. Make sure you have completed all parts of the item.

$43 - 18 = 25$ nickels; $25 \cdot \$0.05 = \$1.25$; $18 \cdot \$0.10 = \$1.80$; $\$1.25 + \$1.80 = \$3.05$ ✓

Try These

Solve. Be sure to show or describe your steps.

1. A car traveled 190 miles. For part of the trip, its speed was 35 miles per hour. For the other part, its speed was 55 miles per hour. The car traveled for a total of 4 hours.

    Part A Write a system of equations that you can use to find the number of hours the car traveled at each speed.

    Part B How long did the car travel at each speed?

Go to PRACTICE BOOK page 163 for exercise sets.

Operations with Polynomials

CHAPTER 7

In This Chapter You Will:

- Identify like monomials
- Write and classify polynomials in standard form
- Model the addition and subtraction of polynomials
- Add and subtract polynomials algebraically
- Multiply and divide monomials
- Raise a power or a product to a power and raise a quotient to a power

- Model binomial multiplication using area models
- Multiply binomials using the Distributive Property and using the FOIL method
- Multiply a polynomial by a monomial and by a binomial
- Apply the strategy: *Find a Pattern*
- Look for new vocabulary words **highlighted** in each lesson

Do You Remember?

- Terms of an algebraic expression that have exactly the same literal coefficients, raised to the same power, are called *like terms*.
- To simplify an algebraic expression, combine like terms by applying the properties of real numbers.
  - The Distributive Property of Multiplication Over Addition: When the same factor is distributed across two addends, the product does not change.

For Practice Exercises:

 Go to **PRACTICE BOOK, pp. 169–194**

For Chapter Support: ONLINE

 Go to **www.progressinmathematics.com**

- Skills Update Practice
- Practice Activities
- Audio Glossary
- Vocabulary Activities
- Technology Videos
- Enrichment Activities
- Electronic SourceBook

 VIRTUAL MANIPULATIVES

Critical Thinking

If you were able to line up average-sized atoms, it would take about 1×10^8 of these atoms to reach the length of 1 cm. About how many atoms of this size would it take to fill a cube that is 1 meter long on each side?

Introduction to Polynomials

Objective To identify like monomials • To write polynomials in standard form • To classify polynomials

▶ A **monomial** is an expression that is a number, a variable, or the product of a number and one or more variables with nonnegative exponents. It is a single term (with no + or − between terms). Monomials that are real numbers are called constants.

Monomials	Not Monomials
n	$x^2 + y$ ◀—The expression contains more than one term.
$-2x^5$	3^n ◀—A variable appears as an exponent.
abc	$\dfrac{3}{x}$ ◀—A variable appears in the denominator; $\dfrac{3}{x} = 3x^{-1}$
7	
$2x^2y^3z^4$	$\sqrt{2x}$ ◀—A variable appears under a radical sign.

▶ Monomials with the same variable(s) to the same power(s) are called *like terms*. If monomials are like terms, only their numerical coefficients can differ.

$3n^3$ and $-2n^3$ are like terms because only their numerical coefficients differ.
$5a$ and $5c$ are *not* like terms because the variables are not the same.

Examples

Are the following monomials like terms? Explain why or why not.

1 $4x^2$ and $-4x^3$

No, the exponents of the variables are not identical.

2 $-4ab, ab,$ and $2ab$

Yes, only their numerical coefficients differ.

3 $4y^5, 5,$ and $-y^5$

No, the terms do not all contain the same variables to the same power.

▶ A **polynomial** is a monomial or a sum of monomials. Each of the monomials is a *term* of the polynomial. To write a polynomial in its simplest form, you must *combine like terms*.

Simplify: $4a^2b - 7ab^2 + 5a^2b$

$(4a^2b + 5a^2b) - 7ab^2$ ◀—Apply the Commutative and Associative Properties to group like terms.

$(4 + 5)a^2b - 7ab^2$ ◀—Apply the Distributive Property.

$9a^2b - 7ab^2$ ◀—Simplify.

▶ A polynomial in simplest form can be classified by its number of terms.

Classifying Polynomials by Number of Terms		
Number of Terms	Classification	Examples
one	monomial	$x, y^4, xy, -3mn^2, c^4d^2, 10$
two	binomial	$2a + 3b, xy - 1, m^2 + 2m, c^3de - 2c^2d^5$
three	trinomial	$a + b - c, -2x^2 + 4xy + 3y^2, e^2 + 5e + 6$

▶ The degree of a monomial is the sum of the exponents of its variables. A term that has no variable part is called a constant term, or simply a constant. The degree of a constant term is 0.

The degree of $5x^3$ is 3.

The degree of $-mn^3$ is 4. ◀— $-mn^3 = -m^1n^3$; add $1 + 3$.

The degree of 9 is 0. ◀— $9 = 9x^0$.

> **Remember:** A variable written without an exponent has an exponent of 1.

▶ The degree of a polynomial is the greatest degree of any of its terms after it has been simplified.

Determine the degree of $x^3y - x^3y^2 + x^3y^4 + 2x^3y^2$.

- First simplify the polynomial.

  $x^3y - x^3y^2 + x^3y^4 + 2x^3y^2$

  $= x^3y + (-x^3y^2 + 2x^3y^2) + x^3y^4$

  $= x^3y + x^3y^2 + x^3y^4$

- Then find the degree of each term.

  $x^3y + x^3y^2 + x^3y^4$

  The degree of x^3y^1 is 4. ◀—Add $3 + 1$.

  The degree of x^3y^2 is 5. ◀—Add $3 + 2$.

  The degree of x^3y^4 is 7. ◀—Add $3 + 4$.

Because 7 is the greatest degree of the terms, the degree of $x^3y - x^3y^2 + x^3y^4 + 2x^3y^2$ is 7.

▶ A polynomial in one variable can also be classified by its degree.

	Classifying Polynomials by Degree	
Degree of Polynomial	**Classification**	**Examples**
one	linear	x, $-3m$, $5c - 2$, $10 + 7y$
two	quadratic	x^2, $2a^2$, $b^2 + 3b$, $x - x^2$, $4 + 2c + c^2$
three	cubic	x^3, $5b^3 + b$, $-2x^3 + 4x^2 + 3x + 6$

▶ A polynomial in one variable is written in *descending order* when the powers of the variable decrease from left to right. When a polynomial in one variable is in its simplest form and the terms are written in descending order, the polynomial is said to be in standard form. The coefficient of the first term of a polynomial in standard form is called the leading coefficient.

Write the polynomial $3x + 6 - x^5 + 12x - 2x^3 - 1$ in standard form.

$(3x + 12x) + (6 - 1) - x^5 - 2x^3$ ◀—Apply the Commutative and Associative Properties to group like terms.

$15x + 5 - x^5 - 2x^3$ ◀—Simplify.

$-x^5 - 2x^3 + 15x + 5$ ◀—Rearrange in descending order: $-x^5 - 2x^3 + 15x^1 + 5$.

-1 is the leading coefficient.

Try These

Classify each as a *monomial*, *binomial*, or *trinomial*. Then state its degree.

1. $3x^3y$ **2.** -19 **3.** $-12p^2q + 4p - 9p^3q^2$ **4.** $7s^4 + 2$

Write the polynomial in standard form.

5. $4k^2 - 2 + 11k^3 - 14k^3$ **6.** $-3x^2 + 5x - 9x^5 + x^2 + 5$

7. Discuss and Write Which phrase, cubic trinomial, cubic monomial, quadratic trinomial, or cubic binomial, best describes $-m^3 + 5m^2 - 7m - 5m^2$? Explain.

Go to   PRACTICE BOOK **Lesson 7-1 for exercise sets.**

Add and Subtract Polynomials

Objective To model the addition and subtraction of polynomials • To add and subtract polynomials algebraically

Michael is building a walkway, as shown in the diagram at the right. The parts of the walkway have areas in square units of x^2, $2x$, $2x^2$, $2x$, and x^2. What polynomial, in simplest form, represents the total area covered by the entire walkway?

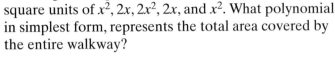

To find the polynomial, add the monomials:
$x^2 + 2x + 2x^2 + 2x + x^2$

► You can model addition of monomials with algebra tiles. The key at the right shows what the various tiles represent. Combine "like tiles" to combine like terms.

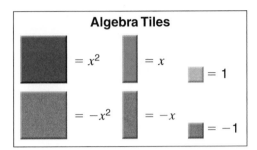

Algebra Tiles

$= x^2$ $= x$ $= 1$

$= -x^2$ $= -x$ $= -1$

1 Model each monomial.

2 Rearrange the tiles so that like tiles are next to each other.

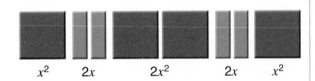

x^2 $2x$ $2x^2$ $2x$ x^2

$4x^2$ $4x$

3 Write the polynomial for the resulting model: $4x^2 + 4x$

So $x^2 + 2x + 2x^2 + 2x + x^2 = 4x^2 + 4x$.

► To add monomials algebraically, combine like terms.

$x^2 + 2x + 2x^2 + 2x + x^2 = (x^2 + 2x^2 + x^2) + (2x + 2x)$ ◄— Apply the Commutative and Associative Properties to group like terms.

$\qquad\qquad = \qquad 4x^2 \qquad + \qquad 4x$ ◄— Combine like terms.

So $4x^2 + 4x$ represents the total area covered by the entire walkway.

► To add polynomials, group like terms and then find the sum. You can add polynomials horizontally or vertically.

Find the sum: $(3x^2 + 4x - 2) + (2x^2 - x + 3) + (x^2 + 4)$

Method 1 Use a horizontal format.

Group and combine like terms.

$(3x^2 + 2x^2 + x^2) + (4x - x) + (-2 + 3 + 4)$
$\qquad 6x^2 \qquad + \quad 3x \quad + \qquad 5$

Method 2 Use a vertical format.

Align like terms in columns.
Add the columns separately.

$$3x^2 + 4x - 2$$
$$2x^2 - 1x + 3$$
$$\underline{+\ 1x^2 \qquad\ \ + 4}$$
$$6x^2 + 3x + 5$$

So the sum of $(3x^2 + 4x - 2) + (2x^2 - x + 3) + (x^2 + 4)$ is equal to $6x^2 + 3x + 5$.

▶ To find the additive inverse of a polynomial, find the opposite, or additive inverse, of each term.

Find the additive inverse of $-3x^3 - 7x^2 + 4x + 2$.

To find the additive inverse, find the polynomial that gives a sum of 0 when added to $-3x^3 - 7x^2 + 4x + 2$.

$$\begin{array}{r} -3x^3 - 7x^2 + 4x + 2 \\ + \qquad\qquad ? \\ \hline \end{array} \longrightarrow \begin{array}{r} -3x^3 - 7x^2 + 4x + 2 \\ + \quad 3x^3 + 7x^2 - 4x - 2 \\ \hline 0 \end{array}$$

Think ....
The sum of a number and its additive inverse is 0.
....

So the additive inverse of $-3x^3 - 7x^2 + 4x + 2$ is $3x^3 + 7x^2 - 4x - 2$.

▶ You can also model subtraction of monomials with algebra tiles. Remember, the red tiles represent negative terms.

Subtract: $4x^2 - x - 2x^2$

1 Model each monomial.

$4x^2 - x - 2x^2 = 4x^2 + (-x) + (-2x^2)$

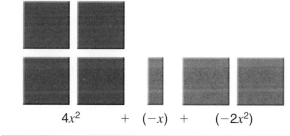

$$4x^2 \qquad + \quad (-x) \quad + \qquad (-2x^2)$$

2 Group tiles and their opposites. Remove zero pairs.

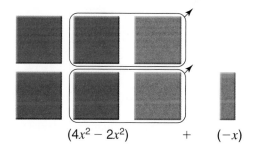

$$(4x^2 - 2x^2) \qquad + \qquad (-x)$$

3 Write the polynomial for the resulting model.

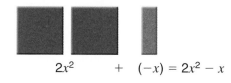

$$2x^2 \qquad + \quad (-x) = 2x^2 - x$$

▶ To subtract monomials algebraically, add the *opposite* of the monomial being subtracted.

$4x^2 - x - 2x^2 = 4x^2 + (-x) + (-2x^2)$ ◀— Add the opposites.

$\qquad = [4x^2 + (-2)x^2] + (-x)$ ◀— Apply the Commutative and Associative Properties to group like terms.

$\qquad = [4 + (-2)]x^2 + (-x)$ ◀— Apply the Distributive Property.

$\qquad = 2x^2 + (-x)$ ◀— Simplify.

$\qquad = 2x^2 - x$ ◀— Apply the definition of subtraction.

So $4x^2 - x - 2x^2 = 2x^2 - x$.

Continue Lesson ➡

▶ To subtract polynomials algebraically, add the *opposite* of the polynomial being subtracted. You can subtract polynomials horizontally or vertically.

Subtract: $(9y^2z + 11yz^2 - 15z^2) - (12y^2z - 3yz^2 + 2z^2)$

Method 1 Use a horizontal format.

Group and combine like terms.

$(9y^2z + 11yz^2 - 15z^2) - (12y^2z - 3yz^2 + 2z^2)$

$(9y^2z + 11yz^2 - 15z^2) + [-(12y^2z - 3yz^2 + 2z^2)]$ ◀—Add the opposite.

$(9y^2z + 11yz^2 - 15z^2) + (-12y^2z + 3yz^2 - 2z^2)$ ◀—Apply the opposite of sums and differences.

$(9y^2z - 12y^2z) + (11yz^2 + 3yz^2) + (-15z^2 - 2z^2)$ ◀—Apply the Commutative and Associative Properties to group like terms.

$(9 - 12)y^2z + (11 + 3)yz^2 + (-15 - 2)z^2$ ◀—Apply the Distributive Property.

$-3y^2z + 14yz^2 - 17z^2$ ◀—Simplify.

Method 2 Use a vertical format.

Align like terms in columns, and subtract the columns separately.
Subtract by adding the opposite.

$$
\begin{array}{l}
9y^2z + 11yz^2 - 15z^2 \\
- (12y^2z - \ 3yz^2 + \ 2z^2) \\
\hline
\end{array}
\quad \longrightarrow \quad
\begin{array}{l}
 \ 9y^2z + 11yz^2 - 15z^2 \\
+ \ -12y^2z + \ 3yz^2 - \ 2z^2 \quad \text{◀—Add the opposites.} \\
\hline
-3y^2z + 14yz^2 - 17z^2
\end{array}
$$

So $(9y^2z + 11yz^2 - 15z^2) - (12y^2z - 3yz^2 + 2z^2) = -3y^2z + 14yz^2 - 17z^2$.

▶ Similar methods can be used to combine more than two polynomials.

Simplify: $(4a^3 - a + 2) - (7a^3 + 2a) - (a^2 - a - 7)$

Method 1 Use a horizontal format.

$(4a^3 - a + 2) - (7a^3 + 2a) - (a^2 - a - 7)$

$(4a^3 - a + 2) + [-(7a^3 + 2a)] + [-(a^2 - a - 7)]$ ◀—Add the opposites.

$(4a^3 - a + 2) + (-7a^3 - 2a) + (-a^2 + a + 7)$ ◀—Apply the opposite of sums and differences.

$(4a^3 - 7a^3) - a^2 + (-a - 2a + a) + (2 + 7)$ ◀—Apply the Commutative and Associative Properties to group like terms.

$(4 - 7)a^3 - a^2 + (-1 - 2 + 1)a + 9$ ◀—Apply the Distributive Property.

$-3a^3 - a^2 - 2a + 9$ ◀—Combine like terms.

Method 2 Use a vertical format.

$$
\begin{array}{l}
 4a^3 - \ a + 2 \\
- (7a^3 + 2a) \\
 - (a^2 - \ a - 7) \\
\hline
\end{array}
\quad \longrightarrow \quad
\begin{array}{l}
 \ 4a^3 - \ a + 2 \\
 \ -7a^3 - 2a \\
+ -a^2 + \ a + 7 \\
\hline
-3a^3 - a^2 - 2a + 9
\end{array}
$$
Add the opposites.

So $(4a^3 - a + 2) - (7a^3 + 2a) - (a^2 - a - 7) = -3a^3 - a^2 - 2a + 9$.

Examples

1 Subtract $(-n^3 - 4n^2 + 2n)$ from the sum of $(7n^3 + 3n - 1)$ and $(5n^3 - n^2 + 8n - 9)$.

$[(7n^3 + 3n - 1) + (5n^3 - n^2 + 8n - 9)] - (n^3 - 4n^2 + 2n)$

$[(7n^3 + 3n - 1) + (5n^3 - 1n^2 + 8n - 9)] + [-(n^3 - 4n^2 + 2n)]$ ←—Add the opposite.

$(7n^3 + 3n - 1) + (5n^3 - 1n^2 + 8n - 9) + (-n^3 + 4n^2 - 2n)$ ←—Apply the opposite of sums and differences.

$(7n^3 + 5n^3 - n^3) + (-n^2 + 4n^2) + (3n + 8n - 2n) + (-1 - 9)$ ←—Group like terms.

$11n^3 + 3n^2 + 9n - 10$ ←—Combine like terms.

So $[(7n^3 + 3n - 1) + (5n^3 - n^2 + 8n - 9)] - (n^3 - 4n^2 + 2n) = 11n^3 + 3n^2 + 9n - 10$.

2 The perimeter of the polygon $ABCD$ at the right is represented by $12x - 9$. Write an expression for the length of $\overline{AD}$.

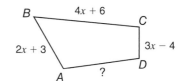

- Find the sum of the lengths of $\overline{AB}, \overline{BC},$ and $\overline{CD}$.

$\begin{array}{r} 2x + 3 \\ 4x + 6 \\ + 3x - 4 \\ \hline 9x + 5 \end{array}$

- Subtract the sum of the lengths of $\overline{AB}, \overline{BC},$ and $\overline{CD}$ from the perimeter of $ABCD$.

$\begin{array}{r} 12x - 9 \\ - (9x + 5) \\ \hline \end{array}$ $\longrightarrow$ $\begin{array}{r} 12x - 9 \\ + -9x - 5 \\ \hline 3x - 14 \end{array}$

So $3x - 14$ represents the length of $\overline{AD}$.

Try These

Simplify.

1. $2m + 3n + 6mn + 5m + mn$

2. $4 + 2x^2 - 3x - 2x^2 - 9$

3. $(-4p^4 - p^3 + 6p^2 - p) - (7p^3 + 5p^2 + p - 4)$

4. $(2t^3 - 3t^2 + 6t - 2) + (7t^3 + 5t^2 + t - 4)$

5. From the sum of $(2j^3 + 5jk^2 - 8k^3)$ and $(-4j^3 - 3j^2k - k^3)$, subtract $(j^3 - 9j^2k + 4jk^2 - k^3)$.

6. If $MNOP$ is a rectangle, write the expression that represents its perimeter.

P _____7x − y_____ O
x + 3y
M _____ N

7. The perimeter of $\triangle PRQ$ is represented by $15x - 1$. Find an expression that represents the length of $\overline{PQ}$.

R ___6x + 5___ Q
4x − 8
P

8. Discuss and Write Write two polynomials with a difference of $3x^2 - 3x - 2$. Explain your answer.

Go to PRACTICE BOOK **Lesson 7-2 for exercise sets.**

Multiply a Polynomial by a Monomial

Objective To multiply monomials • To raise a power or product to a power • To multiply a polynomial by a monomial

The rectangular mat at the right has its length and width represented by the expressions $4x$ and $2x$, respectively. What expression represents the area of the mat?

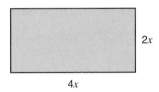

To find the area, multiply: $(4x)(2x)$

▶ You can use an area model to model multiplication of two monomials. The given factors represent the length and width of the rectangles, and the area of the new rectangle represents their product.

① Model a rectangle with a width of $2x$ and a length of $4x$, as shown in the diagram.

② Count the number of x^2 units. The rectangle has eight x^2 units. Its area is $8x^2$ units.

$(4x)(2x) = 8x^2$

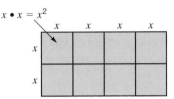

$x \bullet x = x^2$

.Think...........
$\ell = 4x = x + x + x + x$
$w = 2x = x + x$

So $8x^2$ is the expression that represents the area of the mat.

▶ To multiply two monomials algebraically, multiply the coefficients. Then multiply the variables using the Law of Exponents for Multiplication.

Remember:
Law of Exponents for Multiplication
$a^m \bullet a^n = a^{m+n}$

Multiply: $(-5x^2y)(7x^3y^4)$

$(-5x^2y)(7x^3y^4) = (-5 \bullet 7)(x^2 \bullet x^3)(y \bullet y^4)$ ◀— Multiply the coefficients and multiply the variables.

$= -35x^{2+3}\,y^{1+4}$ ◀— Apply the Law of Exponents for Multiplication.

$= -35x^5y^5$ ◀— Simplify.

▶ You can use the definition of an exponent and the Law of Exponents for Multiplication to raise a power to a power.

Simplify: $(m^2)^3$

$(m^2)^3 = m^2 \bullet m^2 \bullet m^2$ ◀— Write the three factors of m^2.

$= m^{2+2+2}$ ◀— Apply the Law of Exponents for Multiplication.

$= m^6$ ◀— Simplify.

Since $6 = 2 \bullet 3$, then $(m^2)^3 = (m)^{2(3)} = m^6$. This result suggests the Law of Exponents for Powers.

_____ **Key Concept** _____
Law of Exponents for Powers
$(a^m)^n = a^{m(n)}$, where m and n are integers

Examples

Simplify using a single exponent.

① $(p^5)^4$

$(p^5)^4 = p^{5(4)} = p^{20}$

② $(9y^3)(y^4)^2$

$(9y^3)(y^4)^2 = (9y^3)(y^{4(2)}) = 9(y^3 \bullet y^8)$

$= 9y^{3+8} = 9y^{11}$

▶ You can also use the definition of an exponent and the Law of Exponents for Powers to raise a product to a power.

Simplify: $(x^2y^3)^2$

$(x^2y^3)^2 = (x^2y^3)(x^2y^3)$ ◀—List the factors of the power.

$\quad = (x^2 \bullet x^2)(y^3 \bullet y^3)$ ◀—Apply the Commutative and Associative Properties to group like factors.

$\quad = (x^2)^2(y^3)^2$ ◀—Write each group of like factors using exponents.

$\quad = x^{2(2)} \bullet y^{3(2)}$ ◀—Apply the Law of Exponents for Powers.

$\quad = x^4y^6$ ◀—Simplify.

The above result suggests the Law of Exponents for a Power of a Product.

Key Concept

Law of Exponents for a Power of a Product

$(ab)^m = a^m b^m$, where m is an integer

Examples

1 Simplify. $(-3g^3h^2)^3$

$(-3g^3h^2)^3 = (-3)^{1(3)}g^{3(3)}h^{2(3)}$

$\quad = (-3)^3g^9h^6$

$\quad = -27g^9h^6$

2 Simplify. $-2(m^3n)^2(-2mn^2)^3$

$-2(m^3n)^2(-2mn^2)^3 = -2[m^{3(2)}n^{1(2)}][(-2)^{1(3)}m^{1(3)}n^{2(3)}]$

$\quad = -2(m^6n^2)(-8m^3n^6)$

$\quad = (-2 \bullet -8)(m^6 \bullet m^3)(n^2 \bullet n^6)$

$\quad = 16(m^{6+3})(n^{2+6})$

$\quad = 16m^9n^8$

▶ To multiply a polynomial by a monomial algebraically, use these steps:

• Apply the Distributive Property to distribute the monomial across the terms of the polynomial.

• Multiply the monomials to simplify.

Multiply: $3a^2b^3(-7ab^2 - 3a^2b)$

$3a^2b^3(-7ab^2 - 3a^2b) = 3a^2b^3(-7ab^2) + 3a^2b^3(-3a^2b)$ ◀—Apply the Distributive Property.

$\quad = 3(-7)(a^2 \bullet a)(b^3 \bullet b^2) + 3(-3)(a^2 \bullet a^2)(b^3 \bullet b)$ ◀—Apply the Commutative and Associative Properties.

$\quad = -21(a^{2+1})(b^{3+2}) - 9(a^{2+2})(b^{3+1})$ ◀—Apply the Law of Exponents for Multiplication.

$\quad = -21a^3b^5 - 9a^4b^4$ ◀—Simplify.

Try These

Simplify.

1. $(5s^2t^2)(-9s^2t)$

2. $(2c^3d^3)^2(5c^{10})$

3. $40x^3y^3 + (-5xy)(\frac{3}{20}xy)^2$

4. $-8ab^3(3a^3b - 2a^2b^2 - ab^3)$

5. $2uv(u^2 + uv - v^2) + (4u^3v - u^2v^2 + 7uv^3)$

6. Discuss and Write Explain the difference between simplifying $-3(x^5y)^2$ and simplifying $(-3x^5y)^2$.

Go to ▶ **PRACTICE BOOK Lesson 7-3 for exercise sets.**

Model Binomial Multiplication

Objective To model binomial multiplication using area models

Mrs. Herrera enlarged her square patio by adding 3 feet to its width and 4 feet to its length. What polynomial represents the area, in square feet, of the expanded patio?

To find the polynomial that represents the area, write the binomials that represent the dimensions of the expanded patio, and then find their product.

Let x = the length of a side of the original patio.

$x + 3$ = the width of the expanded patio

$x + 4$ = the length of the expanded patio

$(x + 3)(x + 4)$ = the area of the expanded patio

▶ You can use an area model to show the product of two binomials.

- Draw a rectangle with a length of $(x + 4)$ and a width of $(x + 3)$. In order to find the area of the rectangle, divide the rectangle into 4 regions, a square and 3 rectangles, as shown in the figure at the right.

- Find the area of each region.

  $x \cdot x = x^2 \qquad x \cdot 4 = 4x$

  $3 \cdot x = 3x \qquad 3 \cdot 4 = 12$

- Find the sum of the areas of the 4 regions.

  $x^2 + 4x + 3x + 12 = x^2 + 7x + 12$

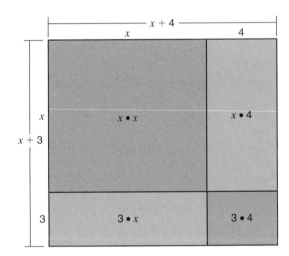

So $x^2 + 7x + 12$ is the polynomial that represents the area, in square feet, of the expanded patio.

▶ Although area is nonnegative, the area model can be used for expressions that are positive or negative.

Find the product: $(x + 1)(x - 2)$

- Draw a rectangle with a length of $(x + 1)$ and a width of x. The area of the rectangle is $x(x + 1)$ or $x^2 + x$.

- Divide the rectangle into 3 rectangles, as shown in the figure at the right. Find the area of each rectangle.

  $(x - 2)(x + 1) \qquad 2(x) = 2x \qquad 2(1) = 2$

- Subtract $(x^2 + x) - (2x + 2)$ to find the product $(x - 2)(x + 1)$.

  $(x - 2)(x + 1) = (x^2 + x) - (2x + 2)$

  $= x^2 + (x - 2x) - 2 = x^2 - x - 2$

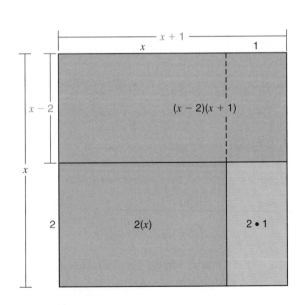

So the product of $(x - 2)(x + 1)$ is $x^2 - x - 2$.

Examples

Find each product.

1 $(2x - 3)(x + 5)$

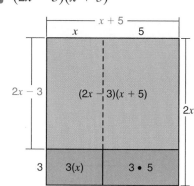

To find $(2x - 3)(x + 5)$,
subtract $(2x^2 + 10x) - (3x + 15)$.

$(2x - 3)(x + 5) = 2x(x + 5) - (3x + 15)$
$\qquad\qquad\qquad = 2x^2 + 10x - 3x - 15$
$\qquad\qquad\qquad = 2x^2 + 7x - 15$

So $(2x - 3)(x + 5) = 2x^2 + 7x - 15$.

2 $(4x - 1)(3x - 2)$

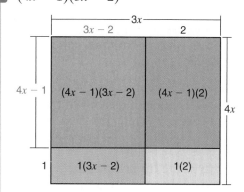

To find $(4x - 1)(3x - 2)$,
subtract $(4x)(3x) - (8x - 2 + 3x - 2 + 2)$.

$(4x - 1)(3x - 2) = (4x)(3x) - (8x - 2 + 3x - 2 + 2)$
$\qquad\qquad\qquad = 12x^2 - (11x - 2)$
$\qquad\qquad\qquad = 12x^2 - 11x + 2$

So $(4x - 1)(3x - 2) = 12x^2 - 11x + 2$.

3 $(x + 2)(x + 2)$

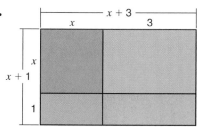

To find $(x + 2)(x + 2)$, add the areas of the 4 regions.

$(x + 2)(x + 2) = x^2 + 2x + 2x + 4$
$\qquad\qquad\qquad = x^2 + 4x + 4$

So $(x + 2)(x + 2) = x^2 + 4x + 4$.

Try These

Write the binomial expressions modeled by each diagram. Then find each product.

1.

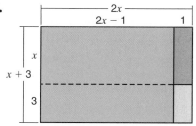

2.

Find each product. Use an area model.

3. $(2x + 5)(x + 3)$ **4.** $(6x - 1)(x + 6)$ **5.** $(x - 4)(4x - 1)$ **6.** $(5x - 2)(2x - 5)$

7. Discuss and Write Mel models $(20 + 8)(30 + 2)$ and Gary models $(30 - 2)(30 + 2)$
to show $(28)(32)$ using an area model. Will the products be the same? Explain.

Multiply Binomials

Objective To multiply binomials using the Distributive Property • To multiply binomials using the FOIL method

Ted plans to frame a 4-inch by 6-inch photograph. If the frame is of uniform width, what polynomial can represent the area of the framed photograph?

To find the polynomial that can represent the area, write the binomials that represent the dimensions of the framed photograph, and then find their product.

Let x = the width of the frame.

$2x + 4$ = the width of the framed photograph

$2x + 6$ = the length of the framed photograph

Then $(2x + 6)(2x + 4)$ represents area of the framed photograph.

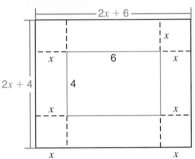

▶To multiply two binomials, apply the Distributive Property. You can multiply two binomials horizontally or vertically.

Method 1 Multiply horizontally.

$(2x + 6)(2x + 4) = (2x + 6)2x + (2x + 6)4$ ◀—Apply the Distributive Property.

$= 2x(2x) + 6(2x) + 2x(4) + 6(4)$ ◀—Apply the Distributive Property.

$= 4x^2 + 12x + 8x + 24$ ◀—Simplify.

$= 4x^2 + 20x + 24$ ◀—Combine like terms.

Method 2 Multiply vertically.

Remember:
Align like terms vertically.

$2x + 4$
$\times\ 2x + 6$
$4x^2 + 12x$ ◀—Apply the Distributive Property: $2x(2x + 6) = 2x(2x) + 2x(6)$
$\quad\quad 8x + 24$ ◀—Apply the Distributive Property: $4(2x + 6) = 4(2x) + 4(6)$
$4x^2 + 20x + 24$ ◀—Combine like terms.

So the area of the framed photograph is $4x^2 + 20x + 24$.

▶One way to multiply two binomials is to use **FOIL**, a memory device for applying the Distributive Property.

Multiply: $(4a + 3)(2a - 1)$

Key Concept

FOIL Method for Multiplying Two Binomials

To multiply two binomials, find the sum of the products of

F the first terms,
O the outer terms,
I the inner terms, and
L the last terms.

F	**O**	**I**	**L**
Multiply the FIRST terms.	Multiply the OUTER terms.	Multiply the INNER terms.	Multiply the LAST terms.

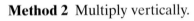

$(4a + 3)(2a - 1) = 4a(2a) +\quad 4a(-1)\quad +\quad 3(2a)\quad +\quad 3(-1)$

$= 8a^2 - 4a + 6a - 3$ ◀—Simplify.

$= 8a^2 + 2a - 3$ ◀—Combine like terms.

So $(4a + 3)(2a - 1) = 8a^2 + 2a - 3$.

Examples

Multiply.

1 $(2z - 5)(z - 8)$

$$\qquad \textbf{First} \qquad \textbf{Outer} \qquad \textbf{Inner} \qquad \textbf{Last}$$

$(2z - 5)(z - 8) = 2z(z) \quad + \quad 2z(-8) \quad + \quad (-5)z \quad + \quad (-5)(-8) \quad \leftarrow$ Apply the Distributive Property.

$\qquad\qquad\qquad = 2z^2 - 16z - 5z + 40 \quad \leftarrow$ Simplify.

$\qquad\qquad\qquad = 2z^2 - 21z + 40 \quad \leftarrow$ Combine like terms.

2 $(a - 1.1b)(a + 0.3b)$

$$\qquad\qquad \textbf{First} \quad \textbf{Outer} \quad \textbf{Inner} \qquad \textbf{Last}$$

$(a - 1.1b)(a + 0.3b) = a(a) + a(0.3b) + (-1.1b)(a) + (-1.1b)(0.3b) \quad \leftarrow$ Apply the Distributive Property.

$\qquad\qquad\qquad\quad = a^2 + 0.3ab - 1.1ab - 0.33b^2 \quad \leftarrow$ Simplify.

$\qquad\qquad\qquad\quad = a^2 - 0.8ab - 0.33b^2 \quad \leftarrow$ Combine like terms.

3 $\left(7r + \frac{1}{2}v\right)\left(9r + \frac{1}{2}v\right)$

$$\qquad\qquad \textbf{First} \quad \textbf{Outer} \quad \textbf{Inner} \qquad \textbf{Last}$$

$\left(7r + \frac{1}{2}v\right)\left(9r + \frac{1}{2}v\right) = 7r(9r) + 7r\left(\frac{1}{2}v\right) + \left(\frac{1}{2}v\right)(9r) + \left(\frac{1}{2}v\right)\left(\frac{1}{2}v\right) \quad \leftarrow$ Apply the Distributive Property.

$\qquad\qquad\qquad\quad = 63r^2 + \frac{7}{2}rv + \frac{9}{2}rv + \frac{1}{4}v^2 \quad \leftarrow$ Simplify.

$\qquad\qquad\qquad\quad = 63r^2 + 8rv + \frac{1}{4}v^2 \quad \leftarrow$ Combine like terms.

Think
$\frac{7}{2} + \frac{9}{2} = \frac{16}{2} = 8$

Try These

Multiply. Watch for the $+$ and $-$ signs.

1. $(x + 3)(3x + 1)$ **2.** $(c - 6)(c + 4)$ **3.** $(y - 3)(y - 2)$

4. $(p - 0.1)(p + 1.5)$ **5.** $\left(\frac{1}{3}d + 9\right)\left(\frac{1}{3}d - 12\right)$ **6.** $(9m - 2n)(2m - 3n)$

7. $(3w - 5)(5w - 3)$ **8.** $(7x + 5y)(6x - 11y)$ **9.** $\left(\frac{2}{5}e + 10f\right)\left(\frac{2}{5}e - 5f\right)$

10. $(0.2a - b)(0.1a + b)$ **11.** $(9w + 3y)(7w + y)$ **12.** $\left(\frac{2}{7}x - 7y\right)\left(\frac{1}{7}x - 14\right)$

Find the area of each polygon.

13. rectangle

$2x - 5$

$x + 5$

14. parallelogram

$x + 10$

$x - 1$

15. Discuss and Write Is the product of two binomials always a trinomial?
Explain. Give examples.

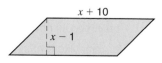

Go to PRACTICE BOOK Lesson 7-5 for exercise sets.

Multiply Polynomials

Objective To multiply a polynomial by a polynomial

Mr. Rizzo is designing storage crates. One type of crate has a base area of $(x^2 + 4x - 12)$ square inches and a height of $(x + 4)$ inches. What polynomial, in cubic inches, represents the volume of the crate?

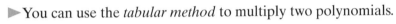

To find a polynomial that represents the volume of the crate, multiply its base area by its height.

$(x^2 + 4x - 12)(x + 4)$

▶ You can use the *tabular method* to multiply two polynomials.

1 Draw a table as shown at the right. Write the first polynomial on the left side of the table. Write the second polynomial above the table.

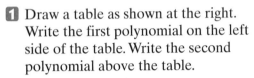

	x	$+4$
x^2	x^3	$+4x^2$
$+4x$	$+4x^2$	$+16x$
-12	$-12x$	-48

2 Mutiply the monomials in the rows and columns to complete the table.

3 Find the sum of the monomial products from the table by combining like terms.

$x^3 + (4x^2 + 4x^2) + (16x - 12x) - 48$

4 Simplify.

$x^3 + 8x^2 + 4x - 48$

So the volume of the crate is $(x^3 + 8x^2 + 4x - 48)$ cubic inches.

▶ You can also multiply two polynomials horizontally or vertically. To multiply two polynomials, apply the Distributive Property.

Multiply: $(x - 3)(2x^2 - x + 2)$

Method 1 Multiply horizontally.

$(x - 3)(2x^2 - x + 2) = x(2x^2 - x + 2) - 3(2x^2 - x + 2)$ ◄—Apply the Distributive Property.

$\qquad = x(2x^2) + x(-x) + x(2) + (-3)(2x^2) + (-3)(-x) + (-3)(2)$ ◄—Apply the Distributive Property.

$\qquad = 2x^3 - x^2 + 2x - 6x^2 + 3x - 6$ ◄—Simplify.

$\qquad = 2x^3 + (-x^2 - 6x^2) + (2x + 3x) - 6$ ◄—Apply the Commutative and Associative Properties.

$\qquad = 2x^3 - 7x^2 + 5x - 6$ ◄—Combine like terms.

Method 2 Multiply vertically.

> **Remember:**
> Align like terms vertically.

$\begin{array}{r} 2x^2 - x + 2 \\ \times \qquad x - 3 \\ \hline 2x^3 - x^2 + 2x \\ -6x^2 + 3x - 6 \\ \hline 2x^3 - 7x^2 + 5x - 6 \end{array}$

$2x^3 - x^2 + 2x$ ◄—Apply the Distributive Property: $x(2x^2 - x + 2) = x(2x^3) + x(-x) + x(2)$

$-6x^2 + 3x - 6$ ◄—Apply the Distributive Property: $-3(2x^2 - x + 2) = (-3)(2x^2) + (-3)(-x) + (-3)(2)$

$2x^3 - 7x^2 + 5x - 6$ ◄—Combine like terms.

So $(x - 3)(2x^2 - x + 2) = 2x^3 - 7x^2 + 5x - 6$.

Examples

Find each product.

1 $(n^2 + 2n + 6)(2n^2 - 3n - 3)$

$(n^2 + 2n + 6)(2n^2 - 3n - 3)$

$n^2(2n^2 - 3n - 3) + 2n(2n^2 - 3n - 3) + 6(2n^2 - 3n - 3)$

$n^2(2n^2) + n^2(-3n) + n^2(-3) + 2n(2n^2) + 2n(-3n) + 2n(-3) + 6(2n^2) + 6(-3n) + 6(-3)$

$2n^4 - 3n^3 - 3n^2 + 4n^3 - 6n^2 - 6n + 12n^2 - 18n - 18$

$2n^4 + (-3n^3 + 4n^3) + (-3n^2 - 6n^2 + 12n^2) + (-6n - 18n) - 18$

$2n^4 + n^3 + 3n^2 - 24n - 18$

2 $(5a^2 + 2a - 1)(3a^2 - 4a + 4)$

$$
\begin{array}{r}
3a^2 - 4a + 4 \\
\times\ 5a^2 + 2a - 1 \\
\hline
15a^4 - 20a^3 + 20a^2 \quad\leftarrow 5a^2(3a^2 - 4a + 4) = 5a^2(3a^2) + 5a^2(-4a) + 5a^2(4) \\
6a^3 - 8a^2 + 8a \quad\leftarrow 2a(3a^2 - 4a + 4) = 2a(3a^2) + 2a(-4a) + 2a(4) \\
- 3a^2 + 4a - 4 \quad\leftarrow (-1)(3a^2 - 4a + 4) = (-1)(3a^2) + (-1)(-4a) + (-1)(4) \\
\hline
15a^4 - 14a^3 + 9a^2 + 12a - 4 \quad\leftarrow \text{Combine like terms.}
\end{array}
$$

3 $(z + 1)(z + 2)(z - 3)$

• First find the product of $(z + 1)(z + 2)$.

$$
\begin{array}{r}
z + 1 \\
\times\ z + 2 \\
\hline
z^2 + z \\
+ 2z + 2 \\
\hline
z^2 + 3z + 2
\end{array}
$$

• Then multiply the product by $(z - 3)$.

$$
\begin{array}{r}
z^2 + 3z + 2 \\
\times\ z - 3 \\
\hline
z^3 + 3z^2 + 2z \\
- 3z^2 - 9z - 6 \\
\hline
z^3 \qquad - 7z - 6
\end{array}
$$

So $(z + 1)(z + 2)(z - 3) = z^3 - 7z - 6$.

Try These

Multiply. Use the tabular method.

1. $(y + 3)(y^2 + 3y + 9)$

2. $(3x + 2)(x^2 - 6x - 3)$

3. $(a^2 - 3a - 4)(a^2 - 4a - 3)$

Find each product.

4. $(d + 3)(d^2 + d + 12)$

5. $(n^2 + 6)(n^2 + n - 3)$

6. $(2b^2 + 5b + 1)(4b^2 - 7b + 9)$

7. $\begin{array}{r} e^2 + e - 8 \\ \times\ \quad e + 6 \\ \hline \end{array}$

8. $\begin{array}{r} v^2 + 6v - 3 \\ \times\ v^2 - v + 1 \\ \hline \end{array}$

9. $\begin{array}{r} 5x^2 + 2x - 10 \\ \times\ 6x^2 - 3x + 2 \\ \hline \end{array}$

10. Discuss and Write Explain how to find a polynomial, in simplest form, that represents the volume of the prism at the right.

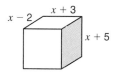

Remember: For a rectangular prism, volume = ℓwh.

Go to ▶ **PRACTICE BOOK Lesson 7-6 for exercise sets.**

Divide a Polynomial by a Monomial

Objective To divide monomials • To divide a polynomial by a monomial • To raise a quotient to a power

Minh is designing a tool shed with a floor that has a length of $4x$ feet and an area of $12x^2$ square feet. What expression represents the width of the floor?

To find an expression for the width of the floor of the shed, divide the area by the length.

$$\text{width} = \frac{\text{area}}{\text{length}} = \frac{12x^2}{4x}$$

Think.......
Area $= \ell w$

► You can use the Law of Exponents for Division to simplify quotients containing monomials.

To divide two monomials:

- First, divide the coefficients.
- Next, divide by subtracting the exponents of the variable factors with the same base.
- Then multiply the quotients obtained in the above steps.

Remember: Law of Exponents for Division

For $a \neq 0$ and m and n as integers,
$$\frac{a^m}{a^n} = a^{m-n}.$$

$$\frac{12x^2}{4x} = \frac{12}{4}\left(\frac{x^2}{x^1}\right) \quad \longleftarrow \frac{ab}{cd} = \left(\frac{a}{b}\right)\left(\frac{c}{d}\right); x = x^1$$

$$= 3(x^{2-1}) = 3x \quad \longleftarrow \text{Apply the Law of Exponents for Division; simplify.}$$

Check:
$$12x^2 \overset{?}{=} 4x(3x)$$
$$12x^2 = 12x^2 \text{ True}$$

So the expression $3x$ represents the width of the floor.

Examples

Find each quotient.

1 $-27a^4 \div 9a^2$

$$\frac{-27a^4}{9a^2} = \frac{\overset{3}{\cancel{-27}}}{\underset{1}{\cancel{9}}}\left(\frac{a^4}{a^2}\right)$$

$$= \frac{-3}{1}(a^{4-2})$$

$$= -3a^2$$

Check:
$$-27a^4 \overset{?}{=} 9a^2(-3a^2)$$
$$-27a^4 = -27a^4 \text{ True}$$

2 $6d^2e^6 \div 24de$

$$\frac{6d^2e^6}{24de} = \frac{\overset{1}{\cancel{6}}}{\underset{4}{\cancel{24}}}\left(\frac{d^2}{d}\right)\left(\frac{e^6}{e}\right)$$

$$= \frac{1}{4}(d^{2-1})(e^{6-1})$$

$$= \frac{1}{4}de^5$$

Check:
$$6d^2e^6 \overset{?}{=} 24de\left(\frac{1}{4}de^5\right)$$
$$6d^2e^6 = 6d^2e^6 \text{ True}$$

3 $-60rs^2t^3 \div (-15rt^2)$

$$\frac{-60rs^2t^3}{-15rt^2} = \frac{\overset{4}{\cancel{-60}}}{\underset{1}{\cancel{-15}}}\left(\frac{r}{r}\right)\left(\frac{s^2}{1}\right)\left(\frac{t^3}{t^2}\right)$$

$$= \frac{4}{1}(r^{1-1})(s^2)(t^{3-2})$$

$$= 4r^0s^2t = 4(1)s^2t$$

$$= 4s^2t$$

Check:
$$-60rs^2t^3 \overset{?}{=} -15rt^2(4s^2t)$$
$$-60rs^2t^3 = -60rs^2t^3 \text{ True}$$

► Dividing by a monomial is the same as multiplying by its reciprocal.

$$\frac{a+b}{c} = \frac{1}{c} \bullet (a+b) \quad \longleftarrow \text{Apply the definition of division.}$$

$$= \frac{1}{c} \bullet a + \frac{1}{c} \bullet b \quad \longleftarrow \text{Apply the Distributive Property.}$$

$$= \frac{a}{c} + \frac{b}{c} \quad \longleftarrow \text{Apply the definition of division.}$$

_____ Key Concept _____

Dividing a Polynomial by a Monomial

To divide a polynomial by a monomial, divide each term of the polynomial by the monomial divisor.
$$\frac{a+b}{c} = \frac{a}{c} + \frac{b}{c}, \text{ where } c \neq 0$$

Divide: $(8x^3 - 12x^2 + 20x) \div 4x$

$\dfrac{8x^3 - 12x^2 + 20x}{4x} = \left(\dfrac{8x^3}{4x}\right) - \left(\dfrac{12x^2}{4x}\right) + \left(\dfrac{20x}{4x}\right)$ ←—Divide each term of the polynomial by the monomial divisor.

$= (2x^{3-1}) - (3x^{2-1}) + (5x^{1-1})$ ←—Divide the coefficients; apply the Law of Exponents for Division to divide the variables.

$= 2x^2 - 3x + 5$ ←—Simplify.

..**Think**..

The number of terms in the polynomial dividend equals the number of terms in the quotient.

So $(8x^3 - 12x^2 + 20x) \div 4x = 2x^2 - 3x + 5$.

Check: $4x(2x^2 - 3x + 5) = 8x^3 - 12x^2 + 20x$

▶ You can use the definition of an exponent and the Law of Exponents for Powers to raise a *quotient to a power*.

Remember: Law of Exponents for Powers

$(a^m)^n = a^{m(n)}$, where m and n are integers

Simplify: $\left(\dfrac{x^3}{y^4}\right)^2$

$\left(\dfrac{x^3}{y^4}\right)^2 = \left(\dfrac{x^3}{y^4}\right)\left(\dfrac{x^3}{y^4}\right) = \dfrac{x^3(x^3)}{y^4(y^4)}$ ←—List the factors of the power. Multiply the numerators. Multiply the denominators.

$= \dfrac{(x^3)^2}{(y^4)^2} = \dfrac{(x)^{3(2)}}{(y)^{4(2)}} = \dfrac{x^6}{y^8}$ ←—Write each group of like factors using exponents. Then simplify by raising a power to a power.

The above result suggests the Law of Exponents for a Power of a Quotient.

___ Key Concept ___

Law of Exponents for a Power of a Quotient

$\left(\dfrac{a}{b}\right)^m = \dfrac{a^m}{b^m}$, where $b \neq 0$ and m is an integer

Examples

Simplify.

1 $\left(\dfrac{a^2}{b^5}\right)^3 = \dfrac{a^{2(3)}}{b^{5(5)}}$

$= \dfrac{a^6}{b^{25}}$

2 $\left(\dfrac{x^{-2}}{y^{-1}}\right)^{-3} = \dfrac{x^{-2(-3)}}{y^{-1(-3)}}$

$= \dfrac{x^6}{y^3}$

3 $\left(\dfrac{3c^0}{d^2}\right)^5 = \left(\dfrac{3 \cdot 1}{d^2}\right)^5$

$= \dfrac{3^5}{d^{2(5)}} = \dfrac{3^5}{d^{10}}$

Try These

Divide and check.

1. $30x^6 \div 6x^2$

2. $9a^4b^3c \div a^3b^3$

3. $-21u^5vw \div 3uvw^2$

4. $(3x^3 - 12x^2 + 6x) \div 6x$

5. $(4xy^3 + 3x^2y^4 + y^2) \div 4y^2$

6. $(27x^4y^5 - 18x^6y^4 - 36x^2y^2) \div 9x^2y^2$

Simplify.

7. $\left(\dfrac{m^4}{n^5}\right)^3$

8. $\left(\dfrac{a^{-4}}{b^{-5}}\right)^{-3}$

9. $\left(\dfrac{2w^0}{t^5}\right)^4$

10. $\dfrac{(4a^2b^3)^2(-ab^2)^3}{-(2a^2b^2)^2(a^3b)^2}$

11. **Discuss and Write** Describe and correct the error made in dividing the monomials, $20a^{10}b^8 \div 10a^5b^4 = 2a^2b^2$.

Go to PRACTICE BOOK **Lesson 7-7 for exercise sets.**

7-8 Divide Polynomials Using Long Division

Objective To divide a polynomial by a binomial

▶When you divide a polynomial by a binomial, you can use a long division process similar to the one you used for dividing whole numbers.

Divide: $(x^2 + 2x - 9) \div (x + 3)$

1 To find the first term of the quotient, divide the first term of the dividend, x^2, by the first term of the divisor, x.

$$\begin{array}{r} x \\ x+3{\overline{\smash{\big)}\,x^2 + 2x - 9}} \quad \leftarrow x^2 \div x = x\\ \underline{(-)\,x^2 + 3x} \quad \leftarrow \text{Multiply: } x(x+3)\\ -x \quad \leftarrow \text{Subtract.}\end{array}$$

Think
(1st term of quotient)(1st term of divisor) = (1st term of dividend)
$\underline{\ ?\ } \cdot x = x^2$

2 To find the next term of the quotient, divide the first term of the partial dividend, $-x$, by the first term of the divisor, x.

$$\begin{array}{r} x - 1 \quad \leftarrow -x \div x = -1\\ x+3{\overline{\smash{\big)}\,x^2 + 2x - 9}}\\ \underline{(-)\,x^2 + 3x} \quad\downarrow\\ -x - 9 \quad \leftarrow \text{Bring down } -9.\\ \underline{(-)\,-x - 3} \quad \leftarrow \text{Multiply: } -1(x+3)\\ -6 \quad \leftarrow \text{Subtract.}\end{array}$$

Think
(2nd term of quotient)(1st term of divisor) = (1st term of partial dividend)
$\underline{\ ?\ } \cdot x = -x$

So the quotient when $(x^2 + 2x - 9)$ is divided by $(x + 3)$ is $(x - 1)$, with a remainder of -6. The degree of the remainder is less than the degree of the divisor. Write the remainder over the divisor.

$$(x^2 + 2x - 9) \div (x + 3) = x - 1 + \frac{-6}{x + 3}$$

Check:
$$x^2 + 2x - 9 \stackrel{?}{=} (x-1)(x+3) - 6$$
$$\stackrel{?}{=} x^2 + 3x - x - 3 - 6$$
$$x^2 + 2x - 9 = x^2 + 2x - 9 \text{ True}$$

▶The dividend must contain every possible power of the variable. If one is missing, you need to insert placeholders for any missing variable term(s) in the dividend using 0 as the coefficient.

Find the quotient: $(y^3 + 15) \div (y - 5)$

$$\begin{array}{r} y^2 + 5y + 25\\ y-5{\overline{\smash{\big)}\,y^3 + 0y^2 + 0y + 15}} \quad \leftarrow y^3 + 15 = y^3 + 0y^2 + 0y + 15\\ \underline{(-)\,y^3 - 5y^2}\\ 5y^2 + 0y\\ \underline{(-)\,5y^2 - 25y}\\ 25y + 15\\ \underline{(-)\,25y - 125}\\ 140\end{array}$$

Check:
$$y^3 + 15 \stackrel{?}{=} (y-5)(y^2 + 5y + 25) + 140$$
$$\stackrel{?}{=} y^3 + 5y^2 + 25y - 5y^2 - 25y - 125 + 140$$
$$y^3 + 15 = y^3 + 15 \text{ True}$$

So $(y^3 + 15) \div (y - 5) = y^2 + 5y + 25 + \frac{140}{y - 5}$.

▶Before dividing, make sure to write all polynomials in standard form.

Divide: $(16y + 12y^2 + 5) \div (5 + 6y)$

$$
\begin{array}{r}
2y + 1 \\
6y + 5 \overline{)12y^2 + 16y + 5} \\
(-)\ \underline{12y^2 + 10y} \downarrow \\
6y + 5 \\
(-)\ \underline{6y + 5} \\
0
\end{array}
$$

←—Write both the dividend and divisor in standard form.

Check:

$16y + 12y^2 + 5 \overset{?}{=} (5 + 6y)(2y + 1)$

$ \overset{?}{=} 10y + 5 + 12y^2 + 6y$

$16y + 12y^2 + 5 = 16y + 12y^2 + 5$ True

So $(16y + 12y^2 + 5) \div (5 + 6y) = 2y + 1$.

Examples

1 $(20 - 22a + 3a^2) \div (a - 6)$

$$
\begin{array}{r}
3a - 4 \\
a - 6 \overline{)3a^2 - 22a + 20} \\
(-)\ \underline{3a^2 - 18a} \downarrow \\
-4a + 20 \\
(-)\ \underline{-4a + 24} \\
-4
\end{array}
$$

Check:

$20 - 22a + 3a^2 \overset{?}{=} (a - 6)(3a - 4) - 4$

$ \overset{?}{=} 3a^2 - 4a - 18a + 24 - 4$

$20 - 22a + 3a^2 = 20 - 22a + 3a^2$ True

So $(20 - 22a + 3a^2) \div (a - 6) = 3a - 4 + \dfrac{-4}{a - 6}$.

2 The product of two polynomials is $t^2 - 81$. If one polynomial is $t - 9$, what is the other one?

To find the other polynomial, divide:
$(t^2 - 81) \div (t - 9)$

So the other polynomial is $t + 9$.

$$
\begin{array}{r}
t + 9 \\
t - 9 \overline{)t^2 + 0t - 81} \\
(-)\ \underline{t^2 - 9t} \downarrow \\
9t - 81 \\
(-)\ \underline{9t - 81} \\
0
\end{array}
$$

Check:

$t^2 - 81$

$\overset{?}{=} (t - 9)(t + 9)$

$\overset{?}{=} t^2 + 9t - 9t - 81$

$= t^2 - 81$ True

Try These

Divide and check.

1. $(4x^2 + 3x - 6) \div (x + 2)$ **2.** $(3y^2 - 4y - 15) \div (y - 4)$ **3.** $(4w^2 - 44w + 121) \div (2w - 11)$

4. $(2b^2 - 9) \div (b + 3)$ **5.** $(n^3 - 5n - n^2 - 3) \div (n - 3)$ **6.** $(v - 5 - 4v^3) \div (3 - 2v)$

Solve.

7. The product of two polynomials is $12x^2 + 5x - 72$. If one polynomial is $3x + 8$, what is the other one?

8. Discuss and Write Explain the meaning of a remainder of 0 in long division of a polynomial by a binomial. Include an example in your explanation.

Go to   **PRACTICE BOOK Lesson 7-8 for exercise sets.**

Problem-Solving Strategy: Find a Pattern

Objective To solve problems using the strategy *Find a Pattern*

Problem 1: A diagonal of a polygon is a segment connecting nonadjacent vertices. How many diagonals does a 15-sided polygon have?

Read ▸ **Read to understand what is being asked.**

List the facts and restate the question.

Facts: A diagonal of a polygon is a segment that connects nonadjacent vertices.

Question: How many diagonals does a polygon with 15 sides have?

Plan ▸ **Select a strategy.**

Start with polygons with fewer sides and see if you can *Find a Pattern*.

Solve ▸ **Apply the strategy.**

First, draw polygons with 3, 4, 5, and 6 sides. Draw and count the diagonals.

Problem-Solving Strategies

1. Make a Drawing
2. Solve a Simpler Problem
3. Reason Logically
4. Consider Extreme Cases
5. Work Backward
6. **Find a Pattern**
7. Account for All Possibilities
8. Adopt a Different Point of View
9. Guess and Test
10. Organize Data

3 sides   4 sides   5 sides   6 sides
0 diagonals   2 diagonals   5 diagonals   9 diagonals

Record the number of sides and number of diagonals in a table and look for a pattern.

Sides	Diagonals
3	0
4	2
5	5
6	9

Notice that the number of diagonals increases by 2, then 3, then 4, and so on. Therefore, a 7-sided polygon would have $(9 + 5)$, or 14, diagonals; an 8-sided polygon would have $(14 + 6)$, or 20, diagonals; and so on.

You can use this pattern to write the sequence below.

0, 2, 5, 9, 14, 20, 27, 35, 44, 54, 65, 77, 90

The thirteenth term, 90, is the number of diagonals in a 15-sided polygon. (Remember, the first term is the number of diagonals in a 3-sided polygon.)

So a 15-sided polygon has 90 diagonals.

Check ▸ **Check to make sure your answer makes sense.**

As a check, observe a different pattern in the polygons above.

In each case, every vertex has the same *total* number of diagonals drawn from it, which is $(n - 3)$, where n is the number of sides. If those numbers are added, the result will be $\frac{1}{2}n(n - 3)$, since each diagonal has its endpoints at two vertices, not one.

So for a 15-gon, the number of diagonals is $\frac{1}{2}(15)(15 - 3)$, or 90. The answer checks.

Problem 2: A machine exactly divided 2^{51} grains of rice among 10 companies. Some grains were left over. Without using a handheld device, determine the number of grains left over.

Read ▸ **Read to understand what is being asked.**

List the facts and restate the question.

Facts: When 2^{51} is divided by 10, there is a remainder.

Question: What is the remainder?

Plan ▸ **Select a strategy.**

Note that, when *any* whole number is divided by 10, the remainder is the units digit of that number.
For example:

$$54 \div 10 = \frac{54}{10} = 5\frac{4}{10} \longrightarrow 5 \text{ R}4 \qquad 4768 \div 10 = \frac{4768}{10} = 476\frac{8}{10} \longrightarrow 476 \text{ R}8$$

So use the strategy, *Find a Pattern*, to find the units digit of 2^{51}.
Begin by finding the units digits of smaller powers of 2.

Solve ▸ **Apply the strategy.**

• Evaluate the first several powers of 2:

   $2^1 = 2$ $2^2 = 4$ $2^3 = 8$ $2^4 = 16$

   $2^5 = 32$ $2^6 = 64$ $2^7 = 128$ $2^8 = 256$

   $2^9 = 512$ $2^{10} = 1024$

• Find a pattern for units digits. The units digits appear to follow a repeating pattern:

   $2, 4, 8, 6, 2, 4, 8, 6, \ldots$

   Notice that as the exponent increases, the group of four units digits 2-4-8-6 repeats again and again.

• Find the units digits of 2^{51}.

   At 2^{48}, the cycle will have repeated 12 times (because $4 \cdot 12 = 48$).

   A new cycle begins with 2^{49}. The units digit of 2^{49} is 2, the units digit of 2^{50} is 4, and the units digit of 2^{51} is 8.

   So there will be 8 grains of rice left over.

Check ▸ **Check to make sure your answer makes sense.**

You can continue to generate powers of 2 to convince yourself that the pattern of units digits continues:

   $2^{10} = 1024$ $2^{11} = 2048$ $2^{12} = 4096$ $2^{13} = 8192$

   $2^{14} = 16,384$ $2^{15} = 32,768$

The pattern holds, so you can be fairly confident that your answer is correct.

Go to **PRACTICE BOOK Lesson 7-9 for exercise sets.**

Enrichment:
Pascal's Triangle and the Expansion of $(x + y)^n$

Objective To apply Pascal's Triangle to the coefficients of $(x + y)^n$ • To investigate other patterns in Pascal's Triangle

Patterns in the Expansion of $(x + y)^n$

▶ If you expand, or write as a sum of terms in an extended form, $(x + y)^n$ for whole number values of n, you will discover some interesting patterns. Look at the expansions of $(x + y)^n$ for $n = 0, 1, 2,$ and 3 below, and find some patterns.

$(x + y)^0 = 1$ $(x + y)^2 = x^2 + 2xy + y^2$

$(x + y)^1 = x + y$ $(x + y)^3 = x^3 + 3x^2y + 3xy^2 + y^3$

Blaise Pascal

- The expansion of $(x + y)^n$ has $n + 1$ terms. For example, the expansion of $(x + y)^2$ has 3 terms.

- The exponents of x start at n and decrease by 1 in each term until they reach 0. The exponents of y start at 0 and increase by 1 in each term until they reach n. For example, in the expansion of $(x + y)^3$, the exponents of x are 3, 2, 1, and 0, while the exponents of y are 0, 1, 2, and 3.

$(x + y)^3 = x^3 + 3x^2y + 3xy^2 + y^3 = x^3y^0 + 3x^2y^1 + 3x^1y^2 + x^0y^3$

▶ Another interesting pattern appears if you look at the *coefficients* of all four expansions, beginning with $(x + y)^0$. At the right, the coefficients are displayed in a triangular arrangement.

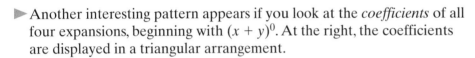

- The pattern is symmetric about a vertical line through the center.
- The numbers along the left and right sides are all 1s.
- The numbers "inside" the triangle—the 2 and the two 3s—are each the sum of the two numbers immediately above them, to the left and to the right.

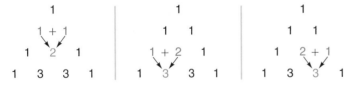

The triangle of coefficients above is the start of a very famous pattern of numbers, known as **Pascal's Triangle**, named for the French mathematician Blaise Pascal. The triangle can be extended indefinitely. The first row is known as Row 0. At the right, Row 0 through Row 8 are shown.

The numbers in Row n are the coefficients of the expansion of $(x + y)^n$.

For example, to expand $(x + y)^5$, use the coefficients found in Row 5 (the sixth row), and use the pattern in the exponents mentioned above.

$(x + y)^5 = x^5 + 5x^4y + 10x^3y^2 + 10x^2y^3 + 5xy^4 + y^5$

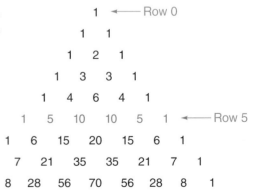

Powers of 2 and Pascal's Triangle

If you find the sum of the numbers in each row of Pascal's Triangle, you will get the *powers of 2*: 1, 2, 4, 8, 16, 32, and so on. This surprising result is related to the expansion of $(x + y)^n$. For example, because $2^5 = (1 + 1)^5$, you can find the value of 2^5 by substituting 1 for both x and y in the expansion of $(x + y)^5$, found on page 196.

$2^5 = (1 + 1)^5$
$\quad = 1^5 + 5(1)^4(1) + 10(1)^3(1)^2 + 10(1)^2(1)^3 + 5(1)(1)^4 + (1)^5$
$\quad = 1 + 5 + 10 + 10 + 5 + 1$
$\quad = 32$

So 2^5 is the sum of the coefficients in the expansion of $(x + y)^5$, the numbers in Row 5 of Pascal's Triangle.

Triangular and Square Numbers

The triangular numbers are the numbers related to the triangular patterns of dots shown below.

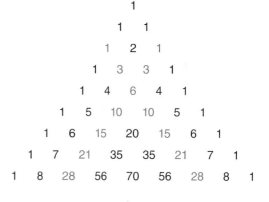

The triangular numbers appear in the *third diagonal of Pascal's Triangle*, as shown at the right.

You can also find the square numbers (perfect squares) along the third diagonal of Pascal's Triangle, by adding any two consecutive numbers.

For example, $1 + 3 = 4$, $3 + 6 = 9$, $6 + 10 = 16$, and so on.

Fibonacci Sequence

The Fibonacci Sequence is the sequence 1, 1, 2, 3, 5, 8, 13, 21, . . . Each term is the sum of the two terms before it. This sequence of numbers can also be found in Pascal's Triangle. Simply add the numbers in the "shallow" diagonals, as shown at the right.

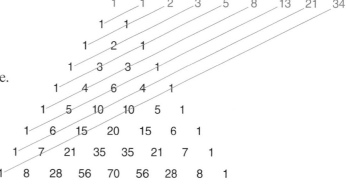

Try These

Solve.

1. Find Row 9 of Pascal's triangle.

2. Use your answer to exercise 1 to find 2^9.

Find the expansion.

3. $(a + b)^5$

4. $(x + 2)^3$

5. $(x - y)^4$

6. $(x + 2y)^3$

7. Discuss and Write Describe a pattern in Pascal's Triangle that is different from the ones mentioned in this lesson.

Test Prep: Multiple-Choice Questions

Strategy: Apply Mathematical Reasoning

To answer some test questions, you can *use a diagram to organize your thinking and to gather and summarize the information.* Pay close attention to labels and scales. Remember that a diagram is not always drawn to scale.

Look at the sample test item.

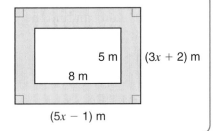
Read the whole test item, including the answer choices.

Examine titles, labels, and scales to interpret diagrams.

• Underline important words.

What is the area of the <u>shaded</u> region?

The *shaded* region is between the perimeters of the two rectangles.

• Restate the question in your own words.

Find the difference in the areas of the large rectangle and the small rectangle.

> **Test-Taking Tips**
>
> • Underline important words.
>
> • Restate the question.
>
> • Use the Test-Prep strategy.
>
> • Analyze and eliminate answer choices.

Solve the problem.

• Use the information given in the diagram.

Area of large rectangle	Area of small rectangle
$\ell w = (3x + 2)(5x - 1)$ ←Use the formula for area.	$\ell w = 8(5)$ ←Use the formula for area.
$\quad = 15x^2 - 3x + 10x - 2$ ←Multiply the binomials.	$\quad = 40$ ←Simplify.
$\quad = 15x^2 + 7x - 2$ ←Combine like terms.	

Subtract the area of the small rectangle from the area of the large rectangle.
$(15x^2 + 7x - 2) - 40 = 15x^2 + 7x - 42$ ←Combine like terms.

Item Analysis

Choose the answer.

• Analyze and eliminate answer choices. Watch out for distractors.

A. $(15x^2 - 42)$ m^2 ←The binomials were not multiplied correctly. Eliminate this choice.

B. $(15x^2 + 7x - 2)$ m^2 ←The area of the small rectangle was not subtracted. Eliminate this choice.

C. $(15x^2 + 7x + 38)$ m^2 ←The areas were added instead of subtracted. Eliminate this choice.

D. $(15x^2 + 7x - 42)$ m^2 ←This is the correct choice!

Try These

1. What is the area of the circle with the indicated diameter?

A. $(2\pi x^2 - 6\pi)$ ft^2 $\qquad$ **C.** $(\pi x^4 - 6\pi x^2 + 9\pi)$ ft^2

B. $(4\pi x^4 - 12\pi)$ ft^2 $\qquad$ **D.** $(4\pi x^4 - 24\pi x^2 + 36\pi)$ ft^2

$(2x^2 - 6)$ ft

Go to PRACTICE BOOK **page 189 for exercise sets.**

Factoring Polynomials

CHAPTER 8

In This Chapter You Will:

- Find the greatest common monomial factor of two or more monomials
- Factor polynomials using the greatest common monomial factor
- Factor quadratic trinomials when the leading coefficient is 1
- Factor quadratic trinomials when the leading coefficient is other than 1
- Square a binomial
- Factor a perfect-square trinomial
- Identify and factor binomials that are differences of two perfect squares
- Find products using mental math
- Factor polynomials by grouping
- Combine factoring techniques to factor a polynomial completely
- Solve problems using a variety of strategies
- Look for new vocabulary words **highlighted** in each lesson

Do You Remember?

- A factor is one of two or more numbers that are multiplied to form a product.
- The greatest common factor (GCF) of two or more numbers is the greatest number that is a factor of all the numbers.
- A polynomial is a monomial or a sum of monomials.

For Practice Exercises:

Go to PRACTICE BOOK, pp. 195–220

For Chapter Support: ONLINE

Go to www.progressinmathematics.com

- Skills Update Practice
- Practice Activities
- Audio Glossary
- Vocabulary Activities
- Technology Videos
- Enrichment Activities
- Electronic SourceBook

VIRTUAL MANIPULATIVES

Critical Thinking

Cicadas can live for several years underground. When they emerge, cicadas are preyed upon by birds and other insects. Praying mantises and certain wasps, with life cycles of 2, 3, 4, or 5 years, are predators that some species of cicada have adapted longer life cycles to avoid. Two longer life cycles of cicadas are between 11 and 19 years, and are whole numbers. What are they?

8-1

Common Monomial Factors

Objective To find the greatest common monomial factor of two or more monomials • To factor polynomials using the greatest common monomial factor

Find the greatest common monomial factor of $36x^2$ and $54x^3$.

▶ The greatest common monomial factor of two or more monomials is the product of all the integer and variable factors that are common to those monomials.

To find the *greatest common monomial factor* of two or more monomials:

- Write the prime factorization of each coefficient. Choose the least power of each prime factor that appears in all coefficients. The GCF is the product of those prime factors.

  GCF of 36 and 54: 18 ◄— $36 = 2^2 \cdot \underline{3^2}$; $54 = \underline{2} \cdot 3^3$; GCF: $2 \cdot 3^2 = 2 \cdot 9 = 18$

- Write the least power of each variable factor that appears in all the monomials. The GCF is the product of those variable factors.

  GCF of x^2 and x^3: x^2 ◄— x appears in both monomials; the least power of x is x^2.

  The greatest common monomial factor of the monomials is the product of these two results.

Greatest common monomial factor: $18x^2$

Examples

Find the greatest common monomial factor.

1 $4m^2n^2$ and m^3n

- GCF of 4 and 1: 1
- GCF of m^2 and m^3: m^2
- GCF of n^2 and n: n

Greatest common monomial factor: $1m^2n$, or m^2n

2 $6a^3c$, $12a^2c^2$, and $-36a^3c$

- GCF of 6, 12, and -36: 6
- GCF of a^3, a^2, and a^3: a^2
- GCF of c, c^2, and c: c

Greatest common monomial factor: $6a^2c$

▶ Factoring is the reverse process of multiplying. If a polynomial can be written as a product of factors, then it is factorable.

You can factor a polynomial by first finding the *greatest monomial* factor of the terms of the polynomial. Divide the polynomial by this factor to find the other factor, and then write the polynomial as the product of the two factors.

Factor using the greatest common monomial factor: $9x^2y^3 + 54x^3y$

- Find the greatest common monomial factor.

  GCF of 9 and 54: 9
  Least power of x: x^2; Least power of y: y
  Greatest common monomial factor: $9x^2y$

- Divide to find the other factor:

  $$\frac{9x^2y^3 + 54x^3y}{9x^2y} = \frac{9x^2y^3}{9x^2y} + \frac{54x^3y}{9x^2y} = y^2 + 6x$$

- Write as the product of the two factors.

  $9x^2y^3 + 54x^3y = 9x^2y(y^2 + 6x)$

So in factored form, $9x^2y^3 + 54x^3y = 9x^2y(y^2 + 6x)$.

▶ You can also use *partial factorization* to factor a polynomial *completely*. A polynomial is factored completely when it is expressed as a product of one or more polynomials that cannot be factored further.

Factor using partial factorization: $28x^5 + 70x^3$

• First factor $28x^5 + 70x^3$ using any common factor—for example, $7x^3$.

$$28x^5 + 70x^3 = 7x^3(4x^2) + 7x^3(10)$$
$$= 7x^3(4x^2 + 10)$$

.Think....................
$4x^2 + 10$ is still factorable.

• Then factor $4x^2 + 10$ using the remaining common factor, 2.

$$7x^3(4x^2 + 10) = 7x^3(2 \cdot 2x^2 + 2 \cdot 5)$$
$$= 2 \cdot 7x^3(2x^2 + 5)$$
$$= 14x^3(2x^2 + 5)$$

So in factored form, $28x^5 + 70x^3 = 14x^3(2x^2 + 5)$.

▶ A polynomial whose terms do not have a common factor other than 1 is called a prime polynomial.

Show that $27y^3 + 35$ is a prime polynomial.

Write each term as a product of prime factors.

$$27y^3 = 3^3 \cdot y^3 \qquad 35 = 5 \cdot 7$$

.Think....................
The terms have no common factor other than 1.

Greatest common monomial factor: 1

So $27y^3 + 35$ is a prime polynomial.

Example

1 Factor using the greatest monomial factor: $18x^3y^2z - 24x^2y^2 + 6xy^2$

$$18x^3y^2z - 24x^2y^2 + 6xy^2 = 6xy^2(3x^2z) + 6xy^2(-4x) + 6xy^2(1)$$ ←— Write each term as a product involving the greatest common monomial factor.

$$= 6xy^2(3x^2z - 4x + 1)$$ ←— Apply the Distributive Property.

So in factored form, $18x^3y^2z - 24x^2y^2 + 6xy^2 = 6xy^2(3x^2z - 4x + 1)$.

Try These

Factor each polynomial using the greatest monomial factor.

1. $x^3 + 2x^2$

2. $-3t^2 + 6t - 9$

3. $6r^3s - 6r^3$

4. $12x^3z^5 + 72x^5y^2z - 60x^2y$

5. $15a^2b^2 - 10ab + 5$

6. $x^2z + xz^2 - xz$

7. $-11n^3 - 22n^2$

8. $10a^3b^3 + 25a^2b^3 - 5a^2b$

9. $24x^2y - 18x^2y^2 - 12xy^2$

10. Discuss and Write Lee, Pat, and Terry each got a different answer when factoring $8x^2 + 12x + 4$. Lee's answer was $2(4x^2 + 6x + 2)$. Pat's answer was $4(2x^2 + 3x)$. Terry's answer was $4(2x^2 + 3x + 1)$. Which student factored the polynomial correctly? Describe the error in the other two students' answers.

Factor Trinomials: $ax^2 + bx + c$, $a = 1$

Objective To factor quadratic trinomials when the leading coefficient is 1

▶ To factor a trinomial of the form $x^2 + bx + c$, where b and c are nonzero integers, express the trinomial as a *product of two binomial factors*.

Since $x^2 + bx + c$ is a trinomial with the leading term x^2, the first terms of the binomial factors must each be x. The second terms of the binomial factors, when added together, must total to b (the coefficient of the linear term) and, when multiplied, must have a product of c (the constant term).

___Key Concept___

Factoring $x^2 + bx + c$

$x^2 + bx + c = (x + m)(x + n)$, when $m + n = b$, $mn = c$, and b and c are nonzero integers.

• $b > 0$ and $c > 0$

Factor: $x^2 + 7x + 12$

For $b = 7$ and $c = 12$: When c is positive, its factors have the same sign. When b is positive, both factors of c must be positive.

Use a table, like the one shown at the right, to list the factors of the constant term, 12, and then add the factors until you find the coefficient, 7, of the linear term.

The factors of 12 whose sum is 7 are 3 and 4.

So in factored form, $x^2 + 7x + 12 = (x + 3)(x + 4)$.

Check: $(x + 3)(x + 4) = x^2 + 4x + 3x + 12 = x^2 + 7x + 12$ ✓

Factors of 12	Sum of Factors
1, 12	13
2, 6	8
3, 4	7

• $b < 0$ and $c > 0$

Factor: $x^2 - 5x + 6$

For $b = -5$ and $c = 6$: When c is positive, its factors have the same sign. When b is negative, both factors of c must be negative.

Factors of 6	Sum of Factors
−1, −6	−7
−2, −3	−5

So in factored form, $x^2 - 5x + 6 = (x - 2)(x - 3)$.

Check: $(x - 2)(x - 3) = x^2 - 3x - 2x + 6$
$= x^2 - 5x + 6$ ✓

..Think.....................................
The sum of the numbers must be equal to −5.

$x^2 - 5x + 6 = (x - \square)(x - \square)$

The product of the numbers must be equal to 6.
The factors of 6 whose sum is −5 are −2 and −3.

• $b > 0$ and $c < 0$

Factor: $x^2 + 3x - 4$

For $b = 3$ and $c = -4$: When c is negative, its factors have opposite signs. When b is positive, the factor with the greater absolute value must be positive.

Factors of −4	Sum of Factors
1, −4	−3
−1, 4	3

So in factored form, $x^2 + 3x - 4 = (x - 1)(x + 4)$.

Check: $(x - 1)(x + 4) = x^2 - x + 4x - 4$
$= x^2 + 3x - 4$ ✓

..Think.....................................
The sum of the numbers must be equal to 3.

$x^2 + 3x - 4 = (x - \square)(x + \square)$

The product of the numbers must be equal to −4.
The factors of −4 whose sum is 3 are −1 and 4.

- $b < 0$ and $c < 0$

  Factor: $x^2 - 2x - 8$

  For $b = -2$ and $c = -8$: When c is negative, its factors have opposite signs. When b is negative, the factor with the greater absolute value must be negative.

  Use a table, such as the one shown at the right, to list the factors of the constant term, -8, and then add the factors until you find the coefficient, -2, of the linear term.

  The factors of -8 whose sum is -2 are 2 and -4.

  So in factored form, $x^2 - 2x - 8 = (x + 2)(x - 4)$.

Factors of −8	Sum of Factors
1, −8	−7
−1, 8	7
2, −4	−2

  Check: $(x + 2)(x - 4) = x^2 - 4x + 2x - 8$
  $$= x^2 - 2x - 8 \checkmark$$

Examples

1 Factor: $13x + x^2 + 42$

- Write the trinomial in standard form.

  $13x + x^2 + 42 \longrightarrow x^2 + 13x + 42$

- Factor the trinomial: $x^2 + 13x + 42$

Factors of 42	Sum of Factors
1, 42	43
2, 21	23
3, 14	17
6, 7	13

  .Think......
  The sum of the numbers must be equal to 13.

  $x^2 + 13x + 42 = (x + \square)(x + \square)$

  The product of the numbers must be equal to 42.
  The factors of 42 whose sum is 13 are 6 and 7.

So in factored form, $13x + x^2 + 42 = (x + 6)(x + 7)$.

Check: $(x + 6)(x + 7) = x^2 + 7x + 6x + 42$
$$= x^2 + 13x + 42$$
$$= 13x + x^2 + 42 \checkmark$$

2 Factor: $-x^2 - 8x + 20$

- Write the trinomial with leading term x^2.

  $-x^2 - 8x + 20 \longrightarrow -(x^2 + 8x - 20)$ ◄—Apply the Property of Opposite of Sums and Differences.

- Factor the trinomial: $x^2 + 8x - 20$

Factors of −20	Sum of Factors
−1, 20	19
−2, 10	8

  .Think.....
  What factors of -20 sum to 8 and include the factor whose greater absolute value is positive?
  The factors of -20 whose sum is 8 are -2 and 10.

So in factored form, $-x^2 - 8x + 20 = -(x - 2)(x + 10)$.

Check: $-(x - 2)(x + 10) = -(x^2 + 10x - 2x - 20)$
$$= -(x^2 + 8x - 20)$$
$$= -x^2 - 8x + 20 \checkmark$$

Continue Lesson ➡

▶Some quadratic trinomials with a leading term of x^2 can be in the form of $x^2 + bxy + cy^2$. To find the binomial factors of these trinomials, consider cy^2 as the constant term and by as the coefficient of the linear term.

Factor: $x^2 + 19xy + 60y^2$

Factors of $60y^2$	Sum of Factors
$1y, 60y$	$61y$
$2y, 30y$	$32y$
$3y, 20y$	$23y$
$4y, 15y$	$19y$

.Think........................
$b = 19y$ and $c = 60y^2$

What factors have a product of $60y^2$ and a sum of $19y$?

The factors of $60y^2$ whose sum is $19y$ are $4y$ and $15y$.

So in factored form, $x^2 + 19xy + 60y^2 = (x + 4y)(x + 15y)$.

Check: $(x + 4y)(x + 15y) = x^2 + 15xy + 4xy + 60y^2$
$= x^2 + 19xy + 60y^2$ ✓

Example

1 Factor: $x^2 - 4xy - 21y^2$

Factors of $-21y^2$	Sum of Factors
$y, -21y$	$-20y$
$3y, -7y$	$-4y$

.Think........................
Consider $x^2 - 4xy - 21y^2$ as being in the form of $x^2 + bx + c$, where $b = -4y$ and $c = -21y^2$.
What factors have a product of $-21y^2$ and a sum of $-4y$?

The factors of $-21y^2$ whose sum is $-4y$ are $3y$ and $-7y$.
So in factored form, $x^2 - 4xy - 21y^2 = (x + 3y)(x - 7y)$.

Check: $(x + 3y)(x - 7y) = x^2 - 7xy + 3xy - 21y^2$
$= x^2 - 4xy - 21y^2$ ✓

▶You can also find the binomial factors of a trinomial of the form $x^2 + bx + c$, where b and c are nonzero integers, by *Guess and Test*. Use a table to list all the possible factors, and then multiply using FOIL.

Factor: $x^2 - 5x - 14$

- Write possible binomial factors using the factors of -14, the constant term, that add up to -5, the coefficient of the linear term.
- Multiply using FOIL to find the correct factors.

.Think........................
$c < 0$, so the factors of c must have opposite signs.

Possible answers include:

Possible Binomial Factors	Multiply Using FOIL	Trinomial Product
$(x + 1)(x - 14)$	$x^2 - 14x + 1x - 14$	$x^2 - 13x - 14$
$(x + 2)(x - 7)$	$x^2 - 7x + 2x - 14$	$x^2 - 5x - 14$

So in factored form, $x^2 - 5x - 14 = (x + 2)(x - 7)$.

Check: $(x + 2)(x - 7) = x^2 - 7x + 2x - 14$
$= x^2 - 5x - 14$ ✓

Examples

1 Factor: $h^2 + 6h + 9$

.Think.

$h^2 + 6h + 9 = (h + \square)(h + \square)$

Possible Binomial Factors	Multiply Using FOIL	Trinomial Product
$(h + 1)(h + 9)$	$h^2 + 9h + 1h + 9$	$h^2 + 10h + 9$
$(h + 3)(h + 3)$	$h^2 + 3h + 3h + 9$	$h^2 + 6h + 9$

So in factored form, $h^2 + 6h + 9 = (h + 3)(h + 3)$.

2 Factor: $x^2 + 9xy + 20y^2$

.Think.

$x^2 + 9xy + 20y^2 = (x + \square)(x + \square)$

Possible Binomial Factors	Multiply Using FOIL	Trinomial Product
$(x + 1y)(x + 20y)$	$x^2 + 20xy + 1xy + 20y^2$	$x^2 + 21xy + 20y^2$
$(x + 2y)(x + 10y)$	$x^2 + 10xy + 2xy + 20y^2$	$x^2 + 12xy + 20y^2$
$(x + 4y)(x + 5y)$	$x^2 + 5xy + 4xy + 20y^2$	$x^2 + 9xy + 20y^2$

So in factored form, $x^2 + 9xy + 20y^2 = (x + 4y)(x + 5y)$.

▶ Not all quadratic trinomials of the form $x^2 + bx + c$ can be factored using integers. If you find that no factor pairs for c have a sum of b, then the trinomial cannot be factored into binomials with integer coefficients. This kind of trinomial is called a *prime polynomial*.

Show that $x^2 + 7x + 9$ cannot be factored using integers.

Factors of 9	Sum of Factors
1, 9	10
3, 3	6

.Think.

What factors of 9 have a sum of 7?

There is no integer solution.

Since none of the factor pairs add up to 7, $x^2 + 7x + 9$ cannot be factored using integers. So $x^2 + 7x + 9$ is a prime polynomial.

Try These

Factor each trinomial, if possible. Check by multiplying the factors. If the trinomial cannot be factored using integers, label it *prime*.

1. $x^2 + 13x + 22$

2. $y^2 - 3y - 2$

3. $n^2 + n - 20$

4. $16d + d^2 + 28$

5. $-n^2 + 10n - 21$

6. $p^2 - 5rp - 24r^2$

Factor each trinomial by *Guess and Test*.

7. $w^2 + 9w + 8$

8. $m^2 - 13m - 48$

9. $d^2 - 11d + 28$

10. $p^2 + 21pq + 110q^2$

11. $x^2 + 8xy - 65y^2$

12. $c^2 - 3cd - 70d^2$

13. Discuss and Write Explain why, when factoring $x^2 + 10x + 21$, it is not necessary to check the sum of the pairs -1 and -21 or -3 and -7.

Go to PRACTICE BOOK **Lesson 8-2 for exercise sets.**

Factor Trinomials: $ax^2 + bx + c$, $a \neq 1$

Objective To factor quadratic trinomials when the leading coefficient is other than 1

▶ To factor quadratic trinomials of the form $ax^2 + bx + c$, $a \neq 1$, find factors of ac (the product of a, the coefficient of the first term, and c, the constant term) that will have a sum of b, the coefficient of the linear term.

$ac = 7(3) = 21$

Factor: $7x^2 + 22x + 3$

$a = 7$, $b = 22$, and $c = 3$ $7x^2 + 22x + 3$

Find two integers that are factors of 21 and that have a sum of 22.

$7x^2 + (\underline{\ ?\ } + \underline{\ ?\ })x + 3$

Use a table, like the one shown at the right, to find the two integers that are factors of 21 and that have a sum of 22.

Factors of 21	Sum of Factors
1, 21	22

$7x^2 + 22x + 3 = 7x^2 + (1 + 21)x + 3$ ◄—Select the factors 1 and 21.

$\qquad = 7x^2 + x + 21x + 3$ ◄—Use the Distributive Property.

$\qquad = (7x^2 + x) + (21x + 3)$ ◄—Group terms that have a common monomial factor.

$\qquad = x(7x + 1) + 3(7x + 1)$ ◄—Factor each binomial using the greatest common monomial factor.

$\qquad = (x + 3)(7x + 1)$ ◄—Use the Distributive Property.

So in factored form, $7x^2 + 22x + 3 = (x + 3)(7x + 1)$.

Check: $(x + 3)(7x + 1) = 7x^2 + x + 21x + 3 = 7x^2 + 22x + 3$ ✓

Examples

1 Factor: $9y^2 + 30y - 11$

$a = 9$, $b = 30$, and $c = -11$

Think
$ac = 9(-11) = -99$
Find two integers that are factors of -99 and that have a sum of 30.

Factors of −99	Sum of Factors
−1, 99	98
−3, 33	30

$9y^2 + 30y - 11 = 9y^2 + (-3 + 33)y - 11$ ◄—Select the factors −3 and 33.

$\qquad = 9y^2 - 3y + 33y - 11$ ◄—Use the Distributive Property.

$\qquad = (9y^2 - 3y) + (33y - 11)$ ◄—Group terms that have a common monomial factor.

$\qquad = 3y(3y - 1) + 11(3y - 1)$ ◄—Factor each binomial using the greatest common monomial factor.

$\qquad = (3y + 11)(3y - 1)$ ◄—Use the Distributive Property.

So in factored form, $9y^2 + 30y - 11 = (3y + 11)(3y - 1)$.

Check: $(3y + 11)(3y - 1) = 9y^2 - 3y + 33y - 11 = 9y^2 + 30y - 11$ ✓

2 Factor: $10m^2 - 43mn + 28n^2$

$a = 10, b = -43n$, and $c = 28n^2$

.Think.....................
$ac = 10(28n^2) = 280n^2$
Find two factors of $280n^2$
that have a sum of $-43n$.

Factors of $280n^2$	Sum of Factors
$-1n, -280n$	$-281n$
$-2n, -140n$	$-142n$
$-4n, -70n$	$-74n$
$-5n, -56n$	$-61n$
$-7n, -40n$	$-47n$
$-8n, -35n$	$-43n$

$$10m^2 - 43mn + 28n^2 = 10m^2 + (-8n - 35n)m + 28n^2$$
$$= 10m^2 - 8mn - 35mn + 28n^2$$
$$= (10m^2 - 8mn) - (35mn - 28n^2)$$
$$= 2m(5m - 4n) - 7n(5m - 4n)$$
$$= (2m - 7n)(5m - 4n)$$

So in factored form, $10m^2 - 43mn + 28n^2 = (2m - 7n)(5m - 4n)$.

Check: $(2m - 7n)(5m - 4n) = 10m^2 - 8mn - 35mn + 28n^2$
$$= 10m^2 - 43mn + 28n^2 \checkmark$$

▶ You can also find the binomial factors of a quadratic trinomial of the form $ax^2 + bx + c, a \neq 1$, by using the strategy *Guess and Test*. Use a table to list all the possible binomial factors, and then multiply using FOIL.

Factor: $3x^2 + 4x - 7$

- Write possible binomial factors using the factors of 3, the coefficient of the first term, and -7, the constant term.

- Look for combinations of factors that have a sum of 4, the coefficient of the linear term. Multiply using FOIL to find the correct factors.

Think...
$c < 0$, so factors of c must have opposite signs.

Possible answers include:

Factors of 3	Factors of -7	Multiply Using FOIL	Trinomial Product
$(3x\ )(1x\ )$	$(3x + 1)(1x - 7)$	$3x^2 - 21x + 1x - 7$	$3x^2 - 20x - 7$
	$(3x - 1)(1x + 7)$	$3x^2 + 21x - 1x - 7$	$3x^2 + 20x - 7$
	$(3x + 7)(1x - 1)$	$3x^2 - 3x + 7x - 7$	$3x^2 + 4x - 7$

So in factored form, $3x^2 + 4x - 7 = (3x + 7)(x - 1)$.

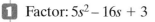

1 Factor: $5s^2 - 16s + 3$

.Think...
$b < 0$, so both factors of c must be negative.

Factors of 5	Factors of 3	Multiply Using FOIL	Trinomial Product
$(5s\ )(1s\ )$	$(5s - 1)(1s - 3)$	$5s^2 - 15s - 1s + 3$	$5s^2 - 16s + 3$

So in factored form, $5s^2 - 16s + 3 = (5s - 1)(s - 3)$.

Continue Lesson ➡

2

Factor: $7x^2 + 27x + 18$

Think..
$b > 0$, so both factors of c must be positive.

Factors of 7	Factors of 18	Multiply Using FOIL	Trinomial Product
$(7x\ )(1x\ )$	$(7x + 1)(1x + 18)$	$7x^2 + 126x + 1x + 18$	$7x^2 + 127x + 18$
	$(7x + 18)(1x + 1)$	$7x^2 + 7x + 18x + 18$	$7x^2 + 25x + 18$
	$(7x + 2)(1x + 9)$	$7x^2 + 63x + 2x + 18$	$7x^2 + 65x + 18$
	$(7x + 9)(1x + 2)$	$7x^2 + 14x + 9x + 18$	$7x^2 + 23x + 18$
	$(7x + 3)(1x + 6)$	$7x^2 + 42x + 3x + 18$	$7x^2 + 45x + 18$
	$(7x + 6)(1x + 3)$	$7x^2 + 21x + 6x + 18$	$7x^2 + 27x + 18$

So in factored form, $7x^2 + 27x + 18 = (7x + 6)(x + 3)$.

3

Factor: $-11x - 6 + 10x^2$

$-11x - 6 + 10x^2 \longrightarrow 10x^2 - 11x - 6$ $\longleftarrow$ Write the trinomial in standard form.

Think..
$c < 0$, so the factors of c must have opposite signs.

Factors of 10	Factors of -6	Multiply Using FOIL	Trinomial Product
$(1x\ )(10x\ )$	$(1x + 1)(10x - 6)$	$10x^2 - 6x + 10x - 6$	$10x^2 + 4x - 6$
	$(1x - 6)(10x + 1)$	$10x^2 + 1x - 60x - 6$	$10x^2 - 59x - 6$
	$(1x + 2)(10x - 3)$	$10x^2 - 3x + 20x - 6$	$10x^2 + 17x - 6$
	$(1x - 3)(10x + 2)$	$10x^2 + 2x - 30x - 6$	$10x^2 - 28x - 6$
$(2x\ )(5x\ )$	$(2x + 1)(5x - 6)$	$10x^2 - 12x + 5x - 6$	$10x^2 - 7x - 6$
	$(2x - 6)(5x + 1)$	$10x^2 + 2x - 30x - 6$	$10x^2 - 28x - 6$
	$(2x + 2)(5x - 3)$	$10x^2 - 6x + 10x - 6$	$10x^2 + 4x - 6$
	$(2x - 3)(5x + 2)$	$10x^2 + 4x - 15x - 6$	$10x^2 - 11x - 6$

So in factored form, $-11x - 6 + 10x^2 = (2x - 3)(5x + 2)$.

▶ Not every trinomial of the form $ax^2 + bx + c, a \neq 1$, can be factored with integer coefficients. If the trinomial cannot be factored using integers, then the trinomial is a prime polynomial.

Show that $5m^2 - 13m + 2$ cannot be factored using integers.

$a = 5, b = -13, c = 2$

$ac = 5(2) = 10$

Find two factors whose product is 10 and whose sum is -13. Since the sum of the factors has to be negative, both factors of 10 have to be negative.

Factors of 10	Sum of Factors
$-10, -1$	-11
$-5, -2$	-7

Since none of the factor pairs have a sum of -13, $5m^2 - 13m + 2$ cannot be factored using integers.

Think........................
There are no factors of 10
whose sum is -13.

So $5m^2 - 13m + 2$ is a prime polynomial.

Example

1 Write the polynomial shown by the area model at the right, and then factor it.

• Write the polynomial by finding the sum of the areas of the four rectangles.

$2x^2 + 5x + 4x + 10 = 2x^2 + 9x + 10$

• Factor the polynomial.

$a = 2, b = 9, c = 10$

$ac = 2(10) = 20$

Find two factors whose product is 20 and whose sum is 9. Since the sum of the factors is positive, both factors of 20 have to be positive.

Factors of 20	Sum of Factors
1, 20	21
2, 10	12
4, 5	9

$2x^2 + 9x + 10 = 2x^2 + (4 + 5)x + 10$ ←—Select the factors 4 and 5.

$= 2x^2 + 4x + 5x + 10$ ←—Use the Distributive Property.

$= (2x^2 + 4x) + (5x + 10)$ ←—Group terms that have a common monomial factor.

$= 2x(x + 2) + 5(x + 2)$ ←—Factor each binomial using the greatest common monomial factor.

$= (2x + 5)(x + 2)$ ←—Use the Distributive Property.

The area model represents the polynomial $2x^2 + 9x + 10$, which is factored as $(2x + 5)(x + 2)$.

Try These

Factor each trinomial. Check by multiplying the factors.

1. $2y^2 + 11y - 6$

2. $11x^2 + 21x - 2$

3. $3n^2 - 20n + 12$

4. $3a^2 - a - 4$

5. $-12y + 9 + 4y^2$

6. $4s^2 + 12st + 5t^2$

7. $3m^2 + 8m + 5$

8. $6x^2 - 19x + 15$

9. $3a^2 - 7ab - 6b^2$

Show that each trinomial is a prime polynomial.

10. $9x^2 - 9x + 2$

11. $3e^2 + 3e - 4$

12. $10s^2 + 21st + 6$

Write the polynomial shown by each area model, and then factor.

13.

14.

15. Discuss and Write For what positive values of b can the polynomial $3x^2 + bx + 5$ be factored with integer coefficients? Explain.

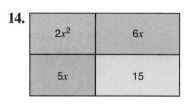

Go to PRACTICE BOOK **Lesson 8-3 for exercise sets.**

Special Product and Factoring:
$(a \pm b)^2 = a^2 \pm 2ab + b^2$

Objective To square a binomial • To factor a perfect-square trinomial

A square patio is bordered on two sides by a flower bed that is 3 feet wide. If the length of a side of the patio is x feet, what expression, in simplest form, represents the area of the larger square?

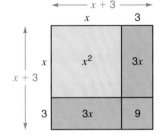

To find the expression, simplify: $(x + 3)^2$

> **Remember:**
> Area of a Square:
> $A = s^2$

$(x + 3)^2 = (x + 3)(x + 3)$

$\qquad$ **F $\quad$ O $\quad$ I $\quad$ L**

$\qquad = x^2 + 3x + 3x + 9 = x^2 + 6x + 9$

The expression $x^2 + 6x + 9$ represents the area of the larger square.

▶ The square of a binomial is a perfect-square trinomial. It is a special product.

$(x + 3)^2$ is a square of a binomial, and $x^2 + 6x + 9$ is a perfect-square trinomial.

Simplify: $(3x - 5)^2$

$(3x - 5)^2 = (3x - 5)(3x - 5)$

$\qquad$ **F $\quad$ O $\quad$ I $\quad$ L**

$\qquad = 9x^2 - 15x - 15x + 25 = x^2 - 30x + 25$

▶ In each case, the square of a binomial consists of the *square of the first term,* plus or minus *twice the product of both of its terms,* plus the *square of the last term.*

___ **Key Concept** ___

**The Square of a Binomial
(Perfect-Square Trinomial)**
$(a + b)^2 = a^2 + 2ab + b^2$
$(a - b)^2 = a^2 - 2ab + b^2$

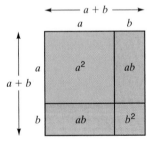

$(a + b)^2$
$a^2 + ab + ab + b^2$
$a^2 + 2ab + b^2$

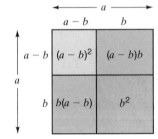

$(a - b)^2$
$a^2 - (a - b)b - b(a - b) - b^2$
$a^2 - ab + b^2 - ab + b^2 - b^2$
$a^2 - 2ab + b^2$

Examples

1 Simplify: $(2n - 1)^2$

Square the first term.	Add twice the product of the terms.	Square the last term.
↓	↓	↓
$(2n)^2$ $-$	$2(2n)(1)$ $+$	$(1)^2$
$4n^2$ $-$	$4n$ $+$	1

$(2n - 1)^2 = 4n^2 - 4n + 1$

2 Simplify: $(7x + 5y)^2$

Square the first term.	Add twice the product of the terms.	Square the last term.
↓	↓	↓
$(7x)^2$ $+$	$2(7x)(5y)$ $+$	$(5y)^2$
$49x^2$ $+$	$70xy$ $+$	$25y^2$

$(7x + 5)^2 = 49x^2 + 70xy + 25y^2$

▶The rules for squaring binomials can be used to identify and factor perfect-square trinomials.

Determine whether $x^2 - 14x + 49$ is a perfect-square trinomial. If so, factor it.

A trinomial is a perfect square if:

$x^2 - 14x + 49$

- The first and last terms are perfect squares.

$x \cdot x - 2(x \cdot 7) + 7 \cdot 7$

x^2 and 49 are perfect squares.
$-14x = -2(\sqrt{x^2})(\sqrt{49})$
$= -2(x)(7)$

- The middle term is twice the product of one factor from the first term and one factor from the last term.

$x^2 - 2(x)(7) + 7^2$
$(x - 7)^2$
$x^2 - 14x + 49$ is a perfect-square trinomial.

So $x^2 - 14x + 49 = (x - 7)(x - 7) = (x - 7)^2$.

Examples

Determine whether the trinomial is a perfect-square trinomial. If so, factor it. If not, explain why not.

1 $25y^2 + 30y + 9$

$5y \cdot 5y - 2(5y \cdot 3) + 3 \cdot 3$

$(5y)^2 + 2(5y)(3) + 3^2$

$(5y + 3)^2$

Check: $(5y + 3)^2 = (5y + 3)(5y + 3)$

$= 25y^2 + 15y + 15y + 9$

$= 25y^2 + 30y + 9$ ✓

2 $t^2 - 10t + 100$

$t \cdot t - 2(t \cdot 10) + 10 \cdot 10$

$t^2 - 10t + 100$ is not a perfect-square trinomial because $-2(t \cdot 10) \neq -10t$.

3 $z^2 - 24zw + 144w^2$

$z \cdot z - 2(z \cdot 12w) + 12w \cdot 12w$

$z^2 - 2(z)(12w) + (12w)^2$

$(z - 12w)^2$

Check: $(z - 12w)^2 = (z - 12w)(z - 12w)$

$= z^2 - 12zw - 12zw + 144w^2$

$= z^2 - 24zw + 144w^2$ ✓

Try These

Square each binomial.

1. $(d + 8)^2$

2. $(y - 11)^2$

3. $[5x + (-4y)]^2$

4. $(3w + 11)^2$

Determine if each trinomial is a perfect square. If so, factor it. If not, explain why not.

5. $x^2 - 24x + 144$

6. $y^2 + 20y + 101$

7. $81p^2 + 18pq + q^2$

8. $4n^2 - 6n + 9$

9. $w^2 - 26wx + 169x^2$

10. $9m^2 + 30mn + 25n^2$

11. $h^2 - 10h + 100$

12. $4c^2 - 60c + 225$

13. Discuss and Write Determine all values of k that make $36x^2 + kx + 25$ a perfect-square trinomial. Explain your answer.

 PRACTICE BOOK Lesson 8-4 for exercise sets.

Special Product and Factoring:
$(a + b)(a - b) = a^2 - b^2$

Objective To identify and factor binomials that are differences of two perfect squares
• To multiply numbers mentally by using the difference of two squares

Dominic and his neighbors are considering two plans for their community garden. One is a square garden that is x feet on each side. The other is a rectangle with a length that is 6 feet longer than the sides of the square garden and a width that is 6 feet shorter than the sides of the square garden. How do the areas of the two gardens compare?

To compare the areas, first find the areas of the gardens, and then subtract.

Square Garden

x | x

$A = x^2$ ←—Area $= s^2$

Rectangular Garden

$x - 6$ | $x + 6$

$A = (x + 6)(x - 6)$ ←—Area $= \ell w$

$\quad = x^2 - 6x + 6x - 36$ ←—Multiply.

$\quad = x^2 - 36$ ←—Simplify.

Compare: $x^2 - (x^2 - 36) = 36$

The area of the rectangular garden is 36 square feet less than the square garden.

► Another *special product* is the result of multiplying the sum of two terms by the difference of the same two terms. Look for patterns in the resulting products.

The "outer" and "inner" terms of the FOIL multiplication are additive inverses. Their sum is zero. The product of the sum and the difference of the same two terms is the *square of the first* term minus the *square of the second* term. Such a product is called the difference of two squares.

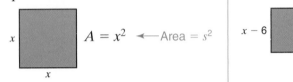

$(a + b)(a - b)$

$= a(a + b) - ab - b^2$

$= a^2 + ab - ab - b^2$

$= a^2 - b^2$

Key Concept

The Difference of Two Squares

$(a + b)(a - b) = a^2 - b^2$

The product of the sum and the difference of the same two terms is the difference of their squares.

Examples

1 Multiply: $\left(8w + \frac{1}{2}\right)\left(8w - \frac{1}{2}\right)$

$(a + b)(a - b) = a^2 - b^2$

$\left(8w + \frac{1}{2}\right)\left(8w - \frac{1}{2}\right) = (8w)^2 - \left(\frac{1}{2}\right)^2$

$\qquad\qquad\qquad = 64w^2 - \frac{1}{4}$

2 Multiply: $(5m + 6n)(5m - 6n)$

$(a + b)(a - b) = a^2 - b^2$

$(5m + 6n)(5m - 6n) = (5m)^2 - (6n)^2$

$\qquad\qquad\qquad = 25m^2 - 36n^2$

▶ You can factor a difference of two squares as the product of two binomials that are the sum and the difference of the same two terms.

To determine whether a binomial is a difference of two squares, the first and second terms must be perfect squares.

Determine whether $x^2 - 225$ is a difference of two squares. If so, factor it.

$x^2 - 225 = x^2 - 15^2$ ◀——The first and second terms are perfect squares.

So $x^2 - 225$ is a difference of two squares.

In factored form, $x^2 - 225 = (x + 15)(x - 15)$.

Check:

$(x + 15)(x - 15) = x^2 - 15x + 15x - 225$

$= x^2 - 225$ ✓

Examples

Factor.

1 $\frac{1}{4}n^2 - 169$

$\frac{1}{4}n^2 - 169 = \left(\frac{1}{2}n\right)^2 - (13)^2$

$= \left(\frac{1}{2}n + 13\right)\left(\frac{1}{2}n - 13\right)$

2 $0.16x^2 - 0.25y^2$

$0.16x^2 - 0.25y^2 = (0.4x)^2 - (0.5y)^2$

$= (0.4x + 0.5y)(0.4x - 0.5y)$

▶ The difference of two squares can be used to multiply numbers mentally.

Show a method for finding the product of 106 and 94 mentally.

Since $106 = 100 + 6$ and $94 = 100 - 6$, the product of $(106)(94)$ can be expressed as $(100 + 6)(100 - 6)$.

$(106)(94) = (100 + 6)(100 - 6)$

$= 100^2 - 6^2 = 10,000 - 36$

$= 9964$

So the product of 106 and 94 is 9964.

Try These

Multiply.

1. $(c + 14)(c - 14)$

2. $(n + 11)(n - 11)$

3. $(-d + 1)(-d - 1)$

4. $(7x + 9y)(7x - 9y)$

5. $(a + 0.3h)(a - 0.3h)$

6. $\left(\frac{1}{5}w + \frac{3}{7}k\right)\left(\frac{1}{5}w - \frac{3}{7}k\right)$

Factor.

7. $t^2 - 144$

8. $36m^2 - n^2$

9. $25q^2 - 256t^2$

10. $4n^2 - \frac{1}{100}$

11. $1.69x^2 - 4$

12. $0.64y^2 - 0.81d^4$

13. Discuss and Write Explain how to use the rule for the difference of two squares to multiply $49 \cdot 51$.

Go to PRACTICE BOOK Lesson 8-5 for exercise sets.

Factor by Grouping

Objective To factor a polynomial by grouping

▶ You can apply the Distributive Property to factor a polynomial with a common binomial factor in the same way you factor a polynomial with a common monomial factor.

Factor: $2x(x - 5) - 3(x - 5)$

$2x(x - 5) - 3(x - 5) = 2x(x - 5) - 3(x - 5)$ ◄—Identify the common binomial factor, $(x - 5)$.

$= (2x - 3)(x - 5)$ ◄—Apply the Distributive Property.

So in factored form, $2x(x - 5) - 3(x - 5) = (2x - 3)(x - 5)$.

Example

1 Factor: $p(p - 2q) + (p - 2q)$

$p(p - 2q) + (p - 2q) = p(p - 2q) + 1(p - 2q)$ ◄—$(p - 2q) = 1(p - 2q)$

$= p(p - 2q) + 1(p - 2q)$ ◄—Identify the common binomial factor, $(p - 2q)$.

$= (p + 1)(p - 2q)$ ◄—Apply the Distributive Property.

So in factored form, $p(p - 2q) + (p - 2q) = (p + 1)(p - 2q)$.

▶ When a polynomial contains four or more terms, you can sometimes factor by grouping if there are two groups of terms that have the same binomial factor.

Factor: $3x^3 - 6x^2 + 2x - 4$

$(3x^3 - 6x^2) + (2x - 4)$ ◄—Arrange in groups with common factors.

$3x^2(x - 2) + 2(x - 2)$ ◄—Factor the GCF from each group.

$(3x^2 + 2)(x - 2)$ ◄—Apply the Distributive Property.

So in factored form, $3x^3 - 6x^2 + 2x - 4 = (3x^2 + 2)(x - 2)$.

Check:

$(3x^2 + 2)(x - 2) =$

F   O   I   L

$3x^3 - 6x^2 + 2x - 4$ ✓

Example

Factor the polynomial by grouping. Check your answer.

1 $12a^3 + 16a^2b + 9ab^2 + 12b^3$

$(12a^3 + 16a^2b) + (9ab^2 + 12b^3)$ ◄—Arrange in groups with common factors.

$4a^2(3a + 4b) + 3b^2(3a + 4b)$ ◄—Factor the GCF from each group.

$(4a^2 + 3b^2)(3a + 4b)$ ◄—Apply the Distributive Property.

So in factored form, $12a^3 + 16a^2b + 9ab^2 + 12b^3 = (4a^2 + 3b^2)(3a + 4b)$.

Check:

$(4a^2 + 3b^2)(3a + 4b) =$

F   O   I   L

$12a^3 + 16a^2b + 9ab^2 + 12b^3$ ✓

▶Sometimes a common binomial factor of a polynomial cannot be found by grouping the first two terms and the second two terms. Try grouping the first and third terms or the first and fourth terms.

Factor: $2r^5 + 2 + r^2 + 4r^3$

$(2r^5 + 2) + (r^2 + 4r^3)$ ◀——Arrange in groups with common factors.

$2(r^5 + 1) + r^2(1 + 4r)$ ◀——Factor out the GCF.

There is no common binomial factor. Use the Commutative and Associative Properties of Equality to rearrange and group the terms differently.

$(2r^5 + 4r^3) + (r^2 + 2)$ ◀——Group the first and fourth terms.

$2r^3(r^2 + 2) + 1(r^2 + 2)$ ◀——Factor out the GCF.

$(2r^3 + 1)(r^2 + 2)$ ◀——Apply the Distributive Property.

Check: F   O   I   L
$(2r^3 + 1)(r^2 + 2) = 2r^5 + 4r^3 + r^2 + 2$

$= 2r^5 + 2 + r^2 + 4r^3$ ✓

▶You can solve factoring problems by grouping.

The area of the rectangle shown at the right is $(x^2 + xy - 6x - 6y)$ square feet. The length is $(x + y)$ feet. Write an expression for the width of the rectangle.

$(x + y)$ feet

To find an expression that represents the width of the rectangle, factor: $x^2 - 6x + xy - 6y$

$(x^2 - 6x) + (xy - 6y)$ ◀——Arrange in groups with common factors.

$x(x - 6) + y(x - 6)$ ◀——Factor out the GCF.

$(x + y)(x - 6)$ ◀——Apply the Distributive Property.

So $(x - 6)$ ft is an expression for the width of the rectangle.

Check: F   O   I   L
$(x + y)(x - 6) = x^2 - 6x + xy - 6y$ ✓

Try These

Factor.

1. $3c(a - b) + 2d(a - b)$

2. $9y(c - d) - 4(c - d)$

3. $4mn(2x - y) - 3p(2x - y)$

4. $7ex^2(4 + a) + 9dy(4 + a)$

Factor each polynomial by grouping. Check your answer.

5. $x^3 - 7x^2 + x - 7$

6. $6p^3 + 15p - 14p^2 - 35$

7. $4y^3 + 10y^2 + 6y + 15$

8. $18n^2 + 2n^3 + 3n^5 + 12$

9. Discuss and Write Show two different ways to factor $2x^3 + 15 + 3x^2 + 10x$ by grouping. Explain your work.

Go to   **PRACTICE BOOK Lesson 8-6 for exercise sets.**

Factor Completely

Objective To combine factoring techniques to factor a polynomial completely

A polynomial is factored *completely* when it is expressed as a product of one or more polynomials that cannot be factored further. It may take several steps to factor a polynomial completely, and it may be necessary to use more than one factoring method. Not all polynomials can be factored.

▶To factor a polynomial completely:

- Identify and factor out the greatest common monomial factor.

- If the degree of the polynomial is 2 or greater, try other methods of factoring that are based on the number of terms in the polynomial. Refer to the table below.

Number of Terms	Type of Factoring	Example
Two	Difference of Two Squares	$16x^2 - 25 = (4x + 5)(4x - 5)$
Three	Perfect Square Trinomial	$x^2 + 12x + 36 = (x + 6)^2$ $x^2 - 12x + 36 = (x - 6)^2$
Three	Product of Two Binomials	$2x^2 + x - 10 = (2x + 5)(x - 2)$
Four	Factoring by Grouping	$x^3 + 7x^2 + 3x + 21 = (x + 7)(x^2 + 3)$

- Check your answer by multiplying.

Factor completely: $12a^2b - 9ab^2$. Check your answer.

$12a^2b - 9ab^2 = 3ab(4a - 3b)$ ◀—The greatest common monomial factor is $3ab$.

Check: $3ab(4a - 3b) = 3ab(4a) - 3ab(3b)$

$$= 12a^2b - 9ab^2 \checkmark$$

Examples

Factor completely. Check your answer.

1 $4x^2 - 144$

$4x^2 - 144 = 4(x^2 - 36)$ ◀—The GCF is 4.

$\qquad = 4(x + 6)(x - 6)$ ◀—$x^2 - 36$ is the difference of two perfect squares.

Check:

$4(x + 6)(x - 6) = 4(x^2 - 36)$

$$= 4x^2 - 144 \checkmark$$

2 $16at^2 - 16at + 4a$

$16at^2 - 16at + 4a = 4a(4t^2 - 4t + 1)$ ◀—The GCF is $4a$.

$\qquad = 4a(2t - 1)^2$ ◀—$4t^2 - 4t + 1$ is a perfect-square trinomial.

Check:

$4a(2t - 1)^2 = 4a(4t^2 - 4t + 1)$

$$= 16at^2 - 16at + 4a \checkmark$$

3 $3m^4n - 5m^3n + 12m^2n - 20mn$

$3m^4n - 5m^3n + 12m^2n - 20mn = mn(3m^3 - 5m^2 + 12m - 20)$ ◄—The GCF is mn.

$= mn[(3m^3 - 5m^2) + (12m - 20)]$ ◄—$3m^3 - 5m^2 + 12m - 20$ can be factored by grouping.

$= mn[m^2(3m - 5) + 4(3m - 5)]$ ◄—Factor each binomial using the greatest common monomial factor.

$= mn(m^2 + 4)(3m - 5)$ ◄—Apply the Distributive Property.

Check:

$mn(m^2 + 4)(3m - 5) = mn(3m^3 - 5m^2 + 12m - 20)$

$= 3m^4n - 5m^3n + 12m^2n - 20mn$ ✓

4 $3x^4y - 243y$ **Check:** $3y(x^2 + 9)(x + 3)(x - 3)$

$3x^4y - 243y = 3y(x^4 - 81)$ $= 3y(x^2 + 9)(x^2 - 9)$

$= 3y(x^2 + 9)(x^2 - 9)$ $= 3y(x^4 - 81)$

$= 3y(x^2 + 9)(x + 3)(x - 3)$ $= 3x^4y - 243y$ ✓

5 $x^4 - 7x^2 + 12$ **Check:** $(x^2 - 3)(x + 2)(x - 2)$

$x^4 - 7x^2 + 12 = (x^2 - 3)(x^2 - 4)$ $= (x^2 - 3)(x^2 - 4)$

$= (x^2 - 3)(x + 2)(x - 2)$ $= x^4 - 7x^2 + 12$ ✓

6 $3b^2 - 3ab - 2a$

$3b^2 - 3ab - 2a$ ◄—There is no GCF. $3b^2 - 3ab - 2a$ is not a perfect-trinomial square and cannot be factored as a product of two binomials.

Remember: Some polynomials cannot be factored.

So $3b^2 - 3ab - 2a$ cannot be factored using integers. It is a prime polynomial.

Try These

Factor completely. Check using multiplication. If the polynomial *cannot* be factored using integers, label it *prime*.

1. $64x^2 + 96xy + 36y^2$ **2.** $3a^2 - 9a - 12$ **3.** $4n^2 - 36$

4. $39m^2n^2 + 65mn^2 + 26n^2$ **5.** $12a^2b + 8b^2c - 15ac^2$ **6.** $c^4 - 13c^2 + 36$

7. $p^2q - q$ **8.** $16t^2 - 100t + 24$ **9.** $7x^4 - 56x^2 + 112$

10. Discuss and Write Write a polynomial that takes more than one step to factor. Factor your polynomial. Explain your work.

Go to **PRACTICE BOOK Lesson 8-7 for exercise sets.**

8-8

Technology:
Factor Polynomials Using a Graph

Objective To use a handheld to factor polynomials

The x-intercepts of the graph of a polynomial function can be used to help factor the polynomial. If the graph has an x-intercept x_1, then $(x - x_1)$ is a factor. Note that sometimes there may be more factors than those found by the x-intercepts. You will learn more about this in a later chapter.

▶ You can use a handheld to find the x-intercepts and factor a polynomial.

Factor $x^2 - 9$ using a handheld. Check your answer.

Step 1 Press ⌂. Then choose **2** to select **Graphs & Geometry**.

Step 2 Input $x^2 - 9$, then press **enter** to graph the polynomial.

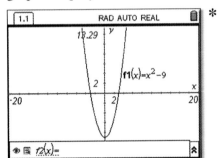

Step 3 Press **menu**. Select **Window**, and then choose **Zoom − Box**.

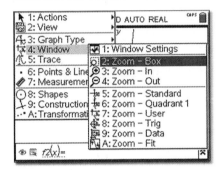

Step 4 Use the arrow keys to make a box that encompasses and zooms in on the x-intercepts. Press **enter** at each corner.

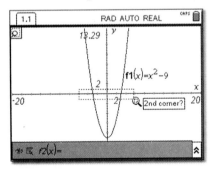

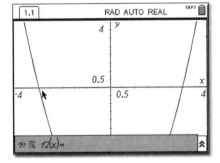

Hint
Mark the corners at integers, such as −4 and 4, so the intervals will be easy to read.

The x-intercepts are at −3 and 3. You may also want to repeat Steps 3 and 4 to zoom in closer.

Note that sometimes a graphed function such as a polynomial may be too large or too small to see the behavior in a set window size. You can set a new window size using the **Menu** key to view the graph more easily.

It appears $(x + 3)$ and $(x - 3)$ are factors.

Check: You can verify the answer by multiplying the two binomials.

$$(x + 3)(x - 3) = x^2 - 3x + 3x - 9 = x^2 - 9 \checkmark$$

So the factored form of $x^2 - 9$ is $(x + 3)(x - 3)$.

＊ Window setting adjusted to fit graph

▶ To find the value of the *x*-intercepts and factor a polynomial, you can also use the trace command on your handheld.

Factor the polynomial $x^2 - 16x + 15$ using a handheld. Check your answer.

Step 1 Press ⌂. Then choose **2** to select **Graphs & Geometry**.

Step 2 Input $x^2 - 16x + 15$, then press ≈enter to graph the polynomial. Notice that the entire graph is not shown.

Step 3 Press menu **4** to select **Window**, then press **1** to select **Window Settings**. Change the *X* and *Y* **Min** to -100 and *X* and *Y* **Max** to 100.

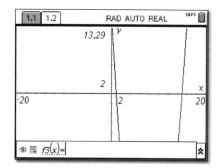

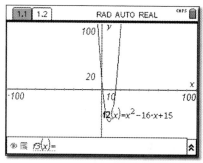

Step 4 Press menu. Select **Trace**, and then choose **Graph Trace**.

Step 5 Press ▶ to move the trace along the line until the *y*-coordinate of the graph equals 0. Repeat to find the second *x*-intercept.

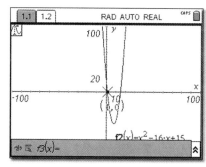

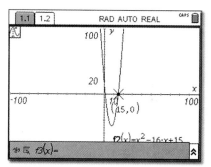

The *x*-intercepts are 1 and 15. It appears $(x - 1)$ and $(x - 15)$ are factors.

Check: You can verify the answer found by multiplying the two binomials.
$$(x - 1)(x - 15) = x^2 - 15x - x + 15$$
$$= x^2 - 16x + 15. ✓$$

So the factored form of $x^2 - 16x + 15$ is $(x - 1)(x - 15)$.

Try These

Use a handheld to factor the polynomial. Check your answer.

1. $x^2 - 25$

2. $x^2 - 5x - 14$

3. $x^2 - 4x - 32$

4. $x^2 + 22x + 40$

5. $2x^2 + 9x + 4$

6. $4x^2 + 5x - 6$

7. Discuss and Write Explain how to use the **Zoom—Box** and the **Trace** command to factor the polynomial $x^2 - 4x - 21$. Then factor the polynomial using both methods.

Problem Solving: Review of Strategies

Read ▷ **Plan** ▷ **Solve** ▷ **Check**

Objective To solve problems by using a variety of strategies

Problem: Two students must be selected from the nine-member chess club to represent the group at a conference. From how many different combinations of 2 students can this selection be made?

Read to understand what is being asked.

List the facts and restate the question.

Facts: Two students must be selected from a group of nine.

Question: From how many different ways can the two students be selected?

Select a strategy.

You can try using the strategy *Find a Pattern*. Or, you can attempt to *Make a Drawing*.

Apply the strategy.

▶**Method I: Find a Pattern**

You need to find the number of ways two students can be chosen from a group of nine students. Start by figuring out how many ways two students can be chosen from groups of two students, three students, four students, and so on, and see if you can *find a pattern*. Use capital letters—A, B, C, and so on—to represent the students.

- From a group of 2 students, A and B, there is only 1 way to choose two students: AB.

- From a group of 3 students, A, B, and C, you can choose the pair AB from above, *plus* 2 new pairs, formed by combining C with each of A and B.

    1 from above (AB) + 2 more (AC, BC) ⟶ 3 pairs in all

- From a group of 4 students, A, B, C, and D, you get the 3 pairs above, *plus* 3 more, created by combining D with each of A, B, and C.

    3 from above (AB, AC, BC) + 3 more (AD, BD, CD) ⟶ 6 pairs in all

- From a group of 5 students, A, B, C, D, E, you get the 6 pairs above, *plus* 4 more created by combining E with each of A, B, C, and D.

    6 from above + 4 more (AE, BE, CE, DE) ⟶ 10 pairs in all

Each time the size of the group increases by 1, the number of pairs increases by one less than the group size. Continue this pattern to solve.

- From a group of 6, you can make (10 + 5), or 15, pairs.
- From a group of 7, you can make (15 + 6), or 21, pairs.
- From a group of 8, you can make (21 + 7), or 28, pairs.
- From a group of 9, you can make (28 + 8), or 36, pairs.

So there are 36 ways two students can be selected from the nine-member chess club.

Problem-Solving Strategies

1. Make a Drawing
2. Solve a Simpler Problem
3. Reason Logically
4. Consider Extreme Cases
5. Work Backward
6. Find a Pattern
7. Account for All Possibilities
8. Adopt a Different Point of View
9. Guess and Test
10. Organize Data

►Method 2: Make a Drawing

Make a drawing to represent the nine students by the nine dots, shown at the right. Draw a segment connecting any two of these dots. Think of drawing such a segment as selecting a pair of students. Note that solving the original problem is the same as answering the question, "How many different segments can be formed by connecting two dots in the figure?"

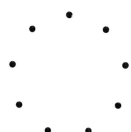

- Start by selecting one of the dots, and then draw every possible segment with that dot as one endpoint. Note that there are 8 segments in all, as shown in the figure to the right, that can be drawn.

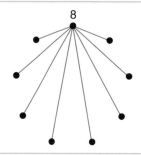

- Move clockwise to the next dot and draw as many *new* segments as you can with that dot as an endpoint. Note that there are 7 new segments, as shown in the figure to the right. The number of new segments is 1 less than before, since the segment from this dot to the first dot has already been drawn.

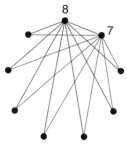

- Continue moving clockwise to each new dot and drawing each new segment. As shown in the figure to the right, note that each time you move to a new dot, the number of segments you can draw is one less than the number you drew for the previous dot.

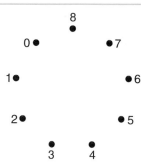

The total number of segments that you can draw is (8 + 7 + 6 + 5 + 4 + 3 + 2 + 1 + 0), or 36.

So there are 36 pairs of students that can be selected from the nine-member chess club.

Check to make sure your answer makes sense.

You can check your answer by solving the problem yet another way. You could try using the strategy, *Reason Logically*.

For example, there are 9 ways to choose one student.

For each of these 9 choices for the first student, there are 8 choices for the second, for a total of (9 • 8), or 72, pairs.

However, since the total, 72, counts every pair twice, like both AB and BA, you need to divide the total by 2 to find the total number of pairs.

So the total number of pairs is (72 ÷ 2), or 36.

The answer checks.

Go to PRACTICE BOOK Lesson 8-9 for exercise sets.

Enrichment:
Factor Sums and Differences of Cubes

Objective To factor sums and differences of two cubes • To find cubes of binomials

You know how to factor the difference of two squares, $a^2 - b^2 = (a - b)(a + b)$.
For example, in factored form, $x^2 - 9 = (x - 3)(x + 3)$.

▶ It is also possible to factor a difference of cubes, such as $x^3 - 27$. In fact, it is possible to factor both differences of cubes *and* sums of cubes.

The formulas for factoring $a^3 + b^3$ and $a^3 - b^3$ are given below.

Factoring Sums or Differences of Cubes	
Sum of Two Cubes	**Difference of Two Cubes**
$a^3 + b^3 = (a + b)(a^2 - ab + b^2)$	$a^3 - b^3 = (a - b)(a^2 + ab + b^2)$

• Factor: $x^3 - 27$

$x^3 - 27 = (x)^3 - (3)^3$ ◀——The expression is in the form $a^3 - b^3$, where $a = x$ and $b = 3$.

$= (x - 3)(x^2 + x \cdot 3 + 3^2)$ ◀——Factor using Difference of Two Cubes:
$a^3 - b^3 = (a - b)(a^2 + ab + b^2)$.

$= (x - 3)(x^2 + 3x + 9)$ ◀——Simplify.

• Factor: $x^3 + 27$

$x^3 + 27 = (x)^3 + (3)^3$ ◀——The expression is in the form $a^3 + b^3$, where $a = x$ and $b = 3$.

$= (x + 3)(x^2 - x \cdot 3 + 3^2)$ ◀——Factor using Sum of Two Cubes:
$a^3 + b^3 = (a + b)(a^2 - ab + b^2)$.

$= (x + 3)(x^2 - 3x + 9)$ ◀——Simplify.

Examples

Factor.

1 $\frac{1}{8}m^3 + 8$

$\frac{1}{8}m^3 + 8 = \left(\frac{1}{2}m\right)^3 + (2)^3$ ◀——The expression is in the form $a^3 + b^3$, where $a = \frac{1}{2}m$ and $b = 2$.

$= \left(\frac{1}{2}m + 2\right)\left[\left(\frac{1}{2}m\right)^2 - \frac{1}{2}m \cdot 2 + 2^2\right]$ ◀——Factor using Sum of Two Cubes:
$a^3 + b^3 = (a + b)(a^2 - ab + b^2)$.

$= \left(\frac{1}{2}m + 2\right)\left(\frac{1}{4}m^2 - m + 4\right)$ ◀——Simplify.

2 $27y^3 - 64$

$27y^3 - 64 = (3y)^3 - (4)^3$ ◀——The expression is in the form $a^3 - b^3$, where $a = 3y$ and $b = 4$.

$= (3y - 4)\left[(3y)^2 + 3y \cdot 4 + 4^2\right]$ ◀——Factor using Difference of Two Cubes:
$a^3 - b^3 = (a - b)(a^2 + ab + b^2)$.

$= (3y - 4)(9y^2 + 12y + 16)$ ◀——Simplify.

▶You can use what you know about factoring sums and differences of cubes to factor polynomials completely.

• Factor completely: $5x^4 + 40x$

$$5x^4 + 40x = 5x(x^3 + 8) \quad \longleftarrow \text{Factor using the greatest common factor: } 5x.$$

$$= 5x(x + 2)(x^2 - 2x + 4) \quad \longleftarrow \text{Factor } x^3 + 8 = x^3 + 2^3, \text{ using Sum of Two Cubes.}$$

• Factor completely: $m^6 - n^6$

$$m^6 - n^6 = (m^3)^2 - (n^3)^2 \quad \longleftarrow \text{Write as a difference of two squares.}$$

$$= (m^3 - n^3)(m^3 + n^3) \quad \longleftarrow \text{Factor using Difference of Two Squares.}$$

$$= (m - n)(m^2 + mn + n^2)(m^3 + n^3) \quad \longleftarrow \text{Factor using Difference of Two Cubes.}$$

$$= (m - n)(m^2 + mn + n^2)(m + n)(m^2 - mn + n^2) \quad \longleftarrow \text{Factor using Sum of Two Cubes.}$$

Perfect Binomial Cubes

You know that perfect square trinomials are squares of binomials. Specifically, $a^2 + 2ab + b^2 = (a + b)^2$ and $a^2 - 2ab + b^2 = (a - b)^2$.

There are similar patterns in the cubes of binomials. To see the patterns, you need to find the expansions of $(a + b)^3$ and $(a - b)^3$.

• $(a + b)^3 = (a + b)(a + b)^2 \quad \longleftarrow \text{Rewrite the expression as a product of two factors.}$

$$= (a + b)(a^2 + 2ab + b^2) \quad \longleftarrow \text{Find the square of the binomial, } (a + b)^2.$$

$$= a^3 + 2a^2b + ab^2 + a^2b + 2ab^2 + b^3 \quad \longleftarrow \text{Apply the Distributive Property.}$$

$$= a^3 + 3a^2b + 3ab^2 + b^3 \quad \longleftarrow \text{Combine like terms.}$$

• $(a - b)^3 = (a - b)(a - b)^2 \quad \longleftarrow \text{Rewrite the expression as a product of two factors.}$

$$= (a - b)(a^2 - 2ab + b^2) \quad \longleftarrow \text{Find the square of the binomial, } (a - b)^2.$$

$$= a^3 - 2a^2b + ab^2 - a^2b + 2ab^2 - b^3 \quad \longleftarrow \text{Apply the Distributive Property.}$$

$$= a^3 - 3a^2b + 3ab^2 - b^3 \quad \longleftarrow \text{Combine like terms.}$$

Perfect Binomial Cubes	
Cube of a Sum	**Cube of a Difference**
$(a + b)^3 = a^3 + 3a^2b + 3ab^2 + b^3$	$(a - b)^3 = a^3 - 3a^2b + 3ab^2 - b^3$

Find each cube.

• $(x + 2)^3 = x^3 + 3x^2(2) + 3x(2)^2 + (2)^3$

$$= x^3 + 6x^2 + 12x + 8$$

• $(3m - 5n)^3 = (3m)^3 - 3(3m)^2(5n) + 3(3m)(5n)^2 - (5n)^3$

$$= 27m^3 - 135m^2n + 225mn^2 - 125n^3$$

Try These

Factor completely.

1. $27z^3 + 1$ **2.** $27a^3 - 1000$ **3.** $-5t^3 + 320$

Find each cube.

4. $(c + 5)^3$ **5.** $(b - 3)^3$ **6.** $(4x + 3y)^3$

7. Discuss and Write Is the statement $x^3 - 2^3 = (x - 2)^3$ true? Explain.

Test Prep: Multiple-Choice Questions
Strategy: Try All the Answers

In a multiple-choice question, the correct answer is one of the choices. If you are not sure how to solve a problem directly, a strategy is to work backward by *testing the answers* in the original problem.

Look at the sample test item.

Read the whole test item, including the answer choices. Use context clues to help determine the meaning of any unfamiliar words.

- Underline important words.

    What is the <u>factored form</u> of $2x^2 + x - 6$?

    The *factored form* is the original expression, written as a product of its factors.

- Restate the question in your own words.

    Which product is equivalent to the polynomial?

Solve the problem.

- Test each answer choice by working backward.
- Apply appropriate rules.

    Find which product of binomials is equal to $2x^2 + x - 6$.

Test-Taking Tips
- Underline important words.
- Restate the question.
- Use the Test-Prep strategy.
- Apply appropriate rules, definitions, properties, or strategies.
- Analyze and eliminate answer choices.

Choice A

$$(x - 2)(2x + 3) = 2x^2 + 3x - 4x - 6 \quad \longleftarrow \text{Multiply.}$$
$$= 2x^2 - x - 6 \quad \longleftarrow \text{Combine like terms.}$$
$$\neq 2x^2 + x - 6$$

Choice B

$$(x + 2)(2x - 3) = 2x^2 - 3x + 4x - 6 \quad \longleftarrow \text{Multiply.}$$
$$= 2x^2 + x - 6 \quad \longleftarrow \text{Combine like terms.}$$

Hint
Even though you have determined the correct answer is letter B, continue to try all of the answer choices to ensure that all incorrect choices are eliminated.

Item Analysis

Choose the answer.

- Analyze and eliminate answer choices. Watch out for distractors.

    A. $(x - 2)(2x + 3)$ ◂— This product is $2x^2 - x - 6$. Eliminate this choice.

    B. $(x + 2)(2x - 3)$ ◂— This is the correct choice!

    C. $(2x - 2)(x + 3)$ ◂— This product is $2x^2 + 4x - 6$. Eliminate this choice.

    D. $(2x + 3)(x - 3)$ ◂— This product is $2x^2 - 3x - 9$. Eliminate this choice.

Try These

Choose the correct answer. Explain how you eliminated answer choices.

1. Which binomial is a factor of $2x^3 + 6x^2 - x - 3$?

    A. $x - 3$ **C.** $2x^2 - 1$

    B. $3 - x$ **D.** $2x^2 + 1$

2. What is the greatest common monomial factor of $12x^5 + 4x^4 + 12x^3, 20x^6 + 4x^4 + 12x^3$, and $4x^6 + 32x^3$?

    F. 4 **H.** $4x^6$

    G. $4x^3$ **J.** $20x^6$

Go to   **PRACTICE BOOK page 215 for exercise sets.**

CHAPTER 9

Radical Expressions and Equations

In This Chapter You Will:

- Write square-root expressions in simplest form
- Add and subtract radical expressions
- Multiply radical expressions and express results in simplest form
- Multiply with sums and differences of radicals
- Divide radical expressions and express results with rational denominators

- Solve radical equations
- Understand and apply the Pythagorean Theorem
- Find the lengths of vertical, horizontal, and oblique segments
- Apply the strategy: *Account for All Possibilities*
- Look for new vocabulary words **highlighted** in each lesson

Do You Remember?

- The square of a number is that number multiplied by itself, or raised to the second power.
- Perfect squares are the squares of natural numbers.
  - If n is a whole number that is not a perfect square, then $\sqrt{n}$ is an irrational number.
  - A right triangle has one 90° (right) angle.

For Practice Exercises:

 Go to **PRACTICE BOOK, pp. 221–242**

For Chapter Support: (ONLINE)

 Go to **www.progressinmathematics.com**

- Skills Update Practice
- Practice Activities
- Audio Glossary
- Vocabulary Activities

- Technology Videos
- Enrichment Activities
- Electronic SourceBook

 VIRTUAL MANIPULATIVES

Critical Thinking

Jonah can rake all the leaves in the front yard in 30 minutes. His friend Jessica can rake all the leaves in 1 hour. How long would it take them working together to rake the leaves?

Simplify Radical Expressions

Objective To write square-root expressions in simplest radical form

 On a softball field, the distance from first base to third base is $\sqrt{7200}$ feet. What is $\sqrt{7200}$ in simplest radical form?

$\sqrt{7200}$ is a called a radical or square-root expression because it contains a radical sign. The number or expression under a radical sign is called the *radicand*. The radicand is in simplest form if it contains no perfect square factors other than 1.

▶ To express a radical expression like $\sqrt{7200}$ in simplest radical form, you can use the Product Property of Square Roots.

To simplify or to find another expression with the *same value*, follow these steps:

- Find two factors of the radicand either by finding the *greatest* perfect square factor or by finding a perfect square and then continuing to simplify.

- Use the Product Property of Square Roots.

- Simplify the perfect square factor.

_____ **Key Concept** _____

Product Property of Square Roots
For any real numbers a and b, where $a \geq 0$ and $b \geq 0$, $\sqrt{ab} = \sqrt{a} \cdot \sqrt{b}$.

Method 1 Find the greatest perfect-square factor.

$$\sqrt{7200} = \sqrt{3600 \cdot 2} \quad \longleftarrow \text{Factor out the greatest perfect square.}$$
$$= \sqrt{3600} \cdot \sqrt{2} \quad \longleftarrow \text{Use the Product Property of Square Roots.}$$
$$= 60\sqrt{2} \quad \longleftarrow \text{Simplify the perfect square: } 3600 = 60^2$$

Method 2 Find a perfect-square factor and then continue to simplify.

$$\sqrt{7200} = \sqrt{100 \cdot 72} \quad \longleftarrow \text{Factor out a perfect square.}$$
$$= \sqrt{100 \cdot 36 \cdot 2} \quad \longleftarrow \text{Look for another perfect square.}$$
$$= \sqrt{100} \cdot \sqrt{36} \cdot \sqrt{2} \quad \longleftarrow \text{Use the Product Property of Square Roots.}$$
$$= 10 \cdot 6\sqrt{2} \quad \longleftarrow \text{Simplify.}$$
$$= 60\sqrt{2} \quad \longleftarrow \text{Simplify.}$$

So $\sqrt{7200}$ in simplest radical form is $60\sqrt{2}$.

Example

1 Express $-2\sqrt{108}$ in simplest radical form.

Method 1 Find the greatest perfect square.

$$-2\sqrt{108} = -2\sqrt{36 \cdot 3}$$
$$= -2\sqrt{36} \cdot \sqrt{3}$$
$$= -2(6\sqrt{3})$$
$$= -12\sqrt{3}$$

So in simplest form, $-2\sqrt{108} = -12\sqrt{3}$.

Method 2 Find a perfect square, and then continue to simplify.

$$-2\sqrt{108} = -2\sqrt{4 \cdot 27}$$
$$= -2\sqrt{4 \cdot 9 \cdot 3}$$
$$= -2\sqrt{4} \cdot \sqrt{9} \cdot \sqrt{3}$$
$$= -2 \cdot 2 \cdot 3 \cdot \sqrt{3}$$
$$= -12\sqrt{3}$$

▶ When simplifying radical expressions containing variables, remember that positive numbers have two square roots, one positive *and* one negative.

For example, $\sqrt{x^2} = +x$ or $-x$.

▶ If the exponent of the variable inside the radical is *even* and the simplified result is *odd*, use absolute value to assure nonnegative results.

$$\sqrt{n^2} = |n|$$
$$\sqrt{n^4} = n^2$$
$$\sqrt{n^6} = |n^3|$$
$$\sqrt{n^8} = n^4$$

Simplify: $\sqrt{147x^2y}$

$\sqrt{147x^2y} = \sqrt{49 \cdot 3 \cdot x^2 \cdot y}$ ◀—Factor out each perfect square wherever possible.

$= \sqrt{49x^2 \cdot 3y}$ ◀—Use the Commutative Property.

$= \sqrt{49x^2} \cdot \sqrt{3y}$ ◀—Use the Product Property of Square Roots.

$= 7|x|\sqrt{3y}$ ◀—Simplify.

So $\sqrt{147x^2y}$ in simplest radical form is $7|x|\sqrt{3y}$.

Remember:
$a^m \cdot a^m = a^{m+m} = a^{2m}$
Therefore, $\sqrt{a^{2m}} = a^m$.

A variable to an even power is a perfect square.

Examples

1 Express $\sqrt{8x^5}$ in simplest radical form.

$= \sqrt{4 \cdot 2 \cdot x^4 \cdot x}$ ◀—Factor out each perfect square wherever possible.

$= \sqrt{4x^4 \cdot 2x}$ ◀—Use the Commutative Property.

$= \sqrt{4x^4} \cdot \sqrt{2x}$ ◀—Use the Product Property of Square Roots.

$= 2x^2\sqrt{2x}$ ◀—Simplify.

So in simplest form, $\sqrt{8x^5} = 2x^2\sqrt{2x}$.

2 Write $3\sqrt{63p^5q^6r}$ in simplest radical form.

$= 3\sqrt{9 \cdot 7 \cdot p^4 \cdot q^6 \cdot p \cdot r}$ ◀—Factor out each perfect square wherever possible.

$= 3\sqrt{9p^4q^6 \cdot 7pr}$ ◀—Use the Commutative Property.

$= 3\sqrt{9p^4q^6} \cdot \sqrt{7pr}$ ◀—Use the Product Property of Square Roots.

$= 3(3p^2|q^3|) \cdot \sqrt{7pr}$ ◀—Simplify.

$= 9p^2|q^3|\sqrt{7pr}$ ◀—Simplify.

So in simplest form, $3\sqrt{63p^5q^6r} = 9p^2|q^3|\sqrt{7pr}$.

Try These

Express each in simplest radical form.

1. $\sqrt{400}$ **2.** $\sqrt{30}$ **3.** $-\sqrt{75}$ **4.** $3\sqrt{160}$

5. $4\sqrt{a^2b^5c^6}$ **6.** $\sqrt{5xy^2}$ **7.** $\sqrt{189m^5n^3}$ **8.** $-9\sqrt{162a^4b}$

9. Discuss and Write Explain how simplifying a square-root expression is similar to simplifying a fraction.

Go to   **PRACTICE BOOK Lesson 9-1 for exercise sets.**

Add and Subtract Radical Expressions

Objective **To add and subtract expressions with like radicands**
• To add and subtract radical expressions that first require simplification

Jay is building a model sailboat. The dimensions of the sail are $2\sqrt{3}$ inches, $4\sqrt{3}$ inches, and $5\sqrt{2}$ inches. What is the perimeter of the sail?

To find the perimeter of the sail, *add* the lengths of the sides.

$$5\sqrt{2} + 4\sqrt{3} + 2\sqrt{3}$$

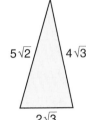

$5\sqrt{2}$ $4\sqrt{3}$

$2\sqrt{3}$

▶ You can combine like radicals by adding or subtracting. The procedures used for combining radical expressions and those used for combining other types of expressions are similar. Just as you apply the Distributive Property to combine like terms, you also apply the Distributive Property to combine like radicands.

$2\sqrt{3} + 4\sqrt{3} + 5\sqrt{2}$ ◀—Identify like radicands. These can be combined.

$(2 + 4)\sqrt{3} + 5\sqrt{2}$ ◀—Apply the Distributive Property.

$6\sqrt{3} + 5\sqrt{2}$

Key Concept

Adding Radical Expressions
For any real numbers a and b, where $a \geq 0$ and $b \geq 0$, $a\sqrt{x} + b\sqrt{x} = (a + b)\sqrt{x}$.

Subtracting Radical Expressions
For any real numbers a and b, where $a \geq 0$ and $b \geq 0$, $a\sqrt{x} - b\sqrt{x} = (a - b)\sqrt{x}$.

$6\sqrt{3}$ and $5\sqrt{2}$ *cannot* be combined in radical form because the radicands are different. Each radicand is in simplest radical form, and there are no common factors.

So the perimeter of the sail is $(6\sqrt{3} + 5\sqrt{2})$ inches.

Examples

Express each sum or difference in simplest radical form.

1 $3\sqrt{5} + 2\sqrt{10} - \sqrt{5} + 8\sqrt{10}$

$3\sqrt{5} + 2\sqrt{10} - \sqrt{5} + 8\sqrt{10}$ ◀—Identify like radicands.

$3\sqrt{5} - \sqrt{5} + 2\sqrt{10} + 8\sqrt{10}$ ◀—Use the Commutative and Associative Properties of Addition.

$(3 - 1)\sqrt{5} + (2 + 8)\sqrt{10}$ ◀—Apply the Distributive Property.

$2\sqrt{5} + 10\sqrt{10}$ ◀—These terms have unlike radicands. Do not combine.

Remember:
$\sqrt{5} = 1\sqrt{5}$

2 $-4n\sqrt{6} + 3n\sqrt{2} + n\sqrt{2} - 5n\sqrt{6}$

$-4n\sqrt{6} + 3n\sqrt{2} + n\sqrt{2} - 5n\sqrt{6}$ ◀—Identify like radicands.

$-4n\sqrt{6} - 5n\sqrt{6} + 3n\sqrt{2} + n\sqrt{2}$ ◀—Use the Commutative and Associative Properties of Addition.

$(-4n - 5n)\sqrt{6} + (3n + n)\sqrt{2}$ ◀—Apply the Distributive Property.

$-9n\sqrt{6} + 4n\sqrt{2}$ ◀—These terms have unlike radicands. Do not combine.

Remember:
$n = 1n$

▶Sometimes you need to simplify radicals *before* you can add or subtract them.

Simplify. Then add or subtract. $3\sqrt{50} + 2\sqrt{98} - \sqrt{2}$

$3\sqrt{25 \cdot 2} + 2\sqrt{49 \cdot 2} - \sqrt{2}$ ◀——Factor out each perfect square in the radicand wherever possible.

$3\sqrt{25} \cdot \sqrt{2} + 2\sqrt{49} \cdot \sqrt{2} - \sqrt{2}$ ◀——Use the Product Property of Square Roots.

$3(5\sqrt{2}) + 2(7\sqrt{2}) - \sqrt{2}$ ◀——Simplify.

$15\sqrt{2} + 14\sqrt{2} - \sqrt{2}$ ◀——Identify like radicands.

$(15 + 14 - 1)\sqrt{2}$ ◀——Apply the Distributive Property.

$28\sqrt{2}$ ◀——Simplify.

Examples

Simplify. Assume that all variables represent nonnegative numbers.

1 $5\sqrt{150} + 12 + \sqrt{54} - 6 + \sqrt{24}$

$5\sqrt{25 \cdot 6} + 12 + \sqrt{9 \cdot 6} - 6 + \sqrt{4 \cdot 6}$ ◀——Factor out each perfect square in the radicand wherever possible.

$5\sqrt{25} \cdot \sqrt{6} + 12 + \sqrt{9} \cdot \sqrt{6} - 6 + \sqrt{4} \cdot \sqrt{6}$ ◀——Use the Product Property of Square Roots.

$5(5\sqrt{6}) + 12 + 3\sqrt{6} - 6 + 2\sqrt{6}$ ◀——Simplify.

$25\sqrt{6} + 12 + 3\sqrt{6} - 6 + 2\sqrt{6}$ ◀——Identify like radicands *and* like terms.

$25\sqrt{6} + 3\sqrt{6} + 2\sqrt{6} + 12 - 6$ ◀——Use the Commutative and Associative Properties of Addition.

$(25 + 3 + 2)\sqrt{6} + 12 - 6$ ◀——Apply the Distributive Property.

$30\sqrt{6} + 6$ ◀——Simplify.

2 $r^2\sqrt{80} - \sqrt{45r^4} + \sqrt{125r^2}$

$r^2\sqrt{16 \cdot 5} - \sqrt{9r^4 \cdot 5} + \sqrt{25r^2 \cdot 5}$ ◀——Factor out each perfect square in the radicand wherever possible.

$r^2\sqrt{16} \cdot \sqrt{5} - \sqrt{9r^4} \cdot \sqrt{5} + \sqrt{25r^2} \cdot \sqrt{5}$ ◀——Use the Product Property of Square Roots.

$r^2(4\sqrt{5}) - 3r^2\sqrt{5} + 5r\sqrt{5}$ ◀——Simplify.

$4r^2\sqrt{5} - 3r^2\sqrt{5} + 5r\sqrt{5}$ ◀——Identify like radicands *and* like terms.

$r^2(\sqrt{5}) + 5r\sqrt{5}$ ◀——Simplify.

$(r^2 + 5r)\sqrt{5}$ ◀——Apply the Distributive Property.

Try These

Express each sum or difference in simplest radical form.

1. $7\sqrt{15} + 15\sqrt{3} - 3\sqrt{15} - \sqrt{3}$

2. $-\sqrt{147} - \sqrt{243} + \sqrt{63} - \sqrt{300}$

3. $15t + 3t\sqrt{11t} + 7t - t\sqrt{11t}$

4. $4y\sqrt{242} + 3\sqrt{18y^6} + y\sqrt{50} - 5\sqrt{32y^6}$

5. Discuss and Write Does $\sqrt{a + b} = \sqrt{a} + \sqrt{b}$? Support your answer with specific examples.

Go to **PRACTICE BOOK Lesson 9-2 for exercise sets.**

Multiply and Divide Radical Expressions

Objective To multiply radical expressions and express results in simplest radical form • To multiply with sums and differences of radicals • To divide radical expressions and express results with rational denominators

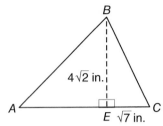

Given triangle ABC, find the area of the inscribed triangle EBC.

To find the area, use the formula for the area of a triangle, $A = \frac{1}{2}bh$.

$A = \frac{1}{2}(\sqrt{7})(4\sqrt{2})$ ←—Substitute $\sqrt{7}$ for b and $4\sqrt{2}$ for h.

▶ To multiply radical expressions, use the Commutative and Associative Properties and the Product Property of Square Roots. Express the product in simplest radical form.

$A = \left(\frac{1}{2} \bullet 4\right)(\sqrt{7} \bullet \sqrt{2})$ ←—Use the Commutative and Associative Properties.

$A = 2\sqrt{7 \bullet 2}$ ←—Use the Product Property of Square Roots.

$A = 2\sqrt{14}$ ←—Simplify.

So the area of triangle EBC is $2\sqrt{14}$ in.²

____ **Key Concept** ____

Multiplying Radical Expressions
For any real numbers a and b,
where $a \geq 0$ and $b \geq 0$,
$a\sqrt{x} \bullet b\sqrt{y} = a \bullet b\sqrt{x \bullet y}$

Examples

Multiply. Write each product in simplest radical form.

1 $3\sqrt{6} \bullet 6\sqrt{10}$

$3(6)\sqrt{6}\sqrt{10}$ ←—Use the Commutative and Associative Properties.

$18\sqrt{6 \bullet 10}$ ←—Use the Product Property of Square Roots.

$18\sqrt{60}$ ←—Simplify.

$18\sqrt{4 \bullet 15}$ ←—Factor out the greatest perfect square from the radicand.

$18\sqrt{4}\sqrt{15}$ ←—Use the Product Property of Square Roots.

$18 \bullet 2\sqrt{15}$

$36\sqrt{15}$

2 $\sqrt{15x} \bullet \sqrt{3x^3} \bullet \sqrt{2x}$

$\sqrt{15x(3x^3)(2x)}$ ←—Use the Product Property of Square Roots.

$\sqrt{90x^5}$ ←—Multiply.

$\sqrt{9x^4(10x)}$ ←—Factor out each perfect square.

$\sqrt{9x^4}\sqrt{10x}$ ←—Use the Product Property of Square Roots.

$3x^2\sqrt{10x}$

3 $(2\sqrt{5a})^2$

$(2\sqrt{5a})(2\sqrt{5a})$ ←—Expand. Express the power as a product.

$2(2)\sqrt{5a}\sqrt{5a}$ ←—Use the Commutative Property.

$4\sqrt{5a(5a)}$ ←—Use the Product Property of Square Roots.

$4\sqrt{25a^2}$ ←—Multiply.

$4 \bullet 5|a|$

$20|a|$

►Sometimes you need to apply the Distributive Property to multiply radical expressions.

Examples

Multiply. Write each product in simplest radical form.
Assume that all variables represent nonnegative numbers.

1 $\sqrt{14}(\sqrt{7} - 5\sqrt{2})$

$\sqrt{14}\sqrt{7} - \sqrt{14}(5\sqrt{2})$ ◄— Apply the Distributive Property.

$\sqrt{14(7)} - 5\sqrt{14(2)}$ ◄— Use the Product Property of Square Roots.

$\sqrt{7 \bullet 2 \bullet 7} - 5\sqrt{7 \bullet 2 \bullet 2}$ ◄— Factor.

$\sqrt{49(2)} - 5\sqrt{4(7)}$ ◄— Factor out each perfect square from the radicand if possible.

$\sqrt{49}\sqrt{2} - 5\sqrt{4}\sqrt{7}$ ◄— Use the Product Property of Square Roots.

$7\sqrt{2} - 5(2)\sqrt{7}$ ◄— Simplify.

$7\sqrt{2} - 10\sqrt{7}$ ◄— Combine like radicands.

2 $\sqrt{2x}(2\sqrt{3x} + 5\sqrt{12x})$

$\sqrt{2x}(2\sqrt{3x}) + \sqrt{2x}(5\sqrt{12x})$ ◄— Apply the Distributive Property.

$2\sqrt{2x(3x)} + 5\sqrt{2x(12x)}$ ◄— Use the Product Property of Square Roots.

$2\sqrt{6x^2} + 5\sqrt{24x^2}$ ◄— Simplify.

$2\sqrt{x^2 \bullet 6} + 5\sqrt{4x^2 \bullet 6}$ ◄— Factor out each perfect square from the radicand if possible.

$2\sqrt{x^2}\sqrt{6} + 5\sqrt{4x^2}\sqrt{6}$ ◄— Use the Product Property of Square Roots.

$2x\sqrt{6} + 5(2x)\sqrt{6}$ ◄— Simplify.

$2x\sqrt{6} + 10x\sqrt{6}$ ◄— Combine like radicals.

$12x\sqrt{6}$

►To multiply sums and differences of two radicals, use the same method that you use to multiply two binomials. You can use FOIL as a memory device to help you remember to apply the Distributive Property twice.

> **Remember:** To multiply two binomials, find the sum of the products of the first terms (**F**), the outer terms (**O**), the inner terms (**I**), and the last terms (**L**).

Multiply: $(6 - \sqrt{3})(4 + \sqrt{3})$

$(6 \bullet 4) + (6 \bullet \sqrt{3}) + (-\sqrt{3} \bullet 4) + (-\sqrt{3} \bullet \sqrt{3})$ ◄—FOIL

$24 + 6\sqrt{3} - 4\sqrt{3} - 3$ ◄— Apply the Distributive Property.
$\sqrt{3}\sqrt{3} = \sqrt{3 \bullet 3} = \sqrt{9} = 3$

$21 + 2\sqrt{3}$ ◄— Simplify.

Examples

1 Multiply: $(2 - \sqrt{5})^2$

$(2 - \sqrt{5})(2 - \sqrt{5})$ ◄—Rewrite as a product.

$(2 \bullet 2) + (2 \bullet -\sqrt{5}) + (-\sqrt{5} \bullet 2) + (-\sqrt{5} \bullet -\sqrt{5})$

$4 - 2\sqrt{5} - 2\sqrt{5} + 5$ ◄— Apply the Distributive Property.

$4 + (-2 - 2)\sqrt{5} + 5$ ◄— Simplify.

$9 - 4\sqrt{5}$

2 Multiply: $(2\sqrt{3} - 3)(2\sqrt{3} + 3)$

$(2\sqrt{3} \bullet 2\sqrt{3}) + (2\sqrt{3} \bullet 3) + (-3 \bullet 2\sqrt{3}) + (-3 \bullet 3)$

$4(3) + 6\sqrt{3} - 6\sqrt{3} - 9$ ◄— Apply the Distributive Property.

$12 + 6\sqrt{3} - 6\sqrt{3} - 9$ ◄— Simplify.

$12 + 0 - 9$

3

Continue Lesson ➡

▶ You can also use the **Quotient Property of Square Roots** to simplify radical expressions.

A radical expression is in *simplest radical form* when the radicand has no perfect-square factors other than 1, the radicand has no fractions, and there is no radical in the denominator of a fraction.

Simplify: $\sqrt{\dfrac{75}{9}}$

$\sqrt{\dfrac{75}{9}} = \dfrac{\sqrt{75}}{\sqrt{9}}$ ◀—Use the Quotient Property of Square Roots.

$= \dfrac{\sqrt{75}}{3}$ ◀—Simplify both the numerator and denominator.

$= \dfrac{\sqrt{25}\sqrt{3}}{3}$ ◀—Use the Product Property of Square Roots.

$= \dfrac{5\sqrt{3}}{3}$ or $\dfrac{5}{3}\sqrt{3}$

Examples

Simplify each expression. All variables represent nonnegative numbers.

1 $\sqrt{\dfrac{28mn}{8n}}$

$\sqrt{\dfrac{14m}{4}}$ ◀—Divide the numerator and denominator by $2n$ to simplify the fraction.

$\dfrac{\sqrt{14m}}{\sqrt{4}}$ ◀—Use the Quotient Property of Square Roots.

$\dfrac{\sqrt{14m}}{2}$ or $\dfrac{1}{2}\sqrt{14m}$

2 $\dfrac{12\sqrt{18}}{3\sqrt{2}}$

$\dfrac{12}{3}\sqrt{\dfrac{18}{2}}$ ◀—Use the Quotient Property of Square Roots.

$\dfrac{12}{3}\sqrt{9}$ ◀—Simplify the fraction in the radicand.

$4(3)$ ◀—Simplify.

12

▶ **Rationalizing the denominator** of a radical expression is a method used to eliminate radicals from the denominator. One way to rationalize the denominator is to multiply both the numerator and denominator by the radical expression in the denominator.

Simplify $\dfrac{3\sqrt{2x}}{\sqrt{11y}}$ by rationalizing the denominator.

$\dfrac{3\sqrt{2x}}{\sqrt{11y}} = \dfrac{3\sqrt{2x}}{\sqrt{11y}} \cdot \dfrac{\sqrt{11y}}{\sqrt{11y}}$ ◀—Multiply by 1 in the form of $\dfrac{\sqrt{11y}}{\sqrt{11y}}$ to make the radicand in the denominator a perfect square.

$= \dfrac{3\sqrt{22xy}}{\sqrt{121y^2}}$ ◀—Simplify.

$= \dfrac{3\sqrt{22xy}}{\sqrt{121}\sqrt{y^2}}$ ◀—Use the Product Property of Square Roots.

$= \dfrac{3\sqrt{22xy}}{11|y|}$ or $\dfrac{3}{11|y|}\sqrt{22xy}$

Examples

Simplify each radical expression. All variables represent nonnegative numbers.

1 $\dfrac{\sqrt{15}}{\sqrt{8}}$

$\dfrac{\sqrt{15}}{\sqrt{8}} = \dfrac{\sqrt{15}}{\sqrt{8}} \cdot \dfrac{\sqrt{2}}{\sqrt{2}}$ ←Multiply by 1 in the form of $\dfrac{\sqrt{2}}{\sqrt{2}}$ to make the denominator a perfect square.

$= \dfrac{\sqrt{30}}{\sqrt{16}}$ ←Simplify.

$= \dfrac{\sqrt{30}}{4}$ or $\dfrac{1}{4}\sqrt{30}$

2 $\dfrac{15n}{2\sqrt{3}}$

$\dfrac{15n}{2\sqrt{3}} = \dfrac{15n}{2\sqrt{3}} \cdot \dfrac{\sqrt{3}}{\sqrt{3}}$ ←Multiply by 1 in the form of $\dfrac{\sqrt{3}}{\sqrt{3}}$ to rationalize the denominator.

$= \dfrac{15n\sqrt{3}}{2\sqrt{9}}$ ←Use the Product Property of Square Roots.

$= \dfrac{15n\sqrt{3}}{2(3)}$ ←Simplify.

$= \dfrac{15n}{6}\sqrt{3}$ ←Simplify.

$= \dfrac{\overset{5}{15n}}{\underset{2}{6}}\sqrt{3}$ ←Divide the numerator and denominator by 3 to simplify the fraction.

$= \dfrac{5n}{2}\sqrt{3}$ or $2\dfrac{1}{2}n\sqrt{3}$

3 $\dfrac{6\sqrt{r} + r\sqrt{6}}{\sqrt{3r}}$

$\dfrac{6\sqrt{r} + r\sqrt{6}}{\sqrt{3r}} = \dfrac{6\sqrt{r} + r\sqrt{6}}{\sqrt{3r}} \cdot \dfrac{\sqrt{3r}}{\sqrt{3r}}$ ←Multiply by 1 in the form of $\dfrac{\sqrt{3r}}{\sqrt{3r}}$ to rationalize the denominator.

$= \dfrac{6\sqrt{3r^2} + r\sqrt{18r}}{\sqrt{9r^2}}$ ←Simplify.

$= \dfrac{6\sqrt{r^2}\sqrt{3} + r\sqrt{9}\sqrt{2r}}{\sqrt{9r^2}} = \dfrac{6r\sqrt{3} + 3r\sqrt{2r}}{3r}$ ←Use the Product Property of Square Roots.

$= \dfrac{\overset{2}{6r}\sqrt{3}}{\underset{1}{3r}} + \dfrac{\overset{1}{3r}\sqrt{2r}}{\underset{1}{3r}}$ ←Divide the numerator and denominator by $3r$ to simplify the fraction.

$= 2\sqrt{3} + \sqrt{2r}$ ←Simplify.

Try These

Simplify each radical expression. Assume that all variables represent nonnegative numbers.

1. $5\sqrt{6} \cdot \sqrt{30} \cdot 2\sqrt{5}$

2. $(5\sqrt{2})^2$

3. $(3x + \sqrt{11})^2$

4. $(\sqrt{5} + \sqrt{2})(3\sqrt{5} + 4\sqrt{2})$

5. $(2\sqrt{13x})^2$

6. $\dfrac{\sqrt{10b^2}}{\sqrt{5}}$

7. $\dfrac{-6 + \sqrt{120}}{-2}$

8. $\dfrac{3\sqrt{120}}{\sqrt{6}}$

9. $\dfrac{8\sqrt{m} - m\sqrt{18}}{\sqrt{2m}}$

10. Discuss and Write Explain why $5\sqrt{21}$ is in simplest form and $5\sqrt{24}$ is not.

Go to   PRACTICE BOOK Lesson 9-3 for exercise sets.

Solve Radical Equations

Objective To solve radical equations

The skid-to-stop formula, $S = \sqrt{30Df}$, relates the speed, S, that a car is traveling in miles per hour and the distance, D, in feet it will skid when the brakes are applied. The variable f is the drag factor that depends on the type and condition of the road. If a car is traveling at 60 miles per hour on a wet road that has a drag factor of 0.5, how far will the car skid when the brakes are applied? Assume that the speed of the automobile can be no more than $\sqrt{30Df}$.

To find how far the car will skid when the brakes are applied, use the skid-to-stop formula, and solve the radical equation.

▶ An equation that contains a variable within a radical is called a radical equation. Solving equations involves inverse operations. Since squaring and finding square roots are inverse operations, to solve an equation with a radical, square both sides.

Solve:
$60 = \sqrt{30(0.5)D}$ ←Substitute the values into the formula.

$60 = \sqrt{15D}$ ←Simplify.

$60^2 = (\sqrt{15D})^2$ ←Square both sides of the equation to eliminate the radical.

$3600 = 15D$ ←Simplify.

$240 = D$ ←Use the Division Property of Equality.

Check:
$60 \overset{?}{=} \sqrt{30(0.5)(240)}$

$60 \overset{?}{=} \sqrt{3600}$

$60 = 60$ True

So the car will skid 240 feet before coming to a stop.

Examples

Solve. Check your solution. Then write the solution set.

1 $\sqrt{x} + 2 = 5$

$\sqrt{x} = 3$ ←Use the Subtraction Property of Equality to isolate the radical expression.

$(\sqrt{x})^2 = 3^2$ ←Square both sides of the equation to eliminate the radical.

$x = 9$

Check: $\sqrt{9} + 2 \overset{?}{=} 5$

$3 + 2 \overset{?}{=} 5$

$5 = 5$ True

Solution set: {9}

2 $5\sqrt{x - 2} = 5$

$\dfrac{5\sqrt{x - 2}}{5} = \dfrac{5}{5}$ ←Use the Division Property of Equality.

$\sqrt{x - 2} = 1$ ←Simplify.

$(\sqrt{x - 2})^2 = 1^2$ ←Square both sides of the equation.

$x - 2 = 1$ ←Use the Addition Property of Equality.

$x = 3$

Check: $5\sqrt{3 - 2} \overset{?}{=} 5$

$5\sqrt{1} \overset{?}{=} 5$

$5(1) \overset{?}{=} 5$

$5 = 5$ True

Solution set: {3}

▶ Sometimes when you square both sides of a radical equation, the resulting equation *may not* have solutions or roots that *satisfy* the original equation. A solution that does not satisfy the equation is called an extraneous solution. It is always important to *check* your solution(s) in the original equation to determine if any are extraneous. *Reject* the extraneous root from the solution set.

Solve: $3\sqrt{x} + 8 = 2$

$3\sqrt{x} = -6$ ◀—Use the Subtraction Property of Equality to isolate the radical expression.

$\sqrt{x} = -2$ ◀—Use the Division Property of Equality.

$(\sqrt{x})^2 = (-2)^2$ ◀—Square both sides of the equation to eliminate the radical.

$x = 4$

Check: $3\sqrt{4} + 8 \overset{?}{=} 2$

$3(2) + 8 \overset{?}{=} 2$

$6 + 8 \overset{?}{=} 2$

$14 = 2$ False

Solution set: { } or $\varnothing$

So the solution, $x = 4$, is an extraneous solution.
There is no real-number solution for $3\sqrt{x} + 8 = 2$.

Examples

Solve each equation. Check your solution. Then write the solution set.

1 $5 - \sqrt{b + 3} = -1$

$-\sqrt{b + 3} = -6$ ◀—Use the Subtraction Property of Equality.

$\sqrt{b + 3} = 6$ ◀—Use the Division Property of Equality.

$(\sqrt{b + 3})^2 = (6)^2$ ◀—Square both sides of the equation.

$b + 3 - 3 = 36 - 3$ ◀—Use the Subtraction Property of Equality.

$b = 33$

The solution, $b = 33$, is a solution.

Check: $5 - \sqrt{33 + 3} \overset{?}{=} -1$

$5 - \sqrt{36} \overset{?}{=} -1$

$5 - 6 \overset{?}{=} -1$

$-1 = -1$ True

Solution set: {33}

2 $5 + \sqrt{a + 3} = 1$

$\sqrt{a + 3} = -4$ ◀—Use the Subtraction Property of Equality.

$(\sqrt{a + 3})^2 = (-4)^2$ ◀—Square both sides of the equation.

$a + 3 - 3 = 16 - 3$ ◀—Use the Subtraction Property of Equality.

$a = 13$

The solution, $a = 13$, is an extraneous solution.
There is no real-number solution for $5 + \sqrt{a + 3} = 1$.

Check: $5 + \sqrt{13 + 3} \overset{?}{=} 1$

$5 + \sqrt{16} \overset{?}{=} 1$

$5 + 4 \overset{?}{=} 1$

$9 = 1$ False

Solution set: { } or $\varnothing$

Try These

Solve each equation. Check your solution. Then write the solution set.

1. $\sqrt{\dfrac{d}{2}} = 8$

2. $\dfrac{\sqrt{n - 15}}{6} = -2$

3. $4\sqrt{3r + 24} = 12$

4. Discuss and Write Explain why $-3\sqrt{2x} = 18$ has no real solutions.

Go to **PRACTICE BOOK Lesson 9-4 for exercise sets.**

The Pythagorean Theorem

The diagram at the right shows a cross section of a
roof whose two halves are congruent right triangles.
The roof peak to a roof edge measures 13 feet.
How far above the floor is the roof peak?

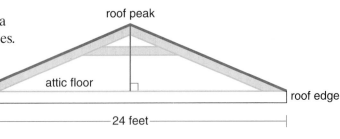

roof peak

attic floor

roof edge

|← 24 feet →|

▶ To find the length of a missing
side of a right triangle, apply the
Pythagorean Theorem.

_____ **Key Concept** _____

Pythagorean Theorem

If a triangle is a right triangle, then the sum of the squares
of the legs, a and b, equals the square of the hypotenuse, c.

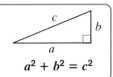

$a^2 + b^2 = c^2$

$a^2 + b^2 = c^2$ ◄—Pythagorean Theorem
$12^2 + b^2 = 13^2$ ◄—Substitute the known values into the Pythagorean Theorem.
$144 + b^2 = 169$ ◄—Simplify.
$b^2 = 25$ ◄—Use the Subtraction Property of Equality.
$\sqrt{b^2} = \sqrt{25}$ ◄—Find the square root of each side.
$b = 5$

.Think.....................
Distance is nonnegative.
Therefore, only consider
the positive root.

So the distance from the attic floor to the peak of the roof is 5 feet.

Examples

1 To find the distance between B and C on opposite ends of a
lake, a surveyor sets a stake at point C. If $\angle C$ is a right angle
and if $AB = 185$ m and $AC = 111$ m, how far apart are B and C?

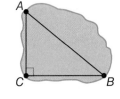

$a^2 + b^2 = c^2$ ◄—Use the Pythagorean Theorem.
$a^2 + 111^2 = 185^2$ ◄—Substitute the known values into the Pythagorean Theorem.
$a^2 + 12{,}321 = 34{,}225$ ◄—Simplify.
$a^2 = 21{,}904$ ◄—Use the Subtraction Property of Equality.
$\sqrt{a^2} = \sqrt{21{,}904}$ ◄—Find the square root of each side.
$a = 148$ ◄—Simplify.

The distance from B to C is 148 meters.

2 Find the length of the diagonal of the rectangle shown.

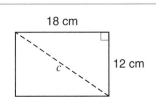

18 cm

12 cm

$a^2 + b^2 = c^2$ ◄—Use the Pythagorean Theorem.
$12^2 + 18^2 = c^2$ ◄—Substitute the known values into the Pythagorean Theorem.
$144 + 324 = c^2$ ◄—Simplify.
$468 = c^2$ ◄—Simplify.
$\sqrt{468} = \sqrt{c^2}$ ◄—Find the square root of each side.
$6\sqrt{13} = c$ ◄—Write in simplest radical form. ($\sqrt{468} = \sqrt{36 \cdot 13}$)

The length of the diagonal is $6\sqrt{13}$ centimeters.

▶ You can use the converse of the Pythagorean Theorem to test whether a triangle is a right triangle.

The lengths of the sides of a triangle are 9 cm, 12 cm, and 8 cm. Is the triangle a right triangle?

$9^2 + 8^2 \overset{?}{=} 12^2$ ◀— Substitute the lengths into the Pythagorean Theorem, using the greatest value for c.

$81 + 64 \overset{?}{=} 144$ ◀— Simplify.

$145 = 144$ False

Since $9^2 + 8^2 \neq 12^2$, the triangle is *not* a right triangle.

Key Concept

Converse of the Pythagorean Theorem

If a triangle has sides of lengths a, b, and c, and if $a^2 + b^2 = c^2$, then the triangle is a right triangle.

Example

1 A builder wants to know if the corner of a room forms a right angle. Does it form a right angle if the walls measure 12 by 16 feet and the diagonal is 20 feet?

$12^2 + 16^2 \overset{?}{=} 20^2$ ◀— Substitute the lengths into the Pythagorean Theorem, using the greatest value for c.

$144 + 256 \overset{?}{=} 400$ ◀— Simplify.

$400 = 400$ True

Since $12^2 + 16^2 = 20^2$, the corner does form a right angle.

▶ A **Pythagorean triple** is a set of three positive whole numbers, a, b, and c, that can be the lengths of the sides of a right triangle. Some Pythagorean triples are {3, 4, 5}, {8, 15, 17}, and {7, 24, 25}.

Determine if {9, 40, 41} is a Pythagorean triple.

$9^2 + 40^2 \overset{?}{=} 41^2$ ◀— Substitute the lengths into the Pythagorean Theorem.

$81 + 1600 \overset{?}{=} 1681$

$1681 = 1681$ True

So the set {9, 40, 41} is a Pythagorean triple.

Try These

Find the length of the third side of each right triangle in simplest radical form.

1.

? 9
12

2. 14
? 50

3. 85
36
?

Determine whether or not a right triangle can have sides of the given lengths.

4. 11, 60, 61

5. 5.4, 7.2, 9

6. 13, 16, $5\sqrt{17}$

7. Discuss and Write Explain whether or not the 3 side lengths of a right triangle can all be odd numbers. Justify your reasoning.

Go to PRACTICE BOOK **Lesson 9-5 for exercise sets.**

Distance in the Coordinate Plane

Objective To find the lengths of vertical and horizontal segments • To find the lengths of oblique segments by using the Distance Formula

▶ The length of a *vertical line segment* is the absolute value of the difference between the y-coordinates of its endpoints.

The distance between (x_1, y_1) and (x_1, y_2) is $|y_2 - y_1|$.

Find the length of a line segment with endpoints $(5, -2)$ and $(5, 4)$.

$|4 - (-2)|$ ◀—Substitute the given values into the formula.

   $|6|$ ◀—Simplify.

    6 ◀—Find the absolute value.

So the length of a line segment with endpoints $(5, -2)$ and $(5, 4)$ is 6 units.

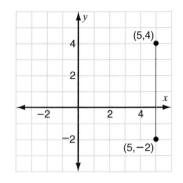

▶ The length of a *horizontal line segment* is the absolute value of the difference between the x-coordinates of its endpoints.

The distance between (x_1, y_1) and (x_2, y_1) is $|x_2 - x_1|$.

Find the length of a line segment with endpoints $(5, -2)$ and $(-3, -2)$.

$|-3 - 5|$ ◀—Substitute the given values into the formula.

   $|-8|$ ◀—Simplify.

    8 ◀—Find the absolute value.

So the length of a line segment with endpoints $(5, -2)$ and $(-3, -2)$ is 8.

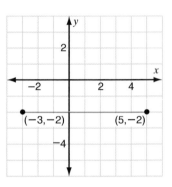

▶ To find the length of a line segment that is neither vertical nor horizontal, you can use the Pythagorean Theorem.

Find the length of a line segment with endpoints $(-3, -2)$ and $(5, 4)$.

1 Create a right triangle by drawing lines parallel to the axes through $(-3, -2)$ and $(5, 4)$. The lines intersect at $(5, -2)$. The vertical and horizontal segments are the legs of the right triangle, and the oblique segment (the one that is neither vertical nor horizontal) is the hypotenuse.

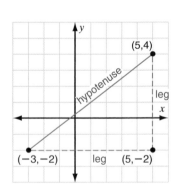

2 Find the lengths of the triangle's legs.

  $|4 - (-2)| = 6$ ◀—Find the length of the vertical leg.

  $|-3 - 5| = 8$ ◀—Find the length of the horizontal leg.

3 Substitute these measurements into the Pythagorean Theorem. Solve for the length of the oblique segment or hypotenuse.

    $6^2 + 8^2 = c^2$ ◀—Use the Pythagorean Theorem to find the length of the hypotenuse.

   $36 + 64 = c^2$ ◀—Simplify.

    $\sqrt{100} = \sqrt{c^2}$ ◀—Find the square root of both sides.

      $10 = c$

So the length of a line segment with endpoints $(-3, -2)$ and $(5, 4)$ is 10.

▶ The **Distance Formula**, which is derived from the Pythagorean Theorem, can be used to find the distance, d, between any two points, (x_1, y_1) and (x_2, y_2).

Create a right triangle by drawing lines parallel to the axes through the points. The lines intersect at (x_2, y_1). Let d represent the length of the hypotenuse.

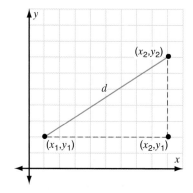

$|x_2 - x_1|$ ◀—Subtract the x-coordinates to find the length of the horizontal leg.

$|y_2 - y_1|$ ◀—Subtract the y-coordinates to find the length of the vertical leg.

$d^2 = (x_2 - x_1)^2 + (y_2 - y_1)^2$ ◀—Use the Pythagorean Theorem.

$\sqrt{d^2} = \sqrt{(x_2 - x_1)^2 + (y_2 - y_1)^2}$ ◀—Find the square root of both sides.

$d = \sqrt{(x_2 - x_1)^2 + (y_2 - y_1)^2}$

_____ **Key Concept** _____

The Distance Formula
The distance, d, between any two points, (x_1, y_1) and (x_2, y_2), can be found using the following formula.

$$d = \sqrt{(x_2 - x_1)^2 + (y_2 - y_1)^2}$$

Examples

Find the distance in simplest radical form between each set of points.

1 $(1, -1)$ and $(3, 5)$

$d = \sqrt{(3 - 1)^2 + [5 - (-1)]^2}$ ◀—Use the Distance Formula.

$d = \sqrt{2^2 + 6^2}$ ◀—Simplify.

$d = \sqrt{4 + 36}$ ◀—Simplify.

$d = \sqrt{40}$ ◀—Simplify.

$d = \sqrt{4}\sqrt{10}$ ◀—Use the Product Property of Square Roots.

$d = 2\sqrt{10}$ ◀—Write in simplest radical form.

The distance between $(1, -1)$ and $(3, 5)$ is $2\sqrt{10}$.

2 $(-3, 8)$ and $(-10, 1)$

$d = \sqrt{[-10 - (-3)]^2 + (1 - 8)^2}$ ◀—Use the Distance Formula.

$d = \sqrt{(-7)^2 + (-7)^2}$ ◀—Simplify.

$d = \sqrt{49 + 49}$ ◀—Simplify.

$d = \sqrt{49 \cdot 2}$ ◀—Simplify.

$d = \sqrt{49}\sqrt{2}$ ◀—Use the Product Property of Square Roots.

$d = 7\sqrt{2}$ ◀—Write in simplest radical form.

The distance between $(-3, 8)$ and $(-10, 1)$ is $7\sqrt{2}$.

Try These

Find the distance in simplest radical form between each set of points.

1. $(4, 1)$ and $(4, -2)$

2. $(3, -3)$ and $(2, -3)$

3. $(2, 4)$ and $(-1, 0)$

4. $(5, 6)$ and $(1, 4)$

5. $(-5, -7)$ and $(-1, -3)$

6. $\left(\frac{3}{4}, -\frac{5}{2}\right)$ and $\left(\frac{1}{4}, 0\right)$

7. Discuss and Write Find the perimeter of a triangle with vertices $(-5, 6)$, $(7, 0)$, and $(4, -3)$. Explain your method.

Go to ▶ PRACTICE BOOK **Lesson 9-6 for exercise sets.**

Problem-Solving Strategy:
⑦ Account for All Possibilities

Objective To solve problems using the strategy *Account for All Possibilities*

Problem I: Mr. and Mrs. Howell are taking their three young children to a theater performance. The family will sit in five consecutive seats. Mr. and Mrs. Howell want to make sure each child sits next to at least one parent. In how many different ways can the parents be seated?

Read ▸ **Read to understand what is being asked.**

List the facts and restate the question.

Facts: Three children and two parents will sit in a row.
Each child must sit next to at least one parent.

Question: In how many ways can the parents be seated?

Plan ▸ **Select a strategy.**

You can use the strategy *Account for All Possibilities*.

Solve ▸ **Apply the strategy.**

Make a table to account for all possibilities.

Let P represent a parent and C a child.

- List all the arrangements with a parent in Seat 1, shown in the first column of the table below. Then list all the *new* arrangements with a parent in Seat 2 in the next column. (Do not list PPCCC because that is in the first column.) Continue in this way. Notice that there are *no new* arrangements with a parent in Seat 5.

- Look carefully through the possibilities and underline those in which each child is sitting next to at least one parent.

Problem-Solving Strategies
1. Make a Drawing
2. Solve a Simpler Problem
3. Reason Logically
4. Consider Extreme Cases
5. Work Backward
6. Find a Pattern
7. Account for All Possibilities
8. Adopt a Different Point of View
9. Guess and Test
10. Organize Data

Arrangements with a Parent in Seat 1	New Arrangements with a Parent in Seat 2	New Arrangements with a Parent in Seat 3	New Arrangements with a Parent in Seat 4	New Arrangements with a Parent in Seat 5
PPCCC PCPCC PCCPC PCCCP	CPPCC CPCPC CPCCP	CCPPC CCPCP	CCCPP	

There are only three possibilities. However, for each one, Mr. and Mrs. Howell can choose *either* P position. Therefore, there are two options for each of these three arrangements, for a total of (3 • 2), or 6, different possibilities. These are listed below with M for mom and D for dad.

MCCDC   DCCMC   CMCDC   CDCMC   CMCCD   CDCCM

So there are 6 different ways in which the parents can be seated.

Check ▸ **Check to make sure your answer makes sense.**

Look back over the list and make sure that no arrangement is missed, in which each child is next to a parent. The answer checks.

Problem 2: Is 713 a prime number?

Read ▶ **Read to understand what is being asked.**

List the facts and restate the question.

Facts: A prime number is a whole number with no factors except itself and 1.

Question: Is 713 a prime number? That is, is there a whole number besides 1 and 713 that divides evenly into 713?

Plan ▶ **Select a strategy.**

Use the strategy *Account for All Possibilities*. Consider every whole number from 2 to 712 and check if the whole number is a factor of 713.

Solve ▶ **Apply the strategy.**

• Start by checking if any power of 2 is a factor of 713. Note that 713 is not an even number, so no power of 2 can be a factor.

• Narrow down the possible factors you have to check.

You need only to check *prime numbers* because, if 713 is divisible by a non-prime number, then it is also divisible by that number's prime factors.

You also need only to check numbers up to $\sqrt{713}$ because any factor greater than $\sqrt{713}$ is paired with a factor less than $\sqrt{713}$.

For example, consider 36, the factors of 36 are 1, 2, 3, 4, 6, 9, 12, 18, and 36. The square root of 36 is 6. Notice that each factor greater than 6 is paired with a factor less than 6 (9 is paired with 4, 12 is paired with 3, 18 is paired with 2, and 36 is paired with 1).

Since $\sqrt{713} \approx 26.7$, you need only to check prime numbers less than 27. These are 2, 3, 5, 7, 11, 13, 17, 19, 23. You can use "divisibility rules" to quickly eliminate 2, 3, and 5. You are left with only six numbers to test. Divide 713 by each number with pencil and paper or a handheld device.

Remember:
A whole number is divisible by 2 if its units digit is even.
A whole number is divisible by 3 if the sum of its digits is divisible by 3.
A whole number is divisible by 5 if its units digit is 0 or 5.

$713 \div 7 = 101\frac{6}{7} \longrightarrow 101 \text{ R}6 \qquad 713 \div 11 = 64\frac{9}{11} \longrightarrow 64 \text{ R}9$

$713 \div 13 = 54\frac{11}{13} \longrightarrow 54 \text{ R}11 \qquad 713 \div 17 = 41\frac{16}{17} \longrightarrow 41 \text{ R}16$

$713 \div 19 = 37\frac{10}{19} \longrightarrow 37 \text{ R}10 \qquad 713 \div 23 = 31$

Note that 23 is a factor of 713. So 713 is *not* a prime number.

Check ▶ **Check to make sure your answer makes sense.**

Multiply 23(31).

23(31) = 713. This shows that 713 is not prime because it has factors besides itself and 1.

The answer checks.

Enrichment:
Extending the Pythagorean Theorem to Three Dimensions

Objective To extend the Pythagorean Theorem to three dimensions • To extend the Distance Formula to three dimensions

Jenny's living room, as shown at the right, is a rectangular prism in shape. The room is 9 feet wide by 12 feet long, and the ceiling is 8 feet high. How can Jenny find the length of the diagonal from one corner of the floor to the opposite corner at the ceiling?

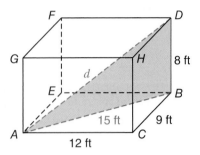

To find the length of the diagonal, use the Pythagorean Theorem.

- Use $\triangle ABC$ of the rectangular base to find the length of the diagonal of the base, $\overline{AB}$. Note that $\overline{AB}$ is the hypotenuse, and $\overline{AC}$ and $\overline{BC}$ are the legs.

$$(AC)^2 + (BC)^2 = (AB)^2 \quad \longleftarrow \text{Apply the Pythagorean Theorem.}$$

$$9^2 + 12^2 = (AB)^2 \quad \longleftarrow \text{Substitute the given values.}$$

$$81 + 144 = (AB)^2 \quad \longleftarrow \text{Simplify.}$$

$$225 = (AB)^2 \quad \longleftarrow \text{Simplify.}$$

$$\sqrt{225} = \sqrt{(AB)^2} \quad \longleftarrow \text{Find the square root of each side of the equation.}$$

$$15 = AB \quad \longleftarrow \text{Simplify.}$$

Remember:
Pythagorean Theorem
$$a^2 + b^2 = c^2$$

- Use $\triangle ABD$ to find the length of the diagonal of the rectangular prism, $\overline{AD}$. Note that $\overline{AD}$ is the hypotenuse, and $\overline{AB}$ and $\overline{DB}$ are the legs.

$$(AB)^2 + (DB)^2 = (AD)^2 \quad \longleftarrow \text{Apply the Pythagorean Theorem.}$$

$$15^2 + 8^2 = (AD)^2 \quad \longleftarrow \text{Substitute the given values.}$$

$$225 + 64 = (AD)^2 \quad \longleftarrow \text{Simplify.}$$

$$289 = (AD)^2 \quad \longleftarrow \text{Simplify.}$$

$$\sqrt{289} = \sqrt{(AD)^2} \quad \longleftarrow \text{Find the square root of each side of the equation.}$$

$$17 = AD \quad \longleftarrow \text{Simplify.}$$

So the length of the diagonal, d, from one corner of the floor to the opposite corner at the ceiling of Jenny's living room is 17 feet.

▶ You can generalize the steps above to extend the Pythagorean Theorem to three dimensions, that is, to find the diagonal of a rectangular prism that has a rectangular base of length, ℓ, and width, w, and a height, h.

- Find the length of a diagonal, d_1, of the rectangular base.

$$d_1 = \sqrt{(\text{length})^2 + (\text{width})^2} = \sqrt{\ell^2 + w^2}$$

- Find the length of a diagonal, d_2, of a rectangular prism.

$$d_2 = \sqrt{\ell^2 + w^2 + h^2}$$

Key Concept

Diagonal of a Rectangular Prism

$d_2 = \sqrt{\ell^2 + w^2 + h^2}$, where

$d_2 = $ the diagonal of the rectangular prism,
$\ell = $ the length of the rectangular base,
$w = $ the width of the rectangular base, and
$h = $ the height of the rectangular prism.

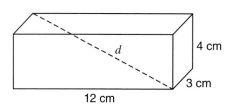

Jenny applied the formula on another rectangular prism. The prism, shown at the right, is 3 cm wide, 12 cm long, and 4 cm high. Find the length of the diagonal, d, of the rectangular prism.

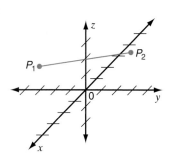

$$d = \sqrt{\ell^2 + w^2 + h^2} \longrightarrow d = \sqrt{3^2 + 4^2 + 12^2} = \sqrt{169}$$
$$= 13$$

So the length of the diagonal, d, of the rectangular prism is 13 cm.

▶ You can also extend the Distance Formula to three dimensions like the Pythagorean Theorem.

Points $P_1(x_1, y_1, z_1)$ and $P_2(x_2, y_2, z_2)$ are points in a three-dimensional coordinate system. The distance, d, between the points P_1 and P_2 is given by the formula:

$$d = \sqrt{(x_2 - x_1)^2 + (y_2 - y_1)^2 + (z_2 - z_1)^2}$$

Find the distance between $(-2, 1, 5)$ and $(1, 3, 7)$.

$$d = \sqrt{[1 - (-2)]^2 + (3 - 1)^2 + (7 - 5)^2}$$
$$= \sqrt{(3)^2 + (2)^2 + (2)^2} = \sqrt{9 + 4 + 4} = \sqrt{17} \approx 4.12$$

Remember:
Distance Formula
The distance between $P_1 (x_1, y_1)$ and $P_2 (x_2, y_2)$ is $d = \sqrt{(x_2 - x_1)^2 + (y_2 - y_1)^2}$.

Try These

Find the length of the diagonal in each rectangular prism. Round to the nearest tenth, if necessary.

1.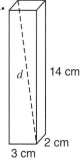

14 cm
2 cm
3 cm

2.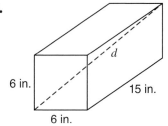

6 in.
15 in.
6 in.

3.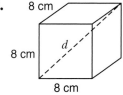

8 cm
8 cm
8 cm

Find the distance between each pair of points. Round to the nearest hundredth, if necessary.

4. $(0, 3, 8)$ and $(1, 5, 0)$

5. $(-3, 4, 5)$ and $(8, 5, 17)$

6. $(1, 2, 6)$ and $(1, -3, 13)$

7. Discuss and Write Consider Jenny's living room from the opening problem. Suppose that the floor of the room is 8 feet wide and 9 feet long and the ceiling is 12 feet high. What would be the length of the diagonal d from one corner of the floor to the opposite corner of the ceiling? How does this length compare to the length of the floor-to-ceiling diagonal in the opening problem? Explain.

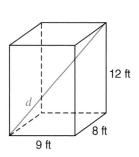

12 ft
8 ft
9 ft

Go to ▶ PRACTICE BOOK pages 235–236 for exercise sets.

Test Prep: Multiple-Choice Questions
Strategy: Apply Mathematical Reasoning

Sometimes you can estimate to help choose the correct answer in a multiple-choice item. If the choices given are not close in value, *an estimate* can help you determine which answers are reasonable and allow you to eliminate those that are not.

Look at the sample test item.

Read the whole test item, including the answer choices.

Ask yourself questions to clarify the meaning of the text.

• Underline important words.

The <u>area</u> of a circle is 10.24π square centimeters. What is its <u>radius</u>?

The *area* of a circle is equal to πr^2.

• Restate the question in your own words.

What is the square root of 10.24?

Solve the problem.

• Find an approximate answer using estimation.

$$A = \pi r^2 \quad \longleftarrow \text{Formula for the area of a circle}$$
$$10.24\pi = \pi r^2 \quad \longleftarrow \text{Substitute the given values.}$$
$$10.24 = r^2 \quad \longleftarrow \text{Use the Division Property of Equality.}$$
$$\sqrt{10.24} = r \quad \longleftarrow \text{Find the square root of each side.}$$

Sample Test Item

The area of a circle is 10.24π square centimeters. What is its radius?

A. 1.6 cm
B. 3.2 cm
C. 5.12 cm
D. 6.4 cm

Test-Taking Tips

• Underline important words.

• Restate the question.

• Use the Test-Prep strategy.

• Analyze and eliminate answer choices.

Estimate: $\sqrt{10.24}$

10.24 falls between two consecutive perfect squares: 9 and 16.

$$\sqrt{9} < \sqrt{10.24} < \sqrt{16} \quad \longleftarrow \text{Write an inequality.}$$
$$3 < \sqrt{10.24} < 4$$

Therefore, $\sqrt{10.24}$ is between 3 and 4.

Item Analysis

Choose the answer.

• Analyze and eliminate answer choices. Watch out for distractors.

A. 1.6 cm ⟵ This is less than 3. Eliminate this choice.

B. 3.2 cm ⟵ This is the correct choice!

C. 5.12 cm ⟵ This is greater than 4. Eliminate this choice.

D. 6.5 cm ⟵ This is greater than 4. Eliminate this choice.

Try These

Choose the correct answer. Explain how you eliminated answer choices.

1. The legs of a right triangle measure 21 inches and 19 inches. What is the length of the hypotenuse? If necessary, round to the nearest tenth.

A. 8.9 in.	**C.** 28.3 in.
B. 20 in.	**D.** 40 in.

2. What is the approximate area of a right triangle with one leg that measures 4 in. and a hypotenuse that measures 10 in.?

F. 18 in.^{2}	**H.** 36 in.^{2}
G. 32 in.^{2}	**J.** 24 in.^{2}

Go to PRACTICE BOOK page 237 for exercise sets.

CHAPTER 10

Quadratic Functions and Equations

In This Chapter You Will:

- Determine the direction of the opening of the graph of a quadratic function and find its maximum or minimum value
- Graph a parabola and determine its vertex and axis of symmetry
- Solve quadratic equations by factoring, completing the square, or with the quadratic formula

- Determine solutions of a quadratic equation by using the discriminant
- Solve linear-quadratic systems of equations
- Apply the strategy: *Adopt a Different Point of View*
- Look for new vocabulary words highlighted in each lesson

Do You Remember?

- A linear function is a function whose graph is a nonvertical line.
- A function table is a table of ordered pairs that represent solutions of a function.
- The Zero Property for Multiplication: Multiplying a number by 0 results in a product of 0.
  - The *radicand* is the expression under a radical sign ($\sqrt{\ }$).

For Practice Exercises:

 PRACTICE BOOK, pp. 243–276

For Chapter Support: (ONLINE)

 www.progressinmathematics.com

- Skills Update Practice
- Practice Activities
- Audio Glossary
- Vocabulary Activities

- Technology Videos
- Enrichment Activities
- Electronic SourceBook

 VIRTUAL MANIPULATIVES

Critical Thinking

While traveling with a group on safari in Africa, Bridget drove the lead vehicle for 90 miles at an average rate of speed. If she had increased her speed by 12 mph, the distance would have been covered in 2 hours less time. What equation can be written to show the difference in travel time had Bridget gone at the greater speed?

Identify Quadratic Functions and Their Graphs

Objective To determine the direction of opening of the graph of a quadratic function • To determine the vertex, axis of symmetry, and intercepts of a parabola, given its graph • To find the maximum or minimum value and the domain and range of a quadratic function, given its graph

Kansas City is known as the City of Fountains. One of its famous fountains is pictured at the right. The streams of water from fountains all take on the same basic shape.

The shape of the water shooting out of a fountain is a curve called a parabola. A parabola is the graph of a quadratic function.

___ **Key Concept** ___

Quadratic Function
A quadratic function is a function that can be written in the form, $f(x) = ax^2 + bx + c, a \neq 0$, or $y = ax^2 + bx + c, a \neq 0$. This form is the standard form of a quadratic function.

▶ When a quadratic function is written in standard form, $y = ax^2 + bx + c, a \neq 0$, the value of the leading coefficient, a, determines the direction that the parabola opens.

- When $a > 0$, the parabola opens upward.
- When $a < 0$, the parabola opens downward.

For $y = -2x^2 + 5x - 2, a = -2$. Since $-2 < 0$, the graph of the function, or the parabola, opens downward.

For $y = 5x^2, a = 5$. Since $5 > 0$, the graph of the function, or the parabola, opens upward.

Examples

Tell whether the graph of the quadratic function opens *upward* or *downward*. Explain.

1 $y - x^2 = 3 + 2x$

$y - x^2 + x^2 = 3 + 2x + x^2$ ◀—Apply the Addition Property of Equality to write the equation in standard form.

$y = 3 + 2x + x^2$ ◀—Simplify.

$y = x^2 + 2x + 3$ ◀—Apply the Commutative Property.

$a = 1$ and $1 > 0$, so the parabola opens upward.

2 $3x^2 + y = 2$

$3x^2 - 3x^2 + y = -3x^2 + 2$ ◀—Apply the Subtraction Property of Equality to write the equation in standard form.

$y = -3x^2 + 2$ ◀—Simplify.

$a = -3$ and $-3 < 0$, so the parabola opens downward.

▶ The point at which a parabola changes direction is called the turning point, or vertex. If a parabola opens upward, the vertex is the lowest point. The y-value of the vertex is the **minimum value** of the function. If a parabola opens downward, the vertex is the highest point. The y-value of the vertex is the **maximum value** of the function.

Look at the parabolas shown at the right.

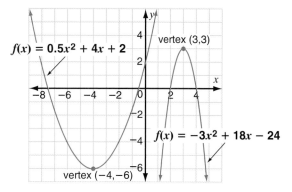

- The graph of $f(x) = 0.5x^2 + 4x + 2$ opens upward. Its vertex, the lowest point, is at $(-4, -6)$. The function has a minimum value of -6.

- The graph of $f(x) = -3x^2 + 18x - 24$ opens downward. Its vertex, the highest point, is at $(3, 3)$. The function has a maximum value of 3.

Examples

Identify the vertex of the parabola. Then give the *minimum* or *maximum value* of the function.

1

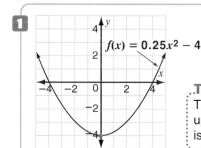

.Think......................
The parabola opens upward, so the vertex is the lowest point.

The vertex is $(0, -4)$.
The function has a minimum value of -4.

2

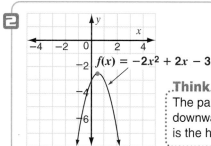

.Think......................
The parabola opens downward, so the vertex is the highest point.

The vertex is $\left(\frac{1}{2}, -2\frac{1}{2}\right)$.
The function has a maximum value of $-2\frac{1}{2}$.

▶ The domain of a quadratic function, $f(x) = ax^2 + bx = c$, where $a \neq 0$, is the set of all real numbers. If the parabola opens upward, the range of the function will be all values greater than or equal to the minimum value. If the parabola opens downward, the range will be all values less than or equal to the maximum value.

State the domain and range of the quadratic function.

$f(x) = 2x^2 - 12x + 11$

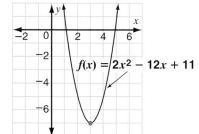

.Think......................
The vertex is at $(3, -7)$; the minimum value is -7.

The domain is the set of all real numbers.
The range is $\{y \mid y \geq -7\}$

$f(x) = -x^2 - 4x - 5$

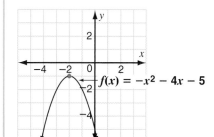

.Think......................
The vertex is at $(-2, -1)$; the maximum value is -1.

The domain is the set of all real numbers.
The range is $\{y \mid y \leq -1\}$

Continue Lesson ➡

▶ You can fold the graph of any quadratic function, $f(x) = ax^2 + bx + c, a \neq 0$, at the vertical line through its vertex, and the two halves will match exactly. This fold line is called the axis of symmetry.

For a quadratic function, the vertex is the only point on the parabola that is on the axis of symmetry.

Remember: The equation of a vertical line is $x = k$, with k as any real number.

Look at the parabola shown at the right.

The vertex of the parabola is $(-2, -7)$.

The equation of its axis of symmetry is $x = -2$.

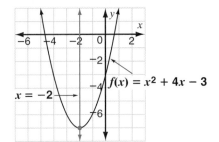

$f(x) = x^2 + 4x - 3$

$x = -2$

Example

1 Identify the vertex of the parabola. Then write the equation of its axis of symmetry.

The vertex of the parabola is $(1.5, 4.5)$.

The equation of the axis of symmetry is $x = 1.5$.

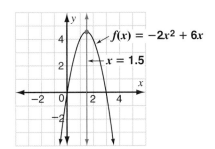

$f(x) = -2x^2 + 6x$

$x = 1.5$

▶ The x-intercepts of a graph are the x-values for the points where the graph intersects the x-axis. A parabola may have *one*, *two*, or *no* x-intercepts. Look at the parabolas shown at the right.

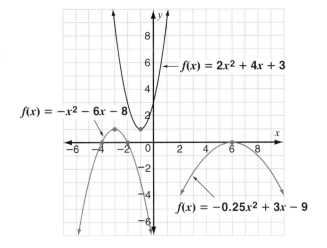

$f(x) = 2x^2 + 4x + 3$

$f(x) = -x^2 - 6x - 8$

$f(x) = -0.25x^2 + 3x - 9$

- The graph of $f(x) = -x^2 - 6x - 8$ intersects the x-axis at $(-4, 0)$ and $(-2, 0)$. Its x-intercepts are -4 and -2.
- The graph of $f(x) = -0.25x^2 + 3x - 9$ intersects the x-axis at one point, $(6, 0)$. Its x-intercept is 6.
- The graph of $f(x) = 2x^2 + 4x + 3$ does not intersect the x-axis. It does *not* have an x-intercept.

Examples

Find the x-intercepts of the parabola.

1

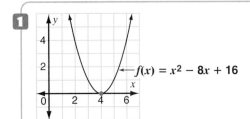

$f(x) = x^2 - 8x + 16$

The graph of $f(x) = x^2 - 8x + 16$ intersects the x-axis at one point, $(4, 0)$.

Its x-intercept is 4.

2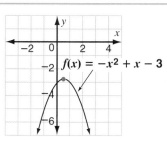

The graph of $f(x) = -x^2 + x - 3$ does not intersect the x-axis.

It does not have an x-intercept.

3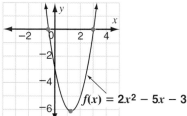

The graph of $f(x) = 2x^2 - 5x - 3$ intersects the x-axis at two points, $(-0.5, 0)$ and $(3, 0)$.

Its x-intercepts are -0.5 and 3.

Try These

Tell whether the graph of the quadratic function opens *upward* or *downward*. Explain.

1. $y = 5x + 3x^2 - 4$

2. $y - 3 = x^2$

3. $y + x^2 = 7$

4. $y - 7x^2 = -11$

5. $y = 6 + x^2 - 2x$

6. $y + 5 + 2x^2 = 3$

For the parabola shown, identify the following:
- **vertex**
- **maximum or minimum value**
- **x-intercept(s)**
- **axis of symmetry**
- **domain and range**

7.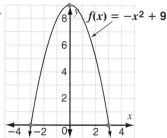

8.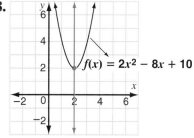

9.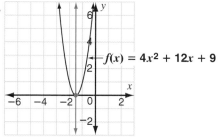

10.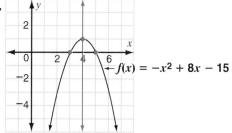

11. Discuss and Write If the graph of a quadratic function has a minimum point, what does that tell you about the function? if the graph has a maximum point? Describe the domain and range for each case.

Go to PRACTICE BOOK **Lesson 10-1 for exercise sets.**

Graph Quadratic Functions: Parabola

Objective To find the coordinates of the vertex of a parabola and the equation of its axis of symmetry, given its function rule • To graph a quadratic function • To use a handheld to investigate the characteristics of families of parabolas

▶ You can graph a quadratic function by making a function table. It is helpful to always include the vertex as one of the points in the table when graphing a quadratic function.

Graph $y = x^2 - 8x + 12$, using the vertex and a function table.

To graph a quadratic function:

___ **Key Concept** ___

Graph of a Quadratic Function
For the graph of a quadratic function,
$f(x) = ax^2 + bx + c$ or $y = ax^2 + bx + c$,
where a, b, and c are real numbers and $a \neq 0$:

• $x = -\dfrac{b}{2a}$ is the equation of its axis of symmetry.

• the x-coordinate of its vertex is $-\dfrac{b}{2a}$.

1 Find the equation of the axis of symmetry.

$a = 1$ and $b = -8$ ◀—Identify the values of a and b in $y = ax^2 + bx + c$.

$x = \dfrac{-b}{2a} = \dfrac{-(-8)}{2 \cdot 1}$ ◀—Substitute 1 for a and -8 for b in $x = \dfrac{-b}{2a}$.

$\quad = \dfrac{8}{2}$

$\quad = 4$ ◀—Simplify.

The equation of the axis of symmetry is $x = 4$.

2 Find the coordinates of the vertex.
The x-coordinate of the vertex is 4.

$y = x^2 - 8x + 12$

$\quad = 4^2 - 8 \cdot 4 + 12$ ◀—Substitute 4 for x in $y = x^2 - 8x + 12$.

$\quad = 16 - 32 + 12 = -4$ ◀—Simplify.

The vertex is at $(4, -4)$.

3 Make a function table. Select three x-values *greater than* 4, the x-coordinate of the vertex, and three x-values *less than* 4. The more points you add to your table, the more accurate your graph will be.

x	y	(x, y)
1	$(1)^2 - 8(1) + 12 = 5$	$(1, 5)$
2	$(2)^2 - 8(2) + 12 = 0$	$(2, 0)$
3	$(3)^2 - 8(3) + 12 = -3$	$(3, -3)$
4	$(4)^2 - 8(4) + 12 = -4$	$(4, -4)$
5	$(5)^2 - 8(5) + 12 = -3$	$(5, -3)$
6	$(6)^2 - 8(6) + 12 = 0$	$(6, 0)$
7	$(7)^2 - 8(7) + 12 = 5$	$(7, 5)$

4 Graph the ordered pairs in the table on a coordinate plane. Draw a smooth curve through them.

The graph of $f(x) = x^2 - 8x + 12$ is shown at the right. Notice that the parabola opens upward because $a = 1$ and $a > 0$.

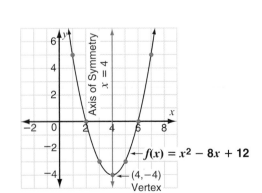

Write the equation of the axis of symmetry, and find the coordinates of the vertex of the parabola. Then make a function table, and graph the function.

 $f(x) = -\frac{1}{4}x^2 + 3x - 9$

- **Find the equation of the axis of symmetry.**

$a = -\frac{1}{4}$ and $b = 3$

$$x = \frac{-b}{2a} = \frac{-(3)}{2\left(-\frac{1}{4}\right)} = \frac{-3}{-\frac{1}{2}} = -3(-2) = 6$$

So the equation of the axis of symmetry is $x = 6$.

- **Find the coordinates of the vertex.**

The x-coordinate of the vertex is 6.

$$y = -\frac{1}{4}x^2 + 3x - 9 = -\frac{1}{4}(6)^2 + 3(6) - 9 = 0$$

So the vertex is at $(6, 0)$.

- Select two x-values *greater than* 6 and two x-values *less than* 6, and make a function table. Then graph.

.Think...

Since $a = -\frac{1}{4}$, even numbers for x-values will be easier to compute.

x	y	(x, y)
2	$-\frac{1}{4}(2)^2 + 3(2) - 9 = -4$	$(2, -4)$
4	$-\frac{1}{4}(4)^2 + 3(4) - 9 = -1$	$(4, -1)$
6	$-\frac{1}{4}(6)^2 + 3(6) - 9 = 0$	$(6, 0)$
8	$-\frac{1}{4}(8)^2 + 3(8) - 9 = -1$	$(8, -1)$
10	$-\frac{1}{4}(10)^2 + 3(10) - 9 = -4$	$(10, -4)$

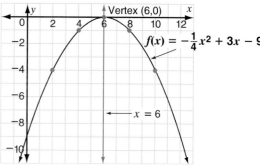

The parabola opens downward because $a = -\frac{1}{4}$ and $a < 0$.

2 $y = 4x^2 - 9$

- **Find the equation of the axis of symmetry.**

$a = 4$ and $b = 0$

$$x = \frac{-b}{2a} = \frac{-0}{2(4)} = 0$$

So the equation of the axis of symmetry is $x = 0$.

- **Find the coordinates of the vertex.**

The x-coordinate of the vertex is 0.

$$y = 4x^2 - 9 = 4(0)^2 - 9 = -9$$

So the vertex is at $(0, -9)$.

- Select two x-values *greater than* 0 and two x-values *less than* 0, and make a function table. Then graph.

x	y	(x, y)
-2	$4(-2)^2 - 9 = 7$	$(-2, 7)$
-1	$4(-1)^2 - 9 = -5$	$(-1, -5)$
0	$4(0)^2 - 9 = -9$	$(0, -9)$
1	$4(1)^2 - 9 = -5$	$(1, -5)$
2	$4(2)^2 - 9 = 7$	$(2, 7)$

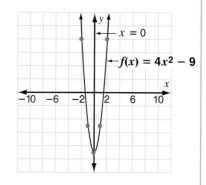

The parabola opens upward because $a = 4$ and $4 > 0$.

Continue Lesson ➡

3 $f(x) = -2x^2 + 4x - 5$

- Find the equation of the axis of symmetry.

  $a = -2$ and $b = 4$

  $x = \dfrac{-b}{2a} = \dfrac{-4}{2(-2)} = 1$

  So the equation of the axis of symmetry is $x = 1$.

- Find the coordinates of the vertex.

  The x-coordinate of the vertex is 1.

  $y = -2x^2 + 4x - 5 = -2(1)^2 + 4(1) - 5$
  $\qquad = -3$

  So the vertex is at $(1, -3)$.

- Select two x-values *greater than* 1 and two x-values *less than* 1 and make a function table. Then graph.

x	y	(x, y)
-1	$-2(-1)^2 + 4(-1) - 5 = -11$	$(-1, -11)$
0	$-2(0)^2 + 4(0) - 5 = -5$	$(0, -5)$
1	$-2(1)^2 + 4(1) - 5 = -3$	$(1, -3)$
2	$-2(2)^2 + 4(2) - 5 = -5$	$(2, -5)$
3	$-2(3)^2 + 4(3) - 5 = -11$	$(3, -11)$

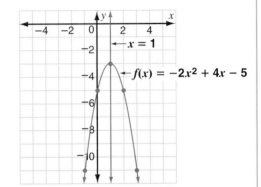

The parabola opens downward because $a = -2$ and $a < 0$.

▶ The simplest function with the defining characteristics of a family of functions is called a *parent function*. Functions in the same family are transformations of their parent function.

Families of parabolas often fall into two categories—those that have the same vertex and those that have the same shape. A handheld can help you investigate the characteristics of families of parabolas.

The parent function of each of the following families of parabolas is $y = x^2$. When analyzing and comparing the shapes of various graphs, you should compare the graphs using the same parameters.

- Graph $y = x^2$ and $y = -x^2$ on the same coordinate plane.

  Press 🏠 . Then choose **2** to select Graphs and Geometry. Input both functions into the handheld.

  Notice that each graph has the same shape and the same axis of symmetry, and that each has its vertex at the origin.

  However, the graph of $y = -x^2$ opens downward, the opposite of the opening of the graph of the parent function, $y = x^2$, which opens upward.

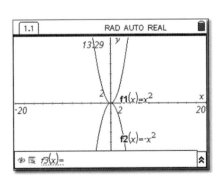

- Graph $y = x^2$, $y = 2x^2$, and $y = \frac{1}{2}x^2$. Press 🔘, **ctrl** , and **clear ⌫** to erase the prior function $-x^2$. Input $2x^2$ and $\frac{1}{2}x^2$.

  Notice that each graph opens upward and has its vertex at the origin, and that each has the same axis of symmetry. However, the graph of $y = 2x^2$ is narrower than the graph of the parent function, $y = x^2$, and the graph of $y = \frac{1}{2}x^2$ is much wider.

  The coefficient of x^2, a, changes the width of the parabola.

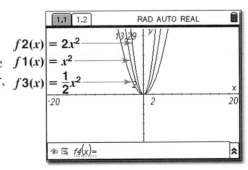

Examples

Graph the group of quadratic functions on the same screen.
Compare and contrast the graphs.

1 Input $y = x^2$ into the handheld.
Then input $y = x^2 + 2$ and $y = x^2 - 2$.

Notice that each graph opens upward and has the same
axis of symmetry. However, the graph of $y = x^2 + 2$ is
two units higher than the graph of the parent function,
$y = x^2$, and the graph of $y = x^2 - 2$ is two units lower.

Adding or subtracting a constant changes the vertical
position of $y = x^2$.

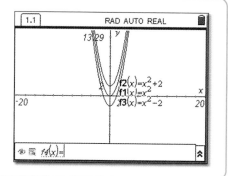

2 Input $y = x^2$ into the handheld.
Then input $y = (x + 2)^2$ and $y = (x - 2)^2$.

Notice that each graph has the same shape and
the same y-value of the vertex. However, the graph
of $y = (x + 2)^2$ is two units to the left of the graph
of the parent function, $y = x^2$, and the graph of
$y = (x - 2)^2$ is two units to its right.

The function $y = (x \pm c)^2$ changes the horizontal
position of $y = x^2$.

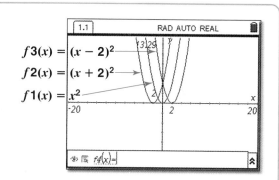

$$f3(x) = (x - 2)^2$$
$$f2(x) = (x + 2)^2$$
$$f1(x) = x^2$$

Try These

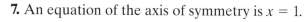

**Write the equation of the axis of symmetry, and find the coordinates of the
vertex of the parabola. Then make a function table and graph the function.**

1. $y = -x^2 + 4$ **2.** $y = x^2 - 5$ **3.** $y = x^2 + 6x + 9$

4. $y = -x^2 + x - 1$ **5.** $y = -3x^2 - 6x + 4$ **6.** $y = 2x^2 + 8x + 3$

**Use the graph at the right. Write if the statement is *true* or *false*.
If false, explain why.**

7. An equation of the axis of symmetry is $x = 1$.

8. The vertex is at $(1, 4)$.

9. The x-intercepts are at -1 and 3.

10. An equation of the parabola is $y = x^2 + 2x + 3$.

11. The parabola intersects the y-axis at $(3, 0)$.

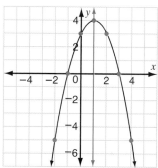

12. Discuss and Write Predict how the graphs of $y = x^2 - 1$ and $y = (x - 1)^2$ are different
from their parent function, $y = x^2$. Check your prediction using a handheld. Describe
how your predictions were the same and different from the actual result.

Go to ▶ PRACTICE BOOK Lesson 10-2 for exercise sets.

Solve Quadratic Equations by Factoring

Objective To solve quadratic equations by factoring • To relate a quadratic equation with a quadratic function • To solve radical equations leading to quadratic equations

Two consecutive integers have a product of 20. What are the integers?

To find the integers, write and solve an algebraic equation. First, define the variable. Then write two equivalent expressions.

Let x = the first integer.

$x + 1$ ◄—represents the next consecutive integer

20 ◄—represents the product of the integers

$x(x + 1) = 20$ ◄—an algebraic equation showing *equal expressions* for the product of the integers

$x^2 + x = 20$ ◄—Apply the Distributive Property.

$x^2 + x - 20 = 20 - 20$ ◄—Apply the Subtraction Property of Equality.

$x^2 + x - 20 = 0$ ◄—Simplify.

▶ The equation $x^2 + x - 20 = 0$ is a quadratic equation in one variable that is in standard form.

The equation $ax^2 + bx + c = 0$, where a, b, and c are real numbers and $a \neq 0$ is a quadratic equation that is written in the standard form. The values of the variable in an equation that make the equation true are called the solutions of the equation.

To solve a quadratic equation by factoring, apply the **Zero-Product Property**. This property enables you to conclude that if a product equals 0, at least one of the factors of the product must equal 0.

___ **Key Concept** ___

Zero-Product Property

$ab = 0$ if and only if $a = 0$ or $b = 0$ where a and b are real numbers.

Solve: $x^2 + x - 20 = 0$

$(x + 5)(x - 4) = 0$ ◄—Factor $x^2 + x - 20$.

$x + 5 = 0 \quad$ or $\quad x - 4 = 0$ ◄—Apply the Zero-Product Property.

$x = -5 \qquad\qquad x = 4$ ◄—Solve for x.

Solution set: $\{-5, 4\}$

Check: $x(x + 1) = 20$

$-5(-5 + 1) \overset{?}{=} 20$

$-5(-4) \overset{?}{=} 20$

$20 = 20$ True

$x(x + 1) = 20$

$4(4 + 1) \overset{?}{=} 20$

$4(5) \overset{?}{=} 20$

$20 = 20$ True

.**Think**.........
If $x = -5$, then $x + 1 = -4$.
If $x = 4$, then $x + 1 = 5$.
....

So the consecutive integers whose product is 20 are -5 and -4 or 4 and 5.

▶ The solutions of the quadratic equation, $ax^2 + bx + c = 0$, are the x-intercepts of the related quadratic function, $f(x) = ax^2 + bx + c$. The solutions of the equation are called the roots of the equation or zeros of the function.

Look at the graph of $y = x^2 + x - 20$ at the right. The solutions of the quadratic equation $x^2 + x - 20 = 0$ are the x-intercepts of the related quadratic function, $y = x^2 + x - 20$.

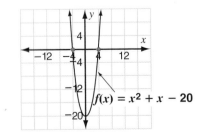

$f(x) = x^2 + x - 20$

Examples

Solve each equation by factoring.

1 **Solve:** $x^2 = 36$

$\quad\quad x^2 - 36 = 0$ ←—Write in standard form.

$(x + 6)(x - 6) = 0$ ←—Write as the product of factors.

$x + 6 = 0 \quad$ or $\quad x - 6 = 0$ ←—Apply the Zero-Product Property; set each factor equal to 0.

$\quad x = -6 \quad\quad\quad\quad x = 6$ ←—Apply the Addition and Subtraction Properties of Equality.

Check: $\quad x^2 \stackrel{?}{=} 36 \quad\quad\quad\quad\quad\quad\quad\quad x^2 \stackrel{?}{=} 36 \quad\quad\quad$ Solution set:

$\quad\quad (-6)^2 \stackrel{?}{=} 36 \quad\quad\quad\quad\quad\quad\quad (6)^2 \stackrel{?}{=} 36 \quad\quad\quad$ $\{-6, 6\}$

$\quad\quad\quad 36 = 36 \ \text{True} \quad\quad\quad\quad\quad\quad\quad 36 = 36 \ \text{True}$

2 **Solve:** $11x = 2x^2 + 14$

$2x^2 - 11x + 14 = 0$ ←—Write the equation in standard form.

$(x - 2)(2x - 7) = 0$ ←—Factor.

$x - 2 = 0 \quad$ or $\quad 2x - 7 = 0$ ←—Apply the Zero-Product Property; set each factor equal to 0.

$\quad x = 2 \quad\quad\quad\quad 2x = 7$ ←—Apply the Addition Property of Equality.

$\quad\quad\quad\quad\quad\quad\quad x = \dfrac{7}{2}$ ←—Apply the Division Property of Equality.

Check: $\quad 2x^2 - 11x + 14 = 0 \quad\quad\quad\quad\quad 2x^2 - 11x + 14 = 0$

$\quad\quad 2(2)^2 - 11(2) + 14 \stackrel{?}{=} 0 \quad\quad\quad\quad 2\left(\dfrac{7}{2}\right)^2 - 11\left(\dfrac{7}{2}\right) + 14 \stackrel{?}{=} 0$

$\quad\quad\quad\quad 8 - 22 + 14 \stackrel{?}{=} 0 \quad\quad\quad\quad\quad\quad \dfrac{49}{2} - \dfrac{77}{2} + 14 \stackrel{?}{=} 0 \quad\quad\quad$ Solution set:

$\quad\quad\quad\quad\quad -14 + 14 \stackrel{?}{=} 0 \quad\quad\quad\quad\quad\quad\quad\quad -14 + 14 \stackrel{?}{=} 0 \quad\quad\quad$ $\left\{2, \dfrac{7}{2}\right\}$

$\quad\quad\quad\quad\quad\quad\quad\quad 0 = 0 \ \text{True} \quad\quad\quad\quad\quad\quad\quad\quad\quad 0 = 0 \ \text{True}$

3 **Solve:** $6x^2 - 14x - 12 = 0$

$2(3x^2 - 7x - 6) = 0$ ←—Factor out the greatest common monomial factor.

$2(x - 3)(3x + 2) = 0$ ←—Factor the trinomial.

$x - 3 = 0 \quad$ or $\quad 3x + 2 = 0$ ←—Apply the Zero-Product Property.

$\quad x = 3 \quad\quad\quad\quad 3x = -2$ ←—Apply the Addition and Subtraction Properties of Equality.

$\quad\quad\quad\quad\quad\quad\quad x = -\dfrac{2}{3}$ ←—Apply the Division Property of Equality.

Check: $\quad 6x^2 - 14x - 12 = 0 \quad\quad\quad\quad\quad 6x^2 - 14x - 12 = 0$

$\quad\quad 6(3)^2 - 14(3) - 12 \stackrel{?}{=} 0 \quad\quad\quad\quad 6\left(-\dfrac{2}{3}\right)^2 - 14\left(-\dfrac{2}{3}\right) - 12 \stackrel{?}{=} 0$

$\quad\quad\quad\quad 54 - 42 - 12 \stackrel{?}{=} 0 \quad\quad\quad\quad\quad\quad\quad \dfrac{8}{3} + \dfrac{28}{3} - 12 \stackrel{?}{=} 0 \quad\quad\quad$ Solution set:

$\quad\quad\quad\quad\quad 12 - 12 \stackrel{?}{=} 0 \quad\quad\quad\quad\quad\quad\quad\quad\quad \dfrac{36}{3} - 12 \stackrel{?}{=} 0 \quad\quad\quad$ $\left\{3, -\dfrac{2}{3}\right\}$

$\quad\quad\quad\quad\quad\quad\quad\quad 0 = 0 \ \text{True} \quad\quad\quad\quad\quad\quad\quad\quad\quad\quad 0 = 0 \ \text{True}$

Continue Lesson ➡

▶Sometimes, there is only one solution to a quadratic equation.

Solve: $x^2 - 10x + 25 = 0$

$(x - 5)(x - 5) = 0$ ←—Factor.

$x - 5 = 0$ ←—Apply the Zero-Product Property.

$x = 5$ ←—Apply the Addition Property of Equality.

Check: $x^2 - 10x + 25 \overset{?}{=} 0$

$(5)^2 - 10(5) + 25 \overset{?}{=} 0$

$25 - 50 + 25 \overset{?}{=} 0$

$0 = 0$ True

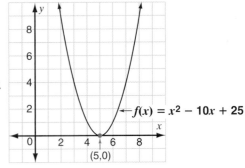

$f(x) = x^2 - 10x + 25$

$(5,0)$

Look at the graph at the right of the related function, $f(x) = x^2 - 10x + 25$. Notice that 5 is its only x-intercept.

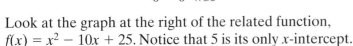

Example

1 Solve by factoring.

Solve: $4x^2 + 64x + 256 = 0$

$4(x^2 + 16x + 64) = 0$ ←—Factor out the greatest common monomial factor.

$4(x + 8)(x + 8) = 0$ ←—Write as the product of factors. Two factors are the same.

$x + 8 = 0$ ←—Apply the Zero-Product Property; $4 \neq 0$.

$x = -8$ ←—Apply the Subtraction Property of Equality.

Check: $4x^2 + 64x + 256 = 0$

$4(-8)^2 + 64(-8) + 256 \overset{?}{=} 0$

$256 - 512 + 256 \overset{?}{=} 0$

$0 = 0$ True

▶Not every quadratic equation can be factored over the integers. Sometimes, the roots of a quadratic equation are irrational numbers, or the roots are not real numbers.

The graph of $f(x) = x^2 - 2x - 5$ has two x-intercepts, x_1 and x_2, that are not integers. They can only be approximated.

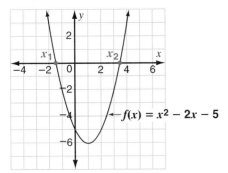

$f(x) = x^2 - 2x - 5$

The graph of $f(x) = x^2 - 5x + 7$ does not have any x-intercepts.

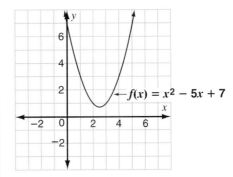

$f(x) = x^2 - 5x + 7$

So the roots of the related quadratic equation, $x^2 - 2x - 5 = 0$, are x_1 and x_2 with $-2 < x_1 < -1$ and $3 < x_2 < 4$.

So the related equation, $x^2 - 5x + 7 = 0$, does not have real-number roots.

▶Some equations containing radicals result in quadratic equations. Sometimes the quadratic equations will have extra roots, called *extraneous roots*, so not all the roots of the quadratic equations are solutions of the original equations.

Solve: $x = \sqrt{x + 6}$

$x^2 = (\sqrt{x + 6})^2$ ◀—Square both sides of the equation.

$x^2 = x + 6$ ◀—Simplify.

$x^2 - x - 6 = 0$ ◀—Write in standard form.

$(x + 2)(x - 3) = 0$ ◀—Factor.

$x + 2 = 0$　or　$x - 3 = 0$ ◀—Apply the Zero-Product Property.

$x = -2$　　　　$x = 3$ ◀—Apply the Addition and Subtraction Properties of Equality.

Check:　$x = \sqrt{x + 6}$　　　　$x = \sqrt{x + 6}$

$-2 \overset{?}{=} \sqrt{-2 + 6}$　　　$3 \overset{?}{=} \sqrt{3 + 6}$

$-2 \overset{?}{=} \sqrt{4}$　　　　　$3 \overset{?}{=} \sqrt{9}$

$-2 \neq 2$　　　　　　$3 = 3$ True

Think........................
⋮ −2 is an extraneous root. ⋮
....

Solution set: {3}

Example

1 **Solve:** $\sqrt{3x - 2} = x$

$(\sqrt{3x - 2})^2 = x^2$ ◀—Square both sides of the equation.

$3x - 2 = x^2$ ◀—Simplify.

$x^2 - 3x + 2 = 0$ ◀—Write in standard form.

$(x - 2)(x - 1) = 0$ ◀—Write as the product of factors.

$x - 2 = 0$　or　$x - 1 = 0$ ◀—Use the Zero-Product Property.

$x = 2$　or　　$x = 1$ ◀—Use the Addition Property of Equality.

Remember: Apply the Addition and Subtraction Properties of Equality to write the equation in standard form.

Check: $\sqrt{3x - 2} = x$　　　$\sqrt{3x - 2} = x$

$\sqrt{3(2) - 2} \overset{?}{=} 2$　　　$\sqrt{3(1) - 2} \overset{?}{=} 1$

$\sqrt{6 - 2} \overset{?}{=} 2$　　　　$\sqrt{3 - 2} \overset{?}{=} 1$

　　　$2 = 2$ True　　　　　$1 = 1$ True

Solution set: {1, 2}

Try These

Solve each equation by factoring. Then check the solutions.

1. $x^2 - 11x + 30 = 0$ 　　**2.** $16x + 1 = -64x^2$ 　　**3.** $10x^2 - 60 = 25x$

4. $9x^2 - 25 = 0$ 　　**5.** $7x^2 - 11x = 6$ 　　**6.** $x = \sqrt{5x + 14}$

7. Discuss and Write Explain how to solve a quadratic equation by factoring.

 Go to **PRACTICE BOOK Lesson 10-3 for exercise sets.**

Solve Verbal Problems Involving Quadratic Equations

Objective To solve verbal problems involving quadratic equations • To write quadratic equations, given their roots

Mrs. Baca's art class is painting a mural on the front of the school. The mural is 3 meters wider than it is high and has an area of 10 m². What are the dimensions of the mural?

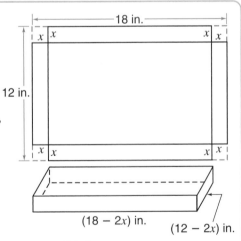

▶ To find the dimensions of the mural, write and solve an equation by using the formula for the area of a rectangle, $A = \ell w$.

Let x = the height of the mural, and
$x + 3$ = the width of the mural.

$x(x + 3) = 10$ ◀——an algebraic equation for the area of the mural
$x^2 + 3x = 10$ ◀——Apply the Distributive Property.
$x^2 + 3x - 10 = 0$ ◀——Write the equation in standard form.
$(x + 5)(x - 2) = 0$ ◀——Factor.
$x + 5 = 0$ or $x - 2 = 0$ ◀——Apply the Zero-Product Property.
     $x = -5$ $x = 2$ ◀——Solve using the Addition and Subtraction Properties of Equality.

If $x = 2$, then the height is 2 meters and the width is $x + 3$, which is 5 meters.

.Think....................................
Reject the solution $x = -5$ because height cannot be a negative number.

Examples

1 Hasim wants to make a tray from a 12-inch by 18-inch sheet of cardboard by cutting a square out of each corner and folding and taping the sides. How long should each side of the square cutout be if Hasim wants the base of the tray to have an area of 112 square inches?

Let x = the length of a side of the square cutout,
$18 - 2x$ = the length of the tray, and
$12 - 2x$ = the width of the tray.

$(18 - 2x)(12 - 2x) = 112$ ◀——Apply the formula for area, $A = \ell w$.
$216 - 60x + 4x^2 = 112$ ◀——Apply the Distributive Property.
$4x^2 - 60x + 104 = 0$ ◀——Write the equation in standard form.
$4(x - 13)(x - 2) = 0$ ◀——Factor.
$x - 13 = 0$ or $x - 2 = 0$ ◀——Apply the Zero-Product Property.
     $x = 13$ $x = 2$ ◀——Apply the Addition Property of Equality.

$x = 2$ is a reasonable answer.

.Think....................................
$x = 13$ does not make sense because the corner squares cannot be longer than the width (12 in.).

Check: $[18 - 2(2)][12 - 2(2)] \overset{?}{=} 112$
$(18 - 4)(12 - 4) \overset{?}{=} 112$
$112 = 112$ True

So the square cutout should be 2 inches on each side.

2 If the formula $d = 16t^2$ gives the number of feet, (d), an object falls in t seconds, how long will it take a pebble to fall 49 feet from a bridge to the water below?

$d = 16t^2 \longrightarrow 49 = 16t^2$ ←——Substitute the information given into the formula.

$\qquad 0 = 16t^2 - 49$ ←——Write the equation in standard form.

$\qquad 0 = (4t - 7)(4t + 7)$ ←——Factor.

$4t - 7 = 0$ or $4t + 7 = 0$ ←——Apply the Zero-Product Property.

$\qquad 4t = 7 \qquad\qquad 4t = -7$ ←——Apply the Addition and Subtraction Properties of Equality.

$\qquad t = \dfrac{7}{4} \qquad\qquad t = -\dfrac{7}{4}$ ←——Apply the Division Property of Equality.

$t = -\dfrac{7}{4}$ does not make sense. The pebble cannot hit the water before it is dropped.

$t = \dfrac{7}{4}$ or $1\dfrac{3}{4}$ is a reasonable answer.

The pebble will take $1\dfrac{3}{4}$ seconds to hit the water.

Check: $49 \overset{?}{=} 16\left(\dfrac{7}{4}\right)^2$ ←——Check the solution using the original problem.

$49 \overset{?}{=} \overset{1}{\cancel{16}} \cdot \dfrac{49}{\underset{1}{\cancel{16}}}$

$49 = 49$ True

▶You can write a quadratic equation, given its roots, by working backward.

• From the roots, write the binomial factors.

• Multiply the factors to write the equation in standard form.

Write an equation with the given roots.

• $\{-3, 5\}$

If -3 and 5 are roots, the factors are $(x + 3)$ and $(x - 5)$.

$(x + 3)(x - 5) = 0$ ←——Multiply.

$x^2 - 2x - 15 = 0$ ←——Apply the Distributive Property.

So $x^2 - 2x - 15 = 0$ is an equation with roots $\{-3, 5\}$.

• $\left\{-\dfrac{1}{2}, -\dfrac{3}{8}\right\}$

If $-\dfrac{1}{2}$ and $-\dfrac{3}{8}$ are roots, the factors are $\left(x + \dfrac{1}{2}\right)$ and $\left(x + \dfrac{3}{8}\right)$.

$(2x + 1)(8x + 3) = 0$ ←——Write each factor using integral coefficients.

$16x^2 + 14x + 3 = 0$ ←——Apply the Distributive Property.

So $16x^2 + 14x + 3 = 0$ is an equation with roots $\left\{-\dfrac{1}{2}, -\dfrac{3}{8}\right\}$.

Try These

Solve and check.

1. Ricardo has 50 feet of fencing to build a rectangular pen. He will use the back of the garage for one side of the pen. Find the dimensions of the enclosure if the area of the pen is to be 300 square feet.

2. The window of Allison's apartment was 64 feet above the sidewalk. She dropped a package of gum out of the window for her friend Brittany. After how many seconds did the gum hit the sidewalk?

Write a quadratic equation with the given roots.

3. $\{-3, 7\}$

4. $\left\{6, \dfrac{3}{4}\right\}$

5. $\left\{-\dfrac{5}{4}, -\dfrac{2}{3}\right\}$

6. Discuss and Write Explain why it is important to check the solutions using the given problem instead of just substituting them into the equation.

 PRACTICE BOOK Lesson 10-4 for exercise sets.

Solve Quadratic Equations by Completing the Square

Objective To model the process of completing the square • To solve quadratic equations by completing the square

One way to solve a quadratic equation is by completing the square. To use this method, you must make the quadratic expression on one side of the equation into a perfect square. You can use algebra tiles to model completing the square.

Use algebra tiles to complete the square for $x^2 + 6x + 4 = 0$.

1 Isolate the constant term on the right side.

$x^2 + 6x + 4 - 4 = 0 - 4$ ◄—Use the Subtraction Property of Equality.

$x^2 + 6x = -4$ ◄—Simplify.

Then model $x^2 + 6x = -4$.

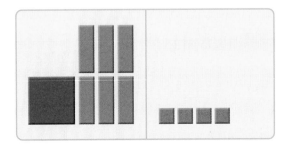

2 Begin to arrange the x^2 tile and the x tiles in a square.

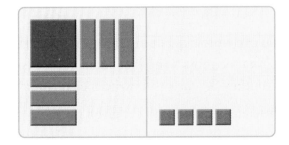

3 To complete the square, add 9 one tiles to the left side of the mat. To keep the equation balanced, add 9 one tiles to the right side of the mat. Then group zero pairs.

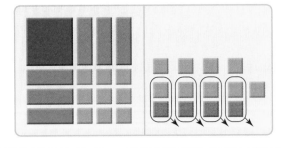

4 Remove the zero pairs on the right side of the mat. You have completed the square, and the equation is $x^2 + 6x + 9 = 5$, or $(x + 3)^2 = 5$.

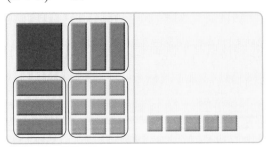

► After completing the square, you can solve the equation by taking the square root of each side.

$(x + 3)^2 = 5$

$\sqrt{(x + 3)^2} = \sqrt{5}$ ◄—Take the square root of both sides.

$|x + 3| = \sqrt{5}$ ◄—$\sqrt{x^2} = |x|$

$x + 3 = \pm \sqrt{5}$ ◄—Apply the definition of absolute value.

$x + 3 = \sqrt{5}$ or $x + 3 = -\sqrt{5}$ ◄—Write as two equations.

$x = -3 + \sqrt{5}$ $x = -3 - \sqrt{5}$ ◄—Apply the Subtraction Property of Equality.

Solution set: $\{-3 + \sqrt{5}, -3 - \sqrt{5}\}$

▶Completing the square is often a good method to use for solving a quadratic equation when the equation is not factorable using integers.

Key Concept

Completing the Square to Solve $ax^2 + bx + c = 0$, $a \neq 0$

1. Write the equation so that the constant term, c, is isolated on the right side. Divide each side of the equation by a; $x^2 + \dfrac{b}{a}x = -\dfrac{c}{a}$

2. Find the square of one half the coefficient of x. Add that number to each side of the equation.

3. Factor the left side of the equation. The result should have the form $(x + r)^2$ where r is a constant.

4. Take the square root of each side. Then solve for x, and simplify the solutions.

Solve: $x^2 + 5x + 4 = 0$ Use completing the square.

$x^2 + 5x + \dfrac{25}{4} = -4 + \dfrac{25}{4}$ ◄—The coefficient of x is 5. Add $\left(\dfrac{5}{2}\right)^2$ to each side.

$\left(x + \dfrac{5}{2}\right)^2 = \dfrac{9}{4}$ ◄—Write $x^2 + 5x + \dfrac{25}{4}$ as the square of a binomial.

$x + \dfrac{5}{2} = \pm\dfrac{3}{2}$ ◄—Find the square root of both sides.

$x + \dfrac{5}{2} = \dfrac{3}{2}$ or $x + \dfrac{5}{2} = -\dfrac{3}{2}$ ◄—Write and solve two equations.

$x = -1$ $\quad x = -4$ ◄—Apply the Subtraction Property of Equality; simplify.

Solution set: $\{-1, -4\}$

Check: $x^2 + 5x \overset{?}{=} -4$

$(-1)^2 + 5(-1) \overset{?}{=} -4$

$1 - 5 \overset{?}{=} -4$

$-4 = -4$

$x^2 + 5x \overset{?}{=} -4$

$(-4)^2 + 5(-4) \overset{?}{=} -4$

$16 - 20 \overset{?}{=} -4$

$-4 = -4$

Example

1 **Solve:** $3x^2 - 7x + 2 = 0$ Use completing the square.

$x^2 - \dfrac{7}{3}x = -\dfrac{2}{3}$ ◄—Write in the form $x^2 + \dfrac{b}{a}x = -\dfrac{c}{a}$.

$x^2 - \dfrac{7}{3}x + \dfrac{49}{36} = -\dfrac{2}{3} + \dfrac{49}{36}$ ◄—Add $\left(\dfrac{7}{6}\right)^2$ to each side to complete the square.

$\left(x - \dfrac{7}{6}\right)^2 = \dfrac{25}{36}$ ◄—Write $x^2 - \dfrac{7}{6}x + \dfrac{49}{36}$ as the square of a binomial.

$x - \dfrac{7}{6} = \pm\dfrac{5}{6}$ ◄—Find the square root of both sides.

$x - \dfrac{7}{6} = \dfrac{5}{6}$ or $x - \dfrac{7}{6} = -\dfrac{5}{6}$ ◄—Write and solve two equations.

$x = 2$ $\quad x = \dfrac{1}{3}$ ◄—Apply the Addition Property of Equality; simplify.

Solution set: $\{2, \dfrac{1}{3}\}$

Check: $3x^2 - 7x + 2 \overset{?}{=} 0$

$3(2)^2 - 7(2) + 2 \overset{?}{=} 0$

$12 - 14 + 2 \overset{?}{=} 0$

$0 = 0$

$3x^2 - 7x + 2 \overset{?}{=} 0$

$3\left(\dfrac{1}{3}\right)^2 - 7\left(\dfrac{1}{3}\right) + 2 \overset{?}{=} 0$

$\dfrac{1}{3} - \dfrac{7}{3} + 2 \overset{?}{=} 0$

$0 = 0$

Try These

Solve each equation by completing the square. Then check.

1. $x^2 + 16x + 6 = 0$

2. $x^2 + 6x - 15 = 0$

3. $4x^2 + 12x + 5 = 0$

4. Discuss and Write Use the method of completing the square to find k such that $x^2 + 4x = k$ has no real solutions. Explain your answer.

Go to **PRACTICE BOOK Lesson 10-5 for exercise sets.**

The Quadratic Formula and the Discriminant

Objective To determine the number and nature of solutions for a quadratic equation by using the discriminant

▶The **Quadratic Formula** is a formula that can be used to solve any quadratic equation. It is derived by solving the standard form of a quadratic equation, $ax^2 + bx + c = 0$, for x by completing the square.

Solve $ax^2 + bx + c = 0$ for x.

$$x^2 + \frac{b}{a}x + \frac{c}{a} = 0 \quad \longleftarrow \text{Apply the Division Property of Equality.}$$

$$x^2 + \frac{b}{a}x = -\frac{c}{a} \quad \longleftarrow \text{Apply the Subtraction Property of Equality.}$$

$$x^2 + \frac{b}{a}x + \frac{b^2}{4a^2} = -\frac{c}{a} + \frac{b^2}{4a^2} \quad \longleftarrow \text{Add } \left(\frac{b}{2a}\right)^2 \text{ to each side to complete the square.}$$

$$x^2 + \frac{b}{a}x + \frac{b^2}{4a^2} = -\frac{c}{a} \cdot \frac{4c}{4c} + \frac{b^2}{4a^2} \quad \longleftarrow \text{Rename } -\frac{c}{a} \text{ using the LCD: } 4a^2$$

$$\left(x + \frac{b}{2a}\right)^2 = -\frac{4ac}{4a^2} + \frac{b^2}{4a^2} \quad \longleftarrow \text{Write } x^2 + \frac{b}{a}x + \frac{b^2}{4a^2} \text{ as the square of a binomial.}$$

$$\left(x + \frac{b}{2a}\right)^2 = \frac{b^2 - 4ac}{4a^2} \quad \longleftarrow \text{Simplify.}$$

$$\sqrt{\left(x + \frac{b}{2a}\right)^2} = \sqrt{\frac{b^2 - 4ac}{4a^2}} \quad \longleftarrow \text{Take the square root of each side of the equation.}$$

$$x + \frac{b}{2a} = \pm \frac{\sqrt{b^2 - 4ac}}{2a} \quad \longleftarrow \text{Simplify.}$$

$$x = \frac{-b \pm \sqrt{b^2 - 4ac}}{2a} \quad \longleftarrow \text{Solve using the Subtraction Property of Equality.}$$

_____ **Key Concept** _____

The Quadratic Formula

If $ax^2 + bx + c = 0$, where $a \neq 0$, then $x = \dfrac{-b \pm \sqrt{b^2 - 4ac}}{2a}$.

▶The expression $b^2 - 4ac$ is called **the discriminant** of the quadratic equation, and it provides important information about the roots of the equation.

The $\pm$ symbol indicates that the discriminant will be both added and subtracted, so the equation will have two roots.

- If $b^2 - 4ac = 0$, then $x = \dfrac{-b \pm \sqrt{0}}{2a}$. The only root of the equation is $\dfrac{-b}{2a}$, which is a rational number.

- If $b^2 - 4ac > 0$, then $x = \dfrac{-b \pm \sqrt{\text{positive number}}}{2a}$. If $b^2 - 4ac$ is a perfect square, both roots will be rational. If it is not, the two roots will be irrational.

- If $b^2 - 4ac < 0$, then $x = \dfrac{-b \pm \sqrt{\text{negative number}}}{2a}$. The equation will have no real roots because the square root of a negative number is not a real number.

Use the discriminant to describe the root(s) of $x^2 - 10x + 25 = 0$.

$a = 1, b = -10,$ and $c = 25$ ←—Identify a, b, and c.

$b^2 - 4ac = (-10)^2 - 4(1)(25) = 100 - 100 = 0$ ←—Substitute into $b^2 - 4ac$ and simplify.

The discriminant is equal to 0.
The equation has one rational root.

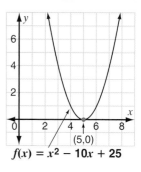

$f(x) = x^2 - 10x + 25$

Examples

Use the discriminant to describe the root(s) of each quadratic equation.

1 $x^2 - 10x + 24 = 0$

$a = 1, b = -10,$ and $c = 24$ ←—Identify a, b, and c.

$b^2 - 4ac = (-10)^2 - 4(1)(24) = 100 - 96 = 4$ ←—Substitute into $b^2 - 4ac$ and simplify.

The discriminant is equal to 4, which is a perfect square.
The equation has two rational roots.

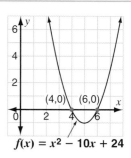

$f(x) = x^2 - 10x + 24$

2 $x^2 - 10x + 20 = 0$

$a = 1, b = -10,$ and $c = 20$ ←—Identify a, b, and c.

$b^2 - 4ac = (-10)^2 - 4(1)(20) = 100 - 80 = 20$ ←—Substitute into $b^2 - 4ac$ and simplify.

The discriminant is equal to 20, which is positive but not a perfect square.
The equation has two irrational roots (x_1 and x_2 in the graph at the right).

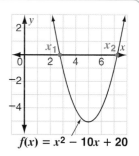

$f(x) = x^2 - 10x + 20$

3 $x^2 - 10x = -30$

$x^2 - 10x + 30 = 0$ ←—Write the equation in standard form.

$a = 1, b = -10,$ and $c = 30$ ←—Identify a, b, and c.

$b^2 - 4ac = (-10)^2 - 4(1)(30) = 100 - 120 = -20$ ←—Substitute into $b^2 - 4ac$ and simplify.

$f(x) = x^2 - 10x + 30$

The discriminant is equal to -20, which is less than zero.
The equation has no real roots.

Try These

**Find the discriminant of each quadratic equation.
Then describe the number and type of roots of the equation.**

1. $2x^2 - 3x - 7 = 0$ **2.** $x^2 - 3x + 5 = 0$ **3.** $7 + 10x^2 = 37x$

4. Discuss and Write If you are trying to graph a quadratic function, what helpful information can you get from the discriminant of the related quadratic equation?

Go to   PRACTICE BOOK **Lesson 10-6 for exercise sets.**

Solve Quadratic Equations with the Quadratic Formula

Objective To solve quadratic equations with the Quadratic Formula

Carla's garden is 3 times longer than it is wide. A 5-foot-wide brick walkway surrounds the garden. Altogether, the area of the garden and walkway is 375 square feet. What are the dimensions of the garden?

▶ To find the dimensions of the garden, write and solve an equation by using the formula for the area of a rectangle, $A = \ell w$.

Let x = the width of the garden,
  $3x$ = the length of the garden,
 $x + 10$ = the width of the garden and walkway, and
$3x + 10$ = the length of the garden and walkway.

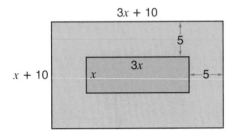

$(3x + 10)(x + 10) = 375$ ◀——$A = \ell w$

$3x^2 + 40x + 100 = 375$ ◀——Apply the Distributive Property.

$3x^2 + 40x - 275 = 0$ ◀——Use the Subtraction Property of Equality to write the equation in standard form.

▶ Although it is possible to solve $3x^2 + 40x - 275 = 0$ by factoring or by completing the square, the Quadratic Formula is a more efficient method for solving this equation.

> **Remember:**
> The Quadratic Formula
> If $ax^2 + bx + c = 0$, where $a \neq 0$, then
> $x = \dfrac{-b \pm \sqrt{b^2 - 4ac}}{2a}$.

$a = 3, b = 40,$ and $c = -275$ ◀——Identify a, b, and c.

$x = \dfrac{-40 \pm \sqrt{40^2 - 4(3)(-275)}}{2(3)}$ ◀——Substitute the values of a, b, and c in the Quadratic Formula.

$= \dfrac{-40 \pm \sqrt{4900}}{6}$ ◀——Simplify.

$x = \dfrac{-40 + 70}{6}$ or $x = \dfrac{-40 - 70}{6}$ ◀——Write as two equations.

$= \dfrac{30}{6}$ $= \dfrac{-110}{6}$ ◀——Simplify.

$= 5$ ◀——Solution.

Think
Use only the positive result because width cannot be negative.

The width of the garden, x, is 5 feet.
The length of the garden is $3x$, or 15 feet.

The outside dimensions of the garden and the walkway are 15 feet by 25 feet.

Check: Area = $(15)(25) = 375$ square feet.

Examples

Use the Quadratic Formula to solve the quadratic equation.

1 $2x^2 + 8x = 5$

$2x^2 + 8x - 5 = 0$ ←—Apply the Subtraction Property of Equality to write in standard form.

$a = 2, b = 8,$ and $c = -5$ ←—Identify a, b, and c.

$x = \dfrac{-8 \pm \sqrt{8^2 - 4(2)(-5)}}{2(2)}$ ←—Substitute values in the Quadratic Formula.

$\quad = \dfrac{-8 \pm \sqrt{64 + 40}}{4} = \dfrac{-8 \pm \sqrt{104}}{4}$

$\quad = \dfrac{-8 \pm \sqrt{4 \cdot 26}}{4} = \dfrac{-8 \pm 2\sqrt{26}}{4} = \dfrac{\overset{1}{-2}(-4 \pm \sqrt{26})}{\underset{2}{4}}$

$\quad = \dfrac{-4 \pm \sqrt{26}}{2}$ ←—Simplify.

$x = \dfrac{-4 + \sqrt{26}}{2}$ or $x = \dfrac{-4 - \sqrt{26}}{2}$ ←—Write as two equations.

Solution set: $\left\{ \dfrac{-4 + \sqrt{26}}{2}, \dfrac{-4 - \sqrt{26}}{2} \right\}$

2 $20 = 16x^2$

$16x^2 - 20 = 0$ ←—Use the Subtraction Property of Equality to write in standard form.

$a = 16, b = 0,$ and $c = -20$ ←—Identify a, b, and c. (If there is no x, the middle term, then $b = 0$.)

$x = \dfrac{-0 \pm \sqrt{0^2 - 4(16)(-20)}}{2(16)}$ ←—Substitute values in the Quadratic Formula.

$\quad = \dfrac{\pm \sqrt{1280}}{32} = \dfrac{\pm \sqrt{256 \cdot 5}}{32}$

$\quad = \dfrac{\pm 16\sqrt{5}}{32} = \dfrac{\pm \sqrt{5}}{2}$ ←—Simplify.

$x = \dfrac{\sqrt{5}}{2}$ or $x = \dfrac{-\sqrt{5}}{2}$ ←—Write as two equations.

Solution set: $\left\{ \dfrac{\sqrt{5}}{2}, \dfrac{-\sqrt{5}}{2} \right\}$

Try These

Solve by using the Quadratic Formula. Write answers in simplest radical form.

1. $2x^2 + 3 = 8x$ **2.** $49x^2 + 14x + 1 = 0$ **3.** $5x^2 = 11x + 3$

4. $-19x + 10 = -6x^2$ **5.** $2x^2 + 6x + 5 = 0$ **6.** $8x + 15x^2 = 0$

7. The base of a triangle is 3 inches shorter than its height. The area of the triangle is 77 square inches. Find the base and the height.

8. Discuss and Write Do you always get two solutions when using the quadratic formula? If so, explain why. If not, describe when you would get a different number of solutions.

Go to   **PRACTICE BOOK Lesson 10-7 for exercise sets.**

Solve Linear-Quadratic Systems

Objective To solve linear-quadratic systems of equations

A waterspout is located at the top of a straight, slanted surface in a perennial garden. It releases water that arcs through the air, landing onto the slanted surface to water the garden's flowers. The arc forms a parabola that is defined by the equation $y = -x^2 + 5x + 18$, and the linear equation $y = -2x + 18$ defines the slanted surface. Find the x-coordinate of the point on the slanted surface where the waterspout lands, and also the point where the arc originates.

The equations $\begin{cases} y = -x^2 + 5x + 18 \\ y = -2x + 18 \end{cases}$ form a system of linear-quadratic equations.

▶ One way to solve a system of a linear-quadratic equations is by substitution. Solve the linear equation for y, and substitute that value into the quadratic equation.

Solve: $\begin{cases} y = -x^2 + 5x + 18 \\ y = -2x + 18 \end{cases}$

$y = -2x + 18$ is already solved for y. So substitute $-2x + 18$ for y in the quadratic equation $y = -x^2 + 5x + 18$.

$-2x + 18 = -x^2 + 5x + 18$

$x^2 - 7x = 0$ ◀——Write the resulting quadratic equation in standard form.

$x(x - 7) = 0$ ◀——Factor.

$x = 0$ or $x - 7 = 0$ ◀——Apply the Zero-Product Property.

$x = 7$ ◀——Use the Addition Property of Equality.

To find y, substitute the values of x in either equation.

If $x = 0$, then $y = -2 \cdot 0 + 18 = 18$.   If $x = 7$, then $y = -2 \cdot 7 + 18 = 4$.
$(0, 18)$ is a solution. $(7, 4)$ is a solution.

Since the waterspout starts at $(0, 18)$, the spout lands on the surface when $x = 7$, and it is 4 units high when it hits the surface.

Graph: $\begin{cases} y = -x^2 + 5x + 18 \\ y = -2x + 18 \end{cases}$

Check if the solutions are reasonable.

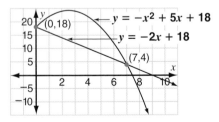

Check: Substitute each ordered pair into both equations.

$(0, 18)$

$y = -x^2 + 5x + 18$ $y = -2x + 18$

$18 \overset{?}{=} -(0)^2 + 5(0) + 18$ $18 \overset{?}{=} -2 \cdot 0 + 18$

$18 \overset{?}{=} 0 + 0 + 18$ $18 \overset{?}{=} 0 + 18$

$18 = 18$ True $18 = 18$ True

$(7, 4)$

$y = -x^2 + 5x + 18$ $y = -2x + 18$

$4 \overset{?}{=} -(7)^2 + 5(7) + 18$ $4 \overset{?}{=} -2 \cdot 7 + 18$

$4 \overset{?}{=} -49 + 35 + 18$ $4 \overset{?}{=} -14 + 18$

$4 = 4$ True $4 = 4$ True

Example

1 Solve: $\begin{cases} 2x + y = 2 \\ y = x^2 - 2x - 14 \end{cases}$

$y = -2x + 2$ ◄——Solve $2x + y = 2$ for y using the Subtraction Property of Equality.

$-2x + 2 = x^2 - 2x - 14$ ◄——Substitute $-2x + 2$ for y in $y = x^2 - 2x - 14$.

$-2x + 2x + 2 = x^2 - 2x + 2x - 14$ ◄——Use the Addition Property of Equality.

$2 - 2 = x^2 - 14 - 2$ ◄——Use the Subtraction Property of Equality.

$0 = x^2 - 16$ ◄——Simplify.

$0 = (x - 4)(x + 4)$ ◄——Factor.

$x - 4 = 0$ or $x + 4 = 0$ ◄——Apply the Zero-Product Property.

$x = 4$ $\qquad$ $x = -4$ ◄——Apply the Addition and Subtraction Properties of Equality.

To find y, substitute the values of x in either equation.

If $x = 4$, then $y = -2(4) + 2 = -6$. $\qquad$ If $x = -4$, then $y = -2(-4) + 2 = 10$.
$(4, -6)$ is a solution. $\qquad\qquad\qquad$ $(-4, 10)$ is a solution.

Graph:

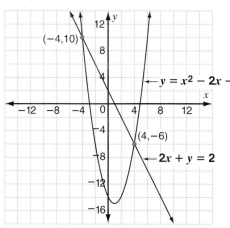

Check:

$(4, -6)$

$y \overset{?}{=} x^2 - 2x - 14$ $\qquad\qquad$ $2x + y = 2$

$-6 \overset{?}{=} (4)^2 - 2(4) - 14$ $\qquad$ $2(4) + (-6) \overset{?}{=} 2$

$-6 = -6$ True $\qquad\qquad\qquad$ $2 = 2$ True

$(-4, 10)$

$y \overset{?}{=} x^2 - 2x - 14$ $\qquad\qquad$ $2x + y = 2$

$10 \overset{?}{=} (-4)^2 - 2(-4) - 14$ $\qquad$ $2(-4) + 10 \overset{?}{=} 2$

$10 = 10$ True $\qquad\qquad\qquad$ $2 = 2$ True

► Systems of linear-quadratic equations can have two solutions (two points), one solution (the parabola and line intersect at one point), or no solutions (no intersection).

$\begin{cases} y = x^2 + 2 \\ y = x + 4 \end{cases}$ $\qquad\qquad$ $\begin{cases} y = x^2 + 2 \\ y = 2 \end{cases}$ $\qquad\qquad$ $\begin{cases} y = x^2 + 2 \\ y = x \end{cases}$

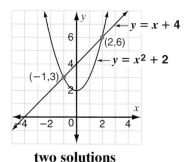 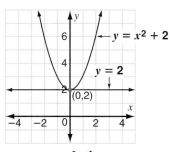 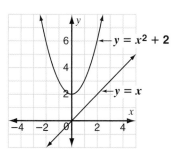

two solutions $\qquad\qquad$ **one solution** $\qquad\qquad$ **no solutions**

Continue Lesson ➡

The height, y, of a ball in feet after x seconds can be described by the equation $y = -16x^2 + 64x + 6$. Use this information to solve Examples 1–3.

1 Jim leaned out the window of his first floor apartment and threw a ball straight up in the air. Ann lives on the 6th floor. Her line of sight through her window can be described by $y = 54$. How many seconds after Jim throws the ball does it pass her window?

To find how many seconds, solve the following linear-quadratic system of equations.

Solve: $\begin{cases} y = 54 \\ y = -16x^2 + 64x + 6 \end{cases}$

$54 = -16x^2 + 64x + 6$ ◄—Substitute 54 for y in $y = -16x^2 + 64x + 6$.

$54 - 54 = -16x^2 + 64x + 6 - 54$ ◄—Use the Subtraction Property of Equality.

$0 = -16x^2 + 64x - 48$ ◄—Simplify.

$0 = -16(x^2 - 4x + 3)$ ◄—Factor out the GCF.

$0 = -16(x - 1)(x - 3)$ ◄—Factor the trinomial.

$x - 1 = 0$　or　$x - 3 = 0$ ◄—Apply the Zero-Product Property.

$x = 1$　　　　$x = 3$ ◄—Apply the Addition Property of Equality.

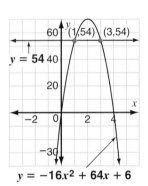

Since we know that $y = 54$, the y-value of the solutions will be 54.

The points of intersection of the path of the ball and Ann's line of sight are $(1, 54)$ and $(3, 54)$.

Ann will see the ball both on its way up and on its way down, 1 and 3 seconds after it is thrown.

2 Tom's line of sight from his 8th floor window can be described by the equation $y = 70$. After how many seconds does Tom see the ball?

To find how many seconds, solve the following linear-quadratic system of equations.

Solve: $\begin{cases} y = 70 \\ y = -16x^2 + 64x + 6 \end{cases}$

$70 = -16x^2 + 64x + 6$ ◄—Substitute 70 for y in $y = -16x^2 + 64x + 6$.

$70 - 70 = -16x^2 + 64x + 6 - 70$ ◄—Use the Subtraction Property of Equality.

$0 = -16x^2 + 64x - 64$ ◄—Simplify.

$0 = -16(x^2 - 4x + 4)$ ◄—Factor out the GCF.

$0 = -16(x - 2)(x - 2)$ ◄—Factor the trinomial.

$0 = x - 2$ ◄—Apply the Zero-Product Property.

$2 = x$ ◄—Apply the Addition Property of Equality.

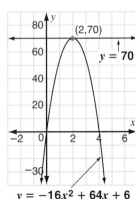

Since we know that $y = 70$, the y-value of the solutions will be 70.

The point of intersection of the ball's path and Tom's line of sight is $(2, 70)$.

Tom will see the ball once it reaches its maximum height 2 seconds after it is thrown.

3 Bill, on the 9th floor, has a line of sight that can be described by $y = 78$.
After how many seconds does Bill see the ball?

To find how many seconds, solve the following linear-quadratic system of equations.

Solve: $\begin{cases} y = 78 \\ y = -16x^2 + 64x + 6 \end{cases}$

$78 = -16x^2 + 64x + 6$ ◄——Substitute 78 for y in $y = -16x^2 + 64x + 6$.

$78 - 78 = -16x^2 + 64x + 6 - 78$ ◄——Use the Subtraction Property of Equality.

$0 = -16x^2 + 64x - 72$ ◄——Simplify.

$0 = -8(2x^2 - 8x + 9)$ ◄——Factor out the GCF.

Since the trinomial cannot be factored over the integers,
you can solve the equation $0 = 2x^2 - 8x + 9$ by completing
the square or by using the Quadratic Formula.

.Think...................................
There are no factors of
9 that add up to -8.
....

You can also check the nature of the roots of the quadratic
equation by finding the value of the discriminant.

$a = 2, b = -8, c = 9$ ◄——Identify the values of a, b, and c.

$b^2 - 4ac = -8^2 - 4(2)(9)$

$= 64 - 72$

$= -8$ ◄——The discriminant is negative, which means
that there are no real-number solutions.

The line and the parabola do not intersect.

Bill will not see the ball. The path of the ball does not intersect
with his line of sight because the ball begins to descend before
reaching his window.

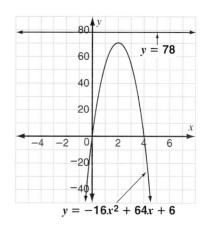

$y = -16x^2 + 64x + 6$

Try These

Solve each linear-quadratic system of equations. Then graph and check your solutions.

1. $\begin{cases} y = -2 \\ y = 6x^2 + 17x + 12 \end{cases}$

2. $\begin{cases} y = 5x + 8 \\ y = 5x^2 + 19x + 5 \end{cases}$

3. $\begin{cases} 3x - y = 3 \\ y = x^2 - 7x + 22 \end{cases}$

4. $\begin{cases} 3x + y = 7 \\ y = 6x^2 - 33x - 29 \end{cases}$

5. $\begin{cases} 2x - y = 4 \\ y = x^2 - 3x - 10 \end{cases}$

6. $\begin{cases} y = 4x + 21 \\ y = 5 - 4x - x^2 \end{cases}$

**Determine the number of points of intersection of the specified graphs.
Justify your answer.**

7. A parabola opens upward and has vertex
$(-2, 5)$. A line has equation $y = 5$.

8. A parabola opens downward and has vertex
$(-2, 5)$. A line has equation $y = 5$.

9. Discuss and Write Describe the graphs of a linear and quadratic system that has
no solutions, one that has exactly one solution, and one that has two solutions.

10-9

Technology:
Find the Zeros of Polynomial Functions

Objective To use a handheld to find the roots of a polynomial equation

▶Sometimes you can solve polynomial equations using a handheld.

Find the roots of the equation $x^2 - x - 12 = 0$ using the **Solve** command on a handheld.

Step 1 Press 🏠, then **1** to select **Calculator**.

Step 2 Press menu. Select **Algebra**, then choose **Solve**.

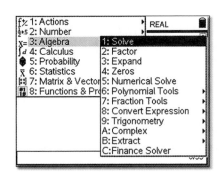

Step 3 Input $x^2 - x - 12 = 0, x$ and press enter.

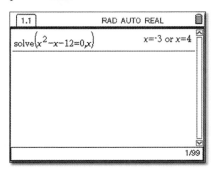

Check: To verify the answer without using a handheld, substitute the values into the polynomial equation.

$$(-3)^2 - (-3) - 12 \overset{?}{=} 0$$
$$9 + 3 - 12 \overset{?}{=} 0$$
$$0 = 0 \checkmark$$

$$(4)^2 - (4) - 12 \overset{?}{=} 0$$
$$16 + (-4) - 12 \overset{?}{=} 0$$
$$0 = 0 \checkmark$$

So the roots are $x = -3$ and $x = 4$.

Example

1 Find the roots of the equation $2x^2 - 11x + 5 = 0$ using the **Solve** command on a handheld.

Step 1 Press menu. Select **Algebra**, and then choose **Solve**.

Step 2 Type in the equation $2x^2 - 11x + 5 = 0$, x, then enter.

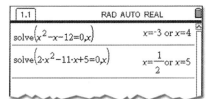

Check: To verify the answer without using a handheld, substitute the values into the polynomial equation.

$$2\left(\tfrac{1}{2}\right)^2 - 11\left(\tfrac{1}{2}\right) + 5 \overset{?}{=} 0$$
$$\tfrac{1}{2} - 5\tfrac{1}{2} + 5 \overset{?}{=} 0$$
$$0 = 0 \checkmark$$

$$2(5)^2 - 11(5) + 5 \overset{?}{=} 0$$
$$50 - 55 + 5 \overset{?}{=} 0$$
$$0 = 0 \checkmark$$

So the roots are $x = \tfrac{1}{2}$ and $x = 5$.

▶ You can also use the **Zeros** command on a handheld to help find the roots.
To do this, rewrite the equation as an expression equal to zero. The displayed
answer is the set of x-values where the graph of the equation intersects the x-axis.

Find the roots of the equation $20x^2 + 7x = 6$ using the **Zeros** command on
a handheld.

$20x^2 + 7x = 6$ ◀——Rewrite the equation as an expression equal to 0.

$20x^2 + 7x - 6 = 0$ ◀——Use the Subtraction Property of Equality.

Step 1 Press (menu). Select **Algebra**, and then
choose **Zeros**.

Step 2 Input in the polynomial expression
$20x^2 + 7x - 6, x$, then (enter).

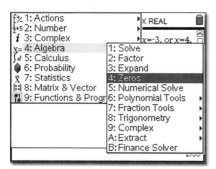

So the roots are $x = -\frac{3}{4}$ and $x = \frac{2}{5}$.

Example

1 Find the roots of the equation $12x^2 - 19x = -5$ using the **Zeros** command on a handheld.

$12x^2 - 19x = -5$ ◀——Rewrite the equation as
an expression equal to 0.

$12x^2 - 19x + 5 = 0$ ◀——Use the Addition Property of Equality.

Step 1 Press (menu) (4) for **Algebra**, then (4) for **Zeros**.

Step 2 Input the polynomial expression $12x^2 - 19x + 5$,
x, then (enter).

So the roots are $x = \frac{1}{3}$ and $x = \frac{5}{4}$.

Try These

Use a handheld to find the roots of the equation.

1. $x^2 - 15x + 56 = 0$

2. $x^2 - 5x = 84$

3. $24x^2 + 5x - 15 = -1$

4. Discuss and Write How are the **Solve** and **Zeros** commands on a handheld
similar and how are they different when finding the roots of an equation?
Use $x^2 + 2x - 3 = 0$ to explain your answer.

Go to ▶ **PRACTICE BOOK** Lesson 10-9 for exercise sets.

See TI-Nspire™ Handbook on pages 415–422.

Technology:
Families of Quadratic Functions

Objective To use a handheld to explore families of quadratic functions

Families of functions are functions that have similar characteristics. Quadratic functions have graphs that are all parabolas. The graph of $y = ax^2 + bx + c$ will change when $a, b,$ or c changes. By graphing families of quadratics, you can observe and explore these relationships.

▶ You can use a handheld to examine how the value of a affects the graph of $y = ax^2$.

Graph the quadratic equation $y = x^2$, using a handheld.

Step 1 Press ⌂ , then **2** to select **Graphs & Geometry**.

Step 2 Input x^2, then press **enter** to graph the parabola.

The most basic of a family of functions is called the *parent function*. The parent quadratic function is $y = x^2$.

Now graph on the same coordinate plane as $y = x^2$, the functions: $y = \frac{1}{2}x^2$, $y = 2x^2$, $y = \frac{1}{4}x^2$, and $y = 4x^2$. Describe how the value of a affects the graph.

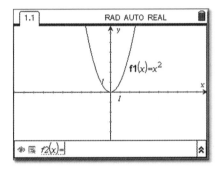

Step 3 Input $\frac{1}{2}x^2$, then press **enter**.

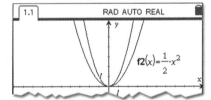

Step 4 Input $2x^2$, then press **enter**.

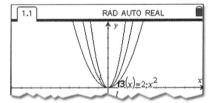

Step 5 Input $\frac{1}{4}x^2$, then press **enter**.

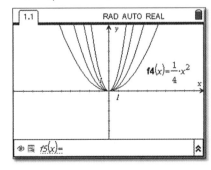

Step 6 Input $4x^2$, then press **enter**.

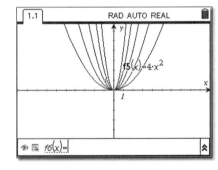

Note that if a is positive and less than 1, the graph of $y = ax^2$ is *wider* than that of the parent function. If a is greater than 1, the parabola is *narrower* than the parent function.

In general, as a becomes *greater*, the parabola gets *narrower*.
As a gets closer to 0, the parabola gets wider.

Example

1 Graph the equations $y = 3x^2$, $y = -3x^2$, $y = \frac{1}{3}x^2$, and $y = -\frac{1}{3}x^2$ using a handheld.

How does the sign of a affect the graph of $y = ax^2$?

Step 1 Press 🏠. Then choose ② to select **Graphs & Geometry**.

Step 2 Input $3x^2$, then press ≈enter to graph the parabola.

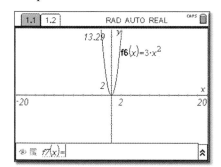

Step 3 Input $-3x^2$, then press ≈enter to graph the parabola.

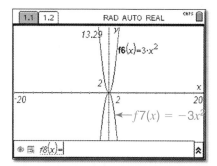

Step 4 Input $\frac{1}{3}x^2$, then press ≈enter to graph the parabola.

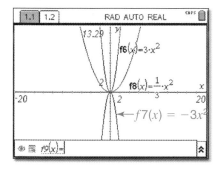

Step 5 Input $-\frac{1}{3}x^2$, then press ≈enter to graph the parabola.

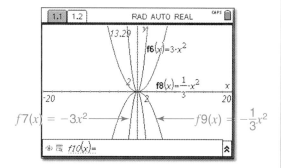

Note that when a is negative, the graph of $y = ax^2$ will have the same width and shape as the graph of $y = |a|x^2$, but will be reflected over the x-axis and open down.

Try These

Predict how the graphs of the second function will compare to that of the first function. Then use a handheld to verify your prediction.

1. $y = x^2$ and $y = 5x^2$

2. $y = 5x^2$ and $y = 3x^2$

3. $y = 10x^2$ and $y = -10x^2$

4. $y = x^2$ and $y = -\frac{1}{8}x^2$

5. $y = \frac{3}{4}x^2$ and $y = -10x^2$

6. $y = \frac{9}{10}x^2$ and $y = \frac{3}{10}x^2$

7. Discuss and Write Explain how the graph of $y = ax^2$ will differ from the parent function $y = x^2$ if a is greater than 1, if a is less than -1, if a is greater than 0 and less than 1, and if a is greater than -1 and less than 0.

Go to ▶ **PRACTICE BOOK Lesson 10-10 for exercise sets.**

Problem-Solving Strategy:
Adopt a Different Point of View

Objective To solve problems using the strategy *Adopt a Different Point of View*

Problem I: In the diagram at the right, *SQRE* is a square. *I* is the midpoint of $\overline{ES}$ and *T* is the midpoint of $\overline{SQ}$. What fraction of the area of the square is inside triangle *TRI*?

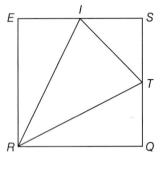

Read ▶ **Read to understand what is being asked.**

List the facts and restate the question.

Facts: *SQRE* is a square. Triangle *TRI* is formed by connecting point *R* and the midpoints of $\overline{ES}$ and $\overline{SQ}$.

Question: The area of triangle *TRI* is what fraction of the area of the square?

Plan ▶ **Select a strategy.**

You can use the strategy *Adopt a Different Point of View*. It would be easier to find the area outside the triangle and then subtract it from the area of the square.

Problem-Solving Strategies

1. Make a Drawing
2. Solve a Simpler Problem
3. Reason Logically
4. Consider Extreme Cases
5. Work Backward
6. Find a Pattern
7. Account for All Possibilities
8. **Adopt a Different Point of View**
9. Guess and Test
10. Organize Data

Solve ▶ **Apply the strategy.**

Let *M* be the midpoint of $\overline{ER}$, and let *N* be the midpoint of $\overline{QR}$. Connect the midpoints of the opposite sides of the square as shown below. Then find the fraction of square *SQRE*'s area *outside* triangle *TRI*.

Notice the following:

- $A_{\text{rectangle } REIN} = \frac{1}{2}(A_{\text{square } SQRE})$

  $A_{\text{triangle } REI} = \frac{1}{2}(A_{\text{rectangle } REIN})$ ◀— A diagonal of a rectangle separates the rectangle into two triangles of equal areas.

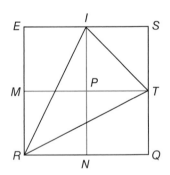

So $A_{\text{triangle } REI} = \frac{1}{2}\left[\frac{1}{2}(A_{\text{square } SQRE})\right] = \frac{1}{4}(A_{\text{square } SQRE})$

- $A_{\text{rectangle } RMTQ} = \frac{1}{2}(A_{\text{square } SQRE})$

  $A_{\text{triangle } RTQ} = \frac{1}{2}(A_{\text{rectangle } RMTQ})$

  So $A_{\text{triangle } RTQ} = \frac{1}{2}\left[\frac{1}{2}(A_{\text{square } SQRE})\right] = \frac{1}{4}(A_{\text{square } SQRE})$

- $A_{\text{rectangle } STPI} = \frac{1}{4}(A_{\text{square } SQRE})$

  $A_{\text{triangle } STI} = \frac{1}{2}(A_{\text{square } STPI})$

  So $A_{\text{triangle } STI} = \frac{1}{2}\left[\frac{1}{4}(A_{\text{square } SQRE})\right] = \frac{1}{8}(A_{\text{square } SQRE})$

The region outside of triangle *TRI* makes up $\left(\frac{1}{4} + \frac{1}{4} + \frac{1}{8}\right)$, or $\frac{5}{8}$, of square *SQRE*.

So the area of triangle *TRI* is $\left(1 - \frac{5}{8}\right)$, or $\frac{3}{8}$, of the area of the square.

Check ▶ **Check to make sure your answer makes sense.**

Estimate whether the answer makes sense by checking each quarter of the square. The triangle occupies $\frac{1}{2}$ of *PTSI*, less than $\frac{1}{2}$ of *EIPM*, less than $\frac{1}{2}$ of *PTQN*, and a little more than $\frac{1}{2}$ of *MPNR*. So $\frac{3}{8}$ is a reasonable answer.

Problem 2: Consider this system of equations:

$$\begin{cases} 51x + 34y = 357 \\ 34x + 51y = 323 \end{cases}$$

Find the value of $x + y$.

Read ► **Read to understand what is being asked.**

List the facts and restate the question.

Facts: You are given a system of linear equations in two variables, x and y.

$$\begin{cases} 51x + 34y = 357 \\ 34x + 51y = 323 \end{cases}$$

Question: What is the value of $x + y$?

Plan ► **Select a strategy.**

To find $x + y$, you can solve for x and y, and then add the results. However, by using the strategy *Adopt a Different Point of View*, you can find the sum of x and y without having to find the individual values of these variables.

Solve ► **Apply the strategy.**

• Add the equations.

$$\begin{array}{r} 51x + 34y = 357 \\ + \ 34x + 51y = 323 \\ \hline 85x + 85y = 680 \end{array}$$

• Factor the sum, $85x + 85y$, using the Greatest Common Factor (GCF).

$$85x + 85y = 680$$
$$85(x + y) = 680$$

......Think..
85 is the GCF of the
coefficients of both x and y.
....

• Simplify using the Division Property of Equality.

$$\frac{85(x + y)}{85} = \frac{680}{85}$$
$$x + y = 8$$

So the value of $x + y = 8$.

Check ► **Check to make sure your answer makes sense.**

Does $85(x + y) = 680$?

$$85(x + y) = 680$$
$$85 \cdot 8 \stackrel{?}{=} 680 \quad \longleftarrow \text{Substitute the value of } x + y.$$
$$680 = 680 \ \checkmark$$

The answer checks.

Go to PRACTICE BOOK Lesson 10-11 for exercise sets.

Enrichment:
Reflective Properties of Parabolic Surfaces

Objective **To explore real-world occurrences of parabolas**

Here is one definition of a parabola:

A *parabola* is the set of all points in a plane whose distance from a fixed point F is the same as their distance from a fixed line d. This definition of a parabola is illustrated at the right.

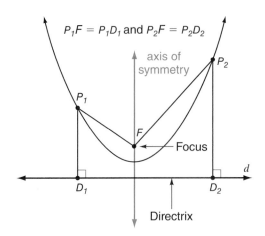

$P_1F = P_1D_1$ and $P_2F = P_2D_2$

axis of symmetry

P_1

P_2

F — Focus

D_1 D_2

d

Directrix

- The fixed point F is called the focus.

- The fixed line d is called the directrix.

- The distance between a point P on the parabola and the focus located on the axis of symmetry is the length of the perpendicular line segment from the point to the directrix.

A point located on the parabola is 10 cm from the focus of the parabola. How far is the point from the directrix?

To find how far, use the definition of the distance from a point on the parabola to the focus, that it is equal to the point's distance to the directrix.

So the point is 10 cm from the directrix.

▶A parabola has some interesting reflective properties that are related to its focus.

- The angle at which a light beam or other ray "hits" any surface is the same as the angle at which it "reflects off" the surface.

    Scientists say, "The angle of incidence equals the angle of reflection." This idea is known as the Law of Reflection.

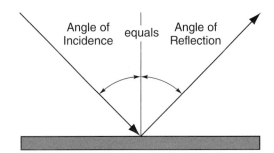

Angle of Incidence   equals   Angle of Reflection

- Because of a parabola's shape, rays that start at the focus and hit the parabola reflect off in rays that are parallel to the axis of symmetry. Also, rays traveling parallel to the axis of symmetry that hit the parabola reflect toward the focus. These properties make the parabola a very useful shape.

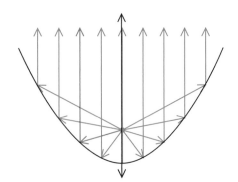
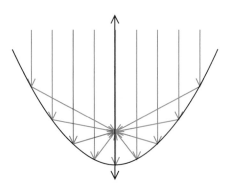

▶ Some real-world objects are designed in the shape of a parabola to utilize its reflective properties.

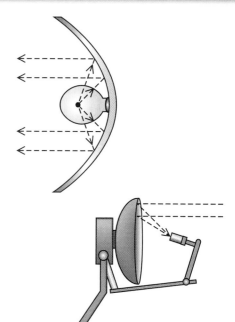

- Flashlights and headlights on cars often have parabolic mirrors. (Imagine a parabola rotated around its axis of symmetry to form a bowl shape.)

- A lightbulb is placed at the focus of the parabola. When rays from the light hit the surface of the mirror, they are reflected off in rays that are parallel to the axis of symmetry, creating a straight beam of light.

- Satellite dishes and reflecting telescopes work in the opposite way.

  A satellite dish is a parabolic surface. Signals hit the satellite dish and reflect off, converging at a device called a "feed horn," which is located at the focus of the dish. The feed horn then sends the signals on to the receiving equipment.

- Solar furnaces also utilize the reflecting properties of a parabola.

  A solar furnace has a parabolic reflecting surface that collects sunlight and focuses it at a single point, creating an enormous amount of heat.

  The world's largest solar furnace is the Odeillo Font-Romeu Solar Furnace (shown at the right) in the French Pyrenees. The furnace is eight stories high. Its parabolic reflective surface is made up of 63 flat mirrors, called heliostats. The heliostats move to track the sun and concentrate its rays toward a focal zone 18 meters in front of the surface. The furnace can create temperatures up to 3800°C (almost 6900°F). It is used to melt iron ore in the production of steel.

  Large solar furnaces are used in science and industry, but even small, handmade solar furnaces can produce temperatures hot enough to melt some metals.

- The reflective properties of parabolic surfaces are used to light the torch used in the modern Olympic Games.

  An actress dressed in the robes of the ancient Greeks holds a torch at the focus of a parabolic mirror. The sun's rays are focused at that point, creating enough heat to ignite the fuel in the torch.

Try These

1. A point on a parabola is 6 cm from the focus of the parabola. How far is the point from the directrix?

2. **Discuss and Write** The word *focus* comes from the Latin word for "fireplace." Explain how the word *fireplace* is related to the idea of the focus of a parabola.

 PRACTICE BOOK pages 269–270 for exercise sets.

Test Prep: Short-Answer Questions
Strategy: Show All Your Work

Short-answer questions require you to provide a solution to the problem that shows all of your work. You should *explain your thinking* to justify the methods you used to arrive at the solution.

Look at the sample test item.

Read the test item for a general idea of the problem.

• Reread the test item carefully. Use context clues to help determine the meaning of any unfamiliar words.

• Identify key ideas. *Use the relationship between the length and width to find the dimensions.*

• Explain the steps you will use to solve the problem.

  First, write and solve an equation to find the width, then use the width to find the length.

Solve the problem.

• Apply appropriate formulas, rules, and properties.

Write and solve an equation using the information in the problem. Let w represent the width and ℓ represent the length.

$\ell = 3w + 2$ ◄— The length is 2 *more than* 3 times the width.

$A = \ell w$ ◄— Use the area formula.

$120 = (3w + 2)w$ ◄— Substitute the expression for length.

$120 = 3w^2 + 2w$ ◄— Apply the Distributive Property.

$0 = 3w^2 + 2w - 120$ ◄— Use the Subtraction Property of Equality.

$\dfrac{-2 \pm \sqrt{2^2 - 4(3)(-120)}}{2(3)}$ ◄— Use the quadratic formula:

$\qquad\qquad\qquad\qquad \dfrac{-b \pm \sqrt{b^2 - 4ac}}{2a}$

6 or $-6\dfrac{2}{3}$ Substitute the values for a, b, and c.

> **Test-Taking Tips**
> • Reread the test item.
> • Use the Test-Prep strategy.
> • Identify key ideas.
> • Apply appropriate rules, definitions, properties, or strategies.
> • Analyze your answers.

A negative value *does not make sense* for the width, so the width is 6 in. Find the length.
Length $= 3w + 2 = 3(6) + 2 = 20$

Answer: The rectangle is 20 in. by 6 in.

Item Analysis

Check your work. Review your notes. Make sure you show all your work.

• Analyze your answer. Does it make sense?

  Find the area of a 20-inch by 6-inch rectangle.

  $A = \ell w \longrightarrow 120 \overset{?}{=} (20)(6) \longrightarrow 120 = 120 \checkmark$

Try These

Solve. Be sure to explain your thinking.

1. The height of an archway, y, in feet, can be modeled by the equation $y = -x^2 + 9$, where the x-axis represents the ground. What is the width across the bottom of the archway? ***Show your work.***

Go to PRACTICE BOOK page 271 for exercise sets.

Ratio, Proportion, and Trigonometry

In This Chapter You Will:

- Write and apply ratios, proportions, rates, and unit rates
- Convert rates from one unit of measure to another
- Solve problems involving scale drawings
- Calculate the relative error in measuring square and cubic units
- Solve problems involving percentage and percent of change

- Write trigonometric ratios, given the lengths of sides of a right triangle
- Use a handheld to find values of trigonometric ratios and angle measures
- Solve verbal problems using trigonometric ratios
- Apply the strategy: *Guess and Test*
- Look for new vocabulary words **highlighted** in each lesson

Do You Remember?

- Equivalent fractions can be found by multiplying or dividing the numerator and denominator by the same number.
- A percent (%) is a ratio that compares a number to 100.
- The sides of a right triangle are called the legs and the hypotenuse.
- To solve equations, use inverse operations and the properties of equality.

For Practice Exercises:

Go to **PRACTICE BOOK, pp. 277–302**

For Chapter Support: (ONLINE)

Go to **www.progressinmathematics.com**

- Skills Update Practice
- Practice Activities
- Audio Glossary
- Vocabulary Activities

- Technology Videos
- Enrichment Activities
- Electronic SourceBook

 VIRTUAL MANIPULATIVES

Critical Thinking

Three cousins own a party supply store, but each cousin's ownership stake differs. One cousin owns $\frac{1}{3}$ of the business, while another cousin owns $\frac{1}{4}$. To the nearest percent, what percent of the business does the third cousin own?

Update your skills. See page 404 V.

11-1

Ratios and Rates

Objective To write and apply ratios, proportions, rates, and unit rates • To convert rates from one unit of measure to another

Ms. Parsons has 48 students enrolled in her after school math lab but has only 32 handheld devices. What is the ratio of handheld devices to students?

► A ratio is a comparison of two numbers *a* and *b*, by division. The numbers, *a* and *b*, are called the terms of the ratio. A ratio can be expressed in three different forms:

Word Form	Ratio Form	Fraction Form
a to *b*	*a* : *b*	$\frac{a}{b}$

The ratio of *handheld devices* to *students* can be written in the following ways:

32 to 48   32 : 48 $\frac{32}{48}$

Ratios are often expressed in simplest form. The ratio of *a* to *b* can be expressed in simplest form by dividing both *a* and *b* by their greatest common factor (GCF).

In simplest form, the ratio of handheld devices to students can be written as 2 to 3, 2 : 3, or $\frac{2}{3}$.

Think
The GCF of 32 and 48 is 16.

So Ms. Parsons has 2 handheld devices for every 3 students.

►An equation showing that two ratios are equal is called a proportion. To check if two ratios form a proportion, use the Cross-Products Rule.

Key Concept

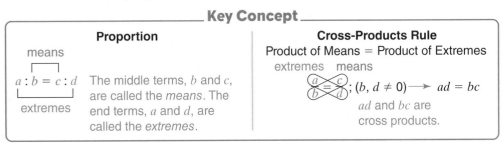

Proportion	**Cross-Products Rule**
means	Product of Means = Product of Extremes
a : *b* = *c* : *d* The middle terms, *b* and *c*, are called the *means*. The end terms, *a* and *d*, are called the *extremes*.	extremes means 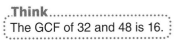 ; (*b*, *d* ≠ 0) → *ad* = *bc* *ad* and *bc* are cross products.

$\frac{32}{48} \overset{?}{=} \frac{2}{3}$ → $32 \cdot 3 \overset{?}{=} 48 \cdot 2$ ←Cross multiply.

96 = 96   True

$\frac{3.6}{4.2} \overset{?}{=} \frac{5}{6}$ → $3.6 \cdot 6 \overset{?}{=} 4.2 \cdot 5$ ←Cross multiply.

21.6 ≠ 21

The cross products are equal, so the two ratios form a proportion.

Since the cross products are *not* equal, the two ratios are not in proportion.

►When there is a relation between two variables, *x* and *y*, such that $y = ax$ and $a \neq 0$, *y* is *proportional* to *x*. This means that there is a *constant ratio* between the corresponding values of *x* and *y*. In these cases, *a* is called the constant of proportionality.

The graph of a proportional relation always contains the origin and has a slope equal to the constant of proportionality.

The table below shows the different disk sizes of Darnel's stacking puzzle. Graph the proportional relation of the: (a) diameter to the radius; (b) circumference to the diameter. Note that $\frac{d}{r}$ is (d, r) and $\frac{C}{d}$ is (C, d) when graphed on the coordinate plane.

Radius (inches)	1	2	3	4
Diameter (inches)	2	4	6	8
Circumference (inches)	2π	4π	6π	8π

Write each ratio as a fraction. Then graph.

Diameter to Radius

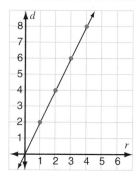

* ratio of diameter to radius:

$$\frac{diameter\ (d)}{radius\ (r)} = \frac{2}{1} = \frac{4}{2} = \frac{6}{3} = \frac{8}{4}$$

The diameter is proportional to the radius.
The ratio of diameter to radius is 2 to 1.

Since $d = 2r$, then 2 is the constant of proportionality.
The constant of proportionality, 2, is the slope of the line, the graph of the proportional relation.

* ratio of circumference to diameter:

$$\frac{C}{d} = \frac{2\pi}{2} = \frac{4\pi}{4} = \frac{6\pi}{6} = \frac{8\pi}{8}$$

The circumference is proportional to the diameter.
The ratio of circumference to diameter is π to 1.

Since $C = \pi d$, then π is the constant of proportionality.
The constant of proportionality, π, is the slope of the line, the graph of the proportional relation.

Circumference to Diameter

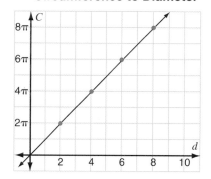

▶ A ratio that compares quantities measured in different types of units is a rate. A unit rate is a rate in which the second term, or denominator, is 1.

For example, speed is a rate that compares distance and time; a unit rate is 50 miles per hour and can be written as 50 mi/h, 50 mph, or $\frac{50\ miles}{1\ hour}$.

To find the unit rate, express a given rate in simplest form.

In the graph of a proportional relation, $y = ax$, the unit rate is the point $(1, a)$. Since $x = 1$, then $y = a(1)$, or $y = a$.

Mark earned $369.00 for 12 hours of work.
* Find the unit rate.
* Then graph: earnings *to* the work hours.

$$\frac{\$369}{12\ hours} \longrightarrow \frac{\$369 \div 12}{12\ hours \div 12} = \frac{\$30.75}{1\ hour} \longleftarrow \boxed{\text{unit rate}}$$

So the rate is $30.75 per hour.

Mark's Earnings

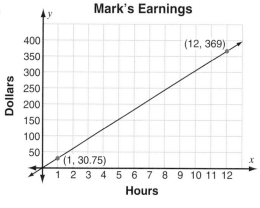

Continue Lesson ➡

► Unit rates are commonly used in everyday life to communicate important measures, such as ounces per quart, miles per gallon, or revolutions per minute. A unit price is a unit rate for an item of purchase.

 Which has the lower unit cost, 8 ounces of shampoo for $2.98 or 12 ounces of shampoo for $5.26? Graph both relations on the *same* coordinate plane.

To find which has the lower unit cost, find and compare the unit prices.

$\dfrac{\$2.98}{8 \text{ oz}} \overset{?}{-} \dfrac{\$5.26}{12 \text{ oz}}$ ◄——Write each rate as a fraction.

$\dfrac{\$2.98 \div 8}{8 \text{ oz} \div 8} \overset{?}{-} \dfrac{\$5.26 \div 12}{12 \text{ oz} \div 12}$ ◄——Divide the numerator and denominator by their GCF.

$\dfrac{\$.3725}{1 \text{ oz}} < \dfrac{\$.483}{1 \text{ oz}}$ ◄——Compare.

So the 8-oz bottle of shampoo has the lower unit cost.

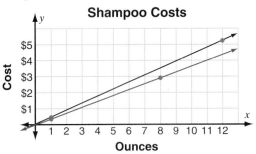

Example

1 Which is the better buy, 3 folders for $2.15 or 20 folders for $10.99?

To find which is the better buy, find and compare the unit prices.

$\dfrac{\$2.15}{3 \text{ folders}} \overset{?}{-} \dfrac{\$10.99}{20 \text{ folders}}$ ◄——Write each rate as a fraction.

$\dfrac{\$2.15 \div 3}{3 \text{ folders} \div 3} \overset{?}{-} \dfrac{\$10.99 \div 20}{20 \text{ folders} \div 20}$ ◄——Divide the numerator and denominator by their GCF.

$\dfrac{\$.73}{1 \text{ folder}} > \dfrac{\$.55}{1 \text{ folder}}$ ◄——Compare.

So the unit price of $0.55 per folder is the better buy.

► You can rename (or convert) rates from one unit of measure to another by using conversion factors. A conversion factor is a rate of equal quantities that is used to multiply a quantity when converting from one unit to another. The process of analyzing units to decide which conversion factor(s) to use is called dimensional, or unit, analysis.

Rename 15 miles per hour as a rate in feet per second.

To rename, set up the conversion factors in sequence so that like units divide, or cancel out. Start with miles per hour and end up with feet per second.

> **Think**
> Rename miles as feet and hours as seconds.

| Conversion factor for hours and minutes | Conversion factor for minutes and seconds | Conversion factor for feet and miles |

$\dfrac{15 \text{ mi}}{\text{h}} = \dfrac{15 \text{ mi}}{1 \text{ h}} \cdot \dfrac{1 \text{ h}}{60 \text{ min}} \cdot \dfrac{1 \text{ min}}{60 \text{ s}} \cdot \dfrac{5280 \text{ ft}}{1 \text{ mi}}$ ◄——Write using the appropriate conversion factors.

$= \dfrac{15 \text{ mi}}{1 \text{ h}} \cdot \dfrac{1 \text{ h}}{60 \text{ min}} \cdot \dfrac{1 \text{ min}}{60 \text{ s}} \cdot \dfrac{5280 \text{ ft}}{1 \text{ mi}} = \dfrac{22 \text{ ft}}{\text{s}}$ ◄——Divide the common units, and simplify the ratios.

So 15 miles per hour = 22 feet per second.

▶ Many verbal problems can be solved by renaming rates from one unit to another.

Machine A processes 3.5 ounces of material per second. Machine B processes 720 pounds of the same material per hour. Which machine is faster?

To determine which machine is faster, compare of 3.5 ounces per second with 720 pounds per hour. You can either convert 3.5 ounces per second to pounds per hour *or* 720 pounds per hour to ounces per second.

Method 1 Convert 3.5 ounces per second to pounds per hour.

$$\frac{3.5 \text{ oz}}{1 \text{ s}} = \frac{3.5 \text{ oz}}{1 \text{ s}} \cdot \frac{60 \text{ s}}{1 \text{ min}} \cdot \frac{60 \text{ min}}{1 \text{ h}} \cdot \frac{1 \text{ lb}}{16 \text{ oz}}$$ ← Write using the appropriate conversion factors.

$$= \frac{3.5 \text{ oz}}{1 \text{ s}} \cdot \frac{\overset{15}{\cancel{60}} \text{ s}}{1 \text{ min}} \cdot \frac{\overset{15}{\cancel{60}} \text{ min}}{1 \text{ h}} \cdot \frac{1 \text{ lb}}{\underset{1}{\cancel{16}} \text{ oz}} = \frac{787.5 \text{ lb}}{1 \text{ h}}$$ ← Divide the common units, and simplify the ratios.

So machine A processes 787.5 pounds of material per hour. Machine A is faster.

Method 2 Convert 720 pounds per hour to ounces per second.

$$\frac{720 \text{ lb}}{1 \text{ h}} = \frac{720 \text{ lb}}{1 \text{ h}} \cdot \frac{1 \text{ h}}{60 \text{ min}} \cdot \frac{1 \text{ min}}{60 \text{ s}} \cdot \frac{16 \text{ oz}}{1 \text{ lb}}$$ ← Write using the appropriate conversion factors.

$$= \frac{\overset{\overset{1}{\cancel{12}}}{\cancel{720}} \text{ lb}}{1 \text{ h}} \cdot \frac{1 \text{ h}}{\underset{1}{\cancel{60}} \text{ min}} \cdot \frac{1 \text{ min}}{\underset{5}{\cancel{60}} \text{ s}} \cdot \frac{16 \text{ oz}}{\underset{1}{\cancel{1 \text{ lb}}}} = \frac{16 \text{ oz}}{5 \text{ s}}$$ ← Divide the common units.

$$= \frac{3.2 \text{ oz}}{1 \text{ s}}$$ ← Simplify.

So machine B processes 3.2 ounces of material per second. Machine A is faster.

Try These

Write each ratio in fractional form, and express in simplest form.

The Chapter 10 test grades were as follows: 6 A's, 8 B's, 10 C's, 3 D's, and 5 F's.

1. A's to D's

2. D's and F's to A's, B's, and C's.

3. A's to all the other grades

Write each as a unit rate.

4. 256 miles on 8 gallons of gas

5. 63 strokes in 18 holes of golf

Convert the units of measure as indicated.

6. 5 centimeters per second to meters per hour

7. 9 quarts per day to fluid ounces per hour

8. Sharon and Maxine are knitting scarves. Sharon can complete $1\frac{1}{2}$ inches per minute. Maxine can complete 3 yards in an hour. Who knits faster?

9. Discuss and Write When using the conversion factor of 1 hour equals 60 minutes, explain how to decide whether you should use $\frac{60 \text{ min}}{1 \text{ h}}$ or $\frac{1 \text{ h}}{60 \text{ min}}$.

Go to PRACTICE BOOK **Lesson 11-1 for exercise sets.**

Apply Proportion to Scale Models

Objective To solve problems involving scale drawings or models

Dave and his friends stop to rest on the way back to the campground after a long hike. The distance on the map from their resting place to the campground is 3 centimeters. The scale on the map shows that 2 centimeters = 1 kilometer. What is the actual distance from the resting place to the campground?

To find the actual distance, use the *scale* on the map to write and solve a proportion.

▶ A scale is a ratio between two sets of measurements, such as 2 m : 1 km. A scale drawing or scale model uses a scale to represent an object smaller than (a reduction) or larger than (an enlargement) the actual object. A map is an example of a scale drawing. The scale of the map is the ratio of the distance on the map *to* the corresponding actual distance.

The scale, 2 cm = 1 km, means that every 2 cm on the map of the campground represents 1 km of actual distance in the campground.

Let x = the actual distance from their resting place to the campground.

$$\frac{\text{map distance (cm)}}{\text{actual distance (km)}} \longrightarrow \frac{2 \text{ cm}}{1 \text{ km}} = \frac{3 \text{ cm}}{x \text{ km}}$$

Solve: $\dfrac{2}{1} = \dfrac{3}{x}$

$2x = 3$ ◀—Use the Cross-Products Rule.

$\dfrac{2x}{2} = \dfrac{3}{2}$ ◀—Use the Division Property of Equality.

$x = 1.5$ ◀—Simplify.

Check: $\dfrac{2}{1} = \dfrac{3}{x}$

$\dfrac{2}{1} \stackrel{?}{=} \dfrac{3}{1.5}$

$2(1.5) = 3(1)$

$3 = 3$ True

So the hikers are 1.5 kilometers from the campground.

Example

Solve using a proportion.

1. Rocky Mountain National Park is about 75 miles from Denver. On a map with a scale of 1 inch : 30 miles, what is its map distance from Denver?

$$\frac{\text{map distance (in.)}}{\text{actual distance (mi)}} \longrightarrow \frac{1 \text{ in.}}{30 \text{ mi}} = \frac{x}{75 \text{ mi}}$$

Solve: $\dfrac{1}{30} = \dfrac{x}{75}$

$30x = 75$ ◀—Use the Cross-Products Rule.

$\dfrac{30x}{30} = \dfrac{75}{30}$ ◀—Use the Division Property of Equality.

$x = 2.5$ ◀—Simplify.

Check: $\dfrac{1}{30} = \dfrac{x}{75}$

$\dfrac{1}{30} \stackrel{?}{=} \dfrac{2.5}{75}$

$1(75) \stackrel{?}{=} 30(2.5)$

$75 = 75$ True

Rocky Mountain National Park is about 2.5 inches from Denver on the map.

▶ Blueprints and scale replicas are other types of scale drawings and scale models.

The blueprint for Selena's new house has a scale of 1 inch : 2.5 feet. Her room is drawn as 4.5 inches by 6 inches. What are the dimensions of the actual room?

Let x = width of Selena's room, and
y = length of Selena's room.

$$\frac{\text{blueprint (in.)}}{\text{actual (ft)}} \longrightarrow \frac{1 \text{ in.}}{2.5 \text{ ft}} = \frac{4.5 \text{ in.}}{x \text{ ft}} \text{ and } \frac{1 \text{ in.}}{2.5 \text{ ft}} = \frac{6 \text{ in.}}{y \text{ ft}}$$

Solve: $\dfrac{1}{2.5} = \dfrac{4.5}{x}$ ◀—Find the width.   **Solve:** $\dfrac{1}{2.5} = \dfrac{6}{y}$ ◀—Find the length.

$x = 11.25$ $y = 15$

So Selena's room is 11.25 feet by 15 feet.

Example

Solve using a proportion.

1 A statue of a Husky, South High School's mascot, stands in front of the school. The ceramics class is making scale replicas of the statue. The students are using the scale 8 centimeters : 0.5 meters. The actual statue is 2 meters long. Jesse's replica is 40 centimeters long. Terry's replica is 32 centimeters long. Which student's replica is the correct length? Explain.

$$\frac{\text{replica (cm)}}{\text{statue (m)}} \longrightarrow \frac{8}{0.5} \longleftarrow \text{Write the scale as a fraction.}$$

Jesse: $\dfrac{8}{0.5} \stackrel{?}{=} \dfrac{40}{2}$ ◀—Write a proportion.—▶   Terry: $\dfrac{8}{0.5} \stackrel{?}{=} \dfrac{32}{2}$

$16 = 20$ False ◀—Use the Cross-Products Rule.—▶ $16 = 16$ True

Terry's statue is the correct length because it was made according to the given scale.

Try These

A map of California has a scale of 2 inches : 75 miles.

1. Sacramento is about 169 miles from Yosemite National Park. About how far apart are they on the map?

2. Los Angeles is shown 10 inches from San Francisco. What is the actual distance between the two cities?

A blueprint has a scale of 7 centimeters : 2 meters.

3. What are the actual dimensions of a room that is drawn as 17.5 centimeters by 14 centimeters on the blueprint?

4. The bathtub that was ordered is 1.7 meters long. The space allowed for the bathtub on the blueprint is 5.6 centimeters. Will the bathtub fit?

5. Discuss and Write When you write a proportion, does it matter which quantity you put in the numerator? Explain why or why not.

Go to PRACTICE BOOK **Lesson 11-2 for exercise sets.**

Calculate Relative Error

Objective To calculate the relative error in measuring square and cubic units

Italian physicist Enrico Fermi came up with a simple way to estimate Earth's circumference. Fermi reasoned as follows:

- It is about 3000 miles from New York to Los Angeles.

- There are four time zones in the continental United States, but you only cross through three of them when traveling from coast to coast.

- This means that each one of the 24 time zones must be about 1000 miles wide.

Therefore, the approximate measure of the Earth's circumference is 24(1000)—or 24,000—miles. If the actual circumference at the equator is about 24,902 miles, how accurate was Fermi's measure?

To find how accurate Fermi's measure was, find the *percent of error* and the *relative error*.

▶ **Percent of error** is one way to describe how accurate a measurement is. **Relative error** is another way to describe the extent of the error.

$$\text{percent of error} = \frac{|\text{measured value} - \text{actual value}|}{\text{actual value}} \cdot 100$$

The relative error is the percent of error written as a decimal.

- percent of error = $\frac{|24,000 - 24,902|}{24,902} \cdot 100$ ◀——Substitute the appropriate values into the formula.

  $= 3.6\%$ ◀——Simplify and round to the nearest tenth of a percent.

- relative error = 3.6% = 0.036 ◀——Write the percent of error as a decimal.

So the percent of error is 3.6% and the relative error is 0.036.

Examples

1 Find the percent of error and the relative error of the area.

measured dimensions: $42\frac{1}{2}$ inches by 68 inches

actual dimensions: 42 inches by $67\frac{1}{2}$ inches

measured area = 42.5 in.(68 in.) = 2890 in.^{2} ⎤ Use the formula
actual area = 42 in.(67.5 in.) = 2835 in.^{2} ⎦ length • width = area

.Think.........
$42\frac{1}{2} = 42.5$
$67\frac{1}{2} = 67.5$

- percent of error = $\frac{|2890 - 2835|}{2835} \cdot 100$ ◀——Substitute the appropriate values into the formula.

  $= 1.9\%$ ◀——Simplify and round to the nearest tenth of a percent.

- relative error = 1.9% = 0.019 ◀——Write the percent of error as a decimal.

The percent of error is 1.9% and the relative error is 0.019.

2 A store owner measured a shipping box and advertised its dimensions as 30 inches by 24 inches by 14 inches. The actual dimensions of the box were $29\frac{1}{2}$ inches by $23\frac{1}{2}$ inches by $13\frac{1}{2}$ inches. What was the percent of error and the relative error of the store owner's measurements in terms of the box's volume?

.Think...

$29\frac{1}{2} = 29.5$ $23\frac{1}{2} = 23.5$ $13\frac{1}{2} = 13.5$

....

measured volume = (30 in.)(24 in.)(14 in.) = 10,080 in.^{3} ⎤ Use the formula
    actual volume = (29.5 in.)(23.5 in.)(13.5 in.) = 9,358.88 in.^{3} ⎦ length • width • height = volume.

• percent of error = $\dfrac{|10,080 - 9,358.88|}{9,358.88} \cdot 100$ ←—Substitute the appropriate values into the formula.

= 7.7% ←—Simplify and round to the nearest tenth of a percent.

• relative error = 7.7% = 0.077 ←—Write the percent of error as a decimal.

The percent of error is 7.7% and the relative error is 0.077.

▶ Percent of error can become aggravated or compounded by multiple measurements.

Find the relative error for each dimension advertised by the store owner above.

$\dfrac{|30 - 29.5|}{29.5} \cdot 100 = 1.7\%$ | $\dfrac{|24 - 23.5|}{23.5} \cdot 100 = 2.1\%$ | $\dfrac{|14 - 13.5|}{13.5} \cdot 100 = 3.7\%$

relative error = 0.017 | relative error = 0.021 | relative error = 0.037

Notice that the relative error for each measure became greater with each measurement. In this case the relative error for the volume of the box is greater than the sum of the relative errors of the individual measurements.

$0.077 > 0.017 + 0.021 + 0.037$

$0.077 > 0.75$

Try These

Find the percent of error and the relative error of the area.

1. measured dimensions: 16 m by 11 m
   actual dimensions: 16.2 m by 11.8 m

2. measured dimensions: $5\frac{1}{2}$ yd by $2\frac{3}{4}$ yd
   actual dimensions: $5\frac{1}{4}$ yd by $2\frac{1}{2}$ yd

Find the percent of error and the relative error of the volume.

3. measured dimensions: 2 ft by 3.5 ft by 7 ft
   actual dimensions: 2.5 ft by 7 ft by 4 ft

4. measured dimensions: 1.2 cm by 1.5 cm by 2.5 cm
   actual dimensions: 1.3 cm by 2.4 cm by 1.5 cm

5. Discuss and Write Explain why the formula for percent of error includes absolute value.

Go to PRACTICE BOOK Lesson 11-3 for exercise sets.

11-4

Apply Percents to Algebraic Problems

Objective To solve problems involving percentage and percent of change

Aran has a part-time job as a salesperson at a computer store. He is paid a 2% commission on his total sales. One week, his total sales were $7000. How much was his commission?

To find Aran's commission, find the *percentage*, $p = 2\%$ *of* $7000 by writing and solving a percent proportion or by using the percentage formula.

> **Remember:** A percent is a ratio that compares a number to 100.
> Percentage = rate • base ($p = rb$)

Method 1 Write and solve a percent proportion.

$$\frac{\text{part}}{\text{whole}} \longrightarrow \frac{p}{7000} = \frac{2}{100}$$

$$100p = 14{,}000$$

$$p = 140$$

Method 2 Use the percentage formula.

$$p = rb \longrightarrow p = 2\% \cdot 7000$$

$$= 0.20 \cdot 7000$$

$$= 140$$

So Aran's commission was $140.

Examples

> **Remember:** T = tax MP = marked price
> R = rate TC = total cost

1 Find the total cost of a $12.96 shirt after a 6.5% sales tax is added.

• Find the sales tax.

$$T = R \cdot MP \longrightarrow T = 6.5\% \cdot 12.96$$

$$= 0.065 \cdot 12.96$$

$$= 0.8424 \approx 0.84$$

The sales tax rounded to the nearest cent is $0.84.

• Find the total cost.

$$TC = MP + T \longrightarrow TC = 12.96 + 0.84$$

$$= 13.80$$

The total cost of the shirt including tax is $13.80.

2 Shelby receives a 20% employee discount at the hardware store where she works. How much would she pay for a can of paint that normally costs $16.99?

> **Remember:** D = discount
> LP = list price
> SP = sale price

• Find the discount.

$$D = R \cdot LP \longrightarrow D = 20\% \cdot 16.99$$

$$= 0.2 \cdot 16.99$$

$$= 3.398 \approx 3.40$$

The discount, rounded to the nearest cent, is $3.40

• Find the sale price.

$$SP = LP - D \longrightarrow SP = 16.99 - 3.40$$

$$= 13.59$$

Shelby would pay $13.59 for the paint.

3 Marcus was charged 5.3% simple interest on a loan of $4600. He paid all the money plus interest after 2 years. How much did he pay altogether?

> **Remember:** P = principal $\quad I$ = interest
> r = rate $\quad B$ = balance
> t = time

- First, find the interest, I, using the simple interest formula.

$$I = Prt \longrightarrow I = 4600 \cdot 5.3\% \cdot 2$$
$$= 4600 \cdot 0.053 \cdot 2$$
$$= 487.6$$

The amount of interest is $487.60

- Then find total amount due, or balance, B.

$$B = P + I \longrightarrow B = 4600 + 487.60$$
$$= 5087.60$$

Marcus paid a total of $5087.60

▶ The percent of change is the percent, or rate, a quantity increases or decreases from its original amount.

When Hannah first started working, she was paid $8.00 an hour. After 6 months, her hourly wage was raised to $8.50. What was the percent of increase in her hourly wage?

___ **Key Concept** ___

Percent of Change

Percent of change = $\dfrac{\text{amount of change}}{\text{original amount}} \cdot 100$

To find the percent of increase, find the percent of change.

- First, find the amount of increase.

new amount − original amount = amount of increase

$8.50 − $8.00 = $0.50

- Then use a formula to find the rate of increase, I.

$$I = \frac{\text{amount of increase}}{\text{original amount}} \cdot 100$$

$$I = \frac{0.50}{8.00} \cdot 100 = 6.25\%$$

So Hannah's hourly wage increased 6.25%.

Try These

Solve each problem.

1. Find the amount of simple interest $900 would earn in 3 years if deposited in an account that paid 3.2% interest.

2. The enrollment at Central High School dropped from 2325 to 2139 students. What was the percent of decrease?

3. Which hourly wage shows the greatest percent of increase: $10.50 to $12.25 or $9.00 to $10.75?

4. Which telescope is less expensive: $150.00 on sale for 25% off or $135.00 on sale for 20% off?

5. **Discuss and Write** The owner of a clothing shop bought some jackets for $40.00 each. She marked up the price 50%. When the jackets did not sell, she put them on the "50% off" sale rack. Because the owner increased the $40.00 cost by 50% and then decreased it by 50%, can you assume that the sale price is $40.00? Explain why or why not.

Go to PRACTICE BOOK Lesson 11-4 for exercise sets.

The Trigonometric Ratios

Objective To define three trigonometric ratios with respect to a right triangle
- To write trigonometric ratios, given the lengths of sides of a right triangle
- To use a handheld to find values of trigonometric ratios and angle measures

The word *trigonometry* means "the measure of triangles." The study of trigonometry involves the relationships among the sides and angles of triangles. Trigonometry is used in engineering, navigation, astronomy, and many other scientific and technical fields.

► A trigonometric ratio is a ratio of the lengths of two sides of a right triangle. The three basic trigonometric ratios are sine, cosine, and tangent. They are abbreviated as sin, cos, and tan, respectively.

Key Concept

Trigonometric Ratios

$$\sin A = \frac{\text{length of leg opposite } \angle A}{\text{length of hypotenuse}} = \frac{a}{c}$$

$$\cos A = \frac{\text{length of leg adjacent to } \angle A}{\text{length of hypotenuse}} = \frac{b}{c}$$

$$\tan A = \frac{\text{length of leg opposite } \angle A}{\text{length of leg adjacent to } \angle A} = \frac{a}{b}$$

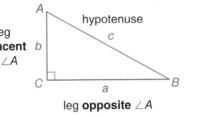

The acronym SOH CAH TOA is a way to remember the definitions of sine, cosine, and tangent.

SOH	**CAH**	**TOA**
$\text{sine} = \dfrac{\text{opposite}}{\text{hypotenuse}}$	$\text{cosine} = \dfrac{\text{adjacent}}{\text{hypotenuse}}$	$\text{tangent} = \dfrac{\text{opposite}}{\text{adjacent}}$

► When the lengths of the sides are known, the trigonometric ratios can be expressed as numerical ratios.

Find the sine, cosine, and tangent of $\angle A$.

$$\sin A = \frac{\text{leg opposite } \angle A}{\text{hypotenuse}} = \frac{15}{17}$$

$$\cos A = \frac{\text{leg adjacent to } \angle A}{\text{hypotenuse}} = \frac{8}{17}$$

$$\tan A = \frac{\text{leg opposite } \angle A}{\text{leg adjacent to } \angle A} = \frac{15}{8}$$

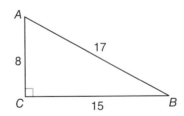

Example

1 Find the sine, cosine, and tangent of $\angle D$ and $\angle E$.

For $\angle D$, adjacent leg $= 4$, opposite leg $= 3$, hypotenuse $= 5$

$$\sin D = \frac{3}{5} \qquad \cos D = \frac{4}{5} \qquad \tan D = \frac{3}{4}$$

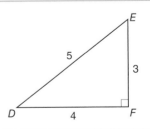

► You can use a handheld to find the values of the sine, cosine, and tangent ratios for a given angle.

Use a handheld to find the value of cos 73°.

Press ⌂. Then press 1 to select Calculator.

Press cos. Input 73. Press enter.

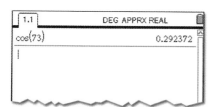

| 1.1 | DEG APPRX REAL |
| cos(73) | 0.292372 |

To find trigonometric values the handheld must be in both the degree mode and the approximate mode.

Rounded to the nearest ten-thousandth, cos 73° = 0.2924.

► You can find the degree measure of an acute angle of a right triangle by using inverse trigonometric functions and a handheld.

Use a handheld to find the measure of ∠A if tan A = 1.1504.

Press ⌂. Then press 1 to select Calculator.

Press ctrl tan. Input 1.1504. Press enter.

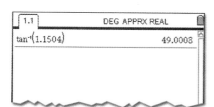

| 1.1 | DEG APPRX REAL |
| tan⁻¹(1.1504) | 49.0008 |

Rounded to the nearest degree, ∠A = 49°.

Key Concept

Inverse Trigonometric Functions

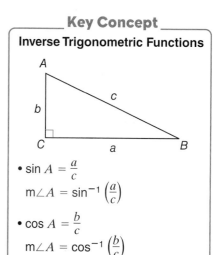

- $\sin A = \frac{a}{c}$

  $m\angle A = \sin^{-1}\left(\frac{a}{c}\right)$

- $\cos A = \frac{b}{c}$

  $m\angle A = \cos^{-1}\left(\frac{b}{c}\right)$

- $\tan A = \frac{a}{b}$

  $m\angle A = \tan^{-1}\left(\frac{a}{b}\right)$

Try These

Find the sine, cosine, and tangent of each angle.

1. ∠A

2. ∠B

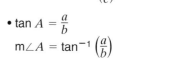

Use a handheld to find the sine, cosine, and tangent of the angle to the nearest ten-thousandth.

3. 71°

4. 36°

Use a handheld to find the measure of ∠A to the nearest degree.

5. cos A = 0.1351

6. tan A = 0.8452

7. sin A = 0.1344

8. **Discuss and Write** What can you say about the range of values of the sine and cosine of the acute angles in every right triangle? Explain.

Go to PRACTICE BOOK **Lesson 11-5 for exercise sets.**

Use Trigonometric Ratios to Solve Right Triangles

Objective To use the trigonometric ratios to solve for lengths of missing sides and degree measures of missing angles of a right triangle

Rebecca is flying a kite and has let out 120 meters of string. If the string forms an angle of 40° with the level ground, to the nearest meter, how high is her kite?

To find how high Rebecca's kite is, first draw and label a picture to represent the problem situation, and then use a trigonometric ratio to solve for the height. Assume that the kite string is close to being a straight line.

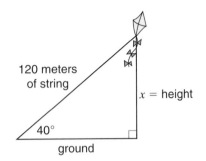

120 meters of string

x = height

40°

ground

►Trigonometric ratios can be used to find missing measures of angles and sides of a right triangle. This process is called *solving a right triangle*.

Since the angle formed by the string with the level ground and the length of the hypotenuse are given, to find how high the kite is, use the sine ratio of the given angle.

Let x = the height of Rebecca's kite.

$$\sin 40° = \frac{\text{opposite}}{\text{hypotenuse}} \longrightarrow \sin 40° = \frac{x}{120} \longleftarrow \text{Substitute the given values.}$$

$$\sin 40°(120) = x \longleftarrow \text{Multiply both sides by 120.}$$

$$(0.6428)(120) = x \longleftarrow \text{Use a handheld to find } \sin 40°.$$

$$77.136 = x \longleftarrow \text{Simplify.}$$

$$77 \approx x$$

So Rebecca's kite is about 77 meters high.

Example

1 Solve $\triangle ABC$. Round the lengths of the sides to the nearest tenth.

- First, find the measure of the missing angle, $\angle B$.

$$m\angle A + m\angle B = 90° \longleftarrow \text{The acute angles of a right triangle are complementary.}$$

$$m\angle B = 90° - 19°$$

$$= 71°$$

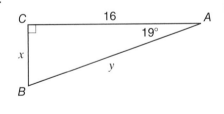

- Then, find the measures of the missing sides, x and y.

To find x:

$$\tan 19° = \frac{\text{opposite}}{\text{adjacent}} \longrightarrow \tan 19° = \frac{x}{16}$$

$$0.3443 = \frac{x}{16}$$

$$(0.3443)(16) = x$$

$$5.5 \approx x$$

To find y:

$$\cos 19° = \frac{\text{adjacent}}{\text{hypotenuse}} \longrightarrow \cos 19° = \frac{16}{y}$$

$$0.9455 = \frac{16}{y}$$

$$0.9455y = 16$$

$$y \approx 16.9$$

▶ Given the length of two sides of a right triangle, you can use trigonometric ratios to find the measures of the acute angles. You can use trigonometric ratios or the Pythagorean Theorem to find the length of the third side.

Solve △ABC. Round the measures of the angles to the nearest degree and the length of the side to the nearest tenth.

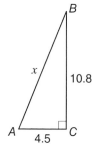

• Find the measures of the missing angles, ∠A and ∠B.

$$\tan A = \frac{\text{opposite}}{\text{adjacent}} \quad \longleftarrow \text{Decide which ratio to use.}$$

$$= \frac{10.8}{4.5} \quad \longleftarrow \text{Substitute the given values.}$$

$$= 2.4 \quad \longleftarrow \text{Simplify.}$$

$$\angle A \approx 67° \quad \longleftarrow \text{Use a handheld to find } \tan^{-1} 2.4.$$

$$\angle B \approx 90° - 67° \quad \longleftarrow \text{The acute angles of a right triangle are complementary.}$$

$$= 23°$$

• Find the measure of the missing side, x.

To find x, you can use the Pythagorean Theorem.

$$(4.5)^2 + (10.8)^2 = x^2$$

$$20.25 + 116.64 = x^2$$

$$136.89 = x^2$$

$$11.7 = x$$

> **Remember:**
> If a triangle is a right triangle, then the sum of the squares of the legs, a and b, equals the square of the hypotenuse, c.
> $$a^2 + b^2 = c^2$$

Try These

Solve each right triangle. Round the lengths of the sides to the nearest tenth, and round angle measures to the nearest degree.

1.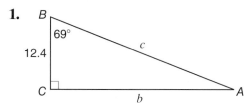

2.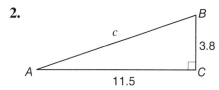

Solve.

3. In right △ABC, m∠A = 38°, m∠C = 90°, and the length of $\overline{BC}$ = 10 cm. Find the length of $\overline{AC}$ to the nearest centimeter.

4. Find, to the nearest integer, the length of the hypotenuse of an isosceles right triangle each of whose legs measures 15 feet.

5. The legs of a right triangle measure 4 in. and 7 in. Find, to the nearest degree, the measure of the smaller acute angle.

6. Find, to the nearest degree, the measure of the larger acute angle of a right triangle whose sides measure 5 cm, 12 cm, and 13 cm.

7. **Discuss and Write** Explain how to decide which trigonometric ratio to use when solving a right triangle.

 PRACTICE BOOK **Lesson 11-6** for exercise sets.

Use Trigonometric Ratios to Solve Verbal Problems

Objective To solve verbal problems using trigonometric ratios

The shadow of a building is 22.5 feet long when the rays of the sun make a 67° angle with the ground. How tall is the building?

To find how tall the building is, first draw and label a picture to represent the problem situation, and then use a trigonometric ratio.

▶ Trigonometric ratios are used to find distances or lengths that cannot be measured directly.

To solve an indirect measurement problem, it is helpful to draw and label a picture to represent the problem situation.

Since the angle formed by the rays of the sun with the ground and the length of the adjacent leg are given, use the tangent ratio of the given angle to find the height of the building. Let h = the height of the building.

$\tan 67° = \dfrac{\text{opposite}}{\text{adjacent}} \longrightarrow \tan 67° = \dfrac{h}{22.5}$ ◀—Substitute the given values.

$2.3559 = \dfrac{h}{22.5}$ ◀—Use a handheld to find tan 67°.

$22.5(2.3559) = h$ ◀—Multiply both sides by 22.5.

$53 \approx h$ ◀—Simplify.

So the building is about 53 feet tall.

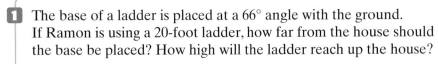

1 The base of a ladder is placed at a 66° angle with the ground. If Ramon is using a 20-foot ladder, how far from the house should the base be placed? How high will the ladder reach up the house?

Draw a picture to represent the problem situation.

Let x = the distance from the base of the ladder to the house.
Let y = the distance the ladder reaches up the house.

To find x, use the cosine ratio.

$\cos 66° = \dfrac{x}{20}$ ◀—Use the ratio of the adjacent side to the hypotenuse.

$0.4067 = \dfrac{x}{20}$ ◀—Use a handheld to find cos 66°.

$8.1 \approx x$ ◀—Simplify.

To find y, use the sine ratio.

$\sin 66° = \dfrac{y}{20}$ ◀—Use the ratio of the opposite side to the hypotenuse.

$0.9135 = \dfrac{y}{20}$ ◀—Use a handheld to find sin 66°.

$18.3 \approx y$ ◀—Simplify.

The ladder should be placed about 8.1 feet from the house. It will reach about 18.3 feet up the house.

2 Josh is designing a skateboard ramp that will be 36 feet long and will make a 10° angle with the ground. How far will the high end of the ramp be above the ground?

Draw a picture to represent the problem situation.

Let x = the height of the high end of the ramp.

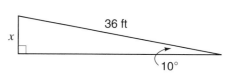

To find x, use the sine ratio.

$\sin 10° = \dfrac{x}{36}$ ◄—Use the ratio of the opposite side to the hypotenuse.

$0.1736 = \dfrac{x}{36}$ ◄—Use a handheld to find sin 10°.

$x = 36(0.1736)$ ◄—Multiply both sides by 36.

$x \approx 6.2$ ◄—Simplify.

The ramp will be about 6.2 feet high at its highest end.

▶ Two terms that are often used in problems about right triangles are angle of elevation and angle of depression. Both angles are formed by an observer's line of sight and a horizontal line.

The *angle of elevation* is formed when the observer is *looking up* at an object.

The *angle of depression* is formed when the observer is *looking down* at an object.

The angle of elevation formed by observer A looking up at observer B and the angle of depression formed by observer B looking down at observer A are *alternate interior angles*. These angles are congruent.

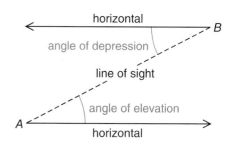

Alden looked out a window 4 meters above ground level. He saw a hot air balloon hovering over the far end of a soccer field 500 meters away. The angle of elevation from his position to the balloon was 33°. How far above the ground was the balloon?

Draw a picture to represent the problem situation.

Let h = the height of the balloon 4 meters above ground level.

To find h, use the tangent ratio.

$\tan 33° = \dfrac{h}{500}$ ◄—Use the ratio of the opposite side to the adjacent.

$0.6494 = \dfrac{h}{500}$ ◄—Use a handheld to find tan 33°.

$h = 500(0.6494)$ ◄—Multiply both sides by 500.

$h \approx 324.7$ ◄—Simplify.

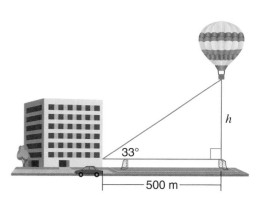

So the balloon is about 325 meters higher than the window. Because the window is 4 meters above the ground, the balloon is about 4 + 325, or 329, meters above the ground.

Continue Lesson ➡

Example

1 A tree is 800 feet from the base of a cliff. The angle of depression of the base of the tree from the top of the cliff is 32°. How high is the cliff?

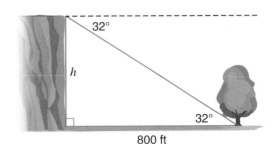
800 ft

Draw a picture to represent the problem situation.

Let h = the height of the cliff.

To find h, use the tangent ratio.

$\tan 32° = \dfrac{h}{800}$ ←—Use the ratio of the opposite side to the adjacent side.

$0.6249 = \dfrac{h}{800}$ ←—Find tan of 32°.

$h = 800(0.6249)$ ←—Multiply both sides by 800.

$h \approx 500$ ←—Simplify.

The cliff is about 500 feet high.

Remember: The angle of depression from point A to point B and the angle of elevation from point B to point A are congruent.

► Sometimes, problems can involve *two* right triangles.

To find the height of a waterfall, a surveyor took two sightings, 200 feet apart. The first angle of elevation was 63°, and the second was 45°. What is the height of the waterfall?

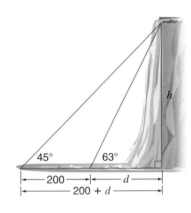

Draw a picture to represent the problem situation.

Let h = the height of the waterfall.

Let d = the surveyor's distance from the waterfall at the first sighting.

To find h and d, use the tangent ratio.

First Sighting

$\tan 63° = \dfrac{h}{d}$ ←—Use the ratio of the opposite to the adjacent.—→

$1.9626 = \dfrac{h}{d}$ ←—Find tan 63° and tan 45°.—→

$h = 1.9626d$ ←—Use the Multiplication Property of Equality.—→

Second Sighting

$\tan 45° = \dfrac{h}{d + 200}$

$1 = \dfrac{h}{d + 200}$

$h = d + 200$

Since both expressions are equal to h, use substitution to solve for d.

$1.9626d = d + 200$ ←—Substitute.

$0.9626d = 200$ ←—Use the Subtraction Property of Equality.

$d \approx 208$ ←—Use the Division Property of Equality.

The first sighting was taken about 208 feet from the base of the waterfall.

$d + 200 = h$ ←—Choose one of the equations to solve for h.

$208 + 200 \approx h$ ←—Use substitution.

$408 \approx h$ ←—Simplify.

So the waterfall is about 408 feet high.

Example

1 To measure the height of a Giant Sequoia, a surveyor took two sightings 30 feet apart. The angle of elevation of the first sighting was 76°; the second was 70°. How tall is the Giant Sequoia?

Draw a picture to represent the problem situation.

Let h = the height of the Giant Sequoia.
Let d = the surveyor's distance from the Giant Sequoia at the first sighting.

First Sighting   **Second Sighting**

$\tan 76° = \dfrac{h}{d}$ ←—Use the tangent ratio.—→ $\tan 70° = \dfrac{h}{d+30}$

$4.0108 = \dfrac{h}{d}$ ←—Find tan 76° and tan 70°.—→ $2.7475 = \dfrac{h}{d+30}$

$h = 4.0108d$ ←—Use the Multiplication—→ $h = 2.7475(d+30)$
             Property of Equality. $= 2.7475d + 82.425$

$4.0108d = 2.7475d + 82.425$ ←—Use substitution to write one equation.
$1.2633d = 82.425$ ←—Use the Subtraction Property of Equality.
$d \approx 65$ ←—Use the Division Property of Equality.

The first sighting was taken about 65 feet from the base of the tree.

$4.0108d = h$ ←—Choose one of the equations to solve for h.
$4.0108(65) = h$ ←—Use substitution.
$261 \approx h$ ←—Simplify.

The Sequoia is about 261 feet high.

Try These

Solve each problem. Round lengths to the nearest whole number.

1. The bottom of a ladder leaning against a building makes a 31° angle with the ground. The horizontal distance from the base of the building to the bottom of the ladder is 12 feet. What is the distance from the base of the building to the top of the ladder? How long is the ladder?

2. A plane carrying emergency supplies to an island is flying 4.5 miles above the ocean. The pilot spots the island in the distance. The angle of depression from the plane to the island is 6°. How much farther must the plane fly before it passes over the island and drops the supplies?

3. A surveyor took two sightings, 92 feet apart, of a rock formation. The first sighting showed an angle of elevation of 84°; the angle of elevation for the second sighting was 75°. How tall is the rock formation?

4. **Discuss and Write** A problem begins, "A lighthouse keeper looked out and saw a boat in the distance. The angle of depression was 38°. . . ." Explain what is meant by the angle of depression. Then sketch the beginning of the problem.

Go to   **PRACTICE BOOK Lesson 11-7 for exercise sets.**

II-8

Technology:
Graph the Sine and Cosine Functions

Objective To use a handheld to graph the sine and cosine functions

Trigonometric functions are functions of an angle. They are important to the study of triangles and the modeling of periodic phenomena.

The graphs of the sine and cosine functions have many real-world applications. You can identify these graphs by their individual characteristics.

▶ Some handhelds allow you to graph trigonometric functions.

Graph the equation $y = \sin(x)$ using a handheld.

Step 1 Change the handheld setting to degrees. Press ⌂. Then choose **8** for **System Info** and **2** for **System Settings**. Change **Angle:** to *Degree*. Tab down to **OK** and press **enter**.

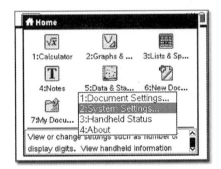 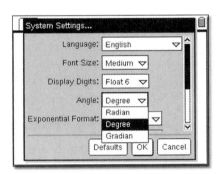

Step 2 Press ⌂. Then choose **2** to select **Graphs & Geometry**.

Step 3 Change the window size to see the graph better. Press **menu** **4** to select **Window**, then **1** to choose **Window Settings**. Change **XMin:** to −90 and **XMax:** to 720. Change **YMin:** to −2 and **YMax:** to 2.

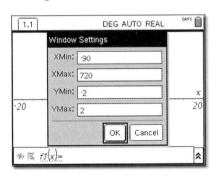

Step 4 Press **sin** *x*. Then press **enter** to graph the sine function.

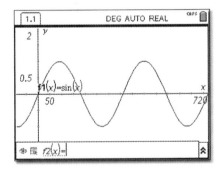

Note that the graph is a repeating pattern of curves with *y*-values between −1 and 1.

As you can see on the graph, the sine function is continuous for negative angle measures as well as those greater than 90°. You will learn more about this in later mathematics courses.

▶ To identify some of the values on the trigonometric graph you can use the **Trace** command on the handheld.

Step 5 Press ⬭menu. Select **Trace**, and then choose **Graph Trace**.

Step 6 Press ⬭menu. Select **Trace**, and then choose **Trace Settings**.
Change **Trace Step** to 10, then press ⬭tab ⬭enter for **OK**.

Step 7 Press ⬭ to move along the line. Note the point $(30, 0.5)$ represents $\sin(30) = 0.5$ and $(90, 1)$ represents $\sin(90) = 1$.

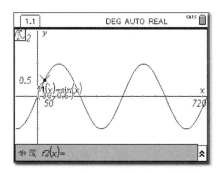 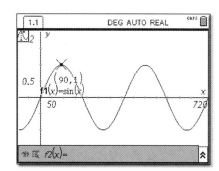

Example

1 Graph the equation $y = \cos(x)$ using a handheld.

Step 1 Press ⬭⌂. Then choose ⬭2 to select **Graphs & Geometry**.

Step 2 Change the window size to see the graph better. Press ⬭menu ⬭4 to select **Window**, then ⬭1 to choose **Window Settings**.
Change **XMin:** to -90 and **XMax:** to 720.
Change **YMin:** to -2 and **YMax:** to 2.

Step 3 Press ⬭cos x. Then press ⬭enter to graph the cosine function.

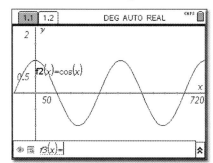

Note that the graph of the cosine function has the same repeating pattern as that of the sine function, but it is shifted so that its y-intercept is 1.

Try These

Use a handheld to graph the trigonometric function. Choose an appropriate window size.

1. $y = 2\sin(x)$ **2.** $y = 2\cos(x)$ **3.** $y = 5\cos(x)$ **4.** $y = 3\sin(x)$

5. Discuss and Write Graph the functions $y = \sin(-x)$ and $y = -\sin(x)$ using a handheld. How do they compare to the graph of the parent function $y = \sin(x)$?

Go to PRACTICE BOOK **Lesson 11-8 for exercise sets.**

Problem-Solving Strategy:
Guess and Test

Objective To solve problems using the strategy *Guess and Test*

Problem 1: The sum of the squares of two consecutive whole numbers is the number of days in a Gregorian calendar non-leap year. What are the two whole numbers?

Read ▶ **Read to understand what is being asked.**

List the facts and restate the question.

Facts: When two consecutive whole numbers are squared and the squares are added, the result is 365. (the number of days in a year that is not a leap year.)

Question: What are the two consecutive whole numbers?

Plan ▶ **Select a strategy.**

You can use the strategy *Guess and Test*.

Solve ▶ **Apply the strategy.**

- Start by choosing two consecutive whole numbers and finding the sum of their squares. Try 9 and 10.

  Square 9 and 10: $9^2 = 81$ and $10^2 = 100$
  Add the squares: $81 + 100 = 181$

  The result is much less than 365.

- Try using greater numbers. Choose 15 and 16.

  Square 15 and 16: $15^2 = 225$ and $16^2 = 256$
  Add the squares: $225 + 256 = 481$

  The result is much greater than 365.

- Try lesser numbers greater than 9 and 10. Choose 12 and 13.

  Square 12 and 13: $12^2 = 144$ and $13^2 = 169$
  Add the squares: $144 + 169 = 313$

  The result, 313, is close to 365.

- Choose 13 and 14.

  Square 13 and 14: $13^2 = 169$ and $14^2 = 196$
  Add the squares: $169 + 196 = 365$

  The sum is 365, so 13 and 14 are the consecutive whole numbers with the sum of their squares equal to the number of days in a Gregorian calendar non-leap year.

Check ▶ **Check to make sure your answer makes sense.**

Are 13 and 14 consecutive whole numbers? Yes ✓
Is the sum of their squares 365?
$13^2 + 14^2 = 169 + 196 = 365$. Yes ✓

Problem-Solving Strategies

1. Make a Drawing
2. Solve a Simpler Problem
3. Reason Logically
4. Consider Extreme Cases
5. Work Backward
6. Find a Pattern
7. Account for All Possibilities
8. Adopt a Different Point of View
9. **Guess and Test**
10. Organize Data

Problem 2: The volume of a box is 1056 cubic feet. Each dimension is a whole number of feet. If the length is 5 feet longer than the width, and the width is 5 feet longer than the height, what are the dimensions of the box?

Read ▶ **Read to understand what is being asked.**

List the facts and restate the question.

Facts: The volume of a box is 1056 cubic feet.

The dimensions are whole numbers.

The length is 5 feet longer than the width.

The width is 5 feet longer than the height.

Question: What are the dimensions of the box?

Plan ▶ **Select a strategy.**

An equation for this situation would be difficult to solve. You can use the strategy *Guess and Test*.

Solve ▶ **Apply the strategy.**

Let ℓ = the length of the box,
$\ell - 5$ = the width of the box, and
$(\ell - 5) - 5 = \ell - 10$ = the height of the box.

Since the box is a rectangular prism, then $V = \ell wh$ is the volume of the box. By substitution:

$$V = \ell wh \longrightarrow 1056 = \ell(\ell - 5)(\ell - 10)$$

> **Remember:** $V = \ell wh$, where V is the volume, ℓ is the length, w is the width, and h is the height of a rectangular prism.

You can guess and test different values of ℓ to find the solution. Making a table can help you keep track of your work.

Start by guessing that the length is 20 feet. Then the width would be $(20 - 5)$, or 15, feet, the height would be $(20 - 10)$, or 10, feet, and the volume with be $(20 \cdot 15 \cdot 10)$, or 3000, cubic feet.

Length (feet)	Width (feet)	Height (feet)	Volume (cubic feet)	
20	15	10	3000	Too big. Try a smaller value.
14	9	4	504	Too small. Try a value between 14 and 20.
17	12	7	1428	Too big. Try slightly smaller value.
15	10	5	750	Too small. 16 must be right.
16	11	6	1056	Correct!

So the dimensions of the box are 16 feet by 11 feet by 6 feet.

Check ▶ **Check to make sure your answer makes sense.**

Are the dimensions whole numbers of feet? Yes, 16 feet by 11 feet by 6 feet ✓
Is the length 5 feet longer than the width? Yes, $16 - 5 = 11$ ✓
Is the width 5 feet longer than the height? Yes, $11 - 6 = 5$ ✓
Is the volume 1056 cubic feet? Yes, $16 \cdot 11 \cdot 6 = 1056$ ✓

Go to ▶ **PRACTICE BOOK Lesson 11-9 for exercise sets.**

Enrichment:
The Law of Sines

Objective To apply the Law of Sines to find unknown side lengths and angle measures of oblique triangles

The Law of Sines

To find an unknown measure in an *oblique triangle*—that is, a triangle with no right angle—sometimes you can use the Law of Sines. The Law of Sines states that the sine of an angle is proportional to the side opposite that angle.

When applying this rule, you should always draw a diagram (if not given) to be certain you have the correct angle and side relationships.

_____ **Key Concept** _____

The Law of Sines

In $\triangle ABC$, where a, b, and c are the lengths of the sides opposite $\angle A$, $\angle B$, and $\angle C$, respectively,

$$\frac{a}{\sin A} = \frac{b}{\sin B} = \frac{c}{\sin C}$$

In writing Law of Sines equations, you use only two of the possible ratios, thus producing a proportion you can solve.

In the given triangle at the right, how could you find the measure of $\angle C$ and the side length b?

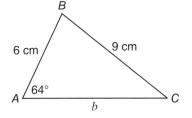

- To find the measure of $\angle C$, use the Law of Sines to set up a proportion in which only one value is unknown.

$$\frac{a}{\sin A} = \frac{c}{\sin C} \quad \longleftarrow \text{The only unknown is } C.$$

$$\frac{9}{\sin 64°} = \frac{6}{\sin C} \quad \longleftarrow \text{Substitute the known values.}$$

$$9(\sin C) = 6(\sin 64°) \quad \longleftarrow \text{Apply the Cross-Products Rule.}$$

$$\frac{9(\sin C)}{9} = \frac{6(\sin 64°)}{9} \quad \longleftarrow \text{Apply the Division Property of Equality.}$$

$$\sin C = \frac{6(\sin 64°)}{9} \quad \longleftarrow \text{Simplify.}$$

$$C \approx 37° \quad \longleftarrow \text{Use a handheld to evaluate the trigonometric function and simplify.}$$

- To find b, first find the measure of $\angle B$, then use the Law of Sines.

$$64° + B + 37° = 180° \quad \longleftarrow \text{The sum of the measures of the angles of a triangle is 180°.}$$

$$B = 79°$$

Use either $\dfrac{a}{\sin A} = \dfrac{b}{\sin B}$ or $\dfrac{b}{\sin B} = \dfrac{c}{\sin C}$.

$$\frac{a}{\sin A} = \frac{b}{\sin B} \longrightarrow \frac{9}{\sin 64°} = \frac{b}{\sin 79°} \quad \longleftarrow \text{Substitute the known values.}$$

$$9(\sin 79°) = b(\sin 64°) \quad \longleftarrow \text{Apply the Cross-Products Rule.}$$

$$\frac{9(\sin 79°)}{\sin 64°} = \frac{b(\sin 64°)}{\sin 64°} \quad \longleftarrow \text{Apply the Division Property of Equality.}$$

$$\frac{9(\sin 79°)}{\sin 64°} = b \quad \longleftarrow \text{Simplify.}$$

$$10 \approx b \quad \longleftarrow \text{Use a handheld to evaluate the trigonometric functions and simplify.}$$

So the degree measure of $\angle C$ is about 37° and the side length b is about 10 cm.

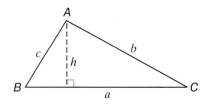

Deriving the Law of Sines

To derive the Law of Sines, use $\triangle ABC$ shown with altitude h.

$\sin B = \dfrac{h}{c}$ and $\sin C = \dfrac{h}{b}$, so $\dfrac{\sin B}{\sin C} = \dfrac{\frac{h}{c}}{\frac{h}{b}} = \dfrac{b}{c}$.

Therefore, $\dfrac{c}{\sin C} = \dfrac{b}{\sin B}$. By drawing another altitude and following a similar argument either for angles A and B or for angles A and C, you can get the third part of the law.

Applying the Law of Sines

Kaya and Zack are staying at cottages 900 m apart along a straight stretch of shore. One morning, they swim from their cottages to the same point on a nearby island. Kaya's path makes a 36° angle with the shore. Zack's path makes a 48° angle with the shore. Who must swim farther to reach the island? How much farther must that person swim?

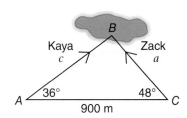

Draw a diagram, as shown at the right to represent the problem situation. Note that $m\angle B = 180° - (36° + 48°) = 96°$. To find the distances Kaya and Zack swam, use the Law of Sines.

Zack's Distance	**Kaya's Distance**
$\dfrac{a}{\sin A} = \dfrac{b}{\sin B}$	$\dfrac{c}{\sin C} = \dfrac{b}{\sin B}$
$\dfrac{a}{\sin 36°} = \dfrac{900}{\sin 96°}$	$\dfrac{c}{\sin 48°} = \dfrac{900}{\sin 96°}$
$a = \dfrac{900(\sin 36°)}{\sin 96°} \approx 532$ m	$c = \dfrac{900(\sin 48°)}{\sin 96°} \approx 673$ m

Kaya must swim about (673 m − 532 m), or 141 m, farther than Zack.

Try These

Find all the unknown side lengths and angle measures.

1.

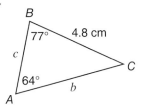

2.

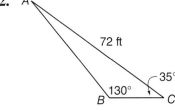

Solve.

3. A cyclist starts from point A and rides in a straight path across a park to point B, which is 630 m away. Then he rides directly to point C. If $m\angle ABC = 48°$ and $m\angle CAB = 31°$, find, to the nearest meter, the distance from C to A.

4. Discuss and Write Suppose you know only the lengths of two sides of a triangle and the measure of their included angle. Explain why you cannot use the Law of Sines to find the unknown side length.

Go to ▶ **PRACTICE BOOK** pages 295–296 for exercise sets.

Chapter 11 303

Test Prep: Short-Answer Questions
Strategy: Organize Information

When a short-answer question involves objects or figures, it may be helpful *to sketch a diagram* using the information given in the problem. This will allow you to visualize the problem and help you organize the given information. Label the diagram with the information you are given, and add new information as you find it.

Look at the sample test item.

Read the test item for a general idea of the problem.

- Reread the test item carefully. Draw conclusions based on written or visual cues.

- Sketch a diagram to help visualize the problem.

  Find the ratio of the side opposite ∠A to the hypotenuse.

Solve the problem.

- Apply an appropriate math strategy.

  Sketch a right triangle, and label it with the given information.

  To find sin *A*, you need to find the length of side *BC*.

  $$AC^2 + BC^2 = AB^2 \quad \longleftarrow \text{Use the Pythagorean Theorem.}$$
  $$24^2 + BC^2 = 26^2 \quad \longleftarrow \text{Substitute the known values.}$$
  $$576 + BC^2 = 676 \quad \longleftarrow \text{Simplify.}$$
  $$576 - 576 + BC^2 = 676 - 576 \quad \longleftarrow \text{Use the Subtraction Property of Equality.}$$
  $$\sqrt{BC^2} = \sqrt{100} \quad \longleftarrow \text{Find the square root of each side.}$$
  $$BC = 10 \quad \longleftarrow \text{Simplify.}$$

  Find sin *A*.
  $$\sin A = \frac{BC}{AB} = \frac{10}{26} = \frac{5}{13} \quad \longleftarrow \text{Use the sine ratio. Substitute in the known values.}$$

  Answer: $\sin A = \dfrac{5}{13}$

Test-Taking Tips

- Reread the test item.
- Use the Test-Prep strategy.
- Apply appropriate rules, definitions, properties, or strategies.
- Analyze your answers.

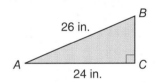

26 in.
24 in.

Remember:
Pythagorean Theorem
$A^2 + B^2 = C^2$

Remember:
$\sin \angle A = \dfrac{\text{opposite leg}}{\text{hypotenuse}}$

Item Analysis

Check your work. Make sure you show all your work.

- Analyze your answer. Does it make sense?

  Check that the side lengths 10 in., 24 in., and 26 in. form a right triangle.
  $$10^2 + 24^2 = 26^2 \longrightarrow 100 + 576 = 676 \longrightarrow 676 = 676 \checkmark$$

Try These

Solve. Be sure to explain your thinking.

1. Mr. Alconada is expanding the size of his rectangular deck by increasing its width. The original deck has a length of 12 feet and a width of 9 feet. The area of the enlarged deck is 153.36 square feet. By what percent was the width increased? ***Show your work.***

Go to PRACTICE BOOK page 297 for exercise sets.

Rational Expressions and Equations

CHAPTER 12

In This Chapter You Will:

- Identify values excluded from the domain of a rational expression
- Simplify rational expressions, mixed expressions, and complex fractions
- Identify the LCM of polynomial expressions
- Add, subtract, multiply, and divide rational expressions
- Solve a rational equation using the Cross-Products Rule, resulting in a linear or a quadratic equation
- Solve a rational equation using the LCD, resulting in a linear or a quadratic equation
- Solve problems using a variety of strategies
- Look for new vocabulary words **highlighted** in each lesson

Do You Remember?

- A rational number is a number that can be written in fractional form, $\frac{a}{b}$, where a and b are integers and $b \neq 0$.
- Division by zero is undefined.
- The least common multiple (LCM) of two or more numbers is the least nonzero multiple that is common to all of the numbers.
- A polynomial is a monomial or the sum or difference of two or more monomials.

For Practice Exercises:

 Go to **PRACTICE BOOK, pp. 303–330**

For Chapter Support: (ONLINE)

 Go to **www.progressinmathematics.com**

- Skills Update Practice
- Practice Activities
- Audio Glossary
- Vocabulary Activities
- Technology Videos
- Enrichment Activities
- Electronic SourceBook

 VIRTUAL MANIPULATIVES

Critical Thinking

Two groups of hikers start at the same spot, one group heading south and the other east. Both groups hike at the same rate, but the southbound group has already completed 1 mile by the time the eastbound group sets off (i.e., if n = the distance traveled by the eastbound group, then $n + 1$ = the distance traveled by the southbound group). When the groups are 13 miles apart, about how far has the eastbound group hiked?

Update your skills. See page 404 V.

Introduction to Rational Expressions

Objective To identify values excluded from the domain of a rational expression • To simplify rational expressions

The parallelogram at the right has a base represented by $x + 2$ and an area represented by $x + 6$. What expression represents the altitude to the base?

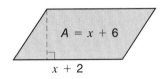

To find the expression that represents the altitude, use the area formula for a parallelogram.

$A = bh$ ◄—area formula for a parallelogram

$x + 6 = (x + 2)h$ ◄—Substitute the known values.

$\dfrac{x + 6}{x + 2} = \dfrac{(x + 2)h}{x + 2}$ ◄—Apply the Division Property of Equality.

$\dfrac{x + 6}{x + 2} = h$ ◄—Simplify.

The *rational expression* $\dfrac{x + 6}{x + 2}$ represents the altitude to the base.

► A rational expression is a quotient of two polynomials. Its domain consists of all values of the variable for which the denominator is not equal to zero. Any values of a variable for which the denominator equals zero are called excluded values of the domain of the rational expression.

Find any excluded values for the rational expression $\dfrac{x + 6}{x + 2}$.

$x + 2 = 0$ ◄—Set the denominator equal to 0.

$x = -2$ ◄—Solve for x, using the Subtraction Property of Equality.

So the excluded value is -2 (or $x \neq -2$).

Examples

Find any excluded values of the domain for each rational expression.

1 $\dfrac{x^2 + 3}{x^2 + 3x}$

$x^2 + 3x = 0$ ◄—Set the denominator equal to 0.

$x(x + 3) = 0$ ◄—Factor the denominator.

$x = 0$ or $x + 3 = 0$ ◄—Apply the Zero-Product Property.

$x = 0$ $\qquad$ $x = -3$ ◄—Solve for x using the Subtraction Property of Equality.

So the excluded values are 0 and -3 (or $x \neq 0, x \neq -3$).

> **Remember:**
> Zero-Product Property
> $ab = 0$ if and only if $a = 0$ or $b = 0$, where a and b are real numbers.

2 $\dfrac{7}{a^2 - 5a + 6}$

$a^2 - 5a + 6 = 0$ ◄—Set the denominator equal to 0.

$(a - 3)(a - 2) = 0$ ◄—Factor the denominator.

$a - 3 = 0$ or $a - 2 = 0$ ◄—Apply the Zero-Product Property.

$a = 3$ $\qquad$ $a = 2$ ◄—Solve for a using the Addition Property of Equality.

The excluded values are 3 and 2 (or $a \neq 3, a \neq 2$).

▶ A rational expression is in *simplest form* when the numerator and denominator have no common factors other than 1 or −1. To simplify a rational expression, you must eliminate any common factors of the numerator and denominator. To do this, you can use the following methods.

Simplify $\dfrac{9x^2}{5x^3 + 3x^2}$. Identify any excluded values.

Method 1 Use the GCF.

$$\dfrac{9x^2}{5x^3 + 3x^2} = \dfrac{9x^2 \div x^2}{(5x^3 + 3x^2) \div x^2}$$

$$= \dfrac{9}{5x + 3} \longleftarrow \boxed{\text{simplest form}}$$

Method 2 Factor completely.

$$\dfrac{9x^2}{5x^3 + 3x^2} = \dfrac{9x^2}{x^2(5x + 3)} \longleftarrow \begin{array}{l}\text{Factor the denominator; the}\\ \text{numerator cannot be factored.}\end{array}$$

$$= \dfrac{9\overset{1}{x^2}}{\underset{1}{x^2}(5x + 3)} \longleftarrow \text{Simplify.}$$

$$= \dfrac{9}{5x + 3} \longleftarrow \boxed{\text{simplest form}}$$

To find any excluded values, use the factored expression of the denominator.

$x^2 = 0$ or $5x + 3 = 0$ ◀— Apply the Zero-Product Property.

$x = 0$ $\qquad\qquad 5x = -3$ ◀— Solve for x using the Subtraction and Division Properties of Equality.

$$x = -\dfrac{3}{5}$$

So the excluded values are 0 and $-\dfrac{3}{5}$ $\left(\text{or } x \neq 0, x \neq -\dfrac{3}{5}\right)$.

Example

Simplify. Identify any excluded values.

1 $\dfrac{3a - 6}{-6a}$

Method 1 Use the GCF.

$$\dfrac{3a - 6}{-6a} = \dfrac{(3a - 6) \div 3}{-6a \div 3}$$

$$= \dfrac{a - 2}{-2a} \longleftarrow \boxed{\text{simplest form}}$$

..Think..
GCF: 3

To find any excluded values, set the denominator equal to 0.

$-6a = 0 \longrightarrow a = 0$

So the excluded value is 0 (or $a \neq 0$).

Method 2 Factor completely.

$$\dfrac{3a - 6}{-6a} = \dfrac{3(a - 2)}{-6a}$$

$$= \dfrac{\overset{1}{3}(a - 2)}{\underset{-2}{-6a}} = \dfrac{a - 2}{-2a} \longleftarrow \boxed{\text{simplest form}}$$

Try These

Find any excluded value of the domain for each rational expression.

1. $\dfrac{y + 6}{2y + 12}$

2. $\dfrac{5x^2 - 5x}{5x^3 + 20x}$

Simplify the rational expression. Identify any excluded values.

3. $\dfrac{15a^2 + 5a}{-5a}$

4. $\dfrac{pqr + 3pq}{pqr^2 + 3pqr}$

5. Discuss and Write Explain why there are no real values of x that would make $\dfrac{x - 2}{x^2 + 4}$ undefined.

Go to PRACTICE BOOK Lesson 12-1 for exercise sets.

Simplify Rational Expressions

Objective To simplify rational expressions using a variety of factoring techniques

▶ In Lesson 12-1, rational expressions are simplified by factoring the numerator and denominator using the greatest common monomial factor. In this lesson, rational expressions are simplified using other techniques, such as factoring a difference of two squares, factoring a trinomial, and factoring by grouping.

Simplify $\dfrac{x^2 - 9}{x^2 - 2x - 3}$. Identify any excluded values.

> **Remember:** $\dfrac{ab}{ac} = \dfrac{b}{c}$; a and $c \neq 0$.

$\dfrac{x^2 - 9}{x^2 - 2x - 3} = \dfrac{(x + 3)(x - 3)}{(x - 3)(x + 1)}$ ◀— Factor the numerator and denominator completely.

$= \dfrac{(x + 3)\cancel{(x - 3)}^{1}}{\cancel{(x - 3)}_{1}(x + 1)}$ ◀— Simplify.

$= \dfrac{x + 3}{x + 1}$ ◀— $\boxed{\text{simplest form}}$

$x - 3 = 0 \quad$ or $\quad x + 1 = 0$ ◀— Apply the Zero-Product Property.

$x = 3 \qquad\qquad\quad x = -1$

> **Remember:** To determine the excluded values of the domain of a rational expression, use the factored expression of the denominator rather than the simplified expression.

The excluded values are 3 and -1 (or $x \neq 3, x \neq -1$).

Examples

Simplify. Identify any excluded values.

1 $\dfrac{3x^2 - 15x + 12}{6x^2 + 24x - 30}$

$\dfrac{3x^2 - 15x + 12}{6x^2 + 24x - 30} = \dfrac{3(x^2 - 5x + 4)}{6(x^2 + 4x - 5)} = \dfrac{3(x - 4)(x - 1)}{6(x - 1)(x + 5)}$ ◀— Factor the numerator and denominator completely.

$= \dfrac{\cancel{3}^{1}(x - 4)\cancel{(x - 1)}^{1}}{\cancel{6}_{2}\cancel{(x - 1)}_{1}(x + 5)} = \dfrac{x - 4}{2(x + 5)}$ ◀— $\boxed{\text{simplest form}}$

$x - 1 = 0 \quad$ or $\quad x + 5 = 0$ ◀— Apply the Zero-Product Property.

$x = 1 \qquad\qquad\quad x = -5$

The excluded values are 1 and -5 (or $x \neq 1, x \neq -5$).

2 $\dfrac{9p^2q + 9pq^2}{3p^3 - 3pq^2}$

$\dfrac{9p^2q + 9pq^2}{3p^3 - 3pq^2} = \dfrac{9pq(p + q)}{3p(p^2 - q^2)} = \dfrac{9pq(p + q)}{3p(p - q)(p + q)}$ ◀— Factor the numerator and denominator completely.

$= \dfrac{\cancel{9}^{3} pq\cancel{(p + q)}^{1}}{\cancel{3}_{1} \cancel{p}_{1}(p - q)\cancel{(p + q)}_{1}} = \dfrac{3q}{p - q}$ ◀— $\boxed{\text{simplest form}}$

$3p = 0 \quad$ or $\quad p - q = 0 \quad$ or $\quad p + q = 0$ ◀— Apply the Zero-Product Property.

$p = 0 \qquad\qquad p = q \qquad\qquad p = -q$

Exclude those values of p and q for which $p = 0, p = q$, and $p = -q$ (or $p \neq 0, p \neq q, p \neq -q$).

▶When the numerator and denominator of a rational expression have binomial factors that are opposites, $\left(\text{such as } \dfrac{x-y}{y-x}\right)$, you can simplify the expression by factoring -1 from one of the binomials.

Simplify $\dfrac{x-y}{y-x}$. Identify the excluded values.

$$\dfrac{x-y}{y-x} = \dfrac{x-y}{-x+y} \longleftarrow \text{Apply the Commutative Property.}$$

$$= \dfrac{x-y}{-1(x-y)} \longleftarrow \text{Apply the Distributive Property to factor } -1.$$

$$= \dfrac{\overset{1}{\cancel{(x-y)}}}{-1\underset{1}{\cancel{(x-y)}}} = \dfrac{1}{-1} = -1 \longleftarrow \text{Simplify.}$$

$y - x = 0 \longleftarrow$ Set the denominator equal to 0.

$\quad y = x$

So the simplest form of $\dfrac{x-y}{y-x}$ is -1; the excluded values of y and x are all values for which $y = x$ (or $y \neq x$).

Example

1 Simplify $\dfrac{4-n}{n^2 - 6n + 8}$. Identify the excluded values.

$$\dfrac{4-n}{n^2 - 6n + 8} = \dfrac{4-n}{(n-2)(n-4)} \longleftarrow \text{Factor the denominator.}$$

$$= \dfrac{-1(n-4)}{(n-2)(n-4)} \longleftarrow \text{Apply the Commutative and Distributive Properties to factor } -1.$$

$$= \dfrac{-1\overset{1}{\cancel{(n-4)}}}{(n-2)\underset{1}{\cancel{(n-4)}}} = \dfrac{-1}{n-2} \longleftarrow \text{Simplify.}$$

$n - 2 = 0 \quad \text{or} \quad n - 4 = 0 \longleftarrow$ Apply the Zero-Product Property.

$\quad n = 2 \qquad\qquad n = 4$

So the simplest form of $\dfrac{4-n}{n^2 - 6n + 8}$ is $\dfrac{-1}{n-2}$; the excluded values are 2 and 4 (or $n \neq 2, n \neq 4$).

Try These

Simplify. Identify the excluded values.

1. $\dfrac{9 - t^2}{t^2 + 6t + 9}$

2. $\dfrac{15a^2 + 10a}{3a^2 + 5a + 2}$

3. $\dfrac{42 - 6d}{d^2 - 5t - 14}$

4. $\dfrac{x^2 + 4x + 3}{x^2 - 2x - 3}$

5. $\dfrac{x^2 - y^2}{x^2y^2 - x^3y}$

6. $\dfrac{2n^2 + 9n - 5}{2n^2 - 3n + 1}$

7. $\dfrac{12 - 6y}{y^2 - 4}$

8. $\dfrac{a^2c - ac^2}{a^2c^2 - a^3c}$

9. $\dfrac{16 - 6m - m^2}{m^2 - 64}$

10. Discuss and Write Does the expression $\dfrac{a+1}{(a-2)(a+1)}$ simplify to $a - 2$? Explain.

 Go to PRACTICE BOOK **Lesson 12-2 for exercise sets.**

12-3

Multiply Rational Expressions

Objective To multiply rational expressions and express the product in simplest form

► Multiplying rational expressions involves the same rules as multiplying fractions—multiply the numerators, then multiply the denominators. You can multiply first and then simplify, or you can simplify first and then multiply.

> **Remember:**
> $\frac{a}{b} \cdot \frac{c}{d} = \frac{ac}{bd}$; $b, d \neq 0$.

From now on, assume that the denominators do not equal zero.

Multiply: $\frac{ab}{3c} \cdot \frac{6a}{b}$

Method 1 Multiply, then simplify.

$$\frac{ab}{3c} \cdot \frac{6a}{b} = \frac{ab \cdot 6a}{3c \cdot b} = \frac{6a^2b}{3bc} \quad \leftarrow \text{Multiply.}$$

$$= \frac{\overset{2}{6}a^2\overset{1}{b}}{\underset{1}{3}\underset{1}{b}c} = \frac{2a^2}{c} \quad \leftarrow \text{Simplify.}$$

Method 2 Simplify, then multiply.

$$\frac{ab}{3c} \cdot \frac{6a}{b} = \frac{a\overset{1}{b}}{\underset{1}{3}c} \cdot \frac{\overset{2}{6}a}{\underset{1}{b}} \quad \leftarrow \text{Simplify.}$$

$$= \frac{2a^2}{c} \quad \leftarrow \text{Multiply.}$$

So the product of $\frac{ab}{3c} \cdot \frac{6a}{b}$ is $\frac{2a^2}{c}$.

Examples

Multiply. Write the product in simplest form.

1 $-8xy \cdot \dfrac{5wz}{2xy^2}$

$$-8xy \cdot \frac{5wz}{2xy^2} = \frac{-8xy}{1} \cdot \frac{5wz}{2xy^2} \quad \leftarrow \text{Write } -8xy \text{ as a fraction.}$$

$$= \frac{\overset{-4}{\cancel{-8}}\,\overset{1}{\cancel{x}}\,\overset{1}{\cancel{y}}}{1} \cdot \frac{5wz}{\underset{1}{\cancel{2}}\,\underset{1}{\cancel{x}}\,\underset{y}{\cancel{y^2}}} \quad \leftarrow \text{Simplify.}$$

$$= \frac{-20wz}{y} \quad \leftarrow \boxed{\text{simplest form}}$$

2 $\dfrac{5m}{3} \cdot \dfrac{6m}{n} \cdot \dfrac{7n}{10m}$

$$\frac{5m}{3} \cdot \frac{6m}{n} \cdot \frac{7n}{10m} = \frac{\overset{1}{5m}}{\underset{1}{\cancel{3}}} \cdot \frac{\overset{\overset{1}{\cancel{2}}}{\cancel{6}m}}{\underset{1}{\cancel{n}}} \cdot \frac{\overset{1}{7\cancel{n}}}{\underset{\underset{1}{\cancel{2}}}{10\cancel{m}}} \quad \leftarrow \text{Simplify.}$$

$$= \frac{7m}{1} \quad \leftarrow \text{Multiply.}$$

$$= 7m \quad \leftarrow \boxed{\text{simplest form}}$$

▶ To multiply rational expressions with numerators and/or denominators that can be factored, first rewrite the expressions in factored form, then simplify.

Multiply: $\dfrac{h^2 - 9}{10h + 30} \bullet \dfrac{5h}{h^2 + 3h}$

$$\dfrac{h^2 - 9}{10h + 30} \bullet \dfrac{5h}{h^2 + 3h} = \dfrac{(h + 3)(h - 3)}{10(h + 3)} \bullet \dfrac{5h}{h(h + 3)}$$ ←Factor the numerators and denominators.

$$= \dfrac{\overset{1}{\cancel{(h + 3)}}(h - 3)}{\underset{2}{\cancel{10}}\underset{1}{\cancel{(h + 3)}}} \bullet \dfrac{\overset{1}{\cancel{5}}\overset{1}{\cancel{h}}}{\underset{1}{\cancel{h}}(h + 3)}$$ ←Simplify.

$$= \dfrac{h - 3}{2(h + 3)}$$ ←Leave the product in factored form.

Examples

Multiply. Write the product in simplest form.

1 $(a^2 - 1) \bullet \dfrac{2a - 14}{a^3 - 6a^2 - 7a}$

$$(a^2 - 1) \bullet \dfrac{2a - 14}{a^3 - 6a^2 - 7a} = \dfrac{(a^2 - 1)}{1} \bullet \dfrac{2a - 14}{a^3 - 6a^2 - 7a}$$ ←Write $(a^2 - 1)$ as a fraction.

$$= \dfrac{(a + 1)(a - 1)}{1} \bullet \dfrac{2(a - 7)}{a(a - 7)(a + 1)}$$ ←Factor.

$$= \dfrac{\overset{1}{\cancel{(a + 1)}}(a - 1)}{1} \bullet \dfrac{2\overset{1}{\cancel{(a - 7)}}}{a\underset{1}{\cancel{(a - 7)}}\underset{1}{\cancel{(a + 1)}}}$$ ←Simplify.

$$= \dfrac{2(a - 1)}{a}$$ ← simplest form

2 $\dfrac{12k - 2k^2}{28k + 4} \bullet \dfrac{7k^2 + 15k + 2}{k^2 - 4k - 12}$

$$\dfrac{12k - 2k^2}{28k + 4} \bullet \dfrac{7k^2 + 15k + 2}{k^2 - 4k - 12} = \dfrac{2k(6 - k)}{4(7k + 1)} \bullet \dfrac{(k + 2)(7k + 1)}{(k + 2)(k - 6)}$$ ←Factor; $(6 - k)$ and $(k - 6)$ are opposites, or additive inverses.

$$= \dfrac{(2k)[-1(k - 6)]}{4(7k + 1)} \bullet \dfrac{(k + 2)(7k + 1)}{(k + 2)(k - 6)}$$ ←Factor -1; $(6 - k) = -1(k - 6)$

$$= \dfrac{(2k)[-1\overset{1}{\cancel{(k - 6)}}]}{\underset{2}{\cancel{4}}\underset{1}{\cancel{(7k + 1)}}} \bullet \dfrac{\overset{1}{\cancel{(k + 2)}}\overset{1}{\cancel{(7k + 1)}}}{\underset{1}{\cancel{(k + 2)}}\underset{1}{\cancel{(k - 6)}}}$$ ←Simplify.

$$= \dfrac{-k}{2}$$ ← simplest form

Try These

Multiply. Write the product in simplest form.

1. $\dfrac{2pq^2}{5} \bullet \dfrac{7p^2qr}{6pr} \bullet \dfrac{15p}{14r^3}$

2. $\dfrac{y^2 + 11y + 28}{3y} \bullet \dfrac{12y - 12y^2}{y^2 + 6y - 7}$

3. $(9m^2 - n^2) \bullet \dfrac{mn}{9m^2 - 3mn}$

4. **Discuss and Write** Is the step shown for multiplying $\dfrac{5a\overset{1}{\cancel{(a + 3)}}}{b^2} \bullet \dfrac{\overset{1}{\cancel{(a + 3)}}}{b - 2}$

correct? Explain.

Go to PRACTICE BOOK Lesson 12-3 for exercise sets.

12-4 Divide Rational Expressions

Objective To divide rational expressions and express the quotient in lowest terms

▶ Dividing rational expressions follows the same rules as dividing fractions. To divide by a rational expression, multiply by the reciprocal of the divisor. The *reciprocal* of a rational expression is the denominator of the expression divided by the numerator.

Remember:
$\dfrac{a}{b} \div \dfrac{c}{d} = \dfrac{a}{b} \cdot \dfrac{d}{c} = \dfrac{ad}{bc},$
$b, c, \text{ and } d \neq 0.$

Divide. Write the quotient in simplest form.

$\dfrac{5ab^2}{6c^2d} \div \dfrac{3a^2c}{2bd}$

$\dfrac{5ab^2}{6c^2d} \div \dfrac{3a^2c}{2bd} = \dfrac{5ab^2}{6c^2d} \cdot \dfrac{2bd}{3a^2c}$ ◀——Multiply by the reciprocal of the divisor.

$= \dfrac{\overset{1}{5ab^2}}{\underset{3}{6c^2}\underset{1}{d}} \cdot \dfrac{\overset{1}{2b}\overset{1}{d}}{\underset{a}{3a^2c}}$ ◀——Simplify.

$= \dfrac{5b^3}{9ac^3}$ ◀—$\boxed{\text{simplest form}}$

Examples

Divide. Write the quotient in simplest form.

1 $12a^3b^2 \div \dfrac{3a^2}{4b}$

$12a^3b^2 \div \dfrac{3a^2}{4b} = \dfrac{12a^3b^2}{1} \div \dfrac{3a^2}{4b}$ ◀——Write $12a^3b^2$ as a rational expression.

$= \dfrac{12a^3b^2}{1} \cdot \dfrac{4b}{3a^2}$ ◀——Multiply by the reciprocal of the divisor.

$= \dfrac{\overset{4}{\overset{}{12}}\overset{a}{a^3}b^2}{1} \cdot \dfrac{4b}{\underset{1}{\underset{}{3}}\underset{1}{a^2}}$ ◀——Simplify.

$= 16ab^3$ ◀—$\boxed{\text{simplest form}}$

2 $\dfrac{3a^2}{4b} \div 12a^3b^2$

$\dfrac{3a^2}{4b} \div 12a^3b^2 = \dfrac{3a^2}{4b} \div \dfrac{12a^3b^2}{1}$ ◀——Write $12a^3b^2$ as a rational expression.

$= \dfrac{3a^2}{4b} \cdot \dfrac{1}{12a^3b^2}$ ◀——Multiply by the reciprocal of the divisor.

$= \dfrac{\overset{1}{\overset{}{3}}\overset{1}{a^2}}{4b} \cdot \dfrac{1}{\underset{4}{\underset{}{12}}\underset{a}{a^3}b^2}$ ◀——Simplify.

$= \dfrac{1}{16ab^3}$ ◀—$\boxed{\text{simplest form}}$

▶ To divide rational expressions with numerators and/or denominators that can be factored, first rewrite the expressions in factored form, then simplify.

Divide $\dfrac{x^2 - y^2}{15xy} \div \dfrac{3x^2 - 3xy}{5xy + 5y^2}$. Write the quotient in simplest form.

$$\dfrac{x^2 - y^2}{15xy} \div \dfrac{3x^2 - 3xy}{5xy + 5y^2} = \dfrac{x^2 - y^2}{15xy} \bullet \dfrac{5xy + 5y^2}{3x^2 - 3xy} \quad \longleftarrow \text{Multiply by the reciprocal of the divisor.}$$

$$= \dfrac{(x + y)(x - y)}{15xy} \bullet \dfrac{5y(x + y)}{3x(x - y)} \quad \longleftarrow \text{Factor the numerators and denominators.}$$

$$= \dfrac{(x + y)(x - y)^{1}}{15xy} \bullet \dfrac{\overset{1}{5}\,\overset{1}{y}(x + y)}{3x(x - y)} \quad \longleftarrow \text{Simplify.}$$

$$= \dfrac{(x + y)^2}{9x^2} \quad \longleftarrow \boxed{\text{simplest form}}$$

Example

Divide. Write the quotient in simplest form.

1 $\dfrac{27 - 9x}{3x} \div (x^2 + 6x - 27)$

$$\dfrac{27 - 9x}{3x} \div (x^2 + 6x - 27) = \dfrac{27 - 9x}{3x} \div \dfrac{(x^2 + 6x - 27)}{1} \quad \longleftarrow \text{Write } x^2 + 6x - 27 \text{ as a rational expression.}$$

$$= \dfrac{27 - 9x}{3x} \bullet \dfrac{1}{(x^2 + 6x - 27)} \quad \longleftarrow \text{Multiply by the reciprocal of the divisor.}$$

$$= \dfrac{9(3 - x)}{3x} \bullet \dfrac{1}{(x - 3)(x + 9)} \quad \longleftarrow \text{Factor; } (3 - x) \text{ and } (x - 3) \text{ are opposites.}$$

$$= \dfrac{9[-1(x - 3)]}{3x} \bullet \dfrac{1}{(x - 3)(x + 9)} \quad \longleftarrow \begin{array}{l}\text{Factor } -1; \\ (3 - x) = -1(x - 3)\end{array}$$

$$= \dfrac{(\overset{3}{9})[-1(x - 3)^{1}]}{3x_{1}} \bullet \dfrac{1}{(x - 3)_{1}(x + 9)} \quad \longleftarrow \text{Simplify.}$$

$$= \dfrac{-3}{x(x + 9)} \quad \longleftarrow \boxed{\text{simplest form}}$$

Try These

Divide. Write the quotient in simplest form.

1. $\dfrac{7y}{2z^2} \div \dfrac{3y^2}{z}$

2. $\dfrac{6r^2}{11s} \div \dfrac{3s}{r^3}$

3. $\dfrac{18xy^2}{5z} \div 15xy$

4. $\dfrac{r^3}{18a} \div \dfrac{14}{21ar}$

5. $\dfrac{1}{m^2 - n^2} \div \dfrac{1}{n^2 - m^2}$

6. $\dfrac{a^2 + 8a - 20}{a^3} \div \dfrac{a^2 + 5a - 50}{a^3 - 5a^2}$

7. $\dfrac{b - 2}{bh + h} \div \dfrac{b^2 - 4}{bh^2 + h^2}$

8. $\dfrac{g^2 - f^2}{f^2} \div \dfrac{3f^2 - 3g^2}{-21f}$

9. $\dfrac{a^2 - 9}{2a^2 + 3a - 35} \div \dfrac{9 - a^2}{49 - 7a - 2a^2}$

10. **Discuss and Write** Find the value of R to make $\dfrac{x^2 + 9x - 36}{2x^2 + 7x + 3} \bullet R = \dfrac{x^2 + 7x - 60}{x^2 - 9}$ a true statement. Describe the process you use.

Go to **PRACTICE BOOK Lesson 12-4 for exercise sets.**

12-5

Combine Rational Expressions with Like Denominators

Objective To add or subtract rational expressions with like denominators

▶ To add or subtract rational expressions with like denominators, add or subtract the numerators, and keep the common denominator. Values of the variables that result in a denominator equal to zero are not in the domain.

> **Remember:**
> $\frac{a}{c} + \frac{b}{c} = \frac{a + b}{c}; c \neq 0$
> $\frac{a}{c} - \frac{b}{c} = \frac{a - b}{c}; c \neq 0$

• Find the length of $\overline{AC}$.

Add: $\frac{3}{2x} + \frac{7}{2x}$ ◀——$AC = AB + BC$

$\frac{3}{2x} + \frac{7}{2x} = \frac{3 + 7}{2x}$ ◀——Add the numerators.

$= \frac{10}{2x} = \frac{\overset{5}{10}}{\underset{1}{2x}} = \frac{5}{x}$

So the length of $\overline{AC}$ is $\frac{5}{x}$ cm.

• Find the length of $\overline{YZ}$.

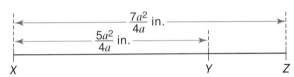

Subtract: $\frac{7a^2}{4a} - \frac{5a^2}{4a}$ ◀——$YZ = XZ - XY$

$\frac{7a^2}{4a} - \frac{5a^2}{4a} = \frac{7a^2 - 5a^2}{4a}$ ◀——Subtract the numerators.

$= \frac{2a^2}{4a} = \frac{\overset{1}{2}\overset{a}{a^2}}{\underset{2}{4}\underset{1}{a}} = \frac{a}{2}$

So the length of $\overline{YZ}$ is $\frac{a}{2}$ in.

Examples

1 Add: $\frac{x}{5x^2} + \frac{4x}{5x^2}$

$\frac{x}{5x^2} + \frac{4x}{5x^2} = \frac{x + 4x}{5x^2}$ ◀——Add the numerators.

$= \frac{5x}{5x^2}$ ◀——Combine like terms.

$= \frac{\overset{1}{5}\overset{1}{x}}{\underset{1}{5}\underset{x}{x^2}} = \frac{1}{x}$ ◀——Simplify.

2 Subtract: $\frac{2c}{3c^2} - \frac{8c}{3c^2}$

$\frac{2c}{3c^2} - \frac{8c}{3c^2} = \frac{2c - 8c}{3c^2}$ ◀——Subtract the numerators.

$= \frac{-6c}{3c^2}$ ◀——Combine like terms.

$= \frac{\overset{-2}{-6}\overset{1}{c}}{\underset{1}{3}\underset{c}{c^2}} = \frac{-2}{c}$ ◀——Simplify.

▶ Sometimes you need to factor the numerator and/or the denominator of each rational expression in order to simplify the result.

Add $\frac{x^2 + 4x}{x + 6} + \frac{3x + 6}{x + 6}$. Write the sum in simplest form. Identify any excluded values.

$\frac{x^2 + 4x}{x + 6} + \frac{3x + 6}{x + 6} = \frac{x^2 + 4x + 3x + 6}{x + 6} = \frac{x^2 + 7x + 6}{x + 6}$ ◀——Add the numerators; combine like terms.

$= \frac{(x + 1)\overset{1}{(x + 6)}}{\underset{1}{(x + 6)}}$ ◀——Factor the numerator, and simplify.

$= x + 1$ ◀——[simplest form]

$x + 6 = 0 \longrightarrow x = -6$

So the excluded value is -6 (or $x \neq -6$).

When subtracting rational expressions, be sure to subtract each term in the numerator of the second expression. Use parentheses to group the terms and apply the rules for opposites of sums and differences.

> **Remember:**
> Opposites of Sums and Differences
> $-(a + b) = -a - b$
> $-(a - b) = -a + b$

Subtract $\dfrac{7h - 3}{2h - 1} - \dfrac{2h - 2h^2}{2h - 1}$. Write the difference in simplest form. Identify any excluded values.

$$\frac{7h - 3}{2h - 1} - \frac{2h - 2h^2}{2h - 1} = \frac{7h - 3 - (2h - 2h^2)}{2h - 1}$$ ←Subtract the numerators.

$$= \frac{7h - 3 - 2h + 2h^2}{2h - 1} = \frac{2h^2 + 5h - 3}{2h - 1}$$ ←Apply the Opposite of a Sum, then combine like terms.

$$= \frac{(h + 3)(2h - 1)^{1}}{2h - 1_{1}}$$ ←Factor and simplify.

$$= h + 3$$ ← simplest form

$2h - 1 = 0 \longrightarrow h = \dfrac{1}{2}$ So the excluded value is $\dfrac{1}{2}$ $\left(\text{or } h \neq \dfrac{1}{2}\right)$.

Examples

1 Add $\dfrac{x - 5}{x^2 - 3x - 4} + \dfrac{x - 3}{x^2 - 3x - 4}$. Write the sum in simplest form.

$$\frac{x - 5}{x^2 - 3x - 4} + \frac{x - 3}{x^2 - 3x - 4} = \frac{x - 5 + x - 3}{x^2 - 3x - 4}$$ ←Add the numerators.

$$= \frac{2x - 8}{x^2 - 3x - 4}$$ ←Combine like terms.

$$= \frac{2(x - 4)^{1}}{(x - 4)_{1}(x + 1)} = \frac{2}{x + 1}$$ ←Factor and simplify.

2 Subtract $\dfrac{4k + 7}{3k - 6} - \dfrac{3k + 9}{6 - 3k}$. Write the difference in simplest form.

$$\frac{4k + 7}{3k - 6} - \frac{3k + 9}{6 - 3k} = \frac{4k + 7}{3k - 6} - \frac{3k + 9}{-(3k - 6)}$$ ←Apply the Commutative Property and the Opposite of a Difference.

$$= \frac{4k + 7}{3k - 6} + \frac{3k + 9}{3k - 6}$$ ← $-\dfrac{a}{-b} = \dfrac{a}{b}$

$$= \frac{4k + 7 + 3k + 9}{3k - 6} = \frac{7k + 16}{3k - 6}$$ ←Simplify.

Try These

Add or subtract. Write the result in simplest form. Identify any excluded values.

1. $\dfrac{7}{2b} - \dfrac{13}{2b}$

2. $\dfrac{6x + 8}{3x} + \dfrac{3x + 7}{3x}$

3. $\dfrac{7}{2q + 12} + \dfrac{13}{2q + 12}$

4. $\dfrac{x^2 - xy}{x - 2y} - \dfrac{xy - x^2}{2y - x}$

5. $\dfrac{-6x - 30}{x - 5} + \dfrac{x^2 + 7x}{x - 5}$

6. $\dfrac{2 - 7d}{5d - 10} - \dfrac{5d + 2}{5d - 10}$

7. Discuss and Write Describe how adding rational expressions with like denominators is similar to adding fractions with like denominators.

Go to PRACTICE BOOK **Lesson 12-5 for exercise sets.**

12-6

Combine Rational Expressions with Unlike Denominators

Objective To identify the LCM of polynomial expressions • To add or subtract rational expressions with unlike denominators

▶To add or subtract rational expressions with unlike denominators, first rename the expressions so that the denominators are alike. Any common denominator could be used. However, the computation is usually easier if you use the least common denominator (LCD), which is the least common multiple (LCM) of the denominators. The domain of the sum or difference consists of all values of the variables in which both denominators are not equal to zero.

To find the least common multiple of polynomials, express each polynomial in factored form, and then use each factor the greatest number of times it appears in any of the factorizations.

• Add $\dfrac{7}{3k} + \dfrac{5k+1}{2k^2}$. Simplify the sum.

LCD: $3 \cdot 2 \cdot k^2 = 6k^2$ ◀——Identify the LCD.

$\dfrac{7}{3k} + \dfrac{5k+1}{2k^2} = \dfrac{7}{3k}\left(\dfrac{2k}{2k}\right) + \dfrac{5k+1}{2k^2}\left(\dfrac{3}{3}\right)$ ◀——Multiply each expression by an appropriate form of 1 to rename it with the LCD.

$= \dfrac{14k}{6k^2} + \dfrac{15k+3}{6k^2} = \dfrac{14k+15k+3}{6k^2}$ ◀——Write each expression over the LCD, then add the numerators.

$= \dfrac{29k+3}{6k^2}$ ◀——Simplify.

• Subtract $\dfrac{3p}{4q} - \dfrac{7p}{q}$. Simplify the difference.

$\dfrac{3p}{4q} - \dfrac{7p}{q} = \dfrac{3p}{4q} - \dfrac{7p}{q}\left(\dfrac{4}{4}\right)$ ◀——Multiply by a form of 1.

Think LCD: $4q$

$= \dfrac{3p}{4q} - \dfrac{28p}{4q} = \dfrac{3p-28p}{4q}$ ◀——Write each expression over the LCD, then subtract the numerators.

$= \dfrac{-25p}{4q}$ ◀——Simplify.

• Add $\dfrac{-4}{x^2-4} + \dfrac{1}{x-2}$. Write the sum in simplest form.

$\dfrac{-4}{x^2-4} + \dfrac{1}{x-2} = \dfrac{-4}{(x+2)(x-2)} + \dfrac{1}{x-2}$ ◀——Factor x^2-4 to identify the LCD.

Think LCD: $(x+2)(x-2)$

$= \dfrac{-4}{(x+2)(x-2)} + \dfrac{1}{(x-2)}\left(\dfrac{x+2}{x+2}\right)$ ◀——Multiply by a form of 1 to rename the expression with the LCD.

$= \dfrac{-4}{(x+2)(x-2)} + \dfrac{x+2}{(x+2)(x-2)}$ ◀——Write each expression over the LCD.

$= \dfrac{-4+x+2}{(x+2)(x-2)} = \dfrac{x-2}{(x+2)(x-2)}$ ◀——Add the numerators; combine like terms.

$= \dfrac{\overset{1}{\cancel{(x-2)}}}{(x+2)\underset{1}{\cancel{(x-2)}}} = \dfrac{1}{x+2}$ ◀——Simplify.

Examples

Add or subtract. Write the result in simplest form, and identify any excluded values.

1 $\dfrac{g-1}{2g} + \dfrac{g+3}{6g}$

..Think...
LCD: $6g$

$\dfrac{g-1}{2g} + \dfrac{g+3}{6g} = \dfrac{g-1}{2g}\left(\dfrac{3}{3}\right) + \dfrac{g+3}{6g}$ ←—Multiply by a form of 1 to rename the expression with the LCD.

$= \dfrac{3g-3}{6g} + \dfrac{g+3}{6g} = \dfrac{3g-3+g+3}{6g}$ ←—Write each expression over the LCD, then add the numerators.

$= \dfrac{4g}{6g} = \dfrac{\overset{2}{\cancel{4}}\overset{1}{\cancel{g}}}{\underset{3}{\cancel{6}}\underset{1}{\cancel{g}}}$ ←—Combine like terms; simplify.

$= \dfrac{2}{3}$

Excluded value: $6g = 0 \longrightarrow g = 0$

So in simplest form, $\dfrac{g-1}{2g} + \dfrac{g+3}{6g} = \dfrac{2}{3}$; the excluded value is 0 (or $g \neq 0$).

2 $\dfrac{1}{y^2 - 3y} - \dfrac{1}{3y - 9}$

$\dfrac{1}{y^2 - 3y} - \dfrac{1}{3y - 9} = \dfrac{1}{y(y-3)} - \dfrac{1}{3(y-3)}$ ←—Factor the denominators.

..Think...
LCD: $3y(y-3)$

$= \dfrac{1}{y(y-3)}\left(\dfrac{3}{3}\right) - \dfrac{1}{3(y-3)}\left(\dfrac{y}{y}\right)$ ←—Multiply each expression by an appropriate form of 1 to rename it with the LCD.

$= \dfrac{3}{3y(y-3)} - \dfrac{y}{3y(y-3)}$ ←—Write each expression over the LCD.

$= \dfrac{3-y}{3y(y-3)} = \dfrac{-1(y-3)}{3y(y-3)}$ ←—Subtract the numerators; factor -1; $(3 \bullet y) = -1(y-3)$

$= \dfrac{-1(\cancel{y-3})^{1}}{3y(\cancel{y-3})_{1}} = \dfrac{-1}{3y}$ ←—Simplify.

Excluded values: $y(y-3) = 0 \longrightarrow y = 0$ or $y = 3$

So in simplest form, $\dfrac{1}{y^2 - 3y} - \dfrac{1}{3y - 9} = \dfrac{-1}{3y}$; the excluded values are 0 and 3 (or $y \neq 0, 3$).

Try These

Find the sum or difference. Write the result in simplest form, and identify any excluded values.

1. $\dfrac{11}{8t^2} + \dfrac{1t}{12t^3}$

2. $\dfrac{6}{7n} - \dfrac{n-1}{5n}$

3. $\dfrac{d-4}{14d} + \dfrac{5d+7}{21d}$

4. $\dfrac{8}{4f} - \dfrac{3}{f+2}$

5. $\dfrac{2}{x+3} + \dfrac{3}{x+1}$

6. $\dfrac{x}{x-3} - \dfrac{3}{x^2 - x - 6}$

7. Discuss and Write Explain the steps you would take to write the sum of $\dfrac{2c+1}{(c-1)^2} + \dfrac{c-2}{c^2 + 3c - 4}$ as a single rational expression.

Go to PRACTICE BOOK **Lesson 12-6 for exercise sets.**

Mixed Expressions and Complex Fractions

Objective To simplify mixed expressions • To simplify complex fractions

▶ A **mixed expression** is the sum (or difference) of a polynomial and a rational expression. An expression such as $3a + \dfrac{a + 2}{a - 3}$ is called a mixed expression because it is the sum of a monomial, $3a$, and a rational expression, $\dfrac{a + 2}{a - 3}$.

Renaming mixed expressions as rational expressions is similar to renaming a mixed number as a fraction greater than 1 or less than -1.

Simplify: $3a + \dfrac{a + 2}{a - 3}$

.**Think**.............
The LCD is $a - 3$.

$3a + \dfrac{a + 2}{a - 3} = \dfrac{3a(a - 3)}{a - 3} + \dfrac{a + 2}{a - 3}$ ←—Rename each term, as necessary, using the LCD.

$= \dfrac{3a(a - 3) + a + 2}{a - 3}$ ←—Add the numerators.

$= \dfrac{3a^2 - 9a + a + 2}{a - 3} = \dfrac{3a^2 - 8a + 2}{a - 3}$ ←—Apply the Distributive Property, then combine like terms.

So the simplest form of $3a + \dfrac{a + 2}{a - 3}$ is $\dfrac{3a^2 - 8a + 2}{a - 3}$.

Example

1 Simplify: $x - 5 + \dfrac{x - 4}{x - 2}$

$x - 5 + \dfrac{x - 4}{x - 2} = \dfrac{(x - 5)(x - 2)}{x - 2} + \dfrac{x - 4}{x - 2}$ ←—Rename each term, as necessary, using the LCD, $x - 2$.

$= \dfrac{(x - 5)(x - 2) + x - 4}{x - 2}$ ←—Add the numerators.

$= \dfrac{x^2 - 2x - 5x + 10 + x - 4}{x - 2} = \dfrac{x^2 - 6x + 6}{x - 2}$ ←—Apply the Distributive Property, then combine like terms.

So the simplest form of $x - 5 + \dfrac{x - 4}{x - 2}$ is $\dfrac{x^2 - 6x + 6}{x - 2}$.

▶ If a fraction has one or more fractions in the numerator or denominator, it is called a **complex fraction**. Some complex fractions are shown below.

Numerical Complex Fractions

$\dfrac{\frac{2}{3}}{\frac{4}{5}}$ $\dfrac{2\frac{1}{2}}{5\frac{3}{4}}$ $\dfrac{1 - \frac{1}{2}}{6 + 1\frac{5}{7}}$

Algebraic Complex Fractions

$\dfrac{\frac{3x}{5}}{\frac{x}{15}}$ $\dfrac{\frac{2x + 6}{5x - 15}}{\frac{3x + 9}{25x - 75}}$ $\dfrac{\frac{1}{x} - \frac{1}{y}}{\frac{1}{x} + \frac{1}{y}}$

Simplifying an algebraic complex fraction is similar to simplifying a numerical complex fraction.

Key Concept

Simplifying a Complex Fraction

Any complex fraction, $\dfrac{\frac{a}{b}}{\frac{c}{d}}$, where $b, c, d \neq 0$, can be expressed as $\dfrac{ad}{bc}$.

Simplify: $\dfrac{\frac{21x^2}{25}}{\frac{7x}{50}}$

Remember: A fraction bar is a division symbol.

Method 1 Multiply by the LCD.

$$\dfrac{\frac{21x^2}{25}}{\frac{7x}{50}} = \dfrac{\frac{21x^2}{25}(50)}{\frac{7x}{50}(50)} \quad \longleftarrow \text{Multiply by the LCD, 50.}$$

$$= \dfrac{\frac{21x^2}{25}\overset{2}{(\cancel{50})}}{\underset{1}{\frac{7x}{50}}\cancel{(50)}} = \dfrac{42x^2}{7x} \quad \longleftarrow \begin{array}{l}\text{Simplify the} \\ \text{numerator and} \\ \text{denominator.}\end{array}$$

$$= \dfrac{\overset{6}{\cancel{42}}\,\overset{x}{\cancel{x^2}}}{\underset{1}{\cancel{7}}\,\underset{1}{\cancel{x}}} = 6x \quad \longleftarrow \begin{array}{l}\text{Simplify the rational} \\ \text{expression.}\end{array}$$

Method 2 Rewrite as a division expression.

$$\dfrac{\frac{21x^2}{25}}{\frac{7x}{50}} = \dfrac{21x^2}{25} \div \dfrac{7x}{50} \quad \longleftarrow \begin{array}{l}\text{Rewrite as a division} \\ \text{expression, since the fraction} \\ \text{bar represents division.}\end{array}$$

$$= \dfrac{21x^2}{25} \cdot \dfrac{50}{7x} \quad \longleftarrow \begin{array}{l}\text{Multiply by the reciprocal} \\ \text{of the divisor.}\end{array}$$

$$= \dfrac{\overset{3}{\cancel{21}}\,\overset{x}{\cancel{x^2}}}{\underset{1}{\cancel{25}}} \cdot \dfrac{\overset{2}{\cancel{50}}}{\underset{1}{\cancel{7}}\,\underset{1}{\cancel{x}}} \quad \longleftarrow \text{Simplify.}$$

$$= 6x$$

So the simplest form of $\dfrac{\frac{21x^2}{25}}{\frac{7x}{50}}$ is $6x$.

Example

1 Simplify: $\dfrac{y - 1 + \frac{3}{y+3}}{y + 1 - \frac{4}{y-2}}$

$$\dfrac{y - 1 + \frac{3}{y+3}}{y + 1 - \frac{4}{y-2}} = \dfrac{\frac{(y-1)(y+3)}{y+3} + \frac{3}{y+3}}{\frac{(y+1)(y-2)}{y-2} - \frac{4}{y-2}} = \dfrac{\frac{y^2 + 3y - y - 3 + 3}{y+3}}{\frac{y^2 - 2y + y - 2 - 4}{y-2}} \quad \longleftarrow \begin{array}{l}\text{Add the numerators; add the} \\ \text{denominators.}\end{array}$$

$$= \dfrac{\frac{y^2 + 2y}{y+3}}{\frac{y^2 - y - 6}{y-2}} = \dfrac{y^2 + 2y}{y+3} \div \dfrac{y^2 - y - 6}{y-2} \quad \longleftarrow \text{Simplify, then write as a division expression.}$$

$$= \dfrac{y(y+2)}{y+3} \div \dfrac{(y-3)(y+2)}{y-2} = \dfrac{y(y+2)}{y+3} \cdot \dfrac{y-2}{(y-3)(y+2)} \quad \longleftarrow \begin{array}{l}\text{Factor, then multiply by} \\ \text{the reciprocal of the} \\ \text{divisor.}\end{array}$$

$$= \dfrac{y\overset{1}{\cancel{(y+2)}}}{y+3} \cdot \dfrac{y-2}{(y-3)\underset{1}{\cancel{(y+2)}}} = \dfrac{y(y-2)}{(y+3)(y-3)} \quad \longleftarrow \text{Simplify.}$$

Try These

Simplify.

1. $3 + \dfrac{4}{x-4}$

2. $\dfrac{1 + \frac{4}{x}}{\frac{x}{y} + \frac{2}{3}}$

3. $\dfrac{a - \frac{a+5}{a-3}}{a+1}$

4. $\dfrac{\frac{x-5}{x}}{\frac{x}{5} - 1}$

5. $\dfrac{\frac{b^2}{4} - 1}{\frac{b}{4} - \frac{1}{2}}$

6. $\dfrac{1 + \frac{7}{x-2}}{1 + \frac{3}{x+2}}$

7. **Discuss and Write** Explain the steps you would use to simplify $\dfrac{1}{\frac{y}{x} + \frac{x}{y}}$.

Go to PRACTICE BOOK **Lesson 12-7 for exercise sets.**

Solve Rational Equations Resulting in Linear Equations

Objective To solve a rational equation using the Cross-Products Rule, resulting in a linear equation • To solve a rational equation using the LCD, resulting in a linear equation

In the time it takes Kevin to run 12 miles, Bodhi runs only 8 miles. Bodhi's running speed is 3 miles per hour less than Kevin's. What is the speed of each runner?

To find the speed of each runner, write and solve an equation.

Let x = speed of Kevin in miles per hour and

$x - 3$ = speed of Bodhi in miles per hour.

$\dfrac{12}{x}$ = time for Kevin to run 12 miles

$\dfrac{8}{x - 3}$ = time for Bodhi to run 8 miles

$\dfrac{12}{x} = \dfrac{8}{x - 3}$ ←— Kevin's time is equal to Bodhi's time.

> **Remember:**
> Distance Formula:
> $d = rt \longrightarrow t = \dfrac{d}{r}$

▶ A rational equation, such as $\dfrac{12}{x} = \dfrac{8}{x - 3}$, contains at least one rational expression. You can solve such equations if you eliminate all denominators other than 1 either by using the Cross-Products Rule or by multiplying each side of the equation by the LCD. Both methods could give an extraneous solution or excluded value, so you must check the solutions using the *original equation*.

Solve: $\dfrac{12}{x} = \dfrac{8}{x - 3}$

Method 1 Use the Cross-Products Rule.

$\dfrac{12}{x} = \dfrac{8}{x - 3} \longrightarrow 12(x - 3) = 8x$ ←— Use the Cross-Products Rule.

$\qquad\qquad\qquad 12x - 36 = 8x$ ←— Apply the Distributive Property.

$\qquad\qquad\qquad\quad -36 = -4x$ ←— Apply the Subtraction Property of Equality.

$\qquad\qquad\qquad\qquad 9 = x$ ←— Apply the Division Property of Equality.

> Use the Cross-Products Rule to solve rational equations only when each side of the equation is a single rational expression.

Method 2 Use the LCD.

LCD = $x(x - 3)$ ←— Find the LCD. Include every factor of the denominators.

$\overset{1}{\cancel{x}}(x - 3)\left(\dfrac{12}{\underset{1}{\cancel{x}}}\right) = x\overset{1}{\cancel{(x - 3)}}\left(\dfrac{8}{\underset{1}{\cancel{x - 3}}}\right)$ ←— Multiply each side by the LCD.

$(x - 3)12 = 8x$ ←— Simplify.

$12x - 36 = 8x$ ←— Apply the Distributive Property.

$-36 = -4x$ ←— Apply the Subtraction Property of Equality.

$9 = x$ ←— Apply the Division Property of Equality.

Check: $\dfrac{12}{x} = \dfrac{8}{x - 3} \longrightarrow \dfrac{12}{9} \overset{?}{=} \dfrac{8}{9 - 3}$

$\qquad\qquad\qquad\qquad\qquad \dfrac{12}{9} \overset{?}{=} \dfrac{8}{6}$

$\qquad\qquad\qquad\qquad\qquad \dfrac{4}{3} = \dfrac{4}{3}$ True

So Kevin's speed is 9 miles per hour, and Bodhi's speed is $(9 - 3)$, or 6, miles per hour.

Example

1 **Solve:** $\dfrac{2x}{x-1} + \dfrac{4x-6}{x-1} = 3$

$(x-1)\dfrac{2x+4x-6}{(x-1)} = (x-1)3$ ← Add, and then multiply each side by the LCD, $x-1$. Simplify.

$2x + 4x - 6 = 3x - 3$ ← Apply the Distributive Property.

$6x - 6 = 3x - 3$ ← Simplify.

$3x = 3$ ← Apply the Addition and Subtraction Properties of Equality.

$x = 1$ ← Apply the Division Property of Equality.

Because 1 is an excluded value, 1 is an extraneous solution.

So $\dfrac{2x}{x-1} + \dfrac{4x-6}{x-1} = 3$ has no solution. Solution set: { }

Check: $\dfrac{2x}{x-1} + \dfrac{4x-6}{x-1} = 3$

$\dfrac{2(1)}{1-1} + \dfrac{4(1)-6}{1-1} \overset{?}{=} 3$

$\dfrac{2}{0} + \dfrac{-2}{0} \neq 3$

.Think..........
: Excluded value:
: $x - 1 = 0 \longrightarrow x = 1 (x \neq 1)$
:..........

▶ Rational equations can be used to solve work problems. After first finding the part of the job that each person does in *one unit of time*, write an equation.

Together Andrew and Dan can complete a job in 10 minutes. How long would it take Dan to do the job alone if Andrew can do it alone in 25 minutes?

To find how long, first find the part of the job each person does in *1 minute*, then write and solve an equation.

Let x = the time in minutes for Dan to complete the job if he works alone.

part of job done by Andrew in 1 minute	*plus*	part of job done by Dan in 1 minute	*equals*	part of job done by both in 1 minute
$\dfrac{1}{25}$	$+$	$\dfrac{1}{x}$	$=$	$\dfrac{1}{10}$

$50x\left(\dfrac{1}{25} + \dfrac{1}{x}\right) = 50x\left(\dfrac{1}{10}\right)$ ← Multiply each side by the LCD, $50x$.

$\overset{2}{50}x\left(\dfrac{1}{25}\right) + 50\overset{1}{x}\left(\dfrac{1}{x}\right) = \overset{5}{50}x\left(\dfrac{1}{10}\right)$ ← Apply the Distributive Property.

$2x + 50 = 5x$ ← Simplify.

$50 = 3x$ ← Apply the Subtraction Property of Equality.

$\dfrac{50}{3} = x$ ← Apply the Division Property of Equality.

So Dan can do the job in $\dfrac{50}{3}$, or $16\dfrac{2}{3}$, minutes.

Try These

Solve and check.

1. $\dfrac{a-2}{a} = \dfrac{3}{4}$

2. $\dfrac{1}{6x} + \dfrac{1}{3} = \dfrac{1}{4}$

3. $\dfrac{p}{p-2} - \dfrac{1}{2} = \dfrac{3}{3p-6}$

4. **Discuss and Write** Two pipes can fill a tank in 9 hours. The larger pipe fills the tank three times as fast as the smaller pipe. How long would it take the smaller pipe to fill the tank? Explain how you got your answer.

Go to PRACTICE BOOK **Lesson 12-8 for exercise sets.**

Solve Rational Equations Resulting in Quadratic Equations

Objective To solve a rational equation using the LCD, resulting in a quadratic equation
• To solve a rational equation using the Cross-Products Rule, resulting in a quadratic equation

The sum of a number and its reciprocal is $\frac{41}{20}$. Find the number.

To find the number, write and solve an equation.

Let x = the number and

$\frac{1}{x}$ = the reciprocal of the number.

$x + \frac{1}{x} = \frac{41}{20}$

▶ When you solve a rational equation by multiplying both sides of the equation by the LCD of all the denominators, the result is sometimes a quadratic equation.

Solve: $x + \frac{1}{x} = \frac{41}{20}$

$20x\left(x + \frac{1}{x}\right) = 20x\left(\frac{41}{20}\right)$ ◀—Multiply both sides of the equation by the LCD, $20x$.

$20x(x) + 20x\left(\frac{1}{x}\right) = 20x\left(\frac{41}{20}\right)$ ◀—Apply the Distributive Property.

$20x^2 + 20 = 41x$ ◀—Simplify.

$20x^2 - 41x + 20 = 0$ ◀—Write the equation in standard form.

$(4x - 5)(5x - 4) = 0$ ◀—Factor.

$4x - 5 = 0$ or $5x - 4 = 0$ ◀—Apply the Zero-Product Property.

$x = \frac{5}{4}$ $\qquad x = \frac{4}{5}$ ◀—Apply the Addition and Division Properties of Equality.

Check: If the number is $\frac{5}{4}$, the reciprocal is $\frac{4}{5}$; and $\qquad$ $\frac{5}{4} + \frac{4}{5} \overset{?}{=} \frac{41}{20} \longrightarrow \frac{25}{20} + \frac{16}{20} = \frac{41}{20}$ True

if the number is $\frac{4}{5}$, the reciprocal is $\frac{5}{4}$.

So the number is either $\frac{5}{4}$ or $\frac{4}{5}$.

▶ When you use the Cross-Products Rule to solve a rational equation, the result is sometimes a quadratic equation.

Solve: $\frac{n - 4}{2} = \frac{3}{n - 5}$ $\qquad\qquad\qquad$ **Check:**

$(n - 4)(n - 5) = 3(2)$ ◀—Apply the Cross-Products Rule. $\qquad$ $\frac{n - 4}{2} = \frac{3}{n - 5}$ $\qquad$ $\frac{n - 4}{2} = \frac{3}{n - 5}$

$n^2 - 9n + 20 = 6$ ◀—Apply the Distributive Property. $\qquad$ $\frac{7 - 4}{2} \overset{?}{=} \frac{3}{7 - 5}$ $\qquad$ $\frac{2 - 4}{2} \overset{?}{=} \frac{3}{2 - 5}$

$n^2 - 9n + 14 = 0$ ◀—Write the equation in standard form.

$(n - 7)(n - 2) = 0$ ◀—Factor. $\qquad\qquad\qquad\qquad$ $\frac{3}{2} = \frac{3}{2}$ True $\qquad$ $\frac{-2}{2} = \frac{3}{-3}$ True

$n - 7 = 0$ or $n - 2 = 0$ ◀—Apply the Zero-Product Property.

$n = 7$ $\qquad n = 2$ ◀—Apply the Addition Property of Equality.

Solution set: $\{2, 7\}$

Examples

1 Solve: $\dfrac{20}{x^2 - 4} + 1 = \dfrac{5}{x - 2}$

$$\dfrac{20}{(x + 2)(x - 2)} + 1 = \dfrac{5}{x - 2}$$ ←— Factor the denominators to find the LCD.

$$(x + 2)(x - 2)\left(\dfrac{20}{(x + 2)(x - 2)} + 1\right) = (x + 2)(x - 2)\left(\dfrac{5}{x - 2}\right)$$ ←— Multiply by the LCD.

$$(x + 2)(x - 2)\left(\dfrac{20}{(x + 2)(x - 2)}\right) + (x + 2)(x - 2)(1) = (x + 2)(x - 2)\left(\dfrac{5}{x - 2}\right)$$ ←— Apply the Distributive Property.

$$(x + 2)(x - 2)\left(\dfrac{20}{(x + 2)(x - 2)}\right) + (x + 2)(x - 2)(1) = (x + 2)(x - 2)\left(\dfrac{5}{x - 2}\right)$$ ←— Simplify.

$$20 + x^2 - 4 = 5x + 10$$ ←— Apply the Distributive Property.

$$x^2 - 5x + 6 = 0$$ ←— Write the equation in standard form.

$$(x - 3)(x - 2) = 0$$ ←— Factor.

$$x - 3 = 0 \text{ or } x - 2 = 0$$ ←— Apply the Zero-Product Property.

$$x = 3 \qquad x = 2$$ ←— Apply the Addition Property of Equality.

Check: $\dfrac{20}{x^2 - 4} + 1 = \dfrac{5}{x - 2}$

$$\dfrac{20}{3^2 - 4} + 1 \stackrel{?}{=} \dfrac{5}{3 - 2}$$

$$\dfrac{20}{5} + 1 = \dfrac{5}{1} \text{ True}$$

$\dfrac{20}{x^2 - 4} + 1 = \dfrac{5}{x - 2}$

$$\dfrac{20}{2^2 - 4} + 1 \stackrel{?}{=} \dfrac{5}{2 - 2}$$

$$\dfrac{20}{0} + 1 = \dfrac{5}{0} \text{ Undefined; exclude 2.}$$

Solution set: {3}

2 Solve: $\dfrac{1}{c + 3} = \dfrac{4}{c^2 - 9}$

$$1(c^2 - 9) = (c + 3)4$$ ←— Apply the Cross-Products Rule.

$$c^2 - 9 = 4c + 12$$ ←— Apply the Distributive Property.

$$c^2 - 4c - 21 = 0$$ ←— Write the equation in standard form.

$$(c - 7)(c + 3) = 0$$ ←— Factor.

$$c - 7 = 0 \text{ or } c + 3 = 0$$ ←— Apply the Zero-Product Property.

$$c = 7 \qquad c = -3$$ ←— Apply the Addition and Subtraction Properties of Equality.

Solution set: {7}

Check: $\dfrac{1}{c + 3} = \dfrac{4}{c^2 - 9}$

$$\dfrac{1}{7 + 3} \stackrel{?}{=} \dfrac{4}{7^2 - 9}$$

$$\dfrac{1}{10} = \dfrac{4}{40}$$

True

$\dfrac{1}{c + 3} = \dfrac{4}{c^2 - 9}$

$$\dfrac{1}{-3 + 3} \stackrel{?}{=} \dfrac{4}{(-3)^2 - 9}$$

$$\dfrac{1}{0} = \dfrac{4}{0}$$

Undefined; exclude −3.

Try These

Solve and check.

1. $\dfrac{1}{a - 4} = \dfrac{2}{a^2 - 16}$

2. $\dfrac{b - 11}{b + 5} = \dfrac{-6}{2b}$

3. $\dfrac{1}{r + 6} + \dfrac{1}{8} = \dfrac{1}{r + 2}$

4. $1 - \dfrac{2}{f + 2} = \dfrac{f}{6}$

5. Discuss and Write Sometimes it is *not* possible to factor a quadratic equation over the integers. Describe two other methods you can use to solve a quadratic equation.

Go to ▶ PRACTICE BOOK Lesson 12-9 for exercise sets.

Problem Solving: Review of Strategies

Read > **Plan** > **Solve** > **Check**

Objective To solve problems by using a variety of strategies

Problem: There are a total of 20 rectangles and triangles on a page of a child's coloring book. Half of the rectangles are squares. In all, the shapes have 74 sides. How many triangles and how many squares are on this page?

Read to understand what is being asked.

List the facts and restate the question.

Facts: There are triangles, squares, and nonsquare rectangles on a page of a coloring book.

There are the same number of squares as nonsquare rectangles.

In all, there are 20 shapes and 74 sides.

Question: How many of the 20 shapes are triangles and how many are squares?

Select a strategy.

You can try using the strategy *Make a Drawing*. Or, you can attempt to *Guess and Test*.

Apply the strategy.

▶**Method 1: Make a Drawing**

You know that each of the 20 shapes has *at least* three sides. So draw 20 three-sided figures, as shown below.

Problem-Solving Strategies

1. Make a Drawing
2. Solve a Simpler Problem
3. Reason Logically
4. Consider Extreme Cases
5. Work Backward
6. Find a Pattern
7. Account for All Possibilities
8. Adopt a Different Point of View
9. Guess and Test
10. Organize Data

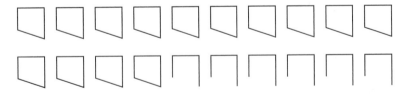

The drawing accounts for 60 sides (3 • 20), or 60, out of the total of 74 sides. To account for the other 14 sides, *add* one side to exactly 14 of the figures.

The 14 four-sided figures represent 14 rectangles, in which half of these rectangles are squares, so there are $\left(\frac{1}{2} \cdot 14\right)$, or 7, squares. The 6 three-sided figures represent the triangles, so there are 6 triangles. The shapes on the page might look something like this:

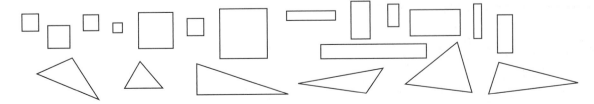

▶Method 2: Guess and Test

You can use the *Guess and Test* strategy. Start by guessing the number of squares. From that guess, you can figure out the number of nonsquare rectangles and the number of triangles. Then you can figure out the number of sides. If it is not 74, adjust your guess and try again.

- Start by guessing that there are 2 squares.

Number of squares:	2
Number of nonsquare rectangles:	2 ◀—Half the rectangles are not squares.
Number triangles:	16 ◀—There are 20 shapes in all.
Total number of sides:	64 ◀—Each square and nonsquare rectangle has 4 sides; each triangle has 3 sides: $2(4) + 2(4) + 16(3) = 64$

The number of sides is too small.

- Increase the guess for the number of squares. Try 8.

Number of squares:	8
Number of nonsquare rectangles:	8 ◀—Half the rectangles are not squares.
Number triangles:	4 ◀—There are 20 shapes in all.
Total number of sides:	76 ◀—$8(4) + 8(4) + 4(3) = 76$

There are too many sides.

- Continue guessing and testing until the total number of sides is 74. You can make a table, like the one below, to keep track of your work.

Number of Squares	Number of Nonsquare Rectangles	Number of Triangles	Number of Sides	
2	2	16	64	too few sides
8	8	4	76	too many sides
5	5	10	70	too few sides
6	6	8	72	close
7	7	6	74	Correct!

So there are 7 squares and 6 triangles on the page.

Check to make sure your answer makes sense.

- Are there 20 shapes in all?

  7 squares + 7 nonsquare rectangles + 6 triangles = 20 shapes ✓

- Are there 74 sides in all?

($7 \cdot 4$) sides for the squares	28 sides
($7 \cdot 4$) sides for the nonsquare rectangles ⟶	28 sides
+ ($6 \cdot 3$) sides for the triangles	+ 18 sides
	74 sides ✓

The answer checks.

Enrichment:
Continued Fractions

Objective **To write rational numbers as continued fractions • To simplify finite continued fractions**

Continued fractions are used as a way to represent rational and real numbers using only integers. Informally, you can think of a fraction as a sequence of fractions within a fraction. Each fractional part gets closer to the actual value of the continued fraction until it is represented exactly.

For example, consider $\frac{58}{13}$.

$\frac{58}{13} \approx 4.4615385$. It is about 4, or 4.0, but a little more; and it is about $4\frac{1}{2}$, or 4.5, but a little less. The correct denominator is a little more than 2.

So $\frac{58}{13} = 4 + \dfrac{1}{2 + \frac{1}{6}}$.

Key Concept

Continued Fraction

A "general" continued fraction representation of a real number is:

$$a + \cfrac{1}{b + \cfrac{1}{c + \cfrac{1}{d + \frac{1}{\ddots}}}}$$

The variable a is an integer, and the other variables b, c, and d are positive integers (a will be 0 if the number is between 0 and 1).

If a number is *rational*, then its continued-fraction form is finite.

If a number is *irrational*, then its continued-fraction form is infinite. For example,

$$\pi = 3 + \cfrac{1}{7 + \cfrac{1}{15 + \frac{1}{\ddots}}}$$

▶When expressing a rational number as a continued fraction, each step involves either writing a fraction greater than 1 as the sum of a whole number and a fraction less than 1 *or* writing a fraction as 1 divided by its reciprocal. The process stops when a fraction with a numerator of 1 is obtained.

Express $\frac{3}{11}$ as a continued fraction.

$\dfrac{3}{11} = \dfrac{1}{\frac{11}{3}}$ ◄—Write $\frac{3}{11}$ as 1 *divided* by its reciprocal.

$= \dfrac{1}{\frac{9+2}{3}} = \dfrac{1}{3 + \frac{2}{3}}$ ◄—Write $\frac{11}{3}$ as $\frac{9+2}{3} = \frac{9}{3} + \frac{2}{3}$, the *sum* of a whole number and a fraction less than 1. Then simplify.

$= \dfrac{1}{3 + \frac{1}{\frac{3}{2}}}$ ◄—Write $\frac{2}{3}$ as 1 *divided* by its reciprocal.

$= \dfrac{1}{3 + \cfrac{1}{1 + \frac{1}{2}}}$ ◄—Write $\frac{3}{2}$ as the *sum* of a whole number and a fraction less than 1. Then simplify.

$= \dfrac{1}{3 + \cfrac{1}{1 + \frac{1}{2}}}$ ◄—This is a fraction with a numerator of 1. The process is complete.

▶To simplify a finite continued fraction, simply start at the lower right and work *upward* step by step.

When simplifying a finite continued fraction, each step involves either adding a whole number and a fraction to get a fraction greater than 1 *or* dividing the fraction greater than 1 by its reciprocal to rewrite it as a fraction.

Simplify: $\dfrac{1}{2 + \dfrac{1}{4 + \dfrac{1}{3 + \frac{1}{2}}}}$

$\dfrac{1}{2 + \dfrac{1}{4 + \dfrac{1}{3 + \frac{1}{2}}}} = \dfrac{1}{2 + \dfrac{1}{4 + \dfrac{1}{\frac{7}{2}}}}$ ◀—Add $3 + \frac{1}{2}$ to get $\frac{7}{2}$.

$= \dfrac{1}{2 + \dfrac{1}{4 + \frac{2}{7}}}$ ◀—Rewrite $\dfrac{1}{\frac{7}{2}}$ as $\dfrac{2}{7}$.

$= \dfrac{1}{2 + \dfrac{1}{\frac{30}{7}}}$ ◀—Add $4 + \frac{2}{7}$ to get $\frac{30}{7}$.

$= \dfrac{1}{2 + \frac{7}{30}}$ ◀—Rewrite $\dfrac{1}{\frac{30}{7}}$ as $\dfrac{7}{30}$.

$= \dfrac{1}{\frac{67}{30}}$ ◀—Add $2 + \frac{7}{30}$ to get $\frac{67}{30}$.

$= \dfrac{30}{67}$ ◀—Rewrite $\dfrac{1}{\frac{67}{30}}$ as $\dfrac{30}{67}$.

Try These

Express as a continued fraction.

1. $\dfrac{28}{18}$

2. $\dfrac{5}{19}$

Simplify each continued fraction.

3. $2 + \dfrac{1}{2 + \dfrac{1}{2 + \frac{1}{2}}}$

4. $\dfrac{1}{5 + \dfrac{1}{4 + \dfrac{1}{3 + \frac{1}{2}}}}$

5. **Discuss and Write** Compare the steps of the process involved in expressing a fraction as a continued fraction with those involved in the process of simplifying a continued fraction.

Go to PRACTICE BOOK pages 323–324 for exercise sets.

Test Prep: Multiple-Choice Questions
Strategy: Understand Distractors

When solving problems, *make notes* to help organize the given information. Include notes about the steps you need to follow in order to complete the problem. Refer to your notes as you work, and then review them as you check your answers.

Look at the sample test item.

Read the test item, including the answer choices. Identify important information.

- Underline important words.

  How many students go to the museum if <u>each student pays</u> <u>$10</u> to cover the cost of the trip?

  The *cost per student* is the total cost divided by the number of students.

- Restate the question in your own words.

  Solve $(75 + 7.5n) \div n = 10$.

Solve the problem.

- Make notes to help organize thoughts and gather information.

  The cost of the bus is $75, and the cost of the tickets is $7.50n. The total cost is $75 + 7.5n$.

- Solve: $(75 + 7.5n) \div n = 10$. Justify your steps.

$$75 + 7.5n = 10n \quad \longleftarrow \text{Use the Multiplication Property of Equality.}$$

$$75 = 2.5n \quad \longleftarrow \text{Use the Subtraction Property of Equality.}$$

$$30 = n \quad \longleftarrow \text{Use the Division Property of Equality.}$$

Test-Taking Tips

- Underline important words.
- Restate the question.
- Use the Test-Prep strategy.
- Apply appropriate rules, definitions, properties, or strategies.
- Analyze and eliminate answer choices.

Item Analysis

Choose the answer.

- Analyze and eliminate answer choices. Watch out for distractors.

  A. -30 $\longleftarrow$ A negative number of students does not make sense. Eliminate this choice.

  B. 8 $\longleftarrow 75 + 7.5(8) \div 8 \approx 16.88 \neq 10$. Eliminate this choice.

  C. 11 $\longleftarrow 75 + 7.5(11) \div 11 \approx 14.32 \neq 10$. Eliminate this choice.

  D. 30 $\longleftarrow$ This is the correct choice!

Try These

1. The length and width of a 15-foot by 10-foot patio are increased by the same amount so that the area is doubled. What is the amount of increase of each dimension?

   A. 5 ft   **B.** 10 ft   **C.** 30 ft   **D.** 150 ft

Go to   **PRACTICE BOOK page 325 for exercise sets.**

Exponential and Other Nonlinear Functions

CHAPTER 13

In This Chapter You Will:

- Recognize, interpret, write, and graph inverse variation
- Solve problems using inverse variation
- Graph rational, radical, and exponential functions
- Identify vertical and horizontal asymptotes
- Graph square-root functions and translated square-root functions

- Simplify rational exponents
- Recognize how changing the coefficients affects the graph of an exponential function
- Solve problems involving exponential growth and decay
- Apply the strategy: *Organize Data*
- Look for new vocabulary words **highlighted** in each lesson

Do You Remember?

- A number in exponential form is a number written with a base and an exponent.
- A proportion is an equation stating that two ratios are equal.
- A function may be expressed in many ways, such as with an equation, table, or graph.
    - A direct variation is described by an equation of the form $y = kx$, where $k \neq 0$.

For Practice Exercises:

 PRACTICE BOOK, pp. 331–358

For Chapter Support: (ONLINE)

 www.progressinmathematics.com

- Skills Update Practice
- Practice Activities
- Audio Glossary
- Vocabulary Activities
- Technology Videos
- Enrichment Activities
- Electronic SourceBook

VIRTUAL MANIPULATIVES

Critical Thinking

The length of time it takes to send information via the Internet depends on connection speed. Use the given table to determine approximately how long it will take Nadine to send a 10-megabyte file with a fiber-optic connection at 640,000 bits per second (bps).

Connection	bps	Minutes : Seconds
Phone Line	14,400	97:05
DSL	128,000	10:55
Fiber Optic	640,000	?

Inverse Variation

Objective To recognize an inverse variation from a table, graph, or equation
• To write and graph inverse variation • To solve problems involving inverse variation

The athletics department recently purchased a new tread climber for the school's athletic facility. This machine allows users to specify a climbing speed. The display on the tread climber then shows how much time it takes to climb 1 mile at that speed. Niles sets the climbing speed at 6 miles per hour. How much time will it take him to climb 1 mile?

To find how much time it will take Niles to climb 1 mile, use the table at the right. Look for a pattern in the (speed, time) pairs, and write a function rule relating speed and time.

Tread Climber Speed (mph)	Time (in minutes)	(Speed, Time)
2	30	(2, 30)
3	20	(3, 20)
4	15	(4, 15)
5	12	(5, 12)
6	?	(6, ?)

▶ A relationship between two variables in which the product is constant is called an inverse variation.

Notice that as the speed of the climber *increases*, the time to climb a mile *decreases*. Additionally, the product of the speed and the time is equal to 60, which is the number of minutes in 1 hour.

You can write a rule to represent this pattern.

  Let x = the speed in miles per hour, and
    y = the time it takes to climb 1 mile.

Then the function rule relating x and y is $xy = 60$, or $y = \dfrac{60}{x}$. Therefore $f(x) = \dfrac{60}{x}$.

This relationship is an example of inverse variation. The constant, k, which equals 60, is called the constant of variation.

$$y = \dfrac{k}{x} \longrightarrow y = \dfrac{60}{x} = \dfrac{60}{6} = 10$$

So it will take Niles 10 minutes to climb 1 mile.

_____ **Key Concept** _____

Inverse Variation

An inverse variation is a function defined by an equation of the form $xy = k$, or $y = \dfrac{k}{x}$, where $x \neq 0$ and k is a nonzero constant.

It is said that y *varies inversely as* x or that y *is inversely proportional to* x.

The constant k is the constant of variation.

▶ The graph of an inverse variation is a hyperbola. The ordered pairs from the table are plotted at the right.

• The hyperbola in this case can only go through Quadrant I, since speed (x) and time (y) can only be positive numbers.

• Neither x nor y can equal 0 for the equation $xy = 60$ to be true. Therefore, the graph *does not intersect* the axes. This indicates that a solution to the inverse variation can never be $(a, 0)$ or $(b, 0)$, where a and b are any real numbers.

• The lines $x = 0$ and $y = 0$ are asymptotes of the hyperbola at the right. An asymptote is a line that a graph approaches more and more closely.

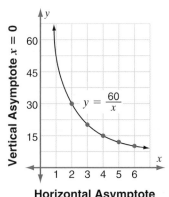

Horizontal Asymptote
$y = 0$

Example

1 Graph the inverse variation, $xy = -18$. Describe the asymptotes.

- Make a function table as shown at the right. Choose both positive and negative values for x.

- Graph the ordered pairs in the table on a coordinate plane. Draw smooth curves through them.

The graph of $xy = -18$ is shown at the right. Notice that the hyperbola gets very close to the lines $x = 0$ and $y = 0$. Therefore, the asymptotes are the axes.

x	y
−18	1
−9	2
−6	3
−3	6
−2	9
−1	18
1	−18
2	−9
3	−6
6	−3
9	−2
18	−1

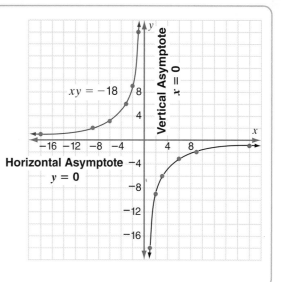

▶ Problems involving inverse variation can be solved by writing and solving an equation of inverse variation, $xy = k$, or a proportion. Since $x_1 y_1 = k$ and $x_2 y_2 = k$, then by using the Transitive Property of Equality, you find that $x_1 y_1 = x_2 y_2$, or $\dfrac{x_1}{x_2} = \dfrac{y_2}{y_1}$.

y varies inversely as x, and $y = 20$ when $x = 5$. Find x when $y = 4$.

Method 1 Use an equation.

$xy = k$

$5(20) = k$ ◀—Find the constant of variation.

$xy = 100$ ◀—Write the equation.

$x \bullet 4 = 100$ ◀—Substitute 4 for y.

$\dfrac{4x}{4} = \dfrac{100}{4}$ ◀—Use the Division Property of Equality.

$x = 25$

Method 2 Use a proportion.

$\dfrac{x_1}{x_2} = \dfrac{y_2}{y_1}$

$\dfrac{5}{x} = \dfrac{4}{20}$ ◀—Substitute the given values.

$4(x) = 5(20)$ ◀—Use the Cross-Products Rule.

$\dfrac{4x}{4} = \dfrac{100}{4}$ ◀—Use the Division Property of Equality.

$x = 25$

Try These

Use a function table to graph each inverse variation.

1. $xy = 12$

2. $y = \dfrac{40}{x}$

3. $xy = 75$

Solve each problem using the equation $xy = k$ or a proportion.

4. y varies inversely as x, and $y = 8$ when $x = 9$. Find x when $y = -3$.

5. y varies inversely as x, and $y = 1.2$ when $x = 7$. Find y when $x = 0.5$.

6. y varies inversely as x, and $y = 8$ when $x = 4$. Find y when $x = 64$.

7. y varies inversely as x, and $y = 9$ when $x = -6$. Find x when $y = -18$.

8. Discuss and Write How does inverse variation differ from direct variation? Give examples.

13-2

Graph Rational Functions

Objective To graph rational functions • To identify vertical and horizontal asymptotes

▶ A rational function is a nonlinear function whose rule includes a quotient of two polynomials in which the denominator has a degree of at least one. Any value of a variable in the denominator that makes the denominator equal to zero is an *excluded value* of the rational function.

Some examples of a rational function are: $y = \dfrac{4}{x}$, $y = \dfrac{4}{x-2}$, and $y = \dfrac{4}{x+3} - 1$

An inverse variation is a type of rational function.

▶ You can graph a rational function by making a function table. It is always helpful to include positive and negative values for x.

Graph $y = \dfrac{4}{x}$. Identify the asymptotes.

• Make a function table as shown below.

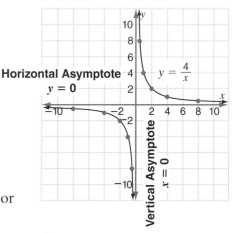

x	-8	-4	-2	-1	-0.5	0.5	1	2	4	8
y	-0.5	-1	-2	-4	-8	8	4	2	1	0.5

Horizontal Asymptote $y = 0$

• Graph the ordered pairs. Draw smooth curves through them.

Vertical asymptote: $x = 0$ Horizontal asymptote: $y = 0$

Notice that the vertical asymptote, $x = 0$, is an excluded value of the rational function, $y = \dfrac{4}{x}$. When the numerator and denominator of a rational function have no common factors other than 1, vertical asymptotes occur at excluded values.

▶ Often, it is easier to graph a function if you relate it to a parent function in a family of functions. The rational function $y = \dfrac{a}{x}$, such as $y = \dfrac{4}{x}$, is a parent function of a family of rational functions.

> **Remember:** A family of functions is a set of functions whose graphs have primary characteristics in common.

Graph $y = \dfrac{4}{x-2}$. Identify the asymptotes.

• Make a function table as shown below. Since $x = 2$ is an excluded value, use values of x near 2.

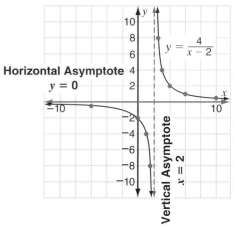

x	-6	0	1	1.5	2.5	3	4	6	10
y	-0.5	-2	-4	-8	8	4	2	1	0.5

Horizontal Asymptote $y = 0$

• Graph the ordered pairs in the table on a coordinate plane. Draw smooth curves through them.

Vertical asymptote: $x = 2$ Horizontal asymptote: $y = 0$

For a rational function written in the form $y = \dfrac{a}{x-b}$, such as $y = \dfrac{4}{x-2}$, the graph is translated b units *to the right* of the graph of $y = \dfrac{a}{x}$ if b is positive or b units *to the left* if b is negative. The vertical asymptote is $x = b$.

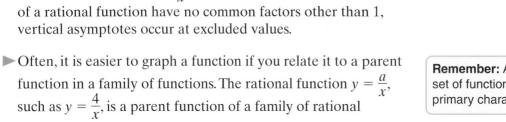

Notice that the graphs of $y = \dfrac{4}{x}$ and $y = \dfrac{4}{x-2}$ on page 332 are identical in shape, but the graph of $y = \dfrac{4}{x-2}$ is translated 2 units to the right of $y = \dfrac{4}{x}$. The horizontal asymptote of *both* graphs is $y = 0$.

▶ You can also see how the graph of a rational function is translated vertically. Consider the graph of a rational function in the form $y = \dfrac{a}{x} + c$ and compare its graph with the graph of the parent function $y = \dfrac{a}{x}$.

 Graph $y = \dfrac{4}{x} + 2$. Identify the asymptotes.

- Make a function table as shown below. $x = 0$ is an excluded value.

x	-8	-4	-2	-1	-0.5	0.5	1	2	4	8
y	1.5	1	0	-2	-6	10	6	4	3	2.5

- Graph the ordered pairs in the table on a coordinate plane. Draw smooth curves through them.

Vertical asymptote: $x = 0$

Horizontal asymptote: $y = 2$

Notice that the graphs of $y = \dfrac{4}{x}$ and $y = \dfrac{4}{x} + 2$ are identical in shape, but the graph of $y = \dfrac{4}{x} + 2$ is translated 2 units above the graph of $y = \dfrac{4}{x}$. The vertical asymptote of *both* graphs is $x = 0$.

For a rational function written in the form $y = \dfrac{a}{x} + c$, such as $y = \dfrac{4}{x} + 2$, the graph is translated *up c* units from the graph of $y = \dfrac{4}{x}$ if c is positive, or *down c* units if c is negative. The horizontal asymptote is $y = c$.

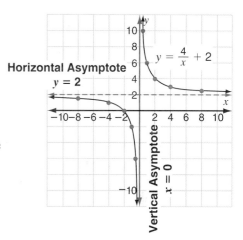

Horizontal Asymptote
$y = 2$

$y = \dfrac{4}{x} + 2$

Vertical Asymptote
$x = 0$

▶ You can use the asymptotes and a function table to graph a rational function in the form of $y = \dfrac{a}{x-b} + c$.

Key Concept

Graph of a Rational Function

The graph of a rational function in the form $y = \dfrac{a}{x-b} + c$ has a vertical asymptote at the excluded value, or $x = b$, and a horizontal asymptote at $y = c$.

The graph is a translation of $y = \dfrac{a}{x}$, b units to the *right* or *left*, and c units *up* or *down*.

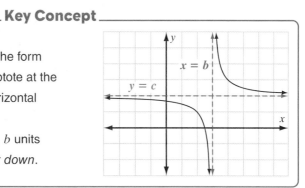

Graph: $y = \dfrac{4}{x - 3} + 1$

- Identify the vertical and horizontal asymptotes.

  vertical asymptote: $x = 3$ ←—Use $x = b$ and $b = 3$.
  horizontal asymptote: $y = 1$ ←—Use $y = c$ and $c = 1$.

- Graph the asymptotes using dashed lines.

- Make a function table. Choose x-values on both sides of the vertical asymptote.

x	−5	−1	1	2	2.5	3.5	4	5	7	11
y	0.5	0	−1	−3	−7	9	5	3	2	1.5

- Graph the ordered pairs. Draw smooth curves through them.

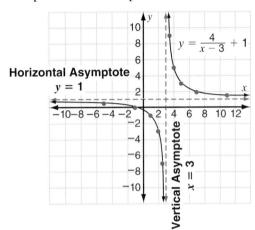

.Think..

The graph of $y = \dfrac{4}{x - 3} + 1$ is a translation

of $y = \dfrac{4}{x}$, 1 unit up and 3 units to the right.

....

Examples

1 Graph: $y = \dfrac{4}{x + 3} - 1$

- Identify the vertical and horizontal asymptotes.

  vertical asymptote: $x = -3$ ←—Use $x = b$ and $b = -3$.
  horizontal asymptote: $y = -1$ ←—Use $y = c$ and $c = -1$.

- Graph the asymptotes using dashed lines.

- Make a function table.

x	−7	−5	−4	−3.5	−2.5	−2	−1	1	5
y	−2	−3	−5	−9	7	3	1	0	−0.5

- Graph the ordered pairs. Draw smooth curves through them.

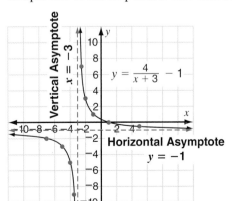

.Think..

The graph of $y = \dfrac{4}{x + 3} - 1$ is a translation

of $y = \dfrac{4}{x}$, 1 unit down and 3 units to the left.

....

2 Graph $y = \dfrac{9}{x}$ and $y = \dfrac{9}{x-1} - 3$.

- Write each function in the form $y = \dfrac{a}{x-b} + c$ to identify the asymptotes.

$y = \dfrac{9}{x-0} + 0$

   vertical asymptote: $x = 0$
   horizontal asymptote: $y = 0$

$y = \dfrac{9}{x-1} - 3$

   vertical asymptote: $x = 1$
   horizontal asymptote: $y = -3$

- Graph the asymptotes of each function using dashed lines.

- Make a function table for each. Choose x-values on both sides of the vertical asymptote.

$y = \dfrac{9}{x} \longrightarrow$

x	−9	−4.5	−3	−2	−1	1	2	3	4.5	9
y	−1	−2	−3	−4.5	−9	9	4.5	3	2	1

$y = \dfrac{9}{x-1} - 3 \longrightarrow$

x	−8	−5	−2	−1	0	2	3	4	7	10
y	−4	−4.5	−6	−7.5	−12	6	1.5	0	−1.5	−2

- Graph the ordered pairs in each table on a coordinate plane. Draw smooth curves through them.

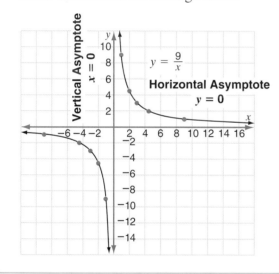

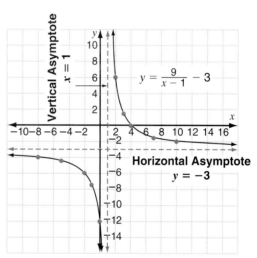

Try These

For each rational function, identify and graph the asymptotes, make a function table, and graph the function.

1. $y = \dfrac{6}{x}$

2. $y = \dfrac{6}{x+2}$

3. $y = \dfrac{6}{x} - 2$

4. $y = \dfrac{6}{x-2} + 2$

5. $y = \dfrac{8}{x+1} + 3$

6. $y = \dfrac{8}{x-1} - 3$

7. Which is the parent function in exercises 1–4? Describe how each of the other functions relates with the parent function.

8. Discuss and Write Explain which of these functions is a rational function: $y = \dfrac{2}{x}$ or $y = \dfrac{x}{2}$. Compare their graphs.

Go to ▶ **PRACTICE BOOK Lesson 13-2 for exercise sets.**

Graph Radical Functions

Objective To graph radical functions

▶ A **square-root function** is a nonlinear function that contains the independent variable in the radicand. The square-root function is the simplest example of a **radical function**. Some examples of a square-root function are: $y = \sqrt{x}$, $y = \sqrt{x} + 3$, and $y = \sqrt{x - 3}$.

> **Remember:** The expression under the radical sign is called the *radicand*.

The function $y = \sqrt{x}$ is a parent function for the family of square-root functions. The domain of a square-root function is restricted to numbers that make the radicand greater than or equal to 0 since the square root of a negative number is not a real number. You can use a function table to graph a square-root function.

Graph: $y = \sqrt{x}$

• Find the domain and range of the function.

    Domain: $x \geq 0$ ◀—The radicand must be greater than or equal to 0.

    Range: $y \geq 0$ ◀—If $x \geq 0$, then $y \geq 0$ in $y = \sqrt{x}$.

• Make a function table. Choose perfect-square values for x.

x	0	1	4	9	16
y	0	1	2	3	4

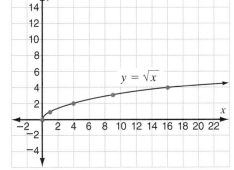

• Graph the ordered pairs in the table on a coordinate plane. Draw a smooth curve through them.

▶ You can graph a radical function $y = \sqrt{x} + k$, and relate its graph with the graph of the parent function $y = \sqrt{x}$.

Key Concept

Graph of $y = \sqrt{x} + k$

The graph of $y = \sqrt{x} + k$ is a vertical translation of $y = \sqrt{x}$.

The graph is translated k units *up* for $k > 0$ and k units *down* for $k < 0$.

Graph: $y = \sqrt{x} + 3$

• Find the domain and range of the function.

    Domain: $x \geq 0$ ◀—The radicand must be greater than or equal to 0.

    Range: $y \geq 3$ ◀—If $x \geq 0$, then $y \geq 3$ in $y = \sqrt{x} + 3$.

• Make a function table. Choose perfect-square values for x.

x	0	1	4	9	16
y	3	4	5	6	7

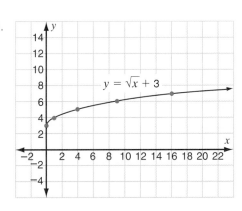

• Graph the ordered pairs. Draw a smooth curve through them.

Notice that the graph of $y = \sqrt{x} + 3$, has been translated 3 units *up* from the graph of $y = \sqrt{x}$.

▶ You can also graph the radical function $y = \sqrt{x - h}$, and relate its graph with the graph of the parent function $y = \sqrt{x}$.

Graph: $y = \sqrt{x - 3}$

• Find the domain and range of the function.

___ **Key Concept** ___

Graph of $y = \sqrt{x - h}$

The graph of $y = \sqrt{x - h}$ is a horizontal translation of $y = \sqrt{x}$. The graph is translated h units to the *right* for $h > 0$ and h units to the *left* for $h < 0$.

Domain: $x - 3 \geq 0$ ◀—The radicand must be greater than or equal to 0.

$x \geq 3$ ◀—Use the Addition Property of Inequality.

Range: $y \geq 0$ ◀—If $x - 3 \geq 0$, then $y \geq 0$ in $y = \sqrt{x - 3}$.

• Make a function table. Then graph the ordered pairs and draw a smooth curve through them.

x	3	4	7	12	19
y	0	1	2	3	4

Notice that the graph of $y = \sqrt{x - 3}$ has been translated 3 units to the *right*.

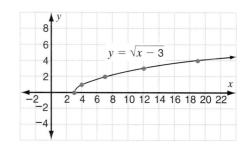

Example

1

Graph: $y = \sqrt{x + 1} - 2$ Describe how the graph relates with the graph of $y = \sqrt{x}$.

• Find the domain and range of the function.

Domain: $x + 1 \geq 0$ ◀—The radicand must be greater than or equal to 0.

$x \geq -1$ ◀—Use the Subtraction Property of Inequality.

Range: $y \geq -2$ ◀—If $x + 1 \geq 0$, then $y \geq -2$ in $y = \sqrt{x + 1} - 2$.

• Make a function table. Then graph the ordered pairs and draw a smooth curve through them.

x	−1	0	3	8	15
y	−2	−1	0	1	2

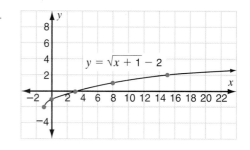

For the graph of $y = \sqrt{x + 1} - 2$, the graph of $y = \sqrt{x}$ has been translated 2 units *down* and 1 unit to the *left*.

Try These

Graph each function. State its domain and range. Describe how its graph relates with the graph of $y = \sqrt{x}$.

1. $y = \sqrt{x + 2}$ **2.** $y = \sqrt{x} - 1$ **3.** $y = \sqrt{x - 2} + 1$

4. Discuss and Write Explain how the graph of the function shown is different from the graph of $y = \sqrt{x}$. Then use your observations to write the function rule for the graph in the form of $y = \sqrt{x - h} + k$.

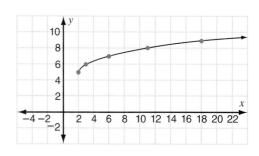

Go to ▶ **PRACTICE BOOK Lesson 13-3 for exercise sets.**

Identify Exponential Functions and Their Graphs

Objective To identify and evaluate exponential functions • To simplify rational exponents • To graph exponential functions • To identify how changing the coefficients affects the graph of an exponential function

To prepare for a marathon, Zalia decided to gradually increase the duration of her practice runs from 2 minutes on day 1, to 4 minutes on day 2, 8 minutes on day 3, and so on, doubling the amount of time each day. If she sticks to her plan, how long will she run on day 7?

▶ To find how long Zalia will run on day 7, write the data in a table, and study the pattern.

Let x = the number of days Zalia runs and
y = the number of minutes she runs each day.

Day (x)	Minutes (y)	Pattern	Exponential Form
1	2	2	2^1
2	4	$2 \cdot 2$	2^2
3	8	$2 \cdot 2 \cdot 2$	2^3
4	16	$2 \cdot 2 \cdot 2 \cdot 2$	2^4
5	32	$2 \cdot 2 \cdot 2 \cdot 2 \cdot 2$	2^5
6	64	$2 \cdot 2 \cdot 2 \cdot 2 \cdot 2 \cdot 2$	2^6
7	128	$2 \cdot 2 \cdot 2 \cdot 2 \cdot 2 \cdot 2 \cdot 2$	2^7
x	$2^x = y$	$2 \cdot 2 \cdot \ldots \cdot 2$ (x factors)	2^x

(The left margin shows $+1$ between each day and $\times 2$ between each minutes value.)

A function rule that describes the pattern above is $y = 2^x$. This type of function, in which the independent variable appears in an exponent is an <u>exponential function</u>. Notice that 2 is the starting time (number of minutes) and 2 is the amount by which the number of minutes is multiplied each day.

So if Zalia follows her plan, she will run 2^7, or 128, minutes on day 7.

▶ Sometimes you may need to simplify rational exponents assigned to the domain.

To simplify numbers with rational exponents, use the Power Law of Exponents, $(x^m)^n = x^{mn}$, and the definition of a radical number.

Simplify: $\left(x^{\frac{1}{2}}\right)^2$

$\left(x^{\frac{1}{2}}\right)^2 = x^{\frac{1}{2}(2)}$ ◀—Use the Power Law of Exponents.

$= x^1 = x$ ◀—Simplify.

Since $\left(x^{\frac{1}{2}}\right)^2 = x$ and $(\sqrt{x})^2 = x$, then $x^{\frac{1}{2}} = \sqrt{x}$.

The $\sqrt{x}$ can also be written as $\sqrt[2]{x}$.

Simplify: $25^{\frac{1}{2}}$
$$25^{\frac{1}{2}} = (\sqrt{25})^1 = (5)^1 = 5$$

Simplify: $49^{\frac{3}{2}}$
$$49^{\frac{3}{2}} = (\sqrt{49})^3 = (7)^3 = 343$$

> **Key Concept**
>
> **Exponential Function**
> An exponential function is a nonlinear function of the form $y = ab^x$, where $a \neq 0$, $b \neq 1$, $b > 0$, and x is a real number.

> **Key Concept**
>
> **Rational Exponent**
> $a^{\frac{m}{n}} = \left(a^{\frac{1}{n}}\right)^m = (\sqrt[n]{a})^m$, where a is a real number and m and n are positive integers.

▶ To graph an exponential function, make a function table, graph the ordered pairs, and then draw a smooth curve through them.

Graph: $y = 4^x$

• Make a function table, as shown below.

• Graph the ordered pairs in the table, and then draw a smooth curve through them.

x	4^x	y
-1	$4^{-1} = \dfrac{1}{4}$	$\dfrac{1}{4}$
0	$4^0 = 1$	1
$\dfrac{1}{2}$	$4^{\frac{1}{2}} = (\sqrt{4})^1 = 2$	2
1	$4^1 = 4$	4
$\dfrac{3}{2}$	$4^{\frac{3}{2}} = (\sqrt{4})^3 = (2)^3 = 8$	8
2	$4^2 = 16$	16

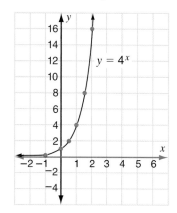

Notice that the graph of $y = 4^x$ has the x-axis, or $y = 0$, as its horizontal asymptote, and that the range of the function is $y > 0$.

▶ The function $y = 4^x$ is the parent function of a family of exponential functions that includes $y = -4^x$ and $y = \left(\dfrac{1}{4}\right)^x$.

To show the relationships of the graphs of $y = 4^x$ and $y = -4^x$, graph both functions on the *same* coordinate plane.

• Make a function table for $y = -4^x$ as shown below. Use the function table above for $y = 4^x$.

Remember:
$-4^x = -(4^x)$

• Graph the ordered pairs in each function table on the same coordinate plane and draw a smooth curve through them.

x	-4^x	y
-1	$-4^{-1} = -\dfrac{1}{4}$	$-\dfrac{1}{4}$
0	$-4^0 = -(1) = -1$	-1
$\dfrac{1}{2}$	$-4^{\frac{1}{2}} = -(\sqrt{4^1}) = -2$	-2
1	$-4^1 = -4$	-4
$\dfrac{3}{2}$	$-4^{\frac{3}{2}} = -(\sqrt{4^3}) = -(2)^3 = -8$	-8
2	$-4^2 = -16$	-16

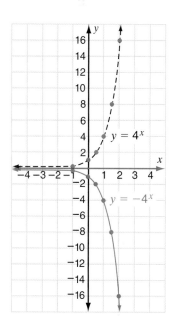

Notice that the graph of $y = -4^x$ is a reflection of $y = 4^x$ across the x-axis. The x-axis, $y = 0$, is an asymptote for both graphs.

The range of $y = -4^x$ is $y < 0$, whereas the range of $y = 4^x$ is $y > 0$.

Continue Lesson ➡

1 Graph $y = 4^x$ and $y = \left(\frac{1}{4}\right)^x$ on the same coordinate plane.
Describe how the graphs are related.

- Make a function table as shown below for $y = \left(\frac{1}{4}\right)^x$.

  Use the function table for $y = 4^x$ shown on page 339.

- Graph the ordered pairs in each function table on the same coordinate plane and draw a smooth curve through them.

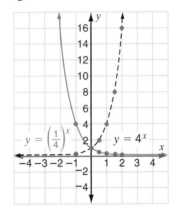

x	$\left(\frac{1}{4}\right)^x$	y
-1	$\left(\frac{1}{4}\right)^{-1} = 4$	4
0	$\left(\frac{1}{4}\right)^{0} = 1$	1
$\frac{1}{2}$	$\left(\frac{1}{4}\right)^{\frac{1}{2}} = \sqrt{\frac{1}{4}} = \frac{1}{2}$	$\frac{1}{2}$
1	$\left(\frac{1}{4}\right)^{1} = \frac{1}{4}$	$\frac{1}{4}$
$\frac{3}{2}$	$\left(\frac{1}{4}\right)^{\frac{3}{2}} = \left(\sqrt{\frac{1}{4}}\right)^3 = \left(\frac{1}{2}\right)^3 = \frac{1}{8}$	$\frac{1}{8}$
2	$\left(\frac{1}{4}\right)^{2} = \frac{1}{16}$	$\frac{1}{16}$

The graph of $y = \left(\frac{1}{4}\right)^x$ is a reflection of the graph of $y = 4^x$ across the y-axis. The x-axis, or $y = 0$, is an asymptote for both graphs and the range for both functions is $y > 0$.

▶ To graph exponential functions of the form $y = ab^x$, choose several values of x (positive, negative, and zero), and solve for the corresponding values of y. Plot the points, and connect them with a smooth curve.

Graph $y = 2(0.4^x)$. Then write an exponential function that would be a reflection of its graph across the x-axis.

- Make a function table, as shown below.

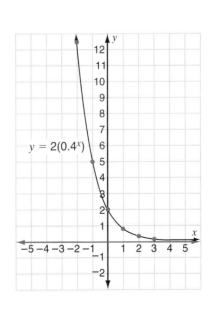

x	$2(0.4^x)$	y
-2	$2(0.4^{-2}) = 2\left(\frac{1}{0.16}\right) = 12.5$	12.5
-1	$2(0.4^{-1}) = 2\left(\frac{1}{0.4}\right) = 5$	5
0	$2(0.4^0) = 2(1) = 2$	2
1	$2(0.4^1) = 2(0.4) = 0.8$	0.8
2	$2(0.4^2) = 2(0.16) = 0.32$	0.32
3	$2(0.4^3) = 2(0.064) = 0.128$	0.128

The reflection of the graph of $y = 2(0.4^x)$ over the x-axis will have the x-coordinates the same and the y-coordinates change to the opposites.

So the graph of $y = -2(0.4^x)$ would be a reflection of the graph of $y = 2(0.4^x)$ over the x-axis.

► The graphs of exponential functions of the form $y = ab^x$ have the same general shape. When the coefficient, a, is changed for any exponential function, it will affect the graph.

• If $b > 1$, then the graph will have one of the following two shapes:	• If $0 < b < 1$, then the graph will have one of the following two shapes:

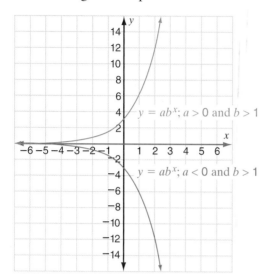

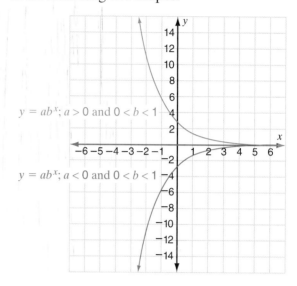

The graph shown in blue above is $y = ab^x$, where $a > 0$.	The graph shown in blue above is $y = ab^x$, where $a > 0$.
The graph shown in red above is $y = ab^x$, where $a < 0$.	The graph shown in red above is $y = ab^x$, where $a < 0$.
The graphs are reflections of each other across the x-axis.	The graphs are reflections of each other across the x-axis.

Try These

Evaluate each function for the given value of x.

1. $y = 6^x$ for $x = 0$

2. $y = 2(3^x)$ for $x = 3$

3. $y = -\frac{1}{2}(2^x)$ for $x = -3$

Simplify.

4. $144^{\frac{1}{2}}$

5. $64^{\frac{3}{2}}$

6. $4^{\frac{5}{2}}$

Make a function table for each exponential function. Then graph each pair of functions on the same coordinate plane. Describe the similarities and differences of the graphs. For exercises 9 and 11, assign rational exponents for the domain.

7. $y = 6^x$ and $y = -6^x$

8. $y = 5^x$ and $y = \left(\frac{1}{5}\right)^x$

9. $y = \frac{1}{3}(2^x)$ and $y = -\frac{1}{3}(2^x)$

10. $y = 3(0.5)^x$ and $y = -3\left(\frac{1}{2}\right)^x$

11. $y = 3(2^x)$ and $y = 3\left(\frac{1}{2}\right)^x$

12. $y = 5(0.25)^x$ and $y = -5\left(\frac{1}{4}\right)^x$

13. Discuss and Write Make a table of values for the function $y = 7(1^x)$. Then graph the function. Is this an exponential function? Explain why or why not.

Go to ► PRACTICE BOOK Lesson 13-4 for exercise sets.

Exponential Growth and Decay

Objective To solve problems involving exponential growth and decay

Suppose a rare quarter that is worth $10 today increases in value, or appreciates, 4% each year. How much will it be worth in 1 year? in 2, 20, and 50 years?

To find how much the quarter will be worth in 1 year, find: $10 + 4%($10)

$$\$10 + 4\%(\$10) = \$10 + 0.04(\$10) \quad \leftarrow \text{Write 4\% as a decimal.}$$
$$= \$10(1 + 0.04) \quad \leftarrow \text{Apply the Distributive Property.}$$
$$= \$10(1.04) \quad \leftarrow \text{Simplify.}$$
$$= \$10.40$$

So the rare quarter will be worth $10.40 in 1 year.

▶ You can use an exponential function to show how the value of the quarter increases in value each year.

starting value

new value⟶ $y = 10(1.04)^x$ ←number of years

Since multiplying over and over by 1.04 causes the value of the quarter to increase, this kind of exponential function is an example of **exponential growth**. Exponential growth occurs when a quantity increases by the same rate each time period, that is, as x increases, y increases exponentially.

To find how much the quarter will be worth in 2, 20, and 50 years, substitute the year values for x in $y = 10(1.04)^x$ as shown in the table below.

___**Key Concept**___

Exponential Growth

For $a > 0$ and $b > 1$, the function $y = ab^x$ models *exponential growth*.

The original quantity is a (when $x = 0$), and the *growth factor* is b.

x	y	Value of the Quarter
1	$10(1.04)^1$	$10.40
2	$10(1.04)^2$	$10.82
20	$10(1.04)^{20}$	$21.91
50	$10(1.04)^{50}$	$71.07

Use a handheld device to simplify the value of y.

So the quarter will be worth $10.82 after 2 years, $21.91 after 5 years, and $71.07 after 50 years.

Example

1 A microbiologist studying a colony of bacteria notices that it has a 32% increase in size each day when at room temperature. If the colony has 1000 organisms one Monday morning and is kept at room temperature, how large will the colony be the following Monday morning if it remains at room temperature?

$$y = ab^x \longrightarrow y = 1000(1.32)^7 \quad \leftarrow \text{Substitute initial quantity, growth factor, and time.}$$
$$= 6982.6056\ldots \quad \leftarrow \text{Use a handheld to simplify.}$$
$$\approx 6983 \quad \leftarrow \text{Round to the nearest whole number.}$$

Think
$a = 1000$
$b = 1 + 32\% = 1.32$
$x = 7$

The colony will have about 6983 organisms the following Monday morning.

▶ *Compound interest* is a common application of exponential growth. Interest is compounded when it is paid on both the amount of the principal and the interest that has already been earned. The formula used to find compound interest is a form of the general equation for exponential growth.

If $5000 is invested at a rate of 8% compounded quarterly, what is the value of the investment after 5 years?

.Think...........
Quarterly means 4 periods per year, so divide the rate by 4, and multiply the number of years by 4.

$$A = P\left(1 + \frac{r}{n}\right)^{nt} \longrightarrow A = 5000\left(1 + \frac{8\%}{4}\right)^{4(5)}$$ ←— Substitute the given values.

$$= 5000(1.02)^{20}$$ ←— Use a handheld to simplify.

$$\approx 7429.74$$ ←— Round to the nearest hundredths.

The investment will be worth about $7429.74 after 5 years.

_____ Key Concept _____

Compound Interest Formula

$A = P\left(1 + \frac{r}{n}\right)^{nt}$, where

P = the principal or initial investment,
r = the annual interest rate written as a decimal,
n = the number of times interest is compounded each year,
t = the time in years, and
A = the final amount after t years.

Examples

Solve using the formula for compound interest.

1 Which investment will be worth more after 20 years, $6000 compounded monthly at 10% or $6000 compounded semiannually at 10.2%? How much more?

.Think...........
monthly ——▶ 12 periods a year
semiannually ——▶ 2 periods a year

• Find the final amount of each investment.

compounded *monthly* at 10%

$$A = P\left(1 + \frac{r}{n}\right)^{nt} \longrightarrow A = 6000\left(1 + \frac{0.10}{12}\right)^{12(20)}$$

$$\approx 6000(1.00833)^{240}$$

$$\approx 43,933.56$$

compounded *semiannually* at 10.2%

$$A = P\left(1 + \frac{r}{n}\right)^{nt} \longrightarrow A = 6000\left(1 + \frac{0.102}{2}\right)^{2(20)}$$

$$= 6000(1.051)^{40}$$

$$= 43,879.32$$

So $6000 compounded monthly at 10% will be worth more after 20 years.

• Find how much more is the $6000 compounded monthly at 10%.
$43,933.56 - $43,879.32 = $54.24

So $6000 compounded monthly at 10% will be worth about $54.24 more after 20 years.

2 How much will Sam owe if he borrows $1000 for 6 months compounded monthly at $18\frac{1}{2}$%?

.Think...........
6 months = $\frac{1}{2}$ year

$$A = P\left(1 + \frac{r}{n}\right)^{nt} \longrightarrow A = 1000\left(1 + \frac{0.185}{12}\right)^{12\left(\frac{1}{2}\right)}$$

$$\approx 1000(1.01542)^{6} \approx 1096.14$$

Sam will owe about $1096.14 after 6 months, compounded monthly.

Continue Lesson ➡

▶You can also use the exponential function $y = ab^x$ to model **exponential decay**. Exponential decay occurs when a quantity decreases by the same rate each time period, that is, as x increases, y decreases exponentially.

The difference between growth and decay is the value of b, the base. With growth, b is greater than 1. With decay, b is between 0 and 1.

Brittany bought a new car for $32,000. If it depreciates, or decreases in value, 15% each year, how much will it be worth in 1 year? in 5 years?

• To find how much the car will be worth in 1 year, subtract: $32,000 − 15% • $32,000

$$\$32{,}000 - 15\% \bullet \$32{,}000 = \$32{,}000 - 0.15 \bullet \$32{,}000 \quad \leftarrow \text{Write 15\% as a decimal.}$$
$$= \$32{,}000(1 - 0.15) \quad \leftarrow \text{Apply the Distributive Property.}$$
$$= \$32{,}000(0.85) \quad \leftarrow \text{Simplify.}$$
$$= \$27{,}200$$

So the car will be worth $27,200 in 1 year.

The equation $y = 32{,}000(0.85)^x$ models the depreciation value of the car after x years. The decay factor is $(1 - 0.15)$, or 0.85.

• To find how much the car will be worth in 5 years, substitute 5 for x in $y = 32{,}000(0.85)^x$.

$$y = 32{,}000(0.85)^x \longrightarrow y = 32{,}000(0.85)^5$$
$$\approx \$14{,}198.57 \quad \leftarrow \text{Use a handheld to simplify.}$$

So the car will be worth $14,198.57 in 5 years.

Examples

1 Suppose the population of a rare lizard on an island is declining by 12% a year. If there are 270 lizards in existence now, how many will there be in 10 years?

$$y = ab^x \longrightarrow y = 270(1 - 12\%)^{10} \quad \leftarrow \text{Substitute the given values.}$$
$$= 270(1 - 0.12)^{10}$$
$$= 270(0.88)^{10} \approx 75 \quad \leftarrow \text{Use a handheld to simplify.}$$
$$\phantom{= 270(0.88)^{10} \approx 75 \quad \leftarrow} \text{Round to the nearest whole number.}$$

If the rate of decline continues, about 75 lizards will be left in 10 years.

2 Suppose a certain medication is absorbed at the rate of 22% per hour. How much of a 12 milligram dose will not yet be absorbed after 6 hours?

$$y = ab^x \longrightarrow y = 12(1 - 22\%)^6 \quad \leftarrow \text{Substitute the given values.}$$
$$= 12(1 - 0.22)^6$$
$$= 12(0.78)^6 \approx 2.7 \quad \leftarrow \text{Use a handheld to simplify.}$$
$$ \text{Round to the nearest tenths.}$$

About 2.7 milligrams of the medication will not yet be absorbed after 6 hours.

► Another example of exponential decay is *radioactive decay*, in which radioactive elements break down by releasing particles and energy. The *half-life* of a radioactive substance is the length of time it takes for half of the substance to decay or decompose.

A new therapy for locating tumors with pinpoint accuracy uses arsenic-74, a radioactive isotope with a short half-life. About how much of a 50-mg sample of arsenic-74 would remain after 60 days if its half-life is 18 days?

To find about how much, write and solve an exponential function, $y = ab^x$, which models an exponential decay.

Let x = number of half-lives, and
y = the amount remaining after x half-lives have occurred.

$a = 50$ mg ◄—the initial amount

$b = 0.5$ ◄—half-life rate of decay

$x = \frac{60}{18} \approx 3.33$ ◄—Divide the time period by the half-life.

$y = ab^x$

$y = 50(0.5)^{3.33}$ ◄—Substitute the given values.

≈ 5 ◄—Use a handheld to simplify. Round to the nearest whole number.

So about 5 mg of arsenic-74 will remain after 60 days.

Try These

**Determine if each represent exponential *growth* or *decay*.
Then solve using an exponential function.**

1. Every time Helene washes her wool blanket, it shrinks by 2%. If it was 92 by 102 inches when it was new, what will its dimensions be to the nearest inch after it is washed 6 times?

2. When Kia was born, her grandparents invested $3,000 in an account that paid 5% interest, compounded annually. How much was it worth on her 18th birthday? How much of that amount was interest?

3. Each one of two cities has a population of 1 million. One is growing 5% annually. The other is growing at an annual rate of 23%. Predict the difference in their populations 25 years from now.

4. Mrs. Chan is deciding whether to buy a car that costs $20,000 but that will depreciate by 15% per year, or a car that costs $18,000 but that will depreciate by 12% per year. What will the cars be worth in 5 years?

5. The half-life of iodine-124 is 4 days. A technician measures a 40-mCi (millicuries, a measure of radiation) sample of iodine-124. How many half-lives of iodine-124 occur in 20 days? How much iodine-124 is in the sample 20 days after the technician measures the original sample?

6. **Discuss and Write** Describe a situation that can be modeled by exponential growth and a situation that can be modeled by exponential decay.

13-6

Technology:
Graph Rational Functions

Objective To use a handheld to graph rational functions

▶ You can graph rational functions and determine asymptote lines using a handheld.

> **Remember:** The asymptotes are lines that a graph approaches more and more closely.

Graph the function $y = \dfrac{1}{x - 3}$ using a handheld. Then identify the asymptotes.

Step 1 Press 🏠. Then choose **2** to select **Graphs & Geometry**.

Step 2 Input $1 \div (x - 3)$. Then press ≈ enter to graph the function.

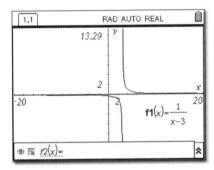

> **Remember:** Use parentheses to group the terms in the denominator.

To determine the asymptote lines, you can use the Trace command to observe the behavior of the x- and y-coordinates to identify where the graph is undefined.

Step 3 Press menu. Select **Trace**, and then choose **Graph Trace**. Use ◀ ▶ to examine the coordinates on the graph.

To verify the asymptote lines, recall that the graph of a rational function,

$y = \dfrac{a}{x - b} + c$, has a *vertical asymptote* at $x = b$ and a *horizontal asymptote* at $y = c$.

So the vertical asymptote is at $x = 3$ and the horizontal asymptote is at $y = 0$.

Example

1 Graph the function $y = \dfrac{1}{x + 2} + 3$ using a handheld. Identify the asymptotes.

Step 1 Press 🏠, then **2** to select **Graphs & Geometry**.

Step 2 Input $y = 1 \div (x + 2) + 3$.

Step 3 Press menu. Select **Trace**, and then choose **Graph Trace**. Use ◀ ▶ to examine the coordinates on the graph.

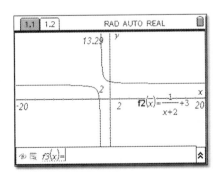

The vertical asymptote is at $x = -2$ and the horizontal asymptote is at $y = 3$.

▶Not all asymptotes are horizontal or vertical. In rational expressions in which the degree of the numerator is exactly one more degree than the degree of the denominator, the graph of the rational function will have a *slant*, or *oblique*, asymptote, which is a line that is neither horizontal nor vertical.

Graph the function $y = \dfrac{x^2}{x - 1}$ using a handheld. Identify the asymptotes.

Step 1 Press ⌂. Then choose ② to select **Graphs & Geometry**.

Step 2 Input $x^2 \div (x + 1)$.

Step 3 Press menu. Select **Trace**, and then choose **Graph Trace**. Use ◀ ▶ to examine the coordinates on the graph for the vertical asymptote.

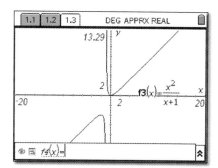

So the graph has two asymptotes, a vertical asymptote at $x = -1$, and a *slant* asymptote.

▶You can find the slant asymptote by performing long division. The slant asymptote is the polynomial part of the answer.

Graph the function $y = \dfrac{x^2 + 3x + 2}{x - 1}$ using a handheld. Identify the asymptotes.

Step 1 Press ⌂. Then choose ② to select **Graphs & Geometry**.

Step 2 Input $(x^2 + 3x + 2) \div (x - 1)$.

Step 3 Press menu. Select **Trace**, and then choose **Graph Trace**. Use ◀ ▶ to examine the coordinates on the graph for the vertical asymptote.

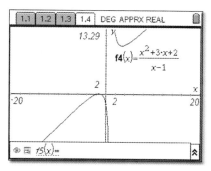

To find the slant asymptote divide: $x - 1 \overline{)\, x^2 + 3x + 2}$ with quotient $x + 4 \ \text{R}6$

$y = x + 4$ is the polynomial part of the answer, and $\dfrac{6}{x - 1}$ is the remainder.

So the graph has two asymptotes, a vertical asymptote at $x = 1$, and a slant asymptote at $y = x + 4$.

Try These

Use a handheld to graph the function. Identify any vertical or horizontal asymptotes.

1. $y = \dfrac{7}{x - 10}$

2. $y = \dfrac{1}{x} + 6$

3. $y = \dfrac{x^2}{x + 1} + 5$

4. Discuss and Write Compare the graphs of $y = \dfrac{1}{x}$ and $y = -\dfrac{1}{x}$.

Go to ▶ **PRACTICE BOOK Lesson 13-6 for exercise sets.**

13-7

Technology:
Graph Radical Functions

Objective To use a handheld to graph radical functions

At the ABC Storage facility, the area of a four-sided storage pod is represented by x square units. What equation can be written and graphed representing the side length of the storage pod?

Since a four equal sided pod is a square shape, the side length of a square *is equal to* the square root of its area. Graph the equation $y = \sqrt{x}$ using a handheld.

Step 1 Press ⌂. Then choose **2** to select **Graphs & Geometry**.

Step 2 Input $\sqrt{x}$. Use **ctrl** **√x²** for the radical symbol.

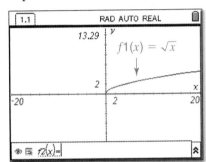

> **Remember:** The domain and range of the square-root function are both *nonnegative numbers*.

So the smooth curve above represents the side length of the pod, which is $y = \sqrt{x}$.

► You can use the **Trace** command to find the approximate side length of the storage pod if its area is 5 square yards.

Step 3 Press **menu**. Select **Trace**, and then choose **Graph Trace**.

Step 4 Press **menu**. Select **Trace**, and then choose **Trace Settings**. Change **Trace Step** to 1, then press **tab** **enter** for **OK**.

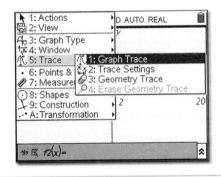

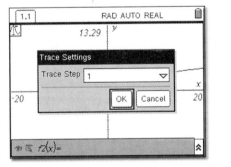

Step 5 Press ▶ to move the trace along the line until the x-coordinate of the graph equals 5. The y-coordinate is 2.23607.

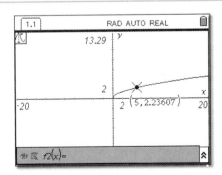

So the side length is about 2.24 yards.

Examples

Graph each radical function using a handheld. Compare this graph to the graph of $y = \sqrt{x}$ shown on the top of page 348.

1 Graph: $y = \sqrt{x} + 3$

Step 1 Press ⌂. Then choose **2** to select **Graphs & Geometry**.

Step 2 Input $\sqrt{x} + 3$. Use ctrl ⁿ√x² for the radical symbol.

.Hint........................

Press ▶ to move the cursor out from under the radical sign before typing + 3.
....

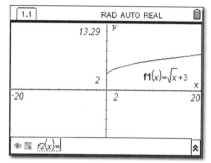

The graph $y = \sqrt{x} + 3$ is shifted *3 units up* from the location of the graph $y = \sqrt{x}$.

2 Graph: $y = \sqrt{x + 4}$

Step 1 Press ⌂. Then choose **2** to select **Graphs & Geometry**.

Step 2 Input $\sqrt{x + 4}$. Use ctrl ⁿ√x² for the radical symbol.

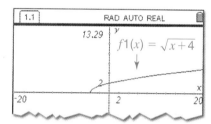

The graph $y = \sqrt{x + 4}$ is shifted *4 units left* from the location of the graph $y = \sqrt{x}$.

3 Graph: $y = \sqrt{x + 4} + 3$

Step 1 Press ⌂. Then choose **2** to select **Graphs & Geometry**.

Step 2 Input $\sqrt{x + 4} + 3$. Use ctrl ⁿ√x² for the radical symbol.

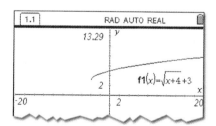

The graph is shifted *4 units left* and *3 units up* from the location of the graph $y = \sqrt{x}$.

Try These

Use a handheld to graph the radical functions.

1. $y = \sqrt{5x}$

2. $y = \sqrt{x} + 7$

3. $y = \sqrt{x - 9}$

4. $y = \sqrt{3x - 6}$

5. $y = \sqrt{-x + 8}$

6. $y = \sqrt{6x + 1} + 4$

7. Discuss and Write Compare the graphs of $y = \sqrt{x}$, $y = -\sqrt{x}$, and $y = \sqrt{-x}$.

  PRACTICE BOOK Lesson 13-7 for exercise sets.

13-8

Technology:
Compare Exponential Growth and Decay

Objective To use a handheld to compare exponential growth and decay

The half-life of a substance is the time it takes for half of the substance to decay. Uranium-238 has a half-life of about 4.5 billion years. What equation can be written to represent the amount of 5 grams of Uranium-238 remaining after x half-lives?

Let y represent the amount of Uranium-238 remaining after x half-lives.

Therefore the exponential decay function for this situation is $y = 5\left(\frac{1}{2}\right)^x$.

▶ You can use a handheld to graph an exponential decay function.

Step 1   Press ⌂ . Then choose ② to select **Graphs & Geometry**.

Step 2   Input $5\left(\frac{1}{2}\right)^x$.

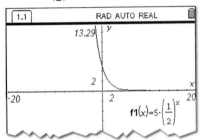

> **Hint**
> Exponential decay graphs *slope downward*, while exponential growth graphs *slope upward*.

▶ You can use the **Trace** command to find how much of the 5 grams of Uranium-238 is left after 9 billion years.

The half-life is 4.5 billion years, so 9 billion years equals 2 half-lives.

Step 3   Press menu . Select **Trace**, and then choose **Graph Trace**.

Step 4   Press menu . Select **Trace**, and then choose **Trace Settings**. Change **Trace Step** to 1, then press tab enter for **OK**.

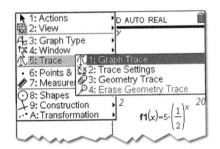

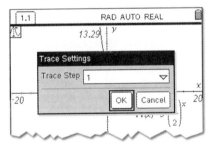

Step 5   Press ▶ to move the trace along the line until the x-coordinate of the graph equals 2. The y-coordinate is 1.25.

So there are 1.25 grams of Uranium-238 remaining after 9 billion years.

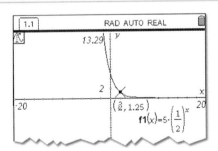

▶ You can also use a handheld to graph an exponential growth function.

Rodney deposits $1000 into an account that pays 5% interest compounded annually. Marcello deposits $900 into an account that pays 3% interest compounded semi-annually. How long will it take for Marcello to have more money in his account than Rodney? Round the answer up to the nearest half year.

Let *f1* represent the amount in Rodney's account and *f2* the amount in Marcello's account. Let *x* represent the number of years.

Then: $f1(x) = 1000(1.05)^x$ and $f2(x) = 900(1.03)^{2x}$.

Step 1   Press 🏠. Then choose **2** to select **Graphs & Geometry**.

Step 2   Press menu **4** for **Window** and **1** for **Window Settings**. Input 0 for **XMin**, 20 for **XMax**, 800 for **YMin**, and 2000 for **YMax**.

Step 3   Input $f1(x) = 1000(1.05)^x$ and $f2(x) = 900(1.03)^{2x}$.

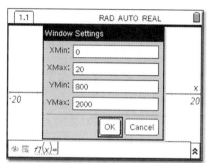

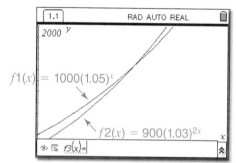

Step 4   Press menu. Select **Trace** and then choose **Graph Trace**.

Step 5   Press menu. Select **Trace** and then choose **Trace Settings**. Change the trace step to 0.5.

Step 6   Press ▶ to move the trace along the line until the first point after the intersection of the lines. The point is (10.5, 1669.12)

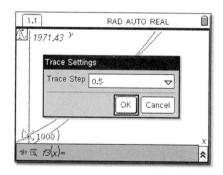

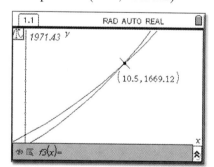

So Marcello will have more money in his account after 10 years 6 months.

Try These

Use a handheld to graph the function. Determine if it represents exponential growth or decay.

1. $y = 0.75^x$ **2.** $y = 4^{2x}$ **3.** $y = 0.2(1.8)^x$ **4.** $y = 4.75 + 2(0.3)^x$

5. Discuss and Write If *a* is not equal to 0, will the exponential growth or decay function $y = a^x$ have any *x*-intercepts? Explain your answer.

PRACTICE BOOK **Lesson 13-8 for exercise sets.**

Problem-Solving Strategy:
Organize Data

Objective To solve problems using the strategy *Organize Data*

Problem I: A survey of 58 high school athletes found that 40 play football, 20 play baseball, and 12 play basketball. Exactly 9 play only baseball. No athlete plays all three sports, but each athlete plays at least one of the three sports. How many play both football and basketball, but not baseball?

Read **Read to understand what is being asked.**

List the facts and restate the question.

Facts: 58 athletes play football, baseball, or basketball.

40 play football, 20 play baseball, and 12 play basketball.

9 play only baseball.

No athlete plays all three sports; each athlete plays at least one sport.

Question: How many play both football and basketball, but not baseball?

Plan **Select a strategy.**

Use the strategy *Organize Data*. A Venn diagram can help you figure out how many athletes are in each category.

Problem-Solving Strategies

1. Make a Drawing
2. Solve a Simpler Problem
3. Reason Logically
4. Consider Extreme Cases
5. Work Backward
6. Find a Pattern
7. Account for All Possibilities
8. Adopt a Different Point of View
9. Guess and Test
10. **Organize Data**

Solve **Apply the strategy.**

Draw three overlapping circles to represent the three sports. In the figure at the right below, the lettered regions represent the six possible categories. To find the number of athletes who play football and basketball, but not baseball, find F.

- Add the number of athletes in each sport.
  $40 + 20 + 12 = 72$

- Subtract 58, the total number of athletes, from 72 to find the sum of D + E + F.
  $72 - 58 = 14 \longrightarrow D + E + F = 14$

- Subtract 9, the number in B, from 20, the number of athletes who play baseball, to find D + E.
  $20 - 9 = 11 \longrightarrow D + E = 11$

- Subtract (D + E) from (D + E + F) to find F.
  $(D + E + F) - (D + E) = F \longrightarrow 14 - 11 = 3 \longrightarrow F = 3$

So 3 athletes play football and basketball, but not baseball.

Football (total 40)   **Baseball (total 20)**

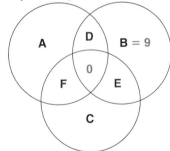

Basketball (total 12)

Check **Check to make sure your answer makes sense.**

Check that the given information is satisfied by your solution using logical reasoning.

Given that there are a total of 58 athletes surveyed and 72 are in all sports, 14 can only play two sports. Since 20 athletes play baseball and 9 *only* play baseball, the sum of the athletes that play both baseball and another sport must be 11. So (14 − 11), or 3, athletes play both football and basketball, but not baseball.

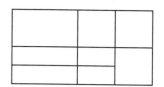

Problem 2: How many rectangles are in this figure?

Read **Read to understand what is being asked.**

List the facts and restate the question.

Facts: A figure includes several (overlapping and nonoverlapping) rectangles.

Question: How many rectangles are in the figure in all?

Plan **Select a strategy.**

You can use the strategy *Organize Data* to count and keep track of the rectangles.

Solve **Apply the strategy.**

Reconstruct the final figure one step at a time, keeping track of the number of new rectangles introduced at each step. Label the vertices, so you can list the rectangles.

Step 1

1 new rectangle:
ABCD

Step 2

2 new rectangles:
AEFD, EBCF

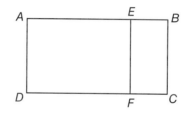

Step 3

3 new rectangles:
AGHD, GEFH, GBCH

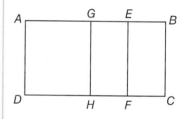

Step 4

12 new rectangles: *AGJI, AEKI, ABLI, GEKJ, GBLJ, EBLK, IJHD, IKFD, ILCD, JKFH, JLCH, KLCF*

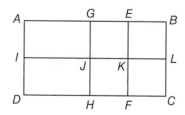

Step 5

9 new rectangles: *AGQP, AERP, GERQ, IJQP, IKRP, JKRQ, PQHD, PRFD, QRFH*

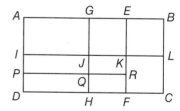

So there are 1 + 2 + 3 + 12 + 9, or 27, rectangles in the figure in all.

Check **Check to make sure your answer makes sense.**

Review the work above to check that every new rectangle is listed at each step. You should find that it is.

You could solve the problem again, building the figure in a different way, to see if you get the same result. (For example, in Step 2, draw the horizontal segment that extends across the figure, instead of the vertical segment.) You should get a total of 27 rectangles no matter how you build the figure.

Go to **PRACTICE BOOK Lesson 13-9 for exercise sets.**

Enrichment:
Geometric Series

Objective To compute partial sums of geometric series

Suppose you are on a game show. You are standing 128 feet from the grand prize. All you have to do is go get it. However, you must follow these rules:

- Walk halfway to the prize and then stop.
- Walk half the remaining distance to the prize and then stop.
- Continue this process of walking half the remaining distance and stopping.

The distances you will walk are 64 ft, 32 ft, 16 ft, 8 ft, 4 ft, 2 ft, and so on, with the distance at each stage half the distance of the stage before. Although you get closer and closer to the prize with every step, you always have some non-zero distance to walk on the next step. You will never reach the prize!

The total distance you would walk on the way to the prize is given by a sum that goes on infinitely: $64 + 32 + 16 + 8 + 4 + 2 + \ldots$

This can also be written as:

$64 + 64 \cdot \dfrac{1}{2} + 64 \cdot \dfrac{1}{4} + 64 \cdot \dfrac{1}{8} + 64 \cdot \dfrac{1}{16} + \ldots$

or

$64 + 64\left(\dfrac{1}{2}\right) + 64\left(\dfrac{1}{2}\right)^2 + 64\left(\dfrac{1}{2}\right)^3 + 64\left(\dfrac{1}{2}\right)^4 + \ldots$

Think
Each term in this sum is $\dfrac{1}{2}$ multiplied by the previous term.

► A sum that goes on infinitely *and* in which each term is some fixed number multiplied by the previous term is called an infinite geometric series. We refer to the fixed number as the *common ratio*. The sum of the first n terms of a series is denoted S_n and is called the nth partial sum. For this series,

$S_1 = 64$ $S_2 = 64 + 32 = 96$ $S_3 = 64 + 32 + 16 = 112$

$S_4 = 64 + 32 + 16 + 8 = 120$ $S_5 = 64 + 32 + 16 + 8 + 4 = 124$

Note that the partial sums get *closer and closer* to 128, which is equal to the distance to the prize, 128 ft. If you kept computing partial sums, you would find that

$S_{10} = 127.875$ $S_{20} = 127.99987793\ldots,$ $S_{30} = 127.999999881\ldots$

Although no partial sum will ever actually be 128, you can get as close to 128 as you add more and more terms. So 128 is the *sum* of the series. However, not all geometric series have sums; some have partial sums that get greater and greater without bound. There is a formula for finding partial sums.

___ **Key Concept** ___

Sum of a Geometric Series

$S_n = a\left(\dfrac{1 - r^n}{1 - r}\right)$, where S_n is the sum of n terms,

a is the first term of the series, and

r is the common ratio.

- Find the sum of the first 5 terms of the geometric series given on the previous page using the formula for sum of a geometric series.

  $a = 64, r = \frac{1}{2},$ and $n = 5.$

  $$S_5 = 64\left(\frac{1 - \left(\frac{1}{2}\right)^5}{1 - \frac{1}{2}}\right) = 124.$$

- Use the formula and your handheld device to find S_5 and S_{10} for this geometric series:

  $$100 + 100(0.8) + 100(0.8)^2 + 100(0.8)^3 + 100(0.8)^4 + \ldots$$

  $a = 100, r = 0.8,$ and $n = 5; 10$

  $$S_5 = 100\left(\frac{1 - 0.8^5}{1 - 0.8}\right) = 336.16 \qquad S_{10} = 100\left(\frac{1 - 0.8^{10}}{1 - 0.8}\right) \approx 446.313$$

▶Geometric series have real-world application.
Suppose you deposit $100 into an account at the start of each month. The account earns 6% interest a year, compounded monthly, which is $6\% \div 12$, or 0.5%, interest each month. This means the balance is multiplied by 1.005 each month. The table below shows how the balance grows.

Month	Balance	
1	100	No interest has been earned yet.
2	$100 + 100\,(1.005)$	New $100 deposit has earned no interest; Month 1 deposit has earned one month's interest.
3	$100 + 100\,(1.005) + 100\,(1.005)^2$	New deposit has earned no interest; Month 2 deposit has earned 1 month's interest; Month 1 deposit has earned 2 month's interest.
4	$100 + 100\,(1.005) + 100(1.005)^2 + 100\,(1.005)^3$	New deposit has earned no interest; Month 3 deposit has earned 1 month's interest; Month 2 deposit has earned 2 month's interest; Month 1 deposit has earned 3 month's interest.

The pattern of growth in the balance is a geometric series:
$$100 + 100(1.005) + 100(1.005)^2 + 100(1.005)^3 + 100(1.005)^4 + 100(1.005)^5 + \ldots$$

You can use the formula for S_n to find the value of the account after any number of months. (In this situation, $a = 100$ and $r = 1.005$.)

After 7 months: $\quad S_7 = 100\left(\frac{1 - (1.005)^7}{1 - 1.005}\right) \approx 710.59$

After 60 months (5 years): $\quad S_{60} = 100\left(\frac{1 - (1.005)^{60}}{1 - 1.005}\right) \approx 6977$

Try These

Find S_4 and S_{20} for each geometric series.

1. $10 + 10\left(\frac{1}{3}\right) + 10\left(\frac{1}{3}\right)^2 + 10\left(\frac{1}{3}\right)^3 + \ldots$ **2.** $25 + 25(1.2) + 25(1.2)^2 + 25(1.3)^3 + \ldots$

3. Discuss and Write The geometric series, $12 + 12\left(\frac{1}{4}\right) + 12\left(\frac{1}{4}\right)^2 + 12\left(\frac{1}{4}\right)^3 + \ldots,$ has a sum. What do you think the sum is? Explain how you found your answer.

Go to ▶ **PRACTICE BOOK pages 351–352 for exercise sets.**

Test Prep: Multiple-Choice Questions
Strategy: Apply Mathematical Reasoning

When answering test questions, it can be helpful to think about a *related problem*. Sometimes breaking a question up into smaller parts can help you to figure out a solution process.

Look at the sample test item.

Sample Test Item

Hank buys a new computer for $1500. Each year, it loses value at a rate of 5%. About how much will the computer be worth after 3 years?

A. $1275   C. $1353.75

B. $1286.06   D. $1485

Read the whole test item, including the answer choices.

- Underline important words.

  Each year, the computer loses value at a rate of 5%.

  Losing value means you need to subtract 5% of the value each year.

- Restate the question in your own words.

  Subtract 5% of the value at the end of each year 3 times.

Solve the problem.

- Use the Test-Prep Strategy.

  To solve this problem, find the computer's calculated worth after each of the 3 passing years. Subtract the 5% lost value from the prior years calculated worth.

  $1500 - (0.05)1500 = 1425$ ←This is the value of the computer at the end of the *first year*.

  $1425 - (0.05)1425 = 1353.75$ ←This is the value at the end of the *second year*.

  $1353.75 - (0.05)1353.75 \approx 1286.06$ ←This is the value at the end of the *third year*.

Test-Taking Tips

- Underline important words.
- Restate the question.
- Use the Test-Prep strategy.
- Apply appropriate rules, definitions, properties, or strategies.
- Analyze and eliminate answer choices.

Item Analysis

Choose the answer.

- Analyze and eliminate answer choices. Watch out for distractors.

  A. $1275 ←$75 was subtracted each year, not 5% of the new value.

  B. $1286.06 ←This is the correct choice!

  C. $1353.75 ←This is the value after 2 years.

  D. $1485 ←$5 was subtracted at the end of each year.

Try These

1. Jackie puts $700 into a certificate of deposit that earns 6% annual interest. What is the approximate value of the certificate after 5 years?

   A. $883.73   C. $936.76

   B. $910   D. $992.96

2. If it takes 8 people 6.5 days to paint a house, approximately how many people would be needed in order to paint the house in no more than 5 days?

   F. 6   H. 10

   G. 7   J. 11

Go to PRACTICE BOOK page 353 for exercise sets.

CHAPTER 14

Data Analysis and Probability

In This Chapter You Will:

- Identify populations and samples for surveys
- Recognize different sampling techniques; identify bias in a sample, question, or display
- Find measures of central tendency and the range of a data set
- Organize and display data in stem-and-leaf, box-and-whisker, and scatter plots
- Find the experimental or theoretical probability of an event
- Compute probabilities of independent and dependent events
- Compute probabilities of mutually exclusive or overlapping events
- Find the number of permutations or combinations in a set of objects
- Solve problems using a variety of strategies
- Look for new vocabulary words **highlighted** in each lesson

Do You Remember?

- Graphs are pictorial representations of data.
- A bar graph is a graph that uses bars to compare sets of data.
- An interval is the number of units between spaces on a graph.
- An outcome is the result of a probability experiment.
- An event is a set of one or more outcomes of a probability experiment.

For Practice Exercises:

 Go to **PRACTICE BOOK, pp. 359–400**

For Chapter Support: (ONLINE)

 Go to **www.progressinmathematics.com**

- Skills Update Practice
- Practice Activities
- Audio Glossary
- Vocabulary Activities
- Technology Videos
- Enrichment Activities
- Electronic SourceBook

 VIRTUAL MANIPULATIVES

Critical Thinking

A survey of 110 college freshmen found that 25 freshmen took psychology, 45 took speech, 48 took mathematics, 10 took psychology and mathematics, 8 took speech and mathematics, 6 took psychology and speech, and 5 took all three subjects. How many of those surveyed did not take any of the three subjects?

Sampling Techniques

Objective To identify populations and samples for surveys • To categorize the nature of the data variable • To recognize different sampling techniques • To identify bias in a sample, question, or display

Darlene wants to determine students' preferences for the location of the 9th-grade, end-of-the-year field trip. How can she find out?

To find out students' preferences, Darlene can conduct a *survey*.

▶ A survey is a method of gathering information about a group. Surveys are usually made up of questions or other items that require responses. The entire group of individuals or objects considered for a survey is called the population.

If it is not practical to survey an entire population, a small part of the population, called a sample, is used. A sample is said to be a representative sample if it has characteristics similar to the entire population. In the situation above, the population is the entire 9th grade. Darlene could choose a sample in many ways, such as surveying students in her biology class.

Identify the population and sample.

Brad goes door to door in his neighborhood to ask people who they will vote for in a town election.

Population: the registered voters in the town   Sample: Brad's neighbors

▶ A variable is a characteristic that differs for various subjects in a survey. Variables can be qualitative or quantitative. Qualitative variables are descriptive and can be separated by category, such as favorite colors. Quantitative variables can be measured or counted, such as heights or the number of students in each math class.

A researcher counts the number of fish in several sections of a pond to estimate the total number of fish in the entire pond. Identify the population, the sample, and the variable. Tell whether the variable is qualitative or quantitative.

population: the entire pond
  sample: the sections of the pond
 variable: the number of fish; quantitative

Examples

Identify the population, the sample, and the variable.
Tell whether the variable is qualitative or quantitative.

1 A gardener writes down each type of flower found in several sections of a wildflower field to find the types of flowers growing in the field.

population: the entire field of flowers
  sample: the sections of the field
 variable: the type of flower; qualitative

2 In order to find the average commuting distance for all of its employees, a company surveys 25 employees to determine the distance they commute to work.

population: all employees
  sample: 25 employees
 variable: the distance that each employee commutes; quantitative

▶ There are different methods of selecting a sample. The table below shows these sampling methods.

Sampling Methods		
Method	**Definition**	**Example**
Convenience Sampling	The sample consists of an easily accessible subset of the population.	In a survey of students who play basketball, Anne surveys members of her basketball team.
Systematic Sampling	A rule is applied to choose the sample.	Every 50th person in the phone book is called.
Cluster Sampling	The population is divided into groups, and a sample is chosen from each group.	Five residents from each of 20 counties are surveyed.
Voluntary Response Sampling	The sample consists of volunteers who choose to participate.	An online survey is conducted.
Random Sampling	All members of the population are equally likely to be chosen.	Students' names are put in a hat and pulled at random.
Stratified Sampling	Subgroups are chosen randomly.	In a citywide school survey, 5 districts are randomly chosen, and 50 students are randomly chosen from each district.

Examples

Identify the sampling method used.

1 A town is divided into 10 different voting districts. Residents from 3 different voting districts are polled.

The population is divided into groups, and members from several of the groups are chosen. This is cluster sampling.

2 In a statewide survey, 5 counties are randomly chosen, and 100 people are randomly chosen from each county.

The 5 counties are the random subgroups. People are chosen randomly from within the counties. This is stratified sampling.

3 Marvin goes door to door in his neighborhood to get opinions about the construction of a new shopping center in town.

A neighborhood is an easy place to conduct a survey. This is convenience sampling.

4 A computer generates the names of 5000 people at random, who will be asked about their number of family members.

Each person is equally likely to be chosen. This is random sampling.

▶ Sometimes survey results may be affected by a bias in the survey or a flaw in the sampling procedure. A bias is anything that favors a particular outcome. A biased sample will not be representative of the population under study.

If Darlene's survey in the opening problem is conducted in a biology class, the students in this class may be more likely to choose a trip to the science museum. The sample is biased and will not be representative of the entire 9th grade.

Continue Lesson ➡

Determine whether or not the sample may be biased. Explain.

1 People at a music store are asked how much money they spend on music each month.

The sample may be biased because the people in the store are more likely to spend money on music while others may spend none.

2 A baseball team is polled to determine how to allocate next year's funds for various athletic programs.

The sample may be biased because the players may be more likely to want more money for the baseball team than any other athletic program.

3 A teacher puts the names of all of the students in a hat and draws 5 names to ask what day they would like to have the test.

This is a random sample. It is unlikely to be biased.

4 Pop music concert goers are asked to complete a survey about their favorite genre of music.

The sample may be biased because most concert goers are likely to choose pop music.

▶ When you conduct a survey, you need to phrase the questions so that the responses accurately reflect the views of the people surveyed. Sometimes questions are biased. A biased question suggests or leads to a specific response or excludes a certain group.

Peter and Dan want to find the favorite spectator sport of the students in school. Peter asks, "Which sport do you think is the most fun to watch?" Dan asks, "Don't you think baseball is the most fun sport to watch?" Explain whose question is biased.

Dan's question is biased toward baseball.

Example

1 Lois surveys her classmates about their favorite kind of cereal. She asks, "What is your favorite kind of cereal?" Is the survey question biased or not? Explain.

The question is not biased. It does not try to persuade the person to respond to a particular kind of cereal.

▶ Data displays such as graphs can be biased and can influence how results are interpreted. For example, art is often used to make a graph more interesting, but it can distort the relationships in the data. These are called misleading graphs.

Look at the bar graph at the right.

Because the scale does not start at 0, the bar for Brand B appears to be three times as tall as the bar for Brand A. In fact, the useful life of Brand B is only about 22% longer than Brand A.

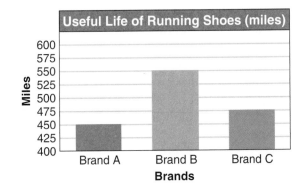

Example

1 Explain how the data display can influence how the results are interpreted.

Different-sized icons represent the same number of vehicles. The number of light trucks is close to one third the number of cars, but in the graph, it looks like more than half. The number of heavy trucks is less than 5% of the total, but it appears much greater.

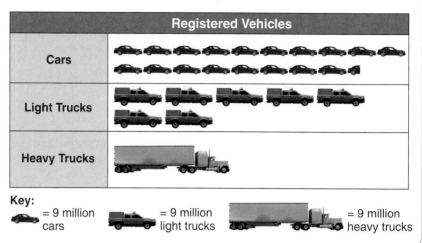

Registered Vehicles

Cars	
Light Trucks	
Heavy Trucks	

Key:
= 9 million cars   = 9 million light trucks   = 9 million heavy trucks

Try These

Identify the population, sample, and variable. Tell whether the variable is qualitative or quantitative.

1. A count of students is taken on 8 school buses to estimate the number of students who ride buses to school.

2. One hundred registered voters are called to determine whom they will vote for in the election.

Identify the sampling method used.

3. Customers are asked to review products online.

4. Bridget asks her friends for the number of siblings they have.

Determine whether or not the sample may be biased. Explain.

5. Mr. Jackson chooses two names out of a hat to determine who will become class representatives.

6. Customers at a car dealership are asked about the age of their current car to estimate the ages of cars driven in the United States.

Tell whether the survey question is biased or not. Explain.

7. Is pizza your favorite choice for lunch?

8. What is your favorite school subject?

9. **Discuss and Write** A survey was conducted on ticket prices for baseball and basketball games in Tony's hometown. The data is displayed at the right. Explain how the data display can influence how the results are interpreted.

Ticket Prices

$75
$60
$45
$30
$15
$0
2001   2008   2001   2008
Baseball   Basketball

14-2

Measures of Central Tendency and Range

Objective To find measures of central tendency and the range of a data set • To determine which measure of central tendency best describes a data set • To recognize how outliers and linear transformations of data affect the measures of central tendency

The points scored by the Hamilton Hurricanes in the games they won in the regular football season are 24, 16, 35, 31, 33, 13, 16, 21, 16, 38.

To analyze and describe the data, you can use the mean, median, mode, or range.

► The mean, median, and mode of a data set are called measures of central tendency. They indicate where the greatest number of items in the data set are concentrated. The measure closest to most of the data in the set best describes the data.

- mean = $\frac{243}{10}$ = 24.3   **Think**.........................
  243 is the sum of the data.

  The average number of points scored per game is 24.3.

- median: First arrange the data values in numerical order.
  13, 16, 16, 16, 21, 24, 31, 33, 35, 38

  $\frac{21 + 24}{2}$ = 22.5

  The median is the mean of the 5th and 6th values.

- mode: The most frequent value in the data is the mode, which is 16.

- range = 38 − 13 = 25

  The range, 25, shows how far the data is spread out from the greatest score to the least score.

Since the mean and median are each close in value to most of the data, the mean or the median best describes the data.

_____ **Key Concept** _____

Measures of Central Tendency and Range

Mean: the average number. Add all the values in the data set, and divide by the total number of values in the set. The mean works best for sets with no very high or low numbers.

Median: the middle number, or the mean of the two middle numbers, in an ordered data set. The median works best when there is an item that is much higher/lower than most of the others.

Mode: the number(s) that occur most often. A data set may have one mode, more than one mode, or no mode. The mode works best when there are many identical cluster numbers.

Range: the difference between the greatest and the least values in a data set

Example

1 Find the mean, median, mode(s), and range of the following data set: 100, 52, 57, 53, 50, 60, 62. Determine which measure of central tendency best describes the data.

- mean = $\frac{434}{7}$ = 62   **Think**...........
  434 is the sum of the data.

- median: 50, 52, 53, 57, 60, 62, 100
  median

- No data value occurs more than any other. There is no mode.

- range: 100 − 50 = 50

Since the median is close in value to most of the data, the median best describes the data.

▶Outliers are numbers set apart from the rest of the data. A set of data may have no outliers, or it may have one or more outliers. Outliers can affect the measures of central tendency and range of a data set.

The number 100 is an outlier of the data set in example 1 on page 362. Find the mean, median, mode, and range of the data set in example 1 on page 362 *without* the outlier. Describe what effect the outlier has on the mean, median, mode, and range of the data set.

• mean $= \dfrac{334}{6} \approx 55.7$ **Think**..........
  334 is the sum
  of the data.

• median: 50, 52, 53, 57, 60, 62
  $\dfrac{53 + 57}{2} = 55$

• No data value occurs more than
  any other. There is no mode.

• range: $62 - 50 = 12$

When the outlier is not included in the data set, the mean decreases by $(62 - 55.7)$, or 6.3; the median decreases by $(57 - 55)$, or 2; there still is no mode; the range decreases by $(50 - 12)$, or 38.

▶A linear transformation of a data set involves multiplying by or adding the same number to each member of the data set. These transformations can affect the measures of central tendency and range of the data set.

Determine the effect on the mean, median, mode, and range of the data set in example 1 on page 362 if you multiply each data value by 2.

The new data values would be 200, 104, 114, 106, 100, 120, and 124.

• mean $= \dfrac{868}{7} = 124$ **Think**..........
  868 is the sum
  of the data.

• median: 100, 104, 106, 114, 120, 124, 200
  median

• No data value occurs more than
  any other. There is no mode.

• range: $200 - 100 = 100$

Doubling each value in the data set doubles the mean, median, and range. There still is no mode.

Try These

Find the mean, median, mode(s), and range of each data set. Determine which measure of central tendency best describes the data.

1. 16, 11, 12, 12, 11, 18   **2.** 49, 46, 50, 18, 49, 48   **3.** 18, 30, 44, 22, 36, 26

4. Identify the outlier of the data set in exercise 2. Find the mean, median, mode(s), and range of the data set *without* the outlier. Then describe what effect the outlier has on the mean, median, mode, and range of the data set.

Use the data set in exercise 3. Determine the effect of each linear transformation on the range, mean, median, and mode.

5. Add 20 to each number.   **6.** Divide each number by 2.

7. Discuss and Write How does multiplying each member of a data set by a number c change the range, mean, median, and mode?

Go to ▶ PRACTICE BOOK **Lesson 14-2 for exercise sets.**

Stem-and-Leaf Plots

Objective To organize and display data in single and back-to-back stem-and-leaf plots
• To analyze data on stem-and-leaf plots

▶A stem-and-leaf plot is a type of graph that arranges numerical data in order of place value. It separates each number in a data set into two parts, called a stem and a leaf. The stem is the front-end digit(s) of each number, and the leaf is the digit with the least place value.

Organize and display the data at the right in a *stem-and-leaf plot*.

To make a stem-and-leaf plot:

• Label two table columns *Stem* and *Leaf*.

• Use all the digits to the left of the last digit of each number as the *Stem*. List these digits in increasing order down the *Stem* column.

• Use the far right digit of each number for the *Leaf*. Write each *Leaf* to the right of its *Stem* in increasing order.

• Write a *key* to show the meaning of each number in the plot.

• Write a *title* for the graph.

Daily High Temperature (°F)		
Day	Week 1	Week 2
Sun.	78°	67°
Mon.	74°	71°
Tues.	69°	79°
Wed.	73°	85°
Thurs.	82°	81°
Fri.	77°	86°
Sat.	70°	74°

Temperatures range from 67° to 86°, so stems are 6 to 8.

Daily High Temperatures (°F)

Stem	Leaf
6	7 9
7	0 1 3 4 4 7 8 9
8	1 2 5 6

Key: 6|7 represents 67.

▶To analyze and describe the data on a stem-and-leaf plot, find the measures of central tendency and the range of the data.

Find the mean, median, and mode of the data on the stem-and-leaf-plot.

• mean $= \dfrac{1066}{14} \approx 76.14$ **Think**......... 1066 is the sum of the data.

The average daily high temperature is about 76.14°F.

• Count the data to find the middle value. There are 14 values in all, so the median is the mean of the 7th and 8th values, which is $\dfrac{74 + 77}{2}$, or 75.5.

• The most frequent value in the data is the mode, which is 74.

Since the mean, median, and mode are each close in value to most of the data, the mean, the median, or the mode best describes the data.

▶If you are given a stem-and-leaf plot, you can use it to list the data values.

Find the data values in the given stem-and-leaf plot at the right.

The key tells you that the stem is the tens digit and the leaf is the ones digit.

So the data values are: 10, 11, 11, 11, 21, 22, 25, 25, 28, 40, 44, and 46.

**School Activities
Club Members**

Stem	Leaf
1	0 1 1 1
2	1 2 5 5 8
3	
4	0 4 6

Key: 1|0 represents 10.

If there are no leaves listed next to a stem, then there are no data values associated with that stem.

Example

1. Make a stem-and-leaf plot of the data in the table shown at the right.

Let each whole-number part be the stem and each decimal part be the leaf. The stems will range from 14 to 17.

• Write each stem on the left-hand side.

• Write each corresponding leaf in ascending order on the right-hand side. Notice that there is no number with a stem of 16, so there is no corresponding leaf.

• Write the key at the bottom.

100-Meter Run Times for 10 Runners (in seconds)
14.9, 15.7, 17.2, 14.8, 15, 15.3, 14.8, 17.7, 17.2, 14.8

100-Meter Run Times for 10 Runners (in seconds)

Stem	Leaf
14	8 8 8 9
15	0 3 7
16	
17	2 2 7

Key: 14|8 represents 14.8.

▶ A back-to-back stem-and-leaf plot, also called a *double stem-and-leaf plot*, can be used to display two sets of related data. The *stems* are in the center, and the *leaves* increase in value from the stem.

How can the data below be displayed in a back-to-back stem-and-leaf plot?

Weights of Male and Female Golden Retrievers (in pounds)	
Female Golden Retrievers	52, 53, 53, 55, 58, 62, 64, 66, 67, 70
Male Golden Retrievers	58, 59, 60, 61, 64, 64, 67, 69, 71, 73

To make a back-to-back stem-and-leaf plot:

• Set up a three-column stem-and-leaf plot.

• Use the tens digits of each number as the *Stem*. Write the tens digits in the center in order down the *Stem* column.

• Use the ones digit of each number as the *Leaf*. Write the ones digits to the left or right in order from their *Stem* outward.

• Include a *key* and a *title*.

Weights of Male and Female Golden Retrievers (in pounds)

Golden Retriever Female Leaf	Stem	Golden Retriever Male Leaf
8 5 3 3 2	5	8 9
7 6 4 2	6	0 1 4 4 7 9
0	7	1 3

Key: 2|5|8 represents 52 and 58.

Try These

Make a stem-and-leaf plot for each data set. Then find the measures of central tendency for each data set.

1.

60-Point Reading Test Scores
58, 39, 40, 58, 51, 32, 52, 43, 45, 36, 24, 39

2.

Softball Throw Distances (in meters)
8, 14, 34, 9, 2, 31, 31, 36, 32, 19, 16, 10

3. List the data values shown in the back-to-back stem-and-leaf plot at the right. Explain your answer.

4. **Discuss and Write** Explain why it is important to give a key when making a stem-and-leaf plot.

Printing Rate of Machines A and B (pages per min)

Machine A Leaf	Stems	Machine B Leaf
6 3 2	10	1 2 4 4 5 8
8 7 3 3 0	11	2 4 5 9
4	12	0 0 3 4
6 1 0 0 0	13	

Key: 2|10|1 represents 102 and 101.

Go to PRACTICE BOOK **Lesson 14-3 for exercise sets.**

Histograms

Objective To create frequency tables and histograms • To analyze histograms

Paolo conducted a survey of his class to determine how much time students spend online each day. The tally chart at the right shows the results. How else can Paolo organize and display the data he collected?

Paolo can make a frequency table and then a histogram to organize and display the data.

► A frequency table shows the frequency of each data value. If the data are divided into intervals, the table shows the frequency of each interval.

Notice that the data in the tally chart are already grouped into equal intervals.

To make a frequency table, list the intervals in the first column of the table. Count the number of tallies in each interval, and write the frequency of each interval as a number. Give the table a title.

Use the intervals and frequencies to construct a histogram.

► A histogram is a bar graph that shows the frequency of equal intervals of data. There are no spaces between the bars unless there is an interval with a frequency of 0.

Time Spent Online	
Number of Minutes	**Number of Students**
0–19	ЖІ
20–39	ЖІІІ
40–59	ЖЖ
60–79	ЖІ
80–99	ІІІІ
100–119	ІІ

Time Spent Online	
Interval	**Frequency**
0–19	6
20–39	8
40–59	10
60–79	6
80–99	4
100–119	2

Frequency Table

To make a histogram:

• Draw and label the horizontal and vertical axes. Use the intervals in order on the horizontal axis. Use the frequencies, starting at 0, on the vertical axis.

• Determine a scale for the vertical axis. For this graph, use a scale ranging from 0 to 12 to include all of the frequency values. Choose a scale that will allow you to read the values clearly.

• Draw bars to show the frequency of each interval. All bars should be the same width. The sides of the bars should touch but not overlap.

• Write a *title* for the histogram.

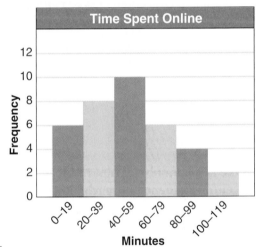

► To analyze data on a histogram, look for trends and patterns by finding intervals where the data are clustered.

• Most data are in the 40–59 minutes interval. Of the 36 students surveyed, $\frac{10}{36}$, or about 28%, spent 40 to 59 minutes online.

• Of those surveyed, there are 14 students who spent less than 40 minutes online, which is $\frac{14}{36}$, or about 39%, of the total frequency.

• Of those surveyed, there are 12 students who spent greater than 59 minutes online, which is $\frac{12}{36}$, or about 33%, of the total frequency.

1 The data in the tally chart below show the ages of students attending a particular dance studio. Construct a histogram using this data.

Age	Number of Students	Age	Number of Students
3	‖	12	卌 卌 卌 卌
4–5	卌 ‖‖	13–14	卌 卌 卌 卌 卌 卌
6–7	卌 卌 ‖	15–17	卌 卌 卌 卌 卌 卌
8	卌 ‖‖	18	卌 卌 ‖
9	卌 卌 卌	19	卌 ‖
10–11	卌 卌 卌 卌 卌	20	‖‖

- Make a frequency table of the data, grouping the data into equal intervals.

  The largest interval given, 15–17, spans three ages. The rest of the data can also be broken into intervals of 3.

- Draw and label the horizontal and vertical axes.

- Determine a scale for the vertical axis. The frequencies are all multiples of 10, so you can use intervals of 10, with the scale ranging from 0 to 50 to include all of the values.

- Draw bars to represent the frequency of each interval.

> **Remember:** There are no gaps between the bars on a histogram.

- Write a title for the histogram.

Ages of Dance Students	
Interval	**Frequency**
3–5	10
6–8	20
9–11	40
12–14	50
15–17	30
18–20	20

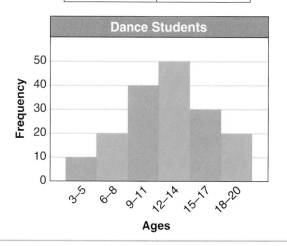

▶ A histogram is a visual summary of a frequency table. You can read information from the graph.

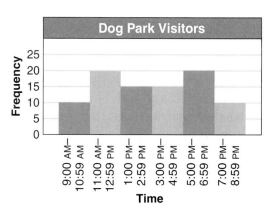

The histogram at the right shows the number of visitors who entered a dog park at different times during one day. The horizontal scale shows times ranging from 9:00 A.M. to 8:59 P.M. in 2-hour intervals. The vertical scale shows the frequency of the data.

Some of the information you can read from the histogram:

- Ten people entered the park between 9:00 A.M. and 10:59 A.M. and also between 7:00 P.M. and 8:59 P.M.

- The least number of people entered the park during the first and last hours of the day.

Continue Lesson ➡

From the histogram on page 367, you can make the frequency table shown at the right. The frequency table can also help you answer questions.

Interval	Frequency
9:00 A.M.–10:59 A.M.	10
11:00 A.M.–12:59 P.M.	20
1:00 P.M.–2:59 P.M.	15
3:00 P.M.–4:59 P.M.	15
5:00 P.M.–6:59 P.M.	20
7:00 P.M.–8:59 P.M.	10

What was total number of visitors before 5:00 P.M.?

$10 + 20 + 15 + 15 = 60$

What was total number of visitors in the park from 9:00 A.M. to 9:00 P.M.?

$10 + 20 + 15 + 15 + 20 + 10 = 90$

▶ A variation of the frequency table is the cumulative frequency table. The graphical display related to a cumulative frequency table is the cumulative frequency histogram.

The data in the frequency table below show how many hours a student spends on school activities each week. Construct a cumulative frequency table and a histogram using this data.

Time Spent on School Activities Each Week						
Hours	1–5	6–10	11–15	16–20	21–25	26–30
Frequency	23	25	18	17	10	7

To construct a cumulative frequency table:

- Add a third row, or a cumulative frequency row, to the table that contains the sum of the frequencies.

Time Spent on School Activities Each Week						
Hours	1–5	6–10	11–15	16–20	21–25	26–30
Frequency	23	25	18	17	10	7
Cumulative Frequency	23	23 + 25 = 48	48 + 18 = 66	66 + 17 = 83	83 + 10 = 93	93 + 7 = 100

- Locate the data intervals in order along the horizontal axis. Choose a scale for the vertical axis.

  Since the greatest cumulative frequency is 100, mark the vertical scale in increments of 20 from 0 to 100.

- For each interval, draw a bar whose height is the cumulative frequency for all the intervals up to and including that interval.

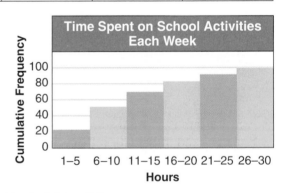

To analyze data on a cumulative frequency histogram, use the heights of the bars. The heights of the bars increase as you read from left to right.

- Of the 100 students surveyed, $\frac{66}{100}$, or 66%, spent less than 16 hours on school activities each week.

- Of those surveyed, there are 93 students who spent at most 25 hours on school activities each week, which is $\frac{93}{100}$, or 93%, of the total frequency.

- Of those surveyed, there are 66 students who spent less than or equal to 15 hours on school activities each week, which is $\frac{66}{100}$, or 66%, of the total frequency.

▶ A cumulative frequency histogram is a visual summary of a cumulative frequency table. You can read information from the graph.

• How many children were weighed?

Read the height of the last bar to get this information. There were 20 children weighed.

• In which interval is the highest frequency?

Look for the largest difference in heights of two adjacent bars, and read the interval for the second of those two bars.

55–59 is the interval in which the highest frequency lies.

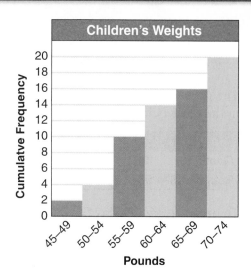

Try These

Make a histogram for each set of data.

1.

Test Scores	
Interval	Frequency
60–69	4
70–79	9
80–89	11
90–99	6
100–109	1

2.

Distance Traveled	
Interval	Frequency
0–19	25
20–39	20
40–59	15
60–79	15
80–99	10

Make a frequency table and a histogram of the data.

3.

Price	Number of Cameras	Price	Number of Cameras
0–$74.99	卌	$200–$224.99	卌
$75–$84.99	l	$225–$299.99	ll
$85–$104.99	卌	$300–$324.99	llll
$105–$149.99	卌 lll	$325–$374.99	ll
$150–$199.99	卌 卌 卌	$375–$449.99	l

Use the histogram at the right to answer the questions.

4. In which months did the greatest number of people join the health club?

5. In which months did the least number of people join the health club?

6. What was the total number of people who joined the health club during the year?

7. How many people joined the health club from May through August?

8. Discuss and Write Explain how to use a frequency table to make a cumulative frequency histogram.

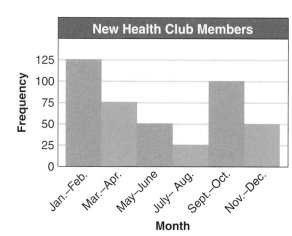

Update your skills. See page 413 XXI.

14-5

Quartiles and Box-and-Whisker Plots

Objective To find the first, second, and third quartiles of a data set • To represent and interpret data on box-and-whisker plots • To analyze box-and-whisker plots

The points scored by a basketball team in 10 games are shown in the table below.

Basketball Scores										
Game	1	2	3	4	5	6	7	8	9	10
Score	48	56	40	38	52	66	70	56	48	62

To organize and display the data distribution, find the quartiles of the data set, and then construct a box-and-whisker plot.

▶ Quartiles separate the data set into four equal parts. The first quartile is the median of the lower half of the data. The second quartile is the median of the entire data set and is usually referred to as the median. The third quartile is the median of the upper half of the data.

To find quartiles of a data set:

• Arrange the data in order from least to greatest.
• Find the median of the entire data set.
• Find the first and third quartiles.

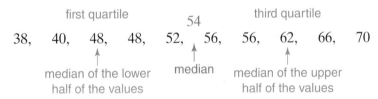

▶ A box-and-whisker plot shows the spread of data over a number line. The box represents the first and third quartiles, and the median, of the data. The whiskers represent the data's extremes (minimum and maximum values).

To make a box-and-whisker plot:

• Order the data, and find the extremes and the quartiles. Display the points corresponding to the extremes and quartiles above a number line.
• Draw a *box* that ends at the the first and third quartiles. Then draw a vertical line segment through the box at the median.
• Draw horizontal line segments, called *whiskers*, from the ends of the box to the extremes.
• Write a *title* for the graph.

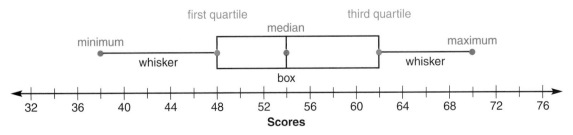

▶Given a box-and-whisker plot like the one below, you can determine information about the data, such as the extremes, quartiles, range, and interquartile range. The interquartile range is the difference between the third quartile and the first quartile.

The minimum value is 6.
The maximum value is 14.
The first quartile is 7; second quartile (median), 8; and third quartile, 9.
The range is 14 − 6, or 8.
The interquartile range is 9 − 7, or 2.

Heights of Some Buildings in Alexandria, Virginia

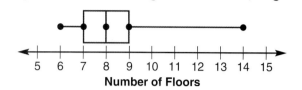

Number of Floors

▶A double box-and-whisker plot compares two or more sets of related data.

The plots below represent the number of letters in 20 students' names. The upper plot includes the number of letters in the last names, and the lower plot includes the number of letters in the first names.

Letters in Names

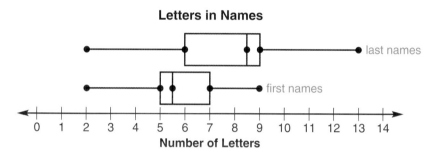

Number of Letters

The minimum number of letters in both the first and last names is 2.
The maximum number of letters in last names is 13 and in first names, 9. The quartiles shift toward the direction of the minimum value.

Try These

Find the first, second, and third quartiles of each data set and the interquartile range. Then make a box-and-whisker plot of the data.

1. 14, 32, 21, 27, 19, 15, 25

2. 68, 49, 53, 71, 70, 65

3. 91, 104, 112, 99, 104

Use the double box-and-whisker plot below to answer exercises 4–5.

Test Scores

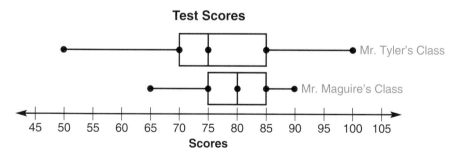

Scores

4. What is the third quartile score in Mr. Tyler's class?

5. How much greater is the interquartile range of scores in Mr. Tyler's class than in Mr. Maguire's?

6. Discuss and Write Explain how to make a box-and-whisker plot from a given data set.

Percentiles

Objective To find the percentile rank of an item in a data set • To find the number in a data set that is at a given percentile • To use a cumulative frequency table to find percentile ranks

Brittany's cat had a litter of 5 kittens. Their weights in grams were 92, 102, 98, 105, and 99. How can you compare the weight of the 99-g kitten to that of the others?

To compare the weight of the 99-g kitten to that of the others, find its percentile rank.

►Data sets can be separated into 100 equal parts, called *percentiles*. A percentile is a measure that tells what percent of the total number of items in a data set is at or below a given measure. The percentile rank of a data value, x, is n if $n\%$ of the data is less than or equal to x.

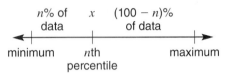

To find the percentile rank of a data value in a data set:

- Write the data in order from least to greatest.

  92, 98, 99, 102, 105

- Count how many data values are less than or equal to the given data value and how many are greater than or equal to the given data value.

  $2\frac{1}{2}$ or 2.5 ◄— There are 2 weights less than 99 and $\frac{1}{2}$ weight equal to 99.

  If a data value belongs to both upper and lower groups, include it in the count as one half of the number of the data value in the lower group and one half of the number of the data value in the upper group.

  .**Think**............................
  : The data value 99 belongs to :
  : both lower and upper groups. :
  ....

- Write a ratio of the number of values less than or equal to the data value compared to the total number of data values.

  $\dfrac{2.5}{5}$ ◄—number of weights less than or equal to 99
  ◄—total number of weights

  $\dfrac{2.5}{5} = 0.50 = 50\%$ ◄—Rewrite as a percent.

So the percentile rank of 99 g is 50. This means that 50% of the kittens in the litter weigh no more than 99 g and 50% weigh no less than 99 g.

Example

1 Find the percentile rank of 87 in the following 30 marks:

57, 65, 65, 68, 73, 74, 75, 78, 78, 79, 79, 79, 81, 81, 81, 83, 84, 85, 85, 85, 86, 87, 87, 87, 88, 91, 92, 93, 95, 98

- Find the sum of the number of marks less than 87 and one half of the number of 87s.

  number of marks less than 87 = 21
  half of the number of 87s = + 1.5
  ‾‾‾‾‾‾‾‾
  22.5

  .**Think**............................
  : There are three 87s. $\frac{1}{2}(3) = 1.5$:
  ....

- Divide the sum by the total number of marks. Write the quotient as a percent.

  $\dfrac{22.5}{30} = 0.75 = 75\%$

A mark of 87 is at the 75th percentile.

▶ You can use a given percentile to find the position of a number in the data set that has that percentile rank.

What is the 50th percentile number in this data set?

.Think..
There are 13 values in the data set.

14, 53, 33, 49, 26, 26, 41, 35, 17, 28, 32, 44, 23

50% of 13 = 6.5 ◀— 6.5 means that there are 6 numbers in the lower group, 6 in the upper group, and 1 that is shared.

14, 17, 23, 26, 26, 28, 32, 33, 35, 41, 44, 49, 53 ◀— Order the numbers from least to greatest, and find the number in the 7th position.

So 32 is the number that is at the 50th percentile of the data set.

Check: There are 6.5 values that are less than or equal to 32 and 6.5 values that are greater than or equal to 32.

$\frac{6.5}{13} = 50\%$

.Think..
There are 6.5 values less than or equal to 32 (6 values less than 32 and 0.5 value equal to 32).

So the percentile rank of 32 is 50. ✓

▶ Certain percentiles can be referred to as quartiles. The 25th percentile is the lower quartile, the 75th percentile is the upper quartile, and the 50th percentile is the median. Given a frequency table, you can add a cumulative frequency column to the table and determine where these percentile ranks fall in the histogram.

Use the cumulative frequency to find the interval that contains the 25th percentile and the 75th percentile.

- Since 25% $\left(\text{or } \frac{1}{4}\right)$ of 50 is 12.5 and 12.5 falls in the cumulative frequency 15, the 25th percentile falls in the interval 0–10.

- Since 75% $\left(\text{or } \frac{3}{4}\right)$ of 50 is 37.5 and 37.5 falls in the cumulative frequency 50, the 75th percentile falls in the interval 41–50.

Interval	Frequency	Cumulative Frequency
0–10	15	15
11–20	8	15 + 8 = 23
21–30	7	23 + 7 = 30
31–40	5	30 + 5 = 35
41–50	15	35 + 15 = 50

Try These

Use the following data to answer exercises 1–2.

62, 69, 73, 77, 77, 80, 84, 86, 88, 91, 95, 97, 100, 101, 108, 112, 115, 119, 123, 126

1. What is the percentile rank of 115?

2. What number is at the 50th percentile?

Use the given frequency table to construct a cumulative frequency table. Then use the cumulative frequency to answer exercise 3.

3. Which interval contains the 25th percentile? the 75th percentile?

4. Discuss and Write Explain how to find the number in a data set that is at the 20th percentile.

Interval	Frequency
100–150	38
151–200	24
201–250	34
251–300	54
301–350	50

Go to **PRACTICE BOOK Lesson 14-6 for exercise sets.**

Scatter Plots

Objective To identify correlation from a scatter plot • To make scatter plots
• To construct lines of best fit for scatter plots and write their equations

Lisa, a nurse practitioner, records the heights of several
children of different ages and displays the data on the graph
shown below. She uses a scatter plot to display the data.

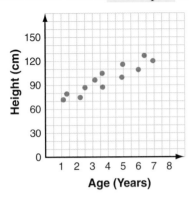

▶A scatter plot is a statistical display using ordered pairs of numbers to show the
relationship between two sets of data. The two data sets have a one-to-one
correspondence—that is, the same number of data in each, as in any relation.

A correlation describes a relationship between two data sets. A scatter plot may
show a positive correlation, a negative correlation, or no correlation at all.

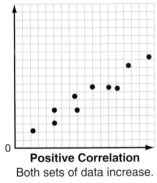

Positive Correlation
Both sets of data increase.

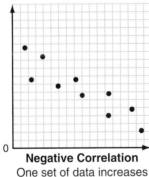

Negative Correlation
One set of data increases
as the other set decreases.

No Correlation
The data sets are not related.

So Lisa's scatter plot shows a positive correlation between the data—that is,
as the ages of the children increase, the heights also tend to increase.

▶When two related sets of data show a correlation, the relationship may be
causal. That is, a change in one quantity causes a change in the other. In the
example involving heights and ages, it is likely that an increase in age causes
an increase in height.

Not every positive or negative correlation
is a causal relationship.

The scatter plot at the right shows a negative
correlation, but it is not likely that a person's
birth date affects his or her shoe size. This
relationship shows correlation, but it is not causal.

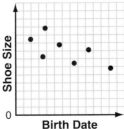

Examples

Identify the correlation (if any) between the two data sets. If there is a correlation, tell if it is likely to be causal.

1 age and number of pets

The age of a person should not affect his or her number of pets.

The relationship is not likely to have any correlation.

2 height of a candle and time it burns

As the candle burns, its height decreases.

The relationship is likely to have a negative correlation that is causal.

3 amount of money earned and amount of money spent

The greater the amount of money you earn, the more you can spend.

The relationship is likely to have a positive correlation that is causal.

4 the number of hours a plane is in flight and the number of passengers on the plane

The number of hours a plane is in flight should not affect the number of passengers on the plane.

The relationship is not likely to have any correlation.

▶ You can analyze or interpret data sets as having positive, negative, or no correlation by making a scatter plot.

Make a scatter plot of the data in the table below. Determine whether there is a positive correlation, a negative correlation, or no correlation. If there is a correlation, determine if the relationship is likely to be causal.

Age of Car (years)	Selling Price
1	$21,000
2	$17,000
3	$15,000
4	$11,000
5	$7,500
6	$6,000
7	$2,500
8	$1,200

To make a scatter plot:

• Draw and label an axis for each set of data. Label the horizontal axis *Age* and the vertical axis *Selling Price*.

• Create a scale for the graph.

• Graph the data, one point per ordered pair (age, selling price) from the table.

The scatter plot shows a negative correlation.

The relationship is likely to be causal because as a car gets older, it decreases in value.

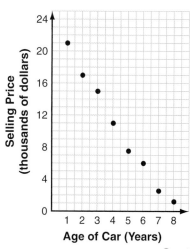

Continue Lesson ➡

Example

1 Make a scatter plot of the data showing the number of hours spent studying and incorrect answers a student gets on a test in the table below. Determine whether there is a positive correlation, a negative correlation, or no correlation. If there is a correlation, determine if the relationship is likely to be causal.

Hours Spent Studying	1	5	6	9	10	8	5	4	10	4	10	7	9	2	8
Incorrect Answers	8	5	3	1	0	3	6	6	2	8	1	4	2	7	2

- Draw and label an axis for each set of data. Label the horizontal axis *Hours Spent Studying* and the vertical axis *Incorrect Answers*.
- Create a scale for the graph.
- Graph the data, one point per ordered pair (hours spent studying, incorrect answers) from the table.

The scatter plot shows a negative correlation.

The relationship is likely to be causal because the more hours a student spends studying for the test, the less number of incorrect answers he or she gets on the test.

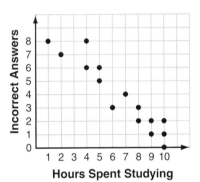

▶ Sometimes a line of best fit can be drawn on a scatter plot to model the relationship between the data sets. A line of best fit best represents the data on a scatter plot. It may pass through some of the points, none of the points, or all of the points.

Make a scatter plot of the data shown in the table. Draw a line of best fit, then write an equation of the line.

Time (minutes)	10	20	30	40	50	60	70	80	90	100	110	120
Distance (miles)	5	15	20	29	38	48	55	62	70	76	82	90

To write an equation for a line of best fit:

- Graph the data from the table.
- Draw a line that shows the trend of the data. Estimate two points on the line.

   $(0, 0)$ and $(40, 30)$ appear to be on the line.

- Use the points to write an equation.

$$m = \frac{30 - 0}{40 - 0} = \frac{3}{4} \quad \longleftarrow \text{Find the slope.}$$

$$y - y_1 = m(x - x_1) \quad \longleftarrow \text{Use the point-slope form of a line.}$$

$$y - 0 = \frac{3}{4}(x - 0) \quad \longleftarrow \text{Substitute } \frac{3}{4} \text{ for } m, 0 \text{ for } y_1, \text{ and } 0 \text{ for } x_1.$$

$$y = \frac{3}{4}x \quad \longleftarrow \text{Simplify.}$$

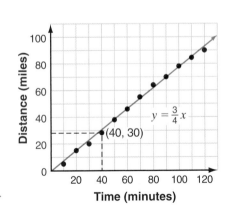

So the equation of the line of best fit is $y = \frac{3}{4}x$.

Example

1 For the data points shown, draw a line of best fit, and write an equation for the line.

• Draw a line that shows the trend of the data. Estimate two points on the line. $(0, 8)$ and $(4, 0)$ appear to be on the line.

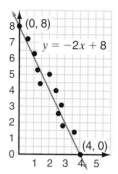

• Use the points to write an equation.

$m = \dfrac{0 - 8}{4 - 0} = -2$ ◀—Find the slope.

$y - y_1 = m(x - x_1)$ ◀—Use the point-slope form.

$y - 8 = -2(x - 0)$ ◀—Substitute -2 for m, 8 for y_1, and 0 for x_1.

$y - 8 = -2x$ ◀—Use the Distributive Property.

$y = -2x + 8$ ◀—Use the Addition Property of Equality.

So the equation of the line of best fit is $y = -2x + 8$.

Try These

Select the graph that most likely represents the relationship.

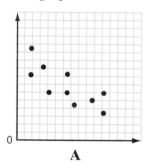

A

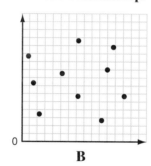

B

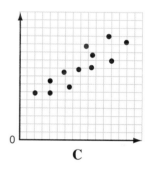

C

1. TV size and price   **2.** computer's age and value   **3.** number of pets and test score

Determine the type of correlation (if any) between the two data sets. If there is a correlation, determine whether the relationship is causal.

4. family size and weekly grocery bill   **5.** time watching TV and time studying

6. distance to school and age   **7.** number of siblings and height

Make a scatter plot of the data. Draw a line of best fit, and then write an equation of the line.

8.

Items Sold	1	2	3	4	5	6	7
Profit ($)	2	6	10	12	16	17	21

9.

Age (years)	1	2	3	4	5	6	7
$ Value (hundreds)	9	8	8	6	4	4	3

10. Discuss and Write Give an example of data sets that are likely to have a causal relationship and a negative correlation.

Go to   PRACTICE BOOK Lesson 14-7 for exercise sets.

Update your skills. See page 414 XXII.

Empirical Probability

Objective To determine the experimental probability of events • To make predictions using empirical probability

Heather and Michelle are playing a board game requiring them to draw tiles from a bag to determine how many spaces to move on the board. After choosing a tile, they place it back in the bag. The table below shows the number of times each tile has been chosen. How likely is it that the next tile chosen is FIVE?

Outcome	Frequency
ONE	5
TWO	4
THREE	6
FOUR	2
FIVE	3

To find how likely it is that the next tile chosen is FIVE, find the *experimental probability* of choosing a FIVE.

▶ **Probability** is a measure of the likelihood that an event will occur. Probabilities are written as fractions or decimals ranging from 0 to 1, or as percents ranging from 0% to 100%.

The greater the probability, the more likely it is that the event will occur.

- An event that is *impossible*, such as rolling a 9 on a 1–6 number cube, has a probability of 0.
- An event that is *certain*, such as rolling a number less than 7 on a 1–6 number cube, has a probability of 1.

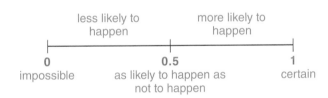

less likely to happen   more likely to happen

| | | |
0   0.5   1
impossible   as likely to happen as   certain
           not to happen

▶ You can use an *empirical approach*, using observations and hands-on activities, to estimate probabilities when conducting experiments.

In empirical probability, also called experimental probability, the likelihood of an event is estimated by repeating a trial many times and observing how many times the event happens. Then that number is divided by the total number of trials. The more the trial is repeated, the more accurate the estimate is likely to be.

_____ **Key Concept** _____

Experimental Probability

$$\text{Exp } P(E) = \frac{\text{number of times the event occurs}}{\text{total number of trials}}$$

To find the experimental probability of choosing a FIVE, find the ratio that represents the number of trials in which the outcome was FIVE divided by the total number of trials.

$$\text{Exp } P(\text{FIVE}) = \frac{\text{number of FIVEs}}{\text{total number of trials}}$$

$$= \frac{3}{5 + 4 + 6 + 2 + 3} = \frac{3}{20} = 0.15 = 15\%$$

So the probability that the next tile chosen will be a FIVE is $\frac{3}{20}$, or 0.15, or 15%.

▶ You can use experimental probability to make *predictions*. A prediction in mathematics is an estimate about something that has not yet happened based on data that has been collected.

In the opening problem, about how many times would you predict that Heather and Michelle will choose TWO in 75 draws?

• Find the experimental probability of choosing TWO:

$$\text{Exp } P(\text{TWO}) = \frac{\text{number of TWOs}}{\text{number of trials}} = \frac{4}{20} = 0.20 = 20\%$$

The experimental probability of choosing TWO is 20%.

• Find 20% of 75:

$(0.2)75 = 15$ ◀—Write 20% as a decimal.

So you would predict that Heather and Michelle will choose about 15 TWOs in 75 draws.

Example

1 In the problem on page 378, about how many times would you predict that Heather and Michelle will choose THREE or FOUR in 125 draws from the bag?

• Find the experimental probability of choosing THREE or FOUR:

$$\text{Exp } P(\text{THREE or FOUR}) = \frac{\text{number of THREEs or FOURs}}{\text{number of trials}}$$

$$= \frac{8}{20} = 0.40 = 40\%$$

.Think......................
THREE was chosen
6 times, and FOUR was
chosen 2 times, so 8 of the
tiles drawn were either
THREE or FOUR.
....

• Find 40% of 125:

$(0.4)125 = 50$ ◀—Write 40% as a decimal.

So you would predict that Heather and Michelle will choose THREE or FOUR about 50 times in 125 draws.

Try These

**Brett spins a spinner and records the outcomes.
Use the table at the right to answer exercises 1–3.**

1. What is the experimental probability of landing on yellow?

2. What is the experimental probability of landing on blue or green?

3. Predict about how many times the spinner would land on red in 225 spins?

Outcome	Frequency
Red	14
Blue	17
Yellow	9
Green	10

4. **Discuss and Write** Marge tosses a coin 40 times, and it lands on heads 22 times. Explain how to use experimental probability to predict the number of times the coin would land on heads in 100 tosses.

Theoretical Probability

Objective To find the theoretical probability of an event • To find the probability of the complement of an event

A spinner is divided into six equal parts, as shown at the right. Joel spins the spinner once. What is the probability that it lands on red?

▶ When the outcomes of an experiment have the same chance of occurring, the outcomes are said to be *equally likely*. On the given spinner, there are six sections, so there are six possible outcomes. The possible outcomes make up the sample space, S.

For experiments with equally likely outcomes, the probability of an event, $P(E)$, occurring is called theoretical probability.

Key Concept

Theoretical Probability

For experiments with equally likely outcomes,
$$P(E) = \frac{\text{number of favorable outcomes}}{\text{total number of possible outcomes}}.$$

To find the theoretical probability that the spinner lands on red, find the ratio of the number of red outcomes to the total number of possible outcomes.

$$P(\text{red}) = \frac{\text{number of favorable outcomes}}{\text{total number of possible outcomes}}$$

$$= \frac{2}{6} = \frac{1}{3}$$

.Think.....................................
6 possible outcomes (6 sections)
2 favorable outcomes (2 red)

So the probability that the spinner lands on red is $\frac{1}{3}$.

Examples

1 The name of a quadrilateral is selected at random from the set {parallelogram, rhombus, rectangle, square, trapezoid}. What is the probability of selecting a quadrilateral with both pairs of opposite sides congruent? all pairs of consecutive angles congruent?

.Think............
total number
of outcomes: 5

• quadrilaterals with both pairs of opposite sides congruent: parallelogram, rhombus, rectangle, square (4 outcomes)

$$P(\text{opposite sides congruent}) = \frac{4}{5}$$

• quadrilaterals with all pairs of consecutive angles congruent: rectangle, square (2 outcomes)

$$P(\text{consecutive angles congruent}) = \frac{2}{5}$$

2 Eric drew the histogram at the right, showing the quantity and the color of the marbles in his collection. If one marble was selected at random, what is the probability that it is green or blue? not white?

• $P(\text{green or blue}) = \frac{8}{15}$

• $P(\text{not white}) = \frac{13}{15}$

.Think ....
15 possible outcomes
(3 + 5 + 2 + 4 + 1)
8 green or blue
13 not white

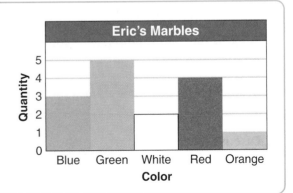

▶The complement of an event includes all of the outcomes that are *not* in the event. An event and its complement, called complementary events, include all outcomes of the sample space, *S*. The sum of their probabilities is equal to 1, or 100%.

Key Concept

Probabilities of Complementary Events

For any event, E, and its complement, E′, $P(E) + P(E') = 1$, or, equivalently, $P(E') = 1 - P(E)$.

The Venn diagram below shows that two students, Jackie and David, take both Biology and U.S. History. The remaining students, Jill, Lindsey, Sarah, Josh, Ryan, and Alex do *not* take both subjects, so they make up the complement of the set of students who *do* take both Biology and U.S. History.

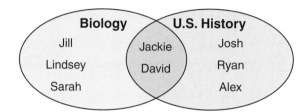

Biology   U.S. History

Jill   Jackie   Josh
Lindsey   David   Ryan
Sarah   Alex

If one of the 8 students is chosen at random, what is the probability that he or she takes both Biology and U.S. History? the probability that he or she does not take both Biology and U.S. History?

• $P(\text{Biology and U.S. History}) = \dfrac{2}{8}$ ←number of students who take both ←total number of students

$$= \dfrac{1}{4}, \text{ or } 0.25, \text{ or } 25\%$$

• $P(not \text{ Biology and U.S. History}) = 1 - \dfrac{1}{4}$

$$= \dfrac{3}{4}, \text{ or } 0.75, \text{ or } 75\%$$

Try These

A 1–6 number cube is rolled. Find the probability of each event.

1. $P(5)$ **2.** $P(1 \text{ or } 2)$ **3.** $P(8)$

4. $P(\text{less than } 5)$ **5.** $P(\text{not } 6)$ **6.** $P(\text{not less than } 5)$

A letter is chosen at random from the word CALIFORNIA. Find the probability of the complement of the event.

7. Choose R **8.** Choose a vowel **9.** Choose a consonant

10. Choose A or I **11.** Choose C or L **12.** Choose C, L, or F

13. Discuss and Write Given the equations $y = x$, $x = 1$, $y = 1$, and $y = x^2$, explain how to find the probability of choosing an equation at random whose graph contains the point $(1, 1)$.

Independent and Dependent Events

Objective To find the number of possible outcomes of an event by making a tree diagram or by using the Counting Principle • To compute probabilities of independent and dependent events

Maria tosses a coin three times. What is the probability that the coin lands on heads exactly twice?

To find the probability, first find the total number of possible and favorable outcomes for the three tosses, and then find the probability of a *compound event*.

▶ A **compound event** consists of two or more events.

- To find the total number of possible outcomes of a compound event, draw a **tree diagram**, or use the Fundamental Counting Principle. A tree diagram is a way to show all the possible outcomes. The Fundamental Counting Principle tells you the number of outcomes, but it does not tell you what they are.

Method 1 Make a tree diagram.

Let H represent heads and T represent tails.

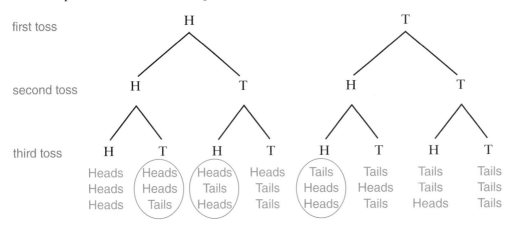

There are 8 possible outcomes, 3 of which contain exactly 2 heads.

Method 2 Use the Fundamental Counting Principle.

When a coin is tossed, there are 2 possible outcomes for each toss. Since the coin is tossed three times, to find the total number of outcomes using the Fundamental Counting Principle, multiply: $2 \cdot 2 \cdot 2 = 8$.

_____ **Key Concept** _____

Fundamental Counting Principle

If one event has m possible outcomes and a second event has n possible outcomes, then there are $m \cdot n$ total possible outcomes for the two events together.

So there are 8 possible outcomes when a coin is tossed three times.

- To find the probability of landing on heads exactly twice in 3 tosses, find the ratio of the number of favorable outcomes to the total number of possible outcomes.

$$P(\text{exactly two heads}) = \frac{\text{number of outcomes with exactly 2 heads}}{\text{number of possible outcomes}} = \frac{3}{8}$$

► All possible outcomes for a compound event can differ depending on whether the event is occurring *with* or *without replacement*.

A bag contains a red marble, a yellow marble, and a green marble. Suppose you choose one marble, and then choose a second marble without looking and record their colors. How many different color pairs are possible?

• You then *put the first marble back* and choose another marble.

Method 1 Make a tree diagram.

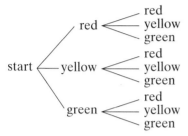

So there are 9 possible color pairs.

Method 2 Use the Fundamental Counting Principle.

• **m** ways for *one activity* to occur;
  3 possibilities for the 1st pick

• **n** ways for *a 2nd activity* to occur;
  3 possibilities for the 2nd pick

• **mn** ways for *both* to occur: 3 • 3 = 9

So there are 9 possible color pairs.

.Think.......
The marble that is first picked is *returned* to the bag.

• *Without putting the first marble back*, you then choose another marble.

Method 1 Make a tree diagram.

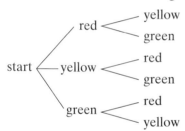

So by counting, you find there are 6 possible color pairs.

Method 2 Use the Fundamental Counting Principle.

• **m** ways for *one activity* to occur;
  3 possibilities for the 1st pick

• **n** ways for *a 2nd activity* to occur;
  2 possibilities for the 2nd pick

• **mn** ways for *both* to occur: 3 • 2 = 6

So there are 6 possible color pairs.

.Think.......
The marble that is first picked is *not returned* to the bag.

Examples

1 A school sells sweatshirts that come in 2 styles (hooded or nonhooded), 4 sizes (S, M, L, and XL), and 3 colors (blue, gray, and gold). How many choices are there?

There are 2 choices for style, 4 choices for size, and 3 choices for color.

$\qquad$ 2 • 4 • 3 = 24 ◄—Apply the Fundamental Counting Principle.

The total number of sweatshirt choices is 24.

2 A computer randomly generates a 5-character license plate of 2 letters followed by 3 digits. Find the possible number of license plates.

1st letter	2nd letter	1st digit	2nd digit	3rd digit
26 •	26 •	10 •	10 •	10 = 676,000

◄—Apply the Fundamental Counting Principle.

The total number of license plates is 676,000.

Continue Lesson ⮕

▶ Events are *independent events* if the outcome of one event does not affect the outcome of another. Events are *dependent events* if the outcome of one does affect the outcome of another.

Determine if the events are dependent or independent.

- tossing a coin twice

  One toss does not affect the outcome of the other. The events are independent.

- drawing 2 marbles from a bag, one after the other

  The marbles drawn cannot be the same marble. The events are dependent.

▶ To find the probability of two independent events, multiply the probabilities of each individual event.

Seven cards are labeled A through G. Sue picks a card at random, replaces it, and then picks another. What is the probability that she picks C both times?

Because Sue replaces the first card, the probabilities for the second pick remain the same. The events are independent.

For each pick, $P(C) = \frac{1}{7}$ ◀— There are 7 cards. One is labeled C.

$P(C, C) = P(C) \cdot P(C)$ ◀— If A and B are independent events, then $P(A, B) = P(A) \cdot P(B)$.

$\quad = \frac{1}{7} \cdot \frac{1}{7} = \frac{1}{49}$

So the probability that Sue picks C both times is $\frac{1}{49}$.

> **_____ Key Concept _____**
>
> **Probability of Independent Events**
> If A and B are independent events, then $P(A, B) = P(A) \cdot P(B)$.
>
> **Probability of Dependent Events**
> If A and B are dependent events, then $P(A, B) = P(A) \cdot P(B \text{ after } A)$.

▶ To find the probability of two dependent events, find the probability of the first event, then find the probability of the second event if the first event has already occurred, and multiply the probabilities. The sample space for the second event will be different from the sample space for the first event.

Suppose you draw two socks at random, one after the other, from a drawer that contains 6 white socks, 4 black socks, 4 brown socks, and 2 red socks. What is the probability you will draw a brown sock, then a white sock if you keep the first sock before drawing the second?

The two draws cannot be the same sock, so the events are dependent.

The total number of socks is $6 + 4 + 4 + 2 = 16$. Four of the socks are brown.

$P(\text{brown}) = \frac{4}{16} = \frac{1}{4}$

After the brown sock is chosen, there are 15 socks left in the drawer, 6 of which are white.

$P(\text{white}) = \frac{6}{15} = \frac{2}{5}$

$P(\text{brown, white}) = P(\text{brown}) \cdot P(\text{white after brown})$

$$= \frac{1}{\overset{}{\underset{2}{4}}} \cdot \frac{\overset{1}{2}}{5} = \frac{1}{10}$$

So the probability that you will draw a brown sock, then a white sock if you keep the first sock before drawing the second is $\frac{1}{10}$.

Examples

1 Pierce spins the spinner shown at the right twice. What is the probability it lands on green first and blue second?

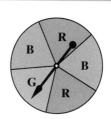

Landing on green first does not affect the probability of landing on blue second. The events are independent.

$P(\text{green, blue}) = P(\text{green}) \cdot P(\text{blue})$ ⟵ $P(A, B) = P(A) \cdot P(B)$

$\qquad = \dfrac{1}{5} \cdot \dfrac{2}{5}$ ⟵ The spinner has 5 sections. One is green and two are blue.

$\qquad = \dfrac{2}{25}$

So the probability that the spinner lands on green first and blue second is $\dfrac{2}{25}$.

2 There are 25 students in Mr. Stone's class, 10 girls and 15 boys. The students' names are put in a hat, and then Mr. Stone draws 2 names at random, one after the other, to present reports on Monday. What is the probability that 1 boy and 1 girl will be chosen?

To find the probability, you need to consider two possibilities:
- Mr. Stone draws a boy's name and then a girl's name.
- Mr. Stone draws a girl's name and then a boy's name.

Find the probability in each case.

$P(\text{boy and then girl}) = P(\text{boy}) \cdot P(\text{girl after boy}) = \dfrac{\overset{3}{\cancel{15}}}{\underset{\underset{1}{\cancel{5}}}{25}} \cdot \dfrac{\overset{1}{\cancel{10}}}{\underset{\underset{4}{\cancel{8}}}{24}} = \dfrac{1}{4}$

$P(\text{girl and then boy}) = P(\text{girl}) \cdot P(\text{boy after girl}) = \dfrac{\overset{2}{\cancel{10}}}{\underset{\underset{1}{\cancel{5}}}{25}} \cdot \dfrac{\overset{3}{\cancel{15}}}{\underset{4}{24}} = \dfrac{1}{4}$

In either case, the probability is $\dfrac{1}{4}$.

So the probability that 1 boy and 1 girl will be chosen is $\dfrac{1}{4}$.

Try These

Draw a tree diagram and use the Fundamental Counting Principle to find the number of possible outcomes.

1. Choose an outfit from 4 pairs of pants and 6 shirts.

2. Toss a coin 2 times and spin a spinner of equal sections labeled 1, 2, and 3.

Determine whether the events are independent or dependent. Then find the probability.

3. Roll a 5, then roll a number less than 5 when rolling a number cube twice.

4. Choose 2 black pens from a drawer containing 8 black, 10 blue, and 4 red pens.

5. Discuss and Write Give an example of a pair of independent events and an example of a pair of dependent events. Explain your answers.

Go to ▶ **PRACTICE BOOK Lesson 14-10 for exercise sets.**

Mutually Exclusive Events

Objective To compute probabilities of mutually exclusive or overlapping events

Milan has 6 comedy DVDs, 4 action DVDs, 3 drama DVDs, and 2 science fiction DVDs. He picks one DVD at random to watch. What is the probability that he chooses a drama or science fiction movie?

Let A = event choosing a drama movie at random, and
      B = event choosing a science fiction movie at random.

▶ Events A and B have no outcome in common, so they are called mutually exclusive, or disjoint events. The number of outcomes in A *or* B is the sum of the number of outcomes in the two events.

total number of possible outcomes: $6 + 4 + 3 + 2 = 15$

number of favorable outcomes: $3 + 2$ ◀— A *or* B contains 5 of the 15 possible outcomes.

$$P(A \text{ or } B) = \frac{3}{15} + \frac{2}{15} \quad \text{◀—} P(A \text{ or } B) = P(A) + P(B)$$

$$= \frac{5}{15} = \frac{1}{3}$$

___ **Key Concept** ___

Probabilities of Mutually Exclusive Events, A and B

• $P(A \text{ and } B) = 0$
• $P(A \text{ or } B) = P(A) + P(B)$

So the probability that Milan chooses a drama or a science fiction movie is $\frac{1}{3}$.

Examples

1 The figure shown at the right is divided into squares of equal size. If a point in the figure is picked at random, what is the probability that the point is in a red square or in a yellow square?

There are 36 squares in the figure, and 6 are red and 12 are yellow.

$$P(\text{red } or \text{ yellow}) = P(\text{red}) + P(\text{yellow}) \quad \text{◀—} P(A \text{ or } B) = P(A) + P(B)$$

$$= \frac{6}{36} + \frac{12}{36}$$

$$= \frac{18}{36} = \frac{1}{2}$$

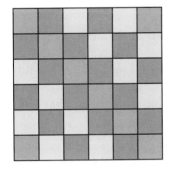

So if a point in the figure is picked at random, the probability that the point is in a red square or in a yellow square is $\frac{1}{2}$.

2 A single piece of mail is randomly selected from a stack of mail containing 4 letters, 3 bills, and 3 advertisements. What is the probability that the piece of mail selected is either a letter or a bill?

$$P(\text{letter } or \text{ bill}) = \frac{4}{10} + \frac{3}{10} = \frac{7}{10} \quad \text{◀—} P(A \text{ or } B) = P(A) + P(B)$$

So the probability that either a letter or a bill is selected is $\frac{7}{10}$.

Think
total possible outcomes:
$4 + 3 + 3 = 10$
4 out of 10 pieces of mail are letters.
3 out of 10 pieces of mail are bills.

▶ If events A and B are *not* mutually exclusive, then they are called overlapping events—that is, they have common outcomes. Finding $P(A \text{ or } B)$ in this case requires an extra step.

Probability of Overlapping Events, A and B

• $P(A \text{ or } B) = P(A) + P(B) - P(A \text{ and } B)$

 Suppose you roll a 1–6 number cube. What is the probability that the number you roll is an even or a prime number?

The Venn diagram at the right shows that these events are overlapping events because 2 is both even and prime.

P(even *or* prime) involves finding the probability that a number is even, is prime, or is *both* even and prime.

$$P(\text{even } or \text{ prime}) = P(\text{even}) + P(\text{prime}) - P(\text{even } and \text{ prime})$$

$$= \frac{3}{6} + \frac{3}{6} - \frac{1}{6} = \frac{5}{6}$$

So the probability of rolling an even or a prime number is $\frac{5}{6}$.

Example

1 Chris makes up 5 sets of cards, each labeled from 1 to 10. One set is red, one set is orange, one set is yellow, one set is green, and one set is blue. If Chris chooses one card at random, what is the probability that it is orange or a multiple of 3?

There are 50 cards in all, 10 of which are orange.

There are 3 multiples of 3 between 1 and 10: 3, 6, and 9. Since there are 5 sets of cards, a total of (5 • 3), or 15, cards are a multiple of 3.

There are 3 cards that are orange and a multiple of 3.

$$P(\text{orange } or \text{ multiple of 3}) = P(\text{orange}) + P(\text{multiple of 3}) - P(\text{orange } and \text{ multiple of 3})$$

$$= \frac{10}{50} + \frac{15}{50} - \frac{3}{50} = \frac{22}{50} = \frac{11}{25}$$

So the probability that Chris chooses a card that is orange or a multiple of 3 is $\frac{11}{25}$.

Try These

Determine if the events are *mutually exclusive* or *overlapping*.

1. rolling a prime number or a 4 when rolling a number cube

2. rolling an even sum or a sum greater than 6 when rolling two number cubes

Use the spinner. Determine if the events are mutually exclusive. Then find the probability.

3. P(red *or* blue)   4. P(green *or* prime)   5. P(blue *or* odd)

6. **Discuss and Write** Give an example of a pair of both mutually exclusive events and overlapping events. Explain your answers.

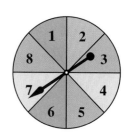

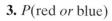 **PRACTICE BOOK Lesson 14-11 for exercise sets.**

Conditional Probability

Objective To find *P*(B GIVEN A)

Ross rolls an odd number on a 1–6 number cube. He then rolls the cube again. What is the probability that the sum of the two rolls is 7?

To find the probability that the sum of the two rolls is 7, you can make an organized list.

(1,1)	(2,1)	(3,1)	(4,1)	(5,1)	(6,1)
(1,2)	(2,2)	(3,2)	(4,2)	(5,2)	(6,2)
(1,3)	(2,3)	(3,3)	(4,3)	(5,3)	(6,3)
(1,4)	(2,4)	(3,4)	(4,4)	(5,4)	(6,4)
(1,5)	(2,5)	(3,5)	(4,5)	(5,5)	(6,5)
(1,6)	(2,6)	(3,6)	(4,6)	(5,6)	(6,6)

There are 18 possible outcomes in which Ross rolls two number cubes that have an odd number for the first roll. Since there are 18 outcomes for the first roll, then the size of the sample space for the second roll will also be 18. Of these 18 outcomes, 3 have a sum of 7.

$$P(\text{sum of 7, given that the first roll is odd}) = \frac{3}{18} = \frac{1}{6}$$

So the probability that the sum of the two rolls adds up to 7 is $\frac{1}{6}$.

▶ When a probability has a condition that may limit the sample space, it is called a conditional probability. In the example above, you are given that the first roll is odd, which limits the sample space to 18. You can write a conditional probability with the notation *P*(B | A), which is read as *the probability of event B given event A*.

Key Concept

Conditional Probability
The probability that event *B* occurs given that *A* has occurred is $P(\text{B} \mid \text{A}) = \dfrac{P(A \text{ and } B)}{P(A)}$

To find the probability that the sum is 7 given that the first roll is odd, use the formula:

$$P(\text{sum of 7} \mid \text{first roll odd}) = \frac{P(\text{first roll is odd and the sum is 7})}{P(\text{first roll is odd})}$$

- $P(\text{first roll odd and } sum \text{ of 7}) = \dfrac{\overset{1}{\cancel{18}}}{\underset{2}{\cancel{36}}} \cdot \dfrac{\overset{1}{\cancel{6}}}{\underset{6}{\cancel{36}}} = \dfrac{1}{12}$ ◀── If *A* and *B* are independent events, then $P(A \text{ and } B) = P(A) \cdot P(B)$

- $P(\text{first roll is odd}) = \dfrac{18}{36} = \dfrac{1}{2}$ ◀── There are 18 favorable outcomes out of 36 possible outcomes.

- $P(\text{sum of 7} \mid \text{first roll odd}) = \dfrac{\frac{1}{12}}{\frac{1}{2}}$ ◀── Substitute the values of *P*(first roll odd and sum of 7) and *P*(first roll is odd).

$$= \dfrac{1}{\underset{6}{\cancel{12}}} \cdot \dfrac{\overset{1}{\cancel{2}}}{1} = \dfrac{1}{6}$$ ◀── Simplify.

Examples

1 A bag contains a number of colored marbles. The probability of choosing a blue marble is $\frac{1}{5}$. The probability of choosing a blue marble and a red marble is $\frac{3}{20}$. What is the probability of choosing a red marble given that the first marble chosen is blue? (Assume the blue marble is replaced in the bag.)

$$P(\text{red} \mid \text{blue}) = \frac{P(\text{blue and red})}{P(\text{blue})} \quad \longleftarrow \text{Use the formula: } P(B \mid A) = \frac{P(A \text{ and } B)}{P(A)}$$

$$= \frac{\frac{3}{20}}{\frac{1}{5}} \quad \longleftarrow \text{Substitute the given values into the formula.}$$

$$= \frac{3}{20} \cdot \frac{\overset{1}{5}}{1} = \frac{3}{4} \quad \longleftarrow \text{Simplify.}$$

So the probability of choosing a red marble given that the first marble chosen is blue is $\frac{3}{4}$.

2 At a high school, 80% of the students take history and 48% of the students take history and chemistry. What is the probability that a student takes chemistry given that he or she takes history?

$$P(\text{chemistry} \mid \text{history}) = \frac{P(\text{history and chemistry})}{P(\text{history})} \quad \longleftarrow \text{Use the formula: } P(B \mid A) = \frac{P(A \text{ and } B)}{P(A)}$$

$$= \frac{0.48}{0.8} \quad \longleftarrow \text{Write the percents as decimals (48\% = 0.48, 80\% = 0.8),} \\ \text{and substitute the given values into the formula.}$$

$$= 0.6 = 60\% \quad \longleftarrow \text{Simplify.}$$

So the probability that a student takes chemistry given that he or she takes history is 60%.

Try These

Find $P(B \mid A)$.

1. $P(A \text{ and } B) = \frac{1}{8}; P(A) = \frac{1}{4}$

2. $P(A \text{ and } B) = \frac{2}{3}; P(A) = \frac{5}{6}$

3. $P(A \text{ and } B) = 21\%; P(A) = 30\%$

4. $P(A \text{ and } B) = 6\%; P(A) = 40\%$

Find the conditional probability.

5. At a school, 20% of the students are in the band, and 13% of the students are in the band and the drama club. What is the probability that a student is in the drama club given that he or she is in the band?

6. Discuss and Write The probability that a basketball team plays a home game and that the team wins is 45%. The probability that the team plays at home is 50%. Explain how to find the probability that the team wins, given that it is playing at home.

Go to PRACTICE BOOK **Lesson 14-12 for exercise sets.**

Permutations

Objective To evaluate factorial expressions • To find the number of permutations in a set of objects

Kristy has 5 songs on a playlist. Her MP3 player plays the songs at random, with no song playing more than once. How many ways can the 5 songs be played?

To find how many ways, find the number of *permutations* of the 5 songs.

▶ A permutation is an arrangement or listing of objects in a specific order. You can use the Fundamental Counting Principle to find the number of permutations.

5 choices   3 choices   1 choice for
for the first   for the third   the fifth

$$5 \bullet 4 \bullet 3 \bullet 2 \bullet 1 = 120$$

4 choices for   2 choices for
the second   the fourth

Remember: If there are m ways to make one selection and n ways to make a second selection, then there are $m \times n$ ways to make the two selections.

There are 120 ways of playing the 5 songs.

▶ In working with permutations, you will find that the result is often a series of factors, each being one less than the preceding factor. This series of factors is called a factorial. For example, $5 \bullet 4 \bullet 3 \bullet 2 \bullet 1$ is written as $5!$ and is read as *five factorial*. $5! = 120$

In general, $n! = n(n - 1)(n - 2) \bullet \ldots \bullet 1$, where n is a positive integer. In particular, $0! = 1$ and $1! = 1$.

Simplify $\dfrac{5!}{3!}$.

$$\frac{5!}{3!} = \frac{5 \bullet 4 \bullet 3 \bullet 2 \bullet 1}{3 \bullet 2 \bullet 1} = \frac{5 \bullet 4 \bullet \cancel{3} \bullet \cancel{2} \bullet \cancel{1}}{\cancel{3} \bullet \cancel{2} \bullet \cancel{1}}$$
$$= 5 \bullet 4 = 20$$

Simplify $\dfrac{5!}{3! \bullet 2!}$.

$$\frac{5!}{3! \bullet 2!} = \frac{5 \bullet 4 \bullet 3 \bullet 2 \bullet 1}{3 \bullet 2 \bullet 1 \bullet 2 \bullet 1} = \frac{5 \bullet \overset{2}{\cancel{4}} \bullet 3 \bullet \overset{1}{\cancel{2}} \bullet 1}{3 \bullet \underset{1}{\cancel{2}} \bullet 1 \bullet 2 \bullet 1}$$
$$= 5 \bullet 2 = 10$$

▶ There are formulas that you can use to find the permutations of n objects taken n at a time and permutations of n objects taken r at a time.

_____ Key Concept _____

Permutations of n Objects Taken n at a Time, $_nP_n$	**Permutations of n Objects Taken r at a Time, $_nP_r$**
$_nP_n = n!$	$_nP_r = \dfrac{n!}{(n - r)!}$

• In how many ways can 6 people be seated in 6 chairs?

To find how many ways, find $_6P_6$.

$_6P_6 = 6! = 6 \bullet 5 \bullet 4 \bullet 3 \bullet 2 \bullet 1$ ←—Use the formula: $_nP_n = n!$; then apply the definition of 6!.

$= 720$ ←—Simplify.

So there are 720 ways 6 people can be seated in 6 chairs.

• Four people enter a room in which there are 6 empty chairs. In how many ways can they take their seats?

To find how many ways, find $_6P_4$.

$$_6P_4 = \frac{6!}{(6-4)!} \quad \longleftarrow \text{Use the formula: } _nP_r = \frac{n!}{(n-r)!}$$

$$= \frac{6!}{2!} = \frac{6 \cdot 5 \cdot 4 \cdot 3 \cdot 2 \cdot 1}{2 \cdot 1} \quad \longleftarrow \text{Apply the definition of factorial.}$$

$$= \frac{6 \cdot 5 \cdot 4 \cdot 3 \cdot 2 \cdot \overset{1}{\cancel{1}}}{\underset{1}{\cancel{2 \cdot 1}}} = 360 \quad \longleftarrow \text{Simplify.}$$

So there are 360 ways 4 people can be seated in 6 chairs.

▶ There are formulas that you can use to find the permutations of n objects when there is one or more than one item with duplicates in a set.

Key Concept

Permutations of n items taken n at a time where r objects are identical	Permutations of n items taken n at a time where r_1 items are identical and r_2 items are identical
$\dfrac{n!}{r!}$	$\dfrac{n!}{r_1! \cdot r_2!}$

How many ways can you arrange the letters in the word NOTEBOOKS?

$\dfrac{n!}{r!} = \dfrac{9!}{3!}$ ← 9 letters total
← 3 O's

$= 9 \cdot 8 \cdot 7 \cdot 6 \cdot 5 \cdot 4$ ← Apply the definition of factorial.

$= 60{,}480$ ← Simplify.

There are 60,480 ways to arrange the 9 letters.

How many ways can you arrange the letters in the word ARKANSAS?

$\dfrac{n!}{r_1! \cdot r_2!} = \dfrac{8!}{3! \cdot 2!}$ ← 8 letters
← 3 A's and 2 S's

$= \dfrac{8 \cdot 7 \cdot 6 \cdot 5 \cdot \overset{2}{\cancel{4}} \cdot 3 \cdot \overset{1}{\cancel{2}} \cdot 1}{\underset{1}{\cancel{3 \cdot 2 \cdot 1}} \cdot \underset{1}{\cancel{2}} \cdot 1}$ ← Apply the definition of factorial.

$= 8 \cdot 7 \cdot 6 \cdot 5 \cdot 2 = 3360$ ← Simplify.

There are 3360 ways to arrange the letters.

Try These

Simplify each expression.

1. $_8P_8$ **2.** $_9P_9$ **3.** $_5P_2$ **4.** $_7P_3$

5. $_8P_6$ **6.** $_{10}P_4$ **7.** $_9P_7$ **8.** $_{10}P_2$

Find the number of possible arrangements of the letters.

9. A, B, C, D **10.** A, B, C, D, E **11.** A, A, C, D, E

12. A, C, C, D, D **13.** A, B, B, C, C, D **14.** A, A, B, B, B, C, D

15. Discuss and Write The face of a lock on a locker door has 10 digits ranging from 0 to 9. The combination that opens the lock is 5 digits long, and no digit is repeated. Explain how to find the number of possible lock combinations.

Combinations

Objective To find the number of combinations in a set of objects

Students are voting for 2 class representatives. The candidates are Arturo, Bella, Clara, Dan, and Edward. How many ways can the representatives be chosen?

To find how many ways, find the number of *combinations* of 2 candidates.

▶ A **combination** is an arrangement of objects where the order is *not* important.

Let A = Arturo; B = Bella; C = Clara; D = Dan; E = Edward.

The possible arrangements of 2 candidates are shown below. The combination of Arturo and Bella is listed twice, once as AB and again as BA. Other combinations are repeated as well. You can eliminate the repeated combinations (shown in red below).

AB	BA	CA	DA	EA
AC	BC	CB	DB	EB
AD	BD	CD	DC	EC
AE	BE	CE	DE	ED

So there are 10 possible combinations of representatives who can be chosen.

▶ There are formulas that you can use to find the combinations of *n* objects taken *n* at a time and combinations of *n* objects taken *r* at a time.

Key Concept

Combinations of *n* Objects Taken *r* at a Time, $_nC_r$

$$_nC_r = \frac{_nP_r}{r!} = \frac{n!}{r!(n-r)!}$$

Use the formula to find the number of possible combinations of class representatives, where $n = 5$ and $r = 2$.

$$_5C_2 = \frac{_5P_2}{2!} = \frac{5!}{2!(5-2)!}$$ ← Use the Combinations Formula.

$$= \frac{5 \cdot 4 \cdot 3 \cdot 2 \cdot 1}{2 \cdot 1 \cdot 3 \cdot 2 \cdot 1} = \frac{5 \cdot \overset{2}{4} \cdot 3 \cdot \overset{1}{2} \cdot 1}{\underset{1}{2} \cdot 1 \cdot 3 \cdot \underset{1}{2} \cdot 1}$$ ← Apply the definition of factorial, and simplify.

$$= 5 \cdot 2 = 10$$

There are 10 possible combinations.

▶ The combination of *n* objects taken *n* at a time, $_nC_n$, is 1.

How many ways can a committee of 5 be chosen from a club of 5 members?

There is only 1 way to choose a committee of 5 from a club of 5 members. That is, every member of the club must be on the committee.

Example

1 A summer camp that has 6 activities—swimming, canoeing, mountain biking, arts and crafts, archery, and hiking—a camper is to choose 3 activities to join. How many different sets of 3 activities can a camper choose?

To find how many sets of 3 activities, find the combinations of 6 objects taken 3 at a time.

$$_6C_3 = \frac{6!}{3!(6-3)!} = \frac{6 \cdot 5 \cdot 4 \cdot 3 \cdot 2 \cdot 1}{3 \cdot 2 \cdot 1 \cdot 3 \cdot 2 \cdot 1}$$ ←—Use the Combinations Formula; apply the definition of factorial.

$$= \frac{6 \cdot 5 \cdot 4 \cdot 3 \cdot 2 \cdot 1}{3 \cdot 2 \cdot 1 \cdot 3 \cdot 2 \cdot 1} = 5 \cdot 4$$ ←—Simplify.

$$= 20$$

So a camper can choose 20 sets of 3 activities.

▶ The Fundamental Counting Principle applies to combinations—that is, if one combination can occur in any of m ways and a second combination can occur in any of n ways, then the total number of ways both combinations can occur is $m \cdot n$.

Three students are chosen to form a team from 4 seventh graders and 6 eighth graders. How many different teams consisting of 1 seventh grader and 2 eighth graders can be chosen?

There are two different sets to select from: seventh graders and eighth graders. Thus, the choices of seventh graders and eighth graders are independent of each other.

• Find the combination of each set.

Seventh graders: $_4C_1 = \frac{4!}{1!(4-1)!}$

$$= \frac{4 \cdot 3 \cdot 2 \cdot 1}{1 \cdot 3 \cdot 2 \cdot 1}$$

$$= 4$$

Eighth graders: $_6C_2 = \frac{6!}{2!(6-2)!}$

$$= \frac{6 \cdot 5 \cdot 4 \cdot 3 \cdot 2 \cdot 1}{2 \cdot 1 \cdot 4 \cdot 3 \cdot 2 \cdot 1}$$

$$= 15$$

• Apply the Fundamental Counting Principle to find the total number of combinations.

$$_4C_1 \cdot {}_6C_2 = 4 \cdot 15 = 60$$

So 60 different teams consisting of 1 seventh grader and 2 eighth graders can be chosen.

Try These

Evaluate each expression.

1. $_4C_3$　　**2.** $_8C_5$　　**3.** $_9C_7$　　**4.** $_7C_4$

5. There are 5 points in a plane, no 3 of which are collinear. How many straight lines are determined?

6. An urn contains 7 red marbles and 5 green marbles. How many selections of 4 marbles will have 2 red and 2 green?

7. Discuss and Write Explain the difference between a combination and a permutation.

Go to PRACTICE BOOK Lesson 14-14 for exercise sets.

14-15

Technology:
Simulate Events

Objective To use a handheld to simulate events

A handheld can be a useful tool in conducting experiments. For example, by assigning numbers such as 1 for heads and 2 for tails, you can generate a list of random numbers to simulate the results of tossing a coin many times.

▶ You can use a handheld to find the experimental probability of landing on heads when tossing a coin.

Step 1 Press (⌂). Then press (1) to select **Calculator**. Press (menu), (1) for Actions, and (1) for Define.

Step 2 Type *x* 5. Then press (menu). Then choose (4) for **Probability**, (4) for **Random**, and (2) for **Integer**.

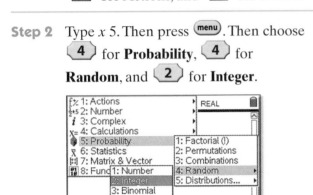

Step 3 Input (1, 2, 20). This will generate a list of 20 randomly generated 1's or 2's.

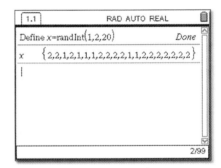

Your list will be different from the one shown because the numbers are generated at random.

If 1 represents heads and 2 represents tails, then in the simulation the coin landed on heads 6 times.

So the experimental probability of landing on heads is $\frac{6}{20}$, or 30%.

Hint
If you press (enter) again, the calculator will generate a different set of numbers.

▶ You can use a handheld to sort a list of randomly generated numbers to help find the experimental probability of landing on red or blue when spinning the spinner.

A spinner is divided into 4 equal sections labeled red, blue, green, and yellow. Find the experimental probability of landing on red or blue.

When dealing with a large quantity of numbers it may be helpful to sort the list. Let 1 represent red, 2 represent blue, 3 represent green, and 4 represent yellow.

Step 1 Press (menu). Then choose (1) for **Actions** and (1) for **Define**.

Step 2 Input *x* =. Then press (menu), (5) for **Probability**, (4) for **Random**, and (2) for **Integer**.

Step 3 Input (1, 4, 20). Then press (enter). This will define *x* as a list of 20 randomly generated integers between 1 and 4, inclusive.

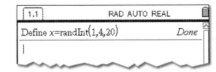

Step 4 Enter *x* to see the list.

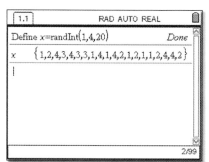

> **Remember:** Your list will be different from the one shown.

Step 5 Press (menu). Then choose (5) for **Statistics**, (4) for **List Operations**, and (1) for **Sort Ascending**. Then input *x*.

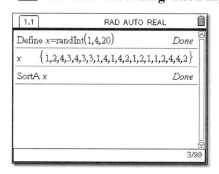

Step 6 Press (≈ enter). Then input *x* and press (≈ enter) to see the sorted list.

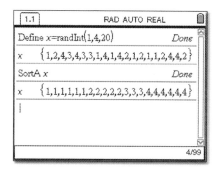

There are six 1's and five 2's in the list. This represents landing on red or blue 11 times. So the experimental probability of landing on red or blue is $\frac{11}{20} = 55\%$.

▶ You can compare the experimental probability with the theoretical probability.

The theoretical probability of landing on red is $\frac{1}{4}$ and the theoretical probability of landing on blue is $\frac{1}{4}$. The theoretical probability of landing on red or blue is $\frac{1}{4} + \frac{1}{4} = \frac{1}{2}$, or 50%.

So, in this case, the experimental probability is greater than the theoretical probability.

Try These

Use a handheld to simulate the experiment and find the experimental probability.

1. Rolling a 5 when rolling a number cube

2. Landing on tails when tossing a coin

3. Landing on C on a spinner divided into 3 equal parts labeled A, B, and C

4. Rolling a number greater than 3 when rolling a number cube

5. **Discuss and Write** Use a handheld to generate a list of random numbers to simulate tossing a coin 10 times. Then find the experimental probability of landing on tails. Repeat the experiment with 25 numbers, 50 numbers, and 100 numbers. What happens to the experimental probability when larger quantities of random numbers are used?

Go to PRACTICE BOOK Lesson 14-15 for exercise sets.

Technology:
Calculator Statistics

Objective **To use a handheld to analyze statistics**

In one game of bowling, Hugh's points per frame were 9, 11, 13, 8, 15, 18, 10, 9, 7, and 12. Find Hugh's total score, then the mean, median, and range for each frame.

▶ You can use a handheld to find the statistics on data.

Step 1 Press ⌂. Then choose **3** to select **Lists & Spreadsheets**.

Step 2 Input the scores in column A.

Step 3 Press menu **4** for **Statistics**, then **1** for **Stat Calculations**. Select **1** for **One-Variable Statistics**.

Step 4 Input 1 for number of lists. The next screen allows you to choose the list for which you will find the statistics and where you will store the statistics. Accept the defaults to use the data in column A (a[]) and to store the results in column B ([]).

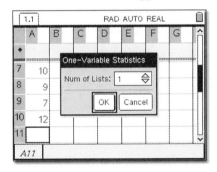
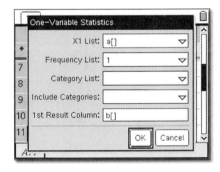

Step 5 Tab to OK and press enter. The statistics you need, in the order in which they appear, are $\bar{x}$, which is the mean, and Σx, which is the sum of the values in the list (that is, the Minimum, the Median, and the Maximum).

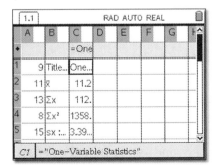

So Hugh's total score was 112.
The mean number of points per frame was 11.2.
The median number of points per frame was 10.5.
The range of the points per frame was the Max score
minus the Min score = 18 − 7 = 11.

► You can also use a handheld to make a scatter plot of
the data.

The table below shows the population of a town during several different years.

Year	1960	1970	1980	1990	2000	2010
Population	8500	9200	10,500	10,700	12,000	12,500

Step 1 Press 🏠. Then choose **3** to select
Lists & Spreadsheets.

Step 2 Name column A *year* and column B
pop. Enter the data from the table in
the appropriate columns.

Step 3 Press 🏠 **5**, then **menu** **2** for
Plot Properties. Then select **4** for
Add X Variable. Choose *year*.

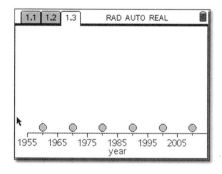

Step 4 Press **menu** **2** for **Plot Properties**.
Then select **6** for **Add Y Variable**.
Choose *pop*.

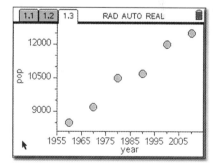

Try These

Use a handheld to find the mean, median, and range of the data.

1. 24, 41, 33, 28, 60, 32, 40, 59   **2.** 12, 18, 14, 28, 24, 22, 20, 16   **3.** 96, 8, 35, 68, 70, 36, 14, 55

4. Discuss and Write Use a handheld to make a scatter plot of the data in the
table. What type of correlation do the data show? Explain.

Day	1	2	3	4	5	6	7
Dog Food (lbs)	35	32	31	27	25	22	19

Go to PRACTICE BOOK **Lesson 14-16 for exercise sets.**

Problem Solving: Review of Strategies

> Read > Plan > Solve > Check >

Objective To solve problems by using a variety of strategies

Problem: Mia is walking from north to south across a pedestrian bridge that runs parallel to a railroad bridge. Each bridge is 1 mile long. Mia is $\frac{3}{8}$ of the way across the pedestrian bridge when she looks back and sees a train approaching the railroad bridge. Mia wonders if she can "beat the train" across. She can run at a top speed of 10 miles per hour. If Mia turns and runs north, she will be able to reach the beginning of her bridge before the train starts across its bridge. If she instead runs south, she will also just make it, reaching the end of her bridge just as the train reaches the end of its bridge. How fast is the train going?

Read to understand what is being asked.

List the facts and restate the question.

Facts: Mia walks from north to south and is $\frac{3}{8}$ of the way across a 1-mile pedestrian bridge that runs parallel to a railroad bridge.

A train approaches the north end of the railroad bridge.

Mia can run 10 miles per hour.

If Mia runs north, she will reach the start of her bridge just as the train reaches the start of its bridge; if Mia runs south, she will reach the end of her bridge, just as the train reaches the end of its bridge.

Question: How fast is the train going?

Select a strategy.

You can try using the strategy *Adopt a Different Point of View.* Or, you can attempt to *Use Logical Reasoning.*

Apply the strategy.

▶ **Method 1: Adopt a Different Point of View**

Imagine that there are two Mias. Mia A runs north toward the beginning of the bridge, and Mia B runs south to the end. Mia A runs $\frac{3}{8}$ mile and reaches the beginning of her bridge just as the train reaches the beginning of the railroad bridge. During this same time, Mia B also runs $\frac{3}{8}$ mile, which is $\left(\frac{3}{8} + \frac{3}{8}\right)$, or $\frac{3}{4}$, of the way along the bridge, leaving her $\frac{1}{4}$ mile to travel when the train reaches the beginning of the railroad bridge.

Problem-Solving Strategies
1. Make a Drawing
2. Solve a Simpler Problem
3. Reason Logically
4. Consider Extreme Cases
5. Work Backward
6. Find a Pattern
7. Account for All Possibilities
8. Adopt a Different Point of View
9. Guess and Test
10. Organize Data

The train will travel the entire 1-mile railroad bridge in the same time it takes Mia B to travel $\frac{1}{4}$ mile. The train must be going 4 times as fast as Mia B, whose speed is 10 miles per hour. The train is therefore traveling at 40 miles per hour.

▶ Method 2: Use Logical Reasoning

Let r represent the train's speed, and let d represent the train's distance from the bridge when Mia sees it.

- If Mia runs $\frac{3}{8}$ mile to the beginning of her bridge at a speed of 10 miles per hour, and since time $= \frac{\text{distance}}{\text{speed}} = \frac{d}{r}$, then it will take her $\left(\frac{3}{8} \div 10\right)$, or $\frac{3}{80}$, hour, to get there. This is the same time it takes the train to reach the start of the railroad bridge. So $\frac{d}{r} = \frac{3}{80}$.

- If Mia runs $\frac{5}{8}$ mile to the end of her bridge at a speed of 10 miles per hour, then it will take her $\left(\frac{5}{8} \div 10\right)$, or $\frac{5}{80}$, hour, to get there. This is the same time it takes the train to travel to the railroad bridge, a distance of d miles, and then across it, a distance of 1 mile. So $\frac{d+1}{r} = \frac{5}{80}$.

- Now, you have two equations in two variables: $\frac{d}{r} = \frac{3}{80}$ and $\frac{d+1}{r} = \frac{5}{80}$. Solve *both* equations for d.

$$\frac{d}{r} = \frac{3}{80}$$

$$r\left(\frac{d}{r}\right) = r\left(\frac{3}{80}\right) \quad \longleftarrow \text{To isolate } d, \text{ use the Multiplication Property of Equality.}$$

$$d = \frac{3}{80}r \quad \longleftarrow \text{Simplify.}$$

$$\frac{d+1}{r} = \frac{5}{80}$$

$$r\left(\frac{d+1}{r}\right) = r\left(\frac{5}{80}\right) \quad \longleftarrow \text{Use the Multiplication Property of Equality.}$$

$$d + 1 - 1 = \frac{5}{80}r - 1 \quad \longleftarrow \text{Use the Subtraction Property of Equality.}$$

$$d = \frac{5}{80}r - 1 \quad \longleftarrow \text{Simplify.}$$

Note that the right sides of these equations are both equal to d, so $\frac{3}{80}r = \frac{5}{80}r - 1$.

- Solve for r.

$$\frac{3}{80}r = \frac{5}{80}r - 1$$

$$80\left(\frac{3}{80}r\right) = 80(5r - 1) \quad \longleftarrow \text{Use the Multiplication Property of Equality.}$$

$$3r + 80 = 5r - 80 + 80 \quad \longleftarrow \text{Use the Addition Property of Equality.}$$

$$3r - 3r + 80 = 5r - 3r \quad \longleftarrow \text{Use the Subtraction Property of Equality.}$$

$$80 \div 2 = 2r \div 2 \quad \longleftarrow \text{Use the Division Property of Equality.}$$

$$40 = r$$

So the train was traveling at a speed of 40 miles per hour.

Check to make sure your answer makes sense.

You can use the equation $d = \frac{3}{80}r$ from Strategy 2 to find that the train's distance (d), from the bridge is $\left(\frac{3}{80} \bullet 40\right)$, or 1.5, miles. The train traveled a total distance of $(1 + 1.5)$, or 2.5, miles. At 40 miles per hour, this would take $(2.5 \div 40)$, or $\frac{1}{16}$, hour. At 10 miles per hour, Mia can run the $\frac{5}{8}$ mile to the end of her bridge in $\left(\frac{5}{8} \div 10\right)$, or $\frac{1}{16}$, hour. These times should be equal, and they are. The answer checks. ✓

Go to ▶ PRACTICE BOOK Lesson 14-17 for exercise sets.

Enrichment:
Geometric Probability

A horizontal segment is 6 feet long. One point is chosen at random from the segment. What is the probability of the point being no more than 1.2 feet from the left end of the segment?

To find the probability, you might try using the definition of the probability of an event E.

> **Remember:**
>
> $P(E) = \dfrac{\text{number of favorable outcomes}}{\text{number of possible outcomes}}$

However, in this situation, it is not possible to count the points. How then can you find the probability?

The sketch below represents the entire 6-foot segment, and the part that is no more than 1.2 feet from the left end of the segment.

|←——————— 6 ft ———————→|
|——| 1.2 ft

You can use the lengths of the segments to determine the probability. The ratio of the number of points in the 1.2-foot section to the number of points in the entire line segment is simply the ratio of the lengths.

$P(\text{point is 1.2 feet from end}) = \dfrac{\text{length of favorable part segment}}{\text{length of entire segment}}$

$= \dfrac{1.2 \text{ feet}}{6 \text{ feet}}$

$= 0.2$

So the probability of the chosen point being no more than 1.2 feet from the left end of the segment is 0.2, or 20%.

▶ Probabilities found by considering lengths, areas, volumes, angles, and other geometric measures are referred to as geometric probabilities.

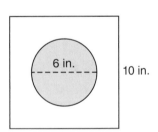

A square board measures 10 inches on each side. On the board is a circle that is 6 inches in diameter. A point on the board is chosen at random. What is the probability that the point lies in the circle?

To find the probability, consider the areas of the regions.

$P(\text{point is in the circle}) = \dfrac{\text{area of circular region}}{\text{area of entire square}}$

> **Remember:**
> Area of a circle: $A = \pi r^2$
> Area of a square: $A = s^2$

$= \dfrac{\pi (3 \text{ in.})^2}{(10 \text{ in.})^2}$

$= \dfrac{9\pi \text{ in.}^2}{100 \text{ in.}^2}$

≈ 0.28

So the probability of the chosen point lying in the circle is about 28%.

▶ You can also create a geometric figure that represents a given probability.

Jon wants to create a figure with red, blue, green, and yellow regions so that when a dart randomly hits the figure, the probabilities are as follows:

$P(\text{red}) = \dfrac{1}{6}$ $P(\text{blue}) = \dfrac{2}{5}$ $P(\text{green}) = \dfrac{1}{3}$ $P(\text{yellow}) = \dfrac{1}{10}$

What might Jon do?

There are many ways, such as the ones given below, Jon could make the figure.

- Jon could make a rectangle that has an area of 30 square units (for example, 3 by 10 or 5 by 6), and draw squares that are each 1 square unit. He could then color 5 squares $\left(\dfrac{1}{6}\text{ of the squares}\right)$ red, 12 squares $\left(\dfrac{2}{5}\text{ of the squares}\right)$ blue, 10 squares $\left(\dfrac{1}{3}\text{ of the squares}\right)$ green, and 3 squares $\left(\dfrac{1}{10}\text{ of the squares}\right)$ yellow.

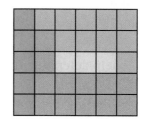

- Jon could also make a circular region with different-colored sectors. He could use the given probabilities to determine the central angle measures of the sectors.

$\text{m}\angle \text{ for red} = \dfrac{1}{6}(360°) = 60°$

$\text{m}\angle \text{ for blue} = \dfrac{2}{5}(360°) = 144°$

$\text{m}\angle \text{ for green} = \dfrac{1}{3}(360°) = 120°$

$\text{m}\angle \text{ for yellow} = \dfrac{1}{10}(360°) = 36°$

Remember:
A complete circle is 360°.

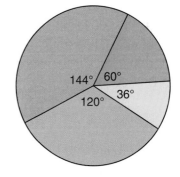

Try These

Solve.

1. A number is chosen at random from the part of a number line from 0 to 2. What is the probability the number will be between 0.8 and 1.4?

2. A target consists of three concentric circles with radii 3 inches, 6 inches, and 9 inches. An arrow is aimed randomly but always hits the target. What is the probability the arrow hits the outermost ring?

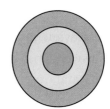

3. A trained skydiver jumps out of a plane and anticipates landing on a 10m by 10m square landing area below. On this area there is a target in the shape of an equilateral triangle with the sides of 2m. Assuming the jumper is certain to land within the square area, what is the probability the skydiver will land in the target?

4. **Discuss and Write** Annie looked at the four-color circular region (blue, red, yellow, and green) that Jon made above. She said, "The drawing is wrong. There are four colors, so the probability of each color must be $\dfrac{1}{4}$." What is incorrect with Annie's reasoning?

Test Prep: Extended-Response Questions
Strategy: Organize Information

Some extended-response questions may require you to work with data or consider multiple possibilities. To solve this type of problem, you can *make an organized list.*

Look at the sample test item.

Read the test item.

- Reread the test item carefully. Pay close attention to diagrams.

- Make a list to help determine the possible outcomes.

  Find the possible outcomes, and determine how many of them satisfy the given conditions.

Solve the problem.

- Apply an appropriate problem-solving strategy.

  Make a list of all of the possible outcomes.
  Note those that have exactly one A or exactly two Cs.

  AAA AAB AAC ABA ABB ABC ACA ACB ACC
  BAA BAB BAC BBA BBB BBC BCA BCB BCC
  CAA CAB CAC CBA CBB CBC CCA CCB CCC

Part A: Count the number of outcomes in the list.

Answer: There are 27 possible outcomes.

Part B: Look at the items in the list. Note that 15 of the 27 possible outcomes have exactly one A or exactly two C's.

Answer: The probability is $\frac{15}{27} = \frac{5}{9}$.

┌─ **Sample Test Item** ─────────
A spinner is divided into 3 equal parts, as shown.

Part A Isaac spins the spinner 3 times. How many possible outcomes are there?

Part B What is the probability that A is landed on exactly once or C is landed on exactly twice?

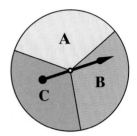

.**Test-Taking Tips**

- Reread the test item.

- Use the Test-Prep strategy.

- Apply appropriate rules, definitions, properties, or strategies.

- Analyze your answers.

.**Hint**
Create the list in a systematic way, such as starting with all of the possibilities if A is landed on first.

Item Analysis

Check your work. Review your organized list.

- Analyze your answer. Does it make sense?

  Use the Fundamental Counting Principle to check that you have listed all possibilities.

  Since the question represents mutually exclusive events, you can add the probabilities.

  $P(A \text{ or } C) = \frac{10}{27} + \frac{5}{27} = \frac{15}{27} = \frac{5}{9}$ ✓

Try These

Solve. Try using an organized list. Answer all parts.

1. The temperatures at noon during one week were 76°F, 74°F, 82°F, 70°F, 63°F, 76°F, and 77°F.

   Part A Find the mean, median, and mode of the temperatures.
   Part B Make a box-and-whisker plot.

A review of prerequisite skills necessary to understand the skills and concepts of Algebra 1

I. Place Value

▶ An **exponent** is a number that tells how many times the base is used as a factor.

Positive powers of 10 are used to show whole-number place value. For positive powers of 10, the exponent indicates the number of zeros in the product.

Negative powers of 10 are used to show decimal place value. For negative powers of 10, the digit in the exponent indicates the number of decimal places.

Any number, except 0, to the zero power is 1.

base   exponent

$$10^3 = 10 \cdot 10 \cdot 10 = 1000$$

power of 10   10 is a factor 3 times

$$10^{-3} = 0.001 \longleftarrow 3 \text{ decimal places}$$

$$10^0 = 1$$

▶ In the decimal system, the value of each place is a different power of 10.

Billions	Hundred Millions	Ten Millions	Millions	Hundred Thousands	Ten Thousands	Thousands	Hundreds	Tens	Ones	Tenths	Hundredths	Thousandths	Ten-Thousandths
1,000,000,000	100,000,000	10,000,000	1,000,000	100,000	10,000	1000	100	10	1	0.1	0.01	0.001	0.0001
10^9	10^8	10^7	10^6	10^5	10^4	10^3	10^2	10^1	10^0	10^{-1}	10^{-2}	10^{-3}	10^{-4}
1	0	4	0	0	0	3	0	6	5.	0	0	2	1

Standard Form: 1,040,003,065.0021

Read as: 1 billion, 40 million, 3 thousand, 65 *and* 21 ten-thousandths

Expanded Form:

$$(1 \times 10^9) + (4 \times 10^7) + (3 \times 10^3) + (6 \times 10^1) + (5 \times 10^0) + (2 \times 10^{-3}) + (1 \times 10^{-4})$$

II. Estimation: Rounding and Compatible Numbers

▶ To use **rounding** to estimate a decimal sum:
- Round each decimal to the greatest nonzero place of the least number.
- Add the rounded numbers.

Estimate: 1.8443 + 0.2715 + 0.3906

$$
\begin{array}{rcr}
 & & 1 \\
1.8443 & \longrightarrow & 1.8 \\
0.2715 & \longrightarrow & 0.3 \\
+ 0.3906 & \longrightarrow & + 0.4 \\
\hline
 & & 2.5 \\
\end{array}
$$

▶ To use **compatible numbers** to estimate decimal quotients:
- Think of nearby numbers that are compatible.
- Divide.

Remember: Compatible numbers are numbers that are easy to compute with mentally.

Estimate: 7.435 ÷ 8

$$8\overline{)7.4\,3\,5} \longrightarrow \overset{0.9}{8\overline{)7.2\,0}}$$

So 7.435 ÷ 8 ≈ 0.9.

.Think.........
8 and 72 are compatible numbers.

Estimate: 1.824 ÷ 32

$$32\overline{)1.8\,2\,4} \longrightarrow \overset{6 \text{ hundredths}}{30\overline{)180}} \text{ hundredths}$$

So 1.824 ÷ 32 ≈ 0.06.

.Think.........
30 and 180 are compatible numbers.

REVIEW OF PREREQUISITE SKILLS

III. Divisibility Rules

▶ A number is **divisible** by another number if there is no remainder when you divide.

Divisibility Rules	
A number is divisible by:	**if:**
2	it is an even number (ends in 0, 2, 4, 6, or 8)
3	the sum of its digits is divisible by 3
4	the last two digits form a number divisible by 4
5	the ones digit is 0 or 5
6	it is divisible by both 2 and 3
8	the last three digits form a number divisible by 8
9	the sum of its digits is divisible by 9
10	the last digit is 0

Determine whether 759,024 is divisible by 2, 3, 4, 5, 6, 8, 9, and/or 10.

2	759,024 ⟶ 4 is an even number.	759,024 is divisible by 2.
3	759,024 ⟶ $7 + 5 + 9 + 0 + 2 + 4 = 27$ and $27 \div 3 = 9$	759,024 is divisible by 3.
4	759,024 ⟶ $24 \div 4 = 6$	759,024 is divisible by 4.
5	759,024 ⟶ 4 is not 0 or 5.	759,024 is *not* divisible by 5.
6	759,024 ⟶ 4 is an even number and $7 + 5 + 9 + 0 + 2 + 4 = 27$ and $27 \div 3 = 9$.	759,024 is divisible by 6.
8	759,024 ⟶ $24 \div 8 = 3$	759,024 is divisible by 8.
9	759,024 ⟶ $7 + 5 + 9 + 0 + 2 + 4 = 27$ and $27 \div 9 = 3$	759,024 is divisible by 9.
10	759,024 ⟶ 4 is not 0.	759,024 is *not* divisible by 10.

IV. Prime and Composite Numbers

▶ A **prime number** is a whole number greater than 1 that has *exactly two factors*, itself and 1.

Find all the factors of 23.

$1 \cdot 23 = 23$ Factors of 23: 1, 23

Since 23 has exactly two factors, 23 is a prime number.

> The numbers 0 and 1 are neither prime nor composite.

▶ A **composite number** is a whole number, other than 0, that has more than two factors.

Find all the factors of 136.

$1 \cdot 136 = 136$ $4 \cdot 34 = 136$
$2 \cdot 68 = 136$ $8 \cdot 17 = 136$

Factors of 136: 1, 2, 4, 8, 17, 34, 68, 136

Since 136 has more than two factors, 136 is a composite number.

V. GCF and LCM (See pp. 404–405)

▶ The **greatest common factor (GCF)** of two or more numbers is the greatest number that is a factor of these numbers. To find the GCF of two or more numbers, first find the prime factors of each number. Then multiply the common prime factors of these numbers to find the GCF.

Find the GCF of 45, 60, and 75.

$45 = 3 \cdot 3 \cdot 5$ $60 = 2 \cdot 2 \cdot 3 \cdot 5$ $75 = 3 \cdot 5 \cdot 5$ GCF: $3 \cdot 5 = 15$

Continue Lesson ➡

► The **least common multiple** (LCM) of two or more numbers is the least number, except 0, that is a common multiple of both (or all) of the numbers. To find the LCM of two or more numbers, first find the prime factors of each number. Then write each prime factor the greatest number of times it occurs in any of the numbers, and multiply these factors to find the LCM.

Find the LCM of 8, 12, and 36.

$8 = 2 \cdot 2 \cdot 2$ $12 = 2 \cdot 2 \cdot 3$ $36 = 2 \cdot 2 \cdot 3 \cdot 3$

LCM: $2 \cdot 2 \cdot 2 \cdot 3 \cdot 3 = 72$

So the LCM of 8, 12, and 36 is 72.

.Think.............
As a factor, 2 occurs at most three times and 3 occurs at most two times.

VI. Multiply and Divide Decimals...

► To **multiply a decimal** by a whole number or another decimal:
  • Multiply as you would with whole numbers.
  • Count the number of decimal places in both factors.
  • Mark off the *same* number of decimal places in the product.

Multiply: 48×0.68

$$
\begin{array}{r}
0.6\,8 \\
\times \quad 4\,8 \\
\hline
5\,4\,4 \\
+2\,7\,2 \quad\; \\
\hline
3\,2.6\,4
\end{array}
$$
2 decimal places

Find the product: 0.42×0.329

$$
\begin{array}{r}
0.3\,2\,9 \quad \leftarrow \text{3 decimal places}\\
\times \quad 0.4\,2 \quad \leftarrow \text{2 decimal places}\\
\hline
6\,5\,8 \\
+1\,3\,1\,6 \quad\;\; \\
\hline
0.1\,3\,8\,1\,8 \quad \leftarrow \text{5 decimal places}
\end{array}
$$

► To **divide by a decimal**:
  • Move the decimal point in the *divisor* to form a whole-number divisor.
  • Move the decimal point in the *dividend* to the right *the same number* of places.
  • Write the decimal point in the quotient directly above the decimal point in the dividend.
  • Divide as you would with whole numbers.

Divide: $1.272 \div 2.4$

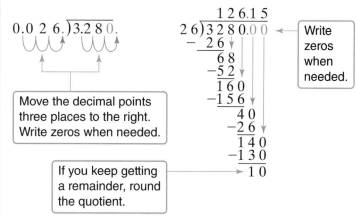

Find the quotient: $3.28 \div 0.026$

Move the decimal points one place to the right.

Move the decimal points three places to the right. Write zeros when needed.

If you keep getting a remainder, round the quotient.

Write zeros when needed.

VII. Mixed Numbers and Fractions

Rename $2\frac{3}{8}$ as a fraction.

▶To **rename a mixed number** as a fraction:
- Multiply the whole number by the denominator.
- Add the product to the numerator.
- Write the sum as the numerator and the given denominator as the denominator.

$$2\frac{3}{8} = \frac{(8 \cdot 2) + 3}{8}$$
$$= \frac{16 + 3}{8} = \frac{19}{8} \quad \longleftarrow \text{fraction}$$

Rename $\frac{38}{4}$ as a mixed number.

▶To **rename a fraction greater than 1** as a mixed number:
- Divide the numerator by the denominator. Write the quotient as the whole number part.
- If there is a remainder, write it over the denominator and express the fraction in simplest form.

$$\frac{38}{4} \longrightarrow 4\overline{)38}\,{}^{9\,R2} \qquad \frac{38}{4} = 9\frac{2}{4}$$
$$= 9\frac{1}{2} \quad \longleftarrow \text{mixed number}$$

VIII. Add and Subtract Fractions

▶To **add**, or **subtract**, **fractions**:
- Find the least common denominator (LCD) of the fractions.
- Rename each fraction as an equivalent fraction with the LCD as the denominator.
- Add, or subtract, the numerators. Write the sum, or difference, over the common denominator and express the answer in simplest form.

Add: $\frac{9}{16} + \frac{7}{8} + \frac{3}{4}$

$$\frac{9}{16} = \frac{9}{16}$$
$$\frac{7}{8} = \frac{7 \cdot 2}{8 \cdot 2} = \frac{14}{16}$$
$$+ \frac{3}{4} = \frac{3 \cdot 4}{4 \cdot 4} = \frac{12}{16}$$
$$\frac{35}{16} = 2\frac{3}{16} \quad \longleftarrow \text{simplest form}$$

Think
LCD of $\frac{9}{16}$, $\frac{7}{8}$, and $\frac{3}{4}$: 16

Subtract: $\frac{1}{2} - \frac{1}{10}$

$$\frac{1}{2} = \frac{1 \cdot 5}{2 \cdot 5} = \frac{5}{10}$$
$$- \frac{1}{10} = \frac{1}{10}$$
$$\frac{4}{10} = \frac{2}{5} \quad \longleftarrow \text{simplest form}$$

Think
LCD of $\frac{1}{2}$ and $\frac{1}{10}$: 10

IX. Multiply and Divide Fractions

▶To **multiply fractions** using the greatest common factor (GCF):
- Divide *any* numerator and denominator by their GCF.
- Multiply the numerators. Then multiply the denominators. The product will be in simplest form.

Multiply: $\frac{2}{3} \cdot \frac{3}{8}$

$$\frac{2}{3} \cdot \frac{3}{8} = \frac{\overset{1}{\cancel{2}}}{\cancel{3}} \cdot \frac{\overset{1}{\cancel{3}}}{\cancel{8}_{4}}$$
$$= \frac{1 \cdot 1}{1 \cdot 4} = \frac{1}{4} \quad \longleftarrow \text{simplest form}$$

▶To **divide fractions**:
- Multiply by the *reciprocal* of the divisor.
- Simplify using the GCF, where possible. Then multiply the numerators and the denominators.
- Rename the product as a whole or mixed number when needed.

Find the quotient: $\frac{9}{10} \div \frac{3}{5}$

$$\frac{9}{10} \div \frac{3}{5} = \frac{9}{10} \cdot \frac{5}{3} = \frac{\overset{3}{\cancel{9}}}{\cancel{10}_{2}} \cdot \frac{\overset{1}{\cancel{5}}}{\cancel{3}_{1}}$$
$$= \frac{3 \cdot 1}{2 \cdot 1} = \frac{3}{2} = 1\frac{1}{2} \quad \longleftarrow \text{mixed number}$$

REVIEW OF PREREQUISITE SKILLS

X. Decimals, Fractions, and Percents

▶ A **percent** is a ratio that compares a number to 100. Percent means *hundredths*, or *per hundred*. The symbol for percent is **%**. A **percent proportion** can be used to write a fraction or a decimal as a percent.

Write $\frac{5}{12}$ as a percent.

$$\frac{5}{12} = \frac{?}{\underline{\quad}} \longrightarrow \frac{5}{12} = \frac{x}{100}$$

$$500 = 12x \longleftarrow \text{Use the Cross-Products Rule.}$$

$$\frac{500}{12} = \frac{12x}{12} \longleftarrow \text{Divide both sides by 12.}$$

$$41\frac{2}{3} = x$$

So $\frac{5}{12} = \frac{41\frac{2}{3}}{100} = 41\frac{2}{3}\%$.

Write 0.123 as a percent.

$$0.123 = \frac{123}{1000} \longrightarrow \frac{123}{1000} = \frac{x}{100}$$

$$12{,}300 = 1000x \longleftarrow \text{Use the Cross-Products Rule.}$$

$$\frac{12{,}300}{1000} = \frac{1000x}{1000} \longleftarrow \text{Divide both sides by 1000.}$$

$$12.3 = x$$

So $0.123 = \frac{12.3}{100} = 12.3\%$.

Write $37\frac{1}{2}\%$ as a fraction in simplest form.

$$37\frac{1}{2}\% = \frac{37\frac{1}{2}}{100} = 37\frac{1}{2} \div 100$$

$$= \frac{\overset{3}{\cancel{75}}}{2} \cdot \frac{1}{\underset{4}{\cancel{100}}} = \frac{3}{8}$$

So $37\frac{1}{2}\% = \frac{3}{8}$.

Write 64.7% as a decimal.

$$64.7\% = \frac{64.7}{100} = 0.647$$

or

$$64.7\% \longrightarrow .64.7 \longrightarrow 0.647$$

So $64.7\% = 0.647$.

Remember: Dividing by 100 is the same as moving the decimal point two places to the *left*.

▶ You can use the **Percentage Formula** to find the percentage, p, of a number, rate, r, or base, b.

Percentage Formula
percentage = rate • base ($p = rb$)

Mrs. Graham receives $2\frac{1}{2}\%$ commission on her total sales at Colony Furniture. In order to earn $300 in commission, what would her total sales have to be?

To find her total sales, find $2\frac{1}{2}\%$ of *what amount* is $300.

• First estimate using compatible numbers.

$$\frac{\$300}{2\frac{1}{2}\%} \approx \frac{\$300}{0.03} = \$10{,}000$$

.Think.......
$2\frac{1}{2}\% \approx 3\%$

• Then use a formula or solve and write a percent proportion to find the base, b.

$$b = \frac{p}{r} = \frac{\$300}{2\frac{1}{2}\%} \longleftarrow \text{Substitute values for } p \text{ and } r; \text{ rename } 2\frac{1}{2}\% \text{ as a decimal.}$$

$$= \frac{\$300}{0.025} = \$12{,}000 \longleftarrow \text{Simplify.}$$

.Think.......
$12,000 is close to the estimate of $10,000.

Mrs. Graham's total sales have to be $12,000.

XI. The Coordinate Plane (See pp. 407–408)

A **coordinate plane**, or grid, is formed by two number lines, called **coordinate axes**, with the horizontal line, as the *x*-axis, and the vertical line, as the *y*-axis. The point where the axes intersect is $(0, 0)$, called the **origin**. The axes divide the coordinate plane into four sections, called **quadrants**.

Continue Lesson ➡

REVIEW OF PREREQUISITE SKILLS

▶ An **ordered pair (x, y)** locates a point on a coordinate plane. The numbers *x* and *y* are called **coordinates**.

To locate, or graph, a point on a coordinate plane:

- Start at (0, 0). Move *right* or *left* the number of units indicated by the *x-coordinate*. The positive (+) sign tells you to move right and the negative (−) sign tells you to move left.
- Then, from that point, move *up* or *down* the number of units indicated by the *y-coordinate*. The positive (+) tells you to move up, and the negative (−) sign tells you to move down.

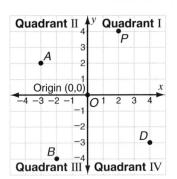

x   y
↓   ↓

$(-3, 2)$ locates the point *A*.

Point *A* is in quadrant II.

XII. Transformations on the Coordinate Plane...............................

A **transformation** is the change in the position or size of a figure. If the pre-image, or original figure, is named *ABC*, then the transformed figure, or image, is named *A′B′C′* (*A* prime, *B* prime, *C* prime). Transformations include **reflections** (flips), **translations** (slides), **rotations** (turns), and **dilations** (enlargements or reductions).

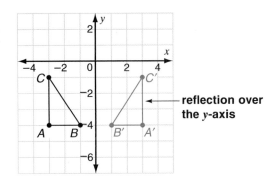

reflection over the *y*-axis

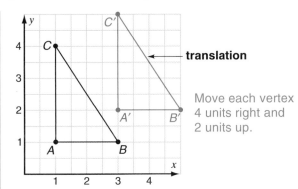

translation

Move each vertex 4 units right and 2 units up.

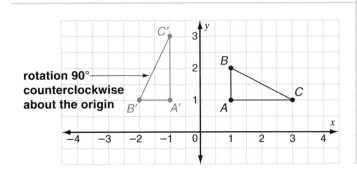

rotation 90° counterclockwise about the origin

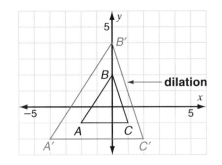

dilation

XIII. Metric and Customary Systems of Measurements (See pp. 408–409)......

▶ For a listing of **metric and customary units of measure**, see the *Measurement Conversions* on page 434. Multiply or divide to rename units of measurement.

- *Multiply* to rename larger units as smaller units.

7 km = __?__ m

7 km = (7 × 1000) m = 7000 m

.Think...........
1 km = 1000 m

18 gal = __?__ qt

18 gal = (18 × 4) qt = 72 qt

.Think.........
1 gal = 4 qt

Continue Lesson ➡

REVIEW OF PREREQUISITE SKILLS

- *Divide* to rename smaller units as larger units.

240 cm = __?__ m

240 cm = (240 ÷ 100) m = 2.4 m

.Think..........
100 cm = 1 m

56 oz = __?__ lb

56 oz = (56 ÷ 16) lb = $3\frac{1}{2}$ lb

.Think..........
16 oz = 1 lb

▶ You can add, subtract, or multiply measures.

$$\begin{array}{r} 5 \text{ m} \quad 90 \text{ cm} \\ + \ 8 \text{ m} \quad 18 \text{ cm} \\ \hline 13 \text{ m } 108 \text{ cm} = 14 \text{ m } 8 \text{ cm or} \\ 14.08 \text{ m} \end{array}$$

.Think..........
13 m 108 cm
= 13 m + 1 m 8 cm
= 14 ft 8 cm

$$\begin{array}{r} \overset{3}{\cancel{4}} \text{ gal } \overset{6}{\cancel{2}} \text{ qt} \\ - \ 2 \text{ gal } 3 \text{ qt} \\ \hline 1 \text{ gal } 3 \text{ qt or } 1\frac{3}{4} \text{ gal} \end{array}$$

.Think..........
4 gal 2 qt
= 3 gal 4 qt + 2 qt
= 3 gal 6 qt

$$\begin{array}{r} 5 \text{ T} \quad 500 \text{ lb} \\ \times \qquad\qquad 9 \\ \hline 45 \text{ T } 4500 \text{ lb} = 47 \text{ T } 500 \text{ lb or} \\ 47\frac{1}{4} \text{ T} \end{array}$$

.Think..........
45 T 4500 lb
= 45 T + 2 T 500 lb
= 47 T 500 lb

XIV. Basic Geometric Terms and Angle Classifications (See pp. 409–410)......

Description	Figure	Symbol	Read
point: an exact location in space, usually represented by a dot	•R	R	"point R"
line: a set of points in place that forms a straight path and extends indefinitely in opposite directions	$\overleftrightarrow{BC}$, $\overleftrightarrow{CB}$	"line BC," "line CB"
line segment: part of a line with two endpoints	$\overline{MN}$, $\overline{NM}$	"segment MN," "segment NM"
ray: part of a line with one endpoint	$\overrightarrow{GH}$	"ray GH"
angle: formed by two rays with a common endpoint, called the vertex	$\angle Q$, $\angle PQR$, $\angle RQP$	"angle Q," "angle PQR," "angle RQP"
plane: a flat surface that extends indefinitely in all directions	RJK	"plane RJK"
intersecting lines: lines that lie in the same plane and meet at a point		"Lines LM and NP intersect at O."

▶ Angles can be classified according to their degree measures.

right
$x = 90$

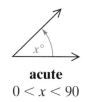
acute
$0 < x < 90$

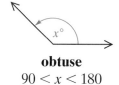
obtuse
$90 < x < 180$

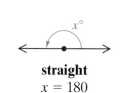
straight
$x = 180$

Continue Lesson ➡

REVIEW OF PREREQUISITE SKILLS

► A **protractor** is used to measure or draw an angle.

To measure ∠*XYZ*:

- Using the inner scale, place the center mark of the protractor on the vertex of the angle, *Y*, with $\overrightarrow{YX}$ pointing to 0°.

- Read the measure of the angle where $\overrightarrow{YZ}$ crosses the protractor.

To draw an angle of 140°:

- Draw a base ray, $\overrightarrow{YN}$. Use the outer scale. Place the center mark of the protractor on *Y* with $\overrightarrow{YN}$ pointing to 0°.

- Mark *P* at 140°. Draw $\overrightarrow{YP}$.

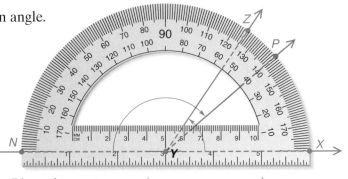

m∠*NYP* = 140°

m∠*XYZ* = 55°

XV. Polygons and Circles..

► **Polygons** are closed plane figures formed by line segments that meet only at their endpoints. In a **regular polygon**, all sides have the same length, and all angles have the same measure. An **irregular polygon** is any polygon that is not regular. Polygons can be classified by the number of sides.

Polygon	Number of Sides	Polygon	Number of Sides
triangle	3	heptagon	7
quadrilateral	4	octagon	8
pentagon	5	nonagon	9
hexagon	6	decagon	10

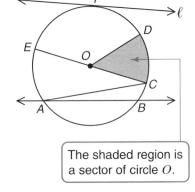

irregular polygon   regular polygon

open plane figure; *not* a polygon

► A **circle** is a set of points in a plane, all of which are the same distance from a given point, called the *center*. A circle is named by its center.

- A **tangent** ℓ, is a line intersecting a circle in exactly one point.

- A **secant** $\overleftrightarrow{AB}$, is a line intersecting a circle in two points.

- A **chord** $\overline{AC}$, of a circle is a segment whose endpoints are on the circle. A **diameter** $\overline{CE}$, is a chord that contains the center of a circle. A **radius** $\overline{OD}$, is a line segment from the center of a circle to any point of the circle.

- A **central angle** ∠*DOC*, has its vertex at the center and its sides contain the radii of the circle.

- An **inscribed angle** ∠*ACE*, has its vertex on the circle and its sides contain the chords of the circle.

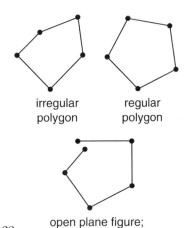

The shaded region is a sector of circle *O*.

► An **arc** is a part of a circle, with all of its points on the circle. The arc measure of a circle is 360°.

- A **semicircle** is an arc that connects the endpoints of a diameter and measures 180°.

- A **major arc** is an arc greater than a semicircle and measures greater than 180°.

- A **minor arc** is an arc less than a semicircle and measures less than 180°.

In circle *O* above, the measure of semicircle $\overparen{EDC}$ = 180°, the measure of minor arc $\overparen{EPD}$ < 180°, and the measure of major arc $\overparen{EBD}$ > 180°.

XVI. Similarity and Congruence

▶ **Similar figures** have the same shape, and the same or different size. Two figures are similar polygons if their corresponding angles are congruent and the lengths of their corresponding sides are proportional.

To determine whether the two polygons $ABCD$ and $EFGH$ shown at the right are similar:

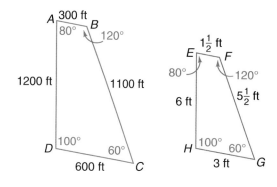

• Compare the corresponding angles.

$\angle A \cong \angle E \qquad \angle B \cong \angle F$
$\angle C \cong \angle G \qquad \angle D \cong \angle H$ — Corresponding angles are congruent.

• Compare the ratios of the lengths of the corresponding sides.

$$\frac{AB}{EF} = \frac{300 \text{ ft}}{1\frac{1}{2} \text{ ft}} = \frac{200}{1} \qquad \frac{BC}{FG} = \frac{1100 \text{ ft}}{5\frac{1}{2} \text{ ft}} = \frac{200}{1}$$

$$\frac{CD}{GH} = \frac{600 \text{ ft}}{3 \text{ ft}} = \frac{200}{1} \qquad \frac{DA}{HE} = \frac{1200 \text{ ft}}{6 \text{ ft}} = \frac{200}{1}$$

The lengths of corresponding sides have equal ratio, so the lengths of the corresponding sides are proportional.

$$\frac{AB}{EF} = \frac{BC}{FG} = \frac{CD}{GH} = \frac{DA}{HE} = \frac{200}{1}.$$

So polygon $ABCD \sim$ polygon $EFGH$.

SYMBOLS	
is similar to	$\sim$
is congruent to	$\cong$
angle	$\angle$
segment (AB)	$\overline{AB}$

When you name similar polygons, list their corresponding vertices in the *same* order.

▶ Polygons with the same size and the same shape are **congruent**. Their sides and angles can be placed in a correspondence so that corresponding sides are congruent and corresponding angles are congruent. For example, $ABCD \cong OPMN$.

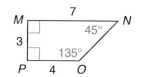

$\overline{AB} \cong \overline{OP} \qquad \overline{BC} \cong \overline{PM} \qquad \overline{CD} \cong \overline{MN} \qquad \overline{DA} \cong \overline{NO}$
$\angle A \cong \angle O \qquad \angle B \cong \angle P \qquad \angle C \cong \angle M \qquad \angle D \cong \angle N$

The vertices correspond in the following order.

$A \leftrightarrow O \qquad B \leftrightarrow P \qquad C \leftrightarrow M \qquad D \leftrightarrow N$

To state the congruence between the polygons, you name the vertices in the same order as this correspondence.

Remember: Segments that are equal in length are congruent. Angles that are equal in measure are congruent.

XVII. Triangles and Quadrilaterals (See pp. 411–412)

▶ **Triangles** are three-sided polygons. They are classified by the lengths of their sides and/or by the measures of their angles.

equilateral triangle (A)—all sides congruent

isosceles triangle (B)—two sides congruent

scalene triangle (C)—no sides congruent

acute triangle (D)—three angles acute

obtuse triangle (E)—one obtuse angle

right triangle (F)—one right angle

Matching tick marks indicate congruent sides.

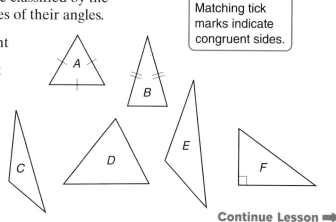

Continue Lesson ➡

REVIEW OF PREREQUISITE SKILLS

▶ **Quadrilaterals** are four-sided polygons. They can be classified according to the special properties of their sides or angles.

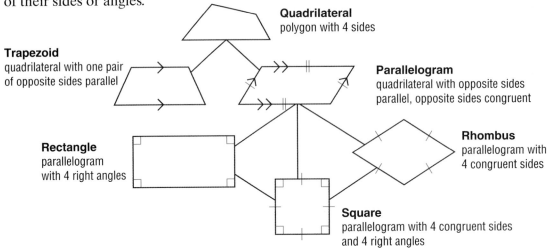

Quadrilateral
polygon with 4 sides

Trapezoid
quadrilateral with one pair
of opposite sides parallel

Parallelogram
quadrilateral with opposite sides
parallel, opposite sides congruent

Rectangle
parallelogram
with 4 right angles

Rhombus
parallelogram with
4 congruent sides

Square
parallelogram with 4 congruent sides
and 4 right angles

XVIII. Perimeter and Area of Polygons

The **perimeter** (P) of a polygon is the distance around the polygon.
The **area** (A) of a figure is the number of square units that cover its surface.

▶ Formulas can be used to find the perimeter and area of polygons.
See Formula Chart on page 435.

Find the perimeter and area of rectangle $ABCD$.

A ⟶ length ⟶ B

12 yd   width

D ⟶ 26 yd ⟶ C

$$P = 2(\ell + w)$$
$$= 2(26 + 12) = 52 + 24$$
$$= 76$$

The perimeter of rectangle $ABCD$ is 76 yd.

$$A = \ell w$$
$$= 26 \bullet 12$$
$$= 312$$

$$\overline{AB} \cong \overline{DC} \qquad \overline{AD} \cong \overline{BC}$$

The area of rectangle $ABCD$ is 312 yd^2.

XIX. Volume and Surface Area

▶ **Three-dimensional figures**, or solids, are objects that do not lie in a plane. They have length, width, and height. They can be classified as **polyhedrons** or **nonpolyhedrons**.

Polyhedrons, such as prisms and pyramids, have faces that are all polygons. Nonpolyhedrons, such as cylinders, cones, and spheres, have curved surfaces.

The **volume** of a three-dimensional figure is the space the figure occupies.

The **lateral area** is the area of all the surfaces of the figure except the base or bases. The **surface area** of a three-dimensional figure is the sum of the areas of all its surfaces.

$h = 30$ in.

$w = 7$ in.

$\ell = 16$ in.

▶ Formulas can be used to find the volume and surface area of three-dimensional figures. See Formula Chart on page 435.

Find the volume, lateral area, and surface area of the rectangular prism above.

$$V = \ell w h$$
$$= 16 \bullet 7 \bullet 30$$
$$= 3360$$
$$= 3360 \text{ in.}^3$$

$$LA = Ph$$
$$= 2(16 + 7) \bullet 30$$
$$= 2(23) \bullet 30 = 46 \bullet 30$$
$$= 1380$$
$$= 1380 \text{ in.}^2$$

$$S = 2(\ell w + \ell h + wh)$$
$$= 2(16 \bullet 7 + 16 \bullet 30 + 7 \bullet 30)$$
$$= 2(112 + 480 + 210) = 2(802)$$
$$= 1604$$
$$= 1604 \text{ in.}^2$$

XX. Double Line and Double Bar Graphs

A **double line graph** and a **double bar graph** are used to compare two sets of data. Each set of data is graphed separately but on the same grid. The *key* identifies the sets of data.

Make a double line graph for the given set of data.

Rico's Marks in Math/Science				
Quarter	1st	2nd	3rd	4th
Math	89	91	88	90
Science	86	89	88	89

Make a double bar graph for the given set of data.

Favorite Types of Literature				
Type	Fantasy	Folk Tales	Science Fiction	Sports
Class 8A	9	6	8	11
Class 8B	4	7	12	11

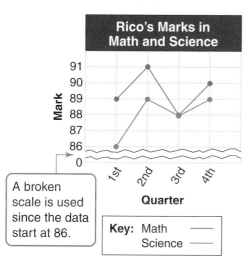

A broken scale is used since the data start at 86.

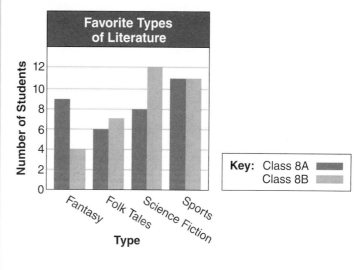

XXI. Line Plots and Circle Graphs (see pp. 413–414)

► A **line plot** is a graph that displays data with X marks above each data value on a number line.

To **make a line plot:**

• Draw a number line. Use the scale to label the intervals. Start with the least score.

• Use an X to represent each data value. Vertically stack the correct number of Xs above each data value on the scale.

Make a line plot for the given set of data.

Nick's Math Test Scores							
Score	100	95	90	85	80	75	70
Frequency	2	2	3	2	0	0	1

Nick's Math Test Scores

```
                              X
              X       X   X   X   X
   X                  X   X   X   X
 ◄─┼───┼───┼───┼───┼───┼───┼──►
   70  75  80  85  90  95  100
```

To **analyze the distribution of data** (or how the data are grouped together or spread out) in the line plot, find *clusters*, *gaps*, and *outliers*.

• **Clusters**: Places on the line plot with high frequency of results. There is a data cluster at score 90.

• **Gaps**: Places on the line plot with no data. A gap exists between 70 and 85.

• **Outliers**: Numbers set apart from the rest of the data. The score 70 is an outlier.

Continue Lesson ➡

▶A **circle graph** shows visually how each part of one set of data compares to the whole set and also to the other parts. The circle represents the whole, or 100%. The sectors of the circle stand for parts of the whole, so each sector can be labeled as a percent.

Make a circle graph for the given set of data.

To **make a circle graph**, follow these steps:

- Copy and extend the given table to include columns for *Percent of Total* and *Angle Measure*.
- Complete the Percent of Total and Angle Measure columns.

TV Survey	
Number of TVs Per Home	**Number of Homes**
1	6
2	12
3	9
4 or more	3

TV Survey			
Number of TVs Per Home	**Number of Homes**	**Percent of Total** $\left(p = \frac{r}{b}\right)$	**Angle Measure** $(p = rb)$
1	6	$r = \frac{6}{30} = 0.2 = 20\%$	$p = 20\% \bullet 360° = 72°$
2	12	$r = \frac{12}{30} = 0.4 = 40\%$	$p = 40\% \bullet 360° = 144°$
3	9	$r = \frac{9}{30} = 0.30 = 30\%$	$p = 30\% \bullet 360° = 108°$
4 or more	3	$r = \frac{3}{30} = 0.10 = 10\%$	$p = 10\% \bullet 360° = 36°$
TOTALS	30	100%	360°

- Use a compass to draw a large circle and a ruler to draw a vertical radius.
- Use a protractor to draw each angle clockwise from the radius.
- Label the graph and each sector. Color the sectors.

TV Survey

2 TVs 72°
3 TVs 108°
1 TV 36°
4 TVs 144°

XXII. Probability and Odds

Probability is the chance that a given *event*, or situation, will occur in an *experiment*.

Spin the spinner at the right. What is the probability of the spinner landing on red? *not* landing on blue? Find the odds in favor of and the odds against the spinner landing on green.

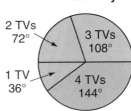

▶For *equally likely outcomes*, the **probability of an event, *P*(E)**, occurring, is given by the formula:

$$P(\text{E}) = \frac{\text{number of favorable outcomes}}{\text{total number of possible outcomes}}$$

$P(\text{red}) = \frac{1}{3}$ ◀ 1 favorable outcome (1 red)
3 possible outcomes

$P(not \text{ blue}) = \frac{2}{3}$

..Think.....................
: *Not* blue: 1 red, 1 green :

▶**Odds** are a way of measuring the chance of success against the chance of failure.

Odds in favor of an event:	**Odds against an event:**
$\dfrac{\text{number of favorable outcomes}}{\text{number of unfavorable outcomes}}$	$\dfrac{\text{number of unfavorable outcomes}}{\text{number of favorable outcomes}}$
Odds in favor of green: $\dfrac{1}{3}$	Odds against green: $\dfrac{2}{1}$

1 favorable outcome:
1 green
2 unfavorable outcomes:
1 red, 1 blue

REVIEW OF PREREQUISITE SKILLS

TI-Nspire™ Handbook

In this overview, you will be introduced to some of the key features of the TI-Nspire™ handheld, including:

- **learning the location and function of the keys;**

- **navigating within the core TI-Nspire™ applications—Calculator, Graphs & Geometry, and Lists & Spreadsheet;**

- **using keyboard shortcuts.**

The technology lessons in this SourceBook will provide an introduction to the use of the handheld, with selected topics from some of the chapters. You may wish to explore these and other topics further on your own.

Here are just a few of the things that the TI-Nspire™ technology allows you to do that will enhance your study of algebra:

- show relationships among the graph of a function, the equation of the function, and a table of values for the function

- transform functions while observing how the equation changes

- display mathematical expressions—including matrices, inequalities, and rational expressions—in a form identical to that shown in your SourceBook

- investigate the intersection and union of systems of inequalities, using high resolution images with boundaries that are easy to see

In applying the TI-Nspire™ handheld technology to your study of algebra and your exploration of graphs, tables, and equations, you will gain a heightened appreciation for the beauty and power of mathematics even as you become aware of a whole new interactive dimension of learning.

TI-Nspire™ Handheld Keys

TECHNOLOGY

esc Removes menus or dialog boxes from the screen.

tab Moves to the next entry field.

ctrl Provides access to the function or character shown above each key.

CAPS ⇧ Makes the next typed character upper-case.

off on Turns on the TI-Nspire™ handheld.

⌂ Displays the home menu.

menu Displays the application or context menu.

clear Clears (erases) the entry line or deletes the selected object.

∞β° ⌨ Displays the catalog for entering commands.

enter Evaluates an expression, executes an instruction, or selects a menu item.

Click Button
Selects an object on the screen.

ctrl + 🖱 or pressing and holding 🖱 displays the grab cursor ✎ so you can grab an object.

NavPad
Press ◀, ▶, ▲, or ▼ to move the cursor.

Getting Started

Turning the Handheld On and Off

To turn the handheld on, press .

To turn the handheld off, press .

After several minutes of inactivity, the handheld turns off automatically. The next time you turn the handheld on, it will be in exactly the same state as when it was turned off.

Using the Keypad

In the upper-right corner of the keypad is the **Home** key ⌂. Press this key to access the **Home** menu. This menu provides a starting point for all activities on your handheld. From here, you can

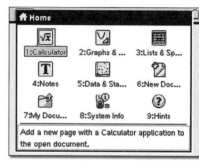

Application choices

- insert a new application;

- create or open a new document or problem;

- change the settings on your handheld;

- view hints for operating the handheld.

Use the arrows (◀, ▶, ▲, or ▼) on the NavPad (top center of keypad, just below the screen) to move among the options on the **Home** menu. To choose an option, press the number associated with that option, or press **enter** when the option you wish to choose is highlighted.

The **Enter** key **enter** is located in the lower-right corner of the keypad. Press this key to evaluate expressions, execute instructions, or select menu items. The screen at the right shows the work area that is displayed when **1: Calculator** is highlighted on the **Home** menu and you press **enter**.

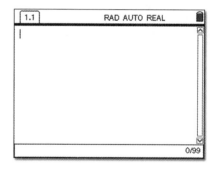

Below the **Home** key is the **Menu** key. Pressing **menu** brings up a menu that is specific to whatever application is being used. From this menu, you can choose the action or function that you want to access. Any menu item with an arrow next to it has more menu choices in it.

To access any option, choose it from the menu by pressing **enter** when the desired option is highlighted, or press the number associated with the desired option. The screen at the right is the result of pressing **menu** **2** **6** and then using the down arrow to move to option 2.

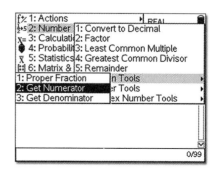

Using the Calculator Application

When you have chosen **1: Calculator** from the **Home** menu, you will be in the Calculator work area. Here, you can enter a numerical expression and have the handheld evaluate it.

One way to do this is to enter a math expression by pressing keys on the handheld keypad. For example, you can follow the following steps to evaluate the expression $\frac{2^8 \cdot 43}{12}$.

Step 1 Select the entry line in the Calculator work area.

Step 2 Type 2 ⬛ 8 to begin the expression.

Step 3 Press ⬤ to return the cursor to the baseline, and then type ⬛ 43 ⬛ 12.

Step 4 Press ⬛ to evaluate the expression. The expression displays in standard mathematical notation, and the result is displayed at the right.

When viewing the menu, you can go back to the previous screen by pressing the ⬛ key. While you are entering values in the Calculator work area, you can use the ⬛ key to delete the last character typed, or you can press ⬛ and ⬛ to erase the entire problem. If you wish to erase a problem you have finished entering, you can press ⬛ and then press the ⬛ key continuously until the problem has been erased, one step at a time. If you wish to enter a new problem and have it appear by itself on the screen, press ⬛ ⬛ before starting the new problem.

- Suppose you want to use the Distance Formula to find the distance a car travels in 3 hours if it is moving at a constant speed of 55 mi/h.

To solve the problem, you will need to use the Calculator menu to define $f(t)$ as $55t$. Press ⬛ to display the menu. The option **Actions** is already highlighted. Then press ⬛ ⬛ to choose **Define**. This takes you out of the menu and back to the Calculator work area. Type ⬛ ⬛ ⬛ ⬛ = 55 ⬛, and press ⬛.

Then type ⬛ ⬛ ⬛ ⬛ to substitute 3 for t, and press ⬛. The number of miles traveled in 3 hours, 165, will be displayed, as shown at the right.

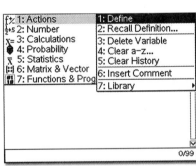

Graphs & Geometry Application

Graphing View

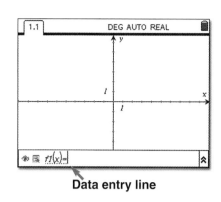

When you choose **2: Graphs & Geometry** from the **Home** menu, you will be in the Graphing work area. The Graphs & Geometry application provides either of these two types of work areas:

- The Graphing view is the default work area. It contains coordinate axes and an entry line at the bottom of the screen, into which you type the function to be graphed.

- The Plane Geometry view removes the axis and the entry line, enabling you to draw Geometric shapes.

Data entry line

To change to the Plane Geometry view, type menu 2 2 .
To return to the Graphing view, type menu 2 1 .

The menu for Graphs & Geometry is shown below at the left. Option 1, **Actions**, provides tools such as accessing the pointer, hiding or showing graph features, adding text, and deleting objects in the work area. The **Graph Type** option allows you to choose the type of graph to plot. The **View** option lets you hide the axes, show the grid, hide the entry line, show the scale, and add a function table. Selecting **Window** (menu shown below in the middle of the first row) and **Window Settings** (shown below in the first row at the right) lets you change the minimum and maximum values for the *x* and *y* axes. The **Trace** option allows you to find the value of the *x*- and *y*-coordinates of points on the graph. These Graphing menu functions are the ones used in this textbook. You may wish to explore other menu options on your own.

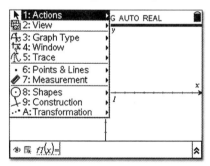
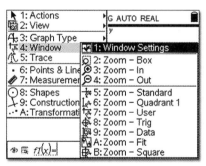
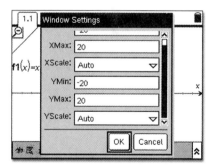

The graph of $y = x + 14$ at the right, is shown with both the default setting (left) and the window settings changed to a minimum of -20 and a maximum of 20 for *x* and *y* (right).

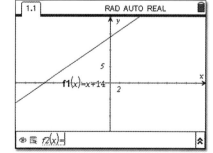

To graph a function, return to the work area, type the function into the data entry line, and press enter. To graph an inequality, you will need to delete the = symbol and use the handheld keypad to enter the appropriate inequality symbol.

To type ≤, press ctrl and <. To type ≥, press ctrl and >.

TECHNOLOGY

Using the Lists & Spreadsheet Applications

Press **3: Lists & Spreadsheet** from the **Home** menu to access the Lists & Spreadsheet work area, the first screen shown at the right.

From here, press menu to display the menu for this application.

A column letter appears at the top of each column, and a row number appears at the left of each row. The top two rows and the left column of the spreadsheet remain in place as you scroll so that you can more easily determine your location.

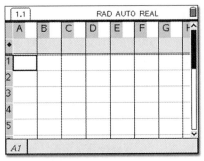

Lists & Spreadsheet

To navigate within a spreadsheet, press the NavPad keys ◁, ▷, △, and ▽. Using these keys, you can move from cell to cell and scroll as necessary to keep the selected cell in view. To move to a specific cell, you can use the **Go To** command on the **Actions** menu. To select a cell, type its column letter and row number (such as **Cell D5**).

The method you use to enter data depends on the type of data and your personal preferences.

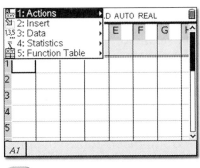

menu **for Lists & Spreadsheet**

- For numbers, text, and simple math expressions and formulas, simply press the handheld keys.

- For more complex mathematical expressions, press ∞β° to display the complete **Catalog** of system functions and commands, symbols, and expression templates.

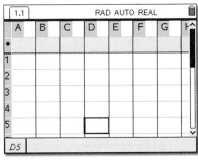

Cell D5

- To display a list of **templates**, press ctrl ⊞×. Here, you will find templates to enter fractions, square roots, matrices, and so on.

- To display only the list of **symbols**, press ctrl ∞β°.

You can enter formulas that refer to spreadsheet data. Formulas begin with the = symbol. Refer to a cell by using its column letter and row number. For example, entering **=3•D5** will give a value that is 3 *times* the data in cell D5.

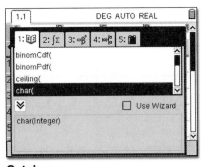

Catalog

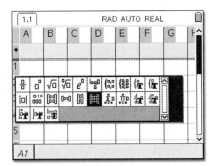

Templates

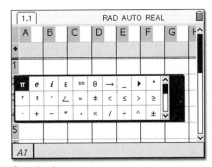

Symbols

TECHNOLOGY

You can enter data on your handheld and then make
a scatter plot to represent the data.

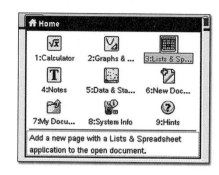

Step 1 Press 🏠 and choose **3** to select
Lists & Spreadsheet.

Step 2 Name the values that will be entered in the first column.
Use the NavPad keys to move to and highlight the white
space at the top of column A that is next to the letter A.

Type a column heading, such as *year*, and press ≈enter.
Then move to the white space at the top of column B next
to the letter B. Type another column heading, such as
courses. Use the NavPad keys to type the data into the
appropriate cells of columns A and B.

Step 3 Press 🏠 **5** to choose the **Data & Statistics** option.
This application is designed as a means of exploring and
visualizing data and graphing statistics. It is, therefore,
best used in conjunction with a numerical application
such as Calculator or Lists & Spreadsheet. From here,
press menu **2** to choose **Plot Properties**. Press **4**
to choose **Add X Variable**. Then choose *year* and ≈enter.

Step 4 Press menu **2** for **Plot Properties** and **6** for
Add Y Variable. Then choose *courses*.

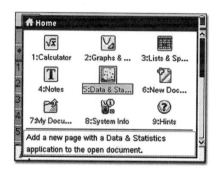

TECHNOLOGY

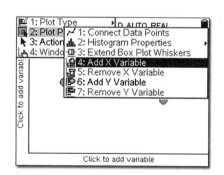

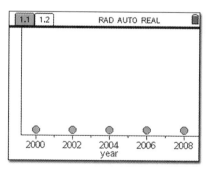

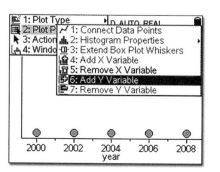

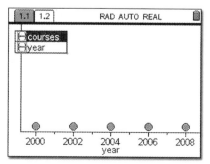

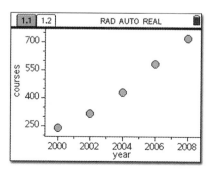

TI-Nspire™ Keypad Shortcuts	
CTRL + (click)	Grab selection
CTRL + (esc)	Undo
CAPS + (esc)	Redo
CTRL + (backspace)	Clear
CTRL + (home)	Tools menu
CTRL + (tab)	Switch between applications on a split page
CTRL + (menu)	Context menu for selection
CTRL + (flag)	Math template palette
CTRL + (less than)	≤ (less than or equal to)
CTRL + (greater than)	≥ (greater than or equal to)
CTRL + (=)	≠ (not equal to)
CTRL + (shift)	Caps Lock
CTRL + (var)	Store
CTRL + (left parenthesis)	[ ] (square brackets)
CTRL + (right parenthesis)	{ } (curly brackets)
CTRL + (catalog)	Character/Symbol palette
CTRL + (apostrophe)	° (degree symbol)
CTRL + (caret)	n^{th} root
CTRL + (sin)	$\sin^{-1}$
CTRL + (cos)	$\cos^{-1}$
CTRL + (tan)	$\tan^{-1}$
CTRL + (quotation mark)	$ (absolute cell reference in spreadsheet)
CTRL + (imaginary)	∞ (infinity)
CTRL + (squared)	$\sqrt{}$ (square root)
CTRL + (1)	End
CTRL + (7)	Beginning
CTRL + (3)	Page Down
CTRL + (9)	Page Up
CTRL + (division)	Fraction template
CTRL + (multiplication)	Math template palette
CTRL + (colon)	; (semicolon)
CTRL + (subtraction)	Decrease screen contrast (lighter)
CTRL + (addition)	Increase screen contrast (darker)
CAPS + (division)	\ (backslash)
CTRL + (negate)	ans (use answer)
CTRL + (space)	Underscore
CAPS + (carriage return)	Adds a column in matrix

A

absolute value (AB-suh-loot VAL-yoo) The distance of a number from zero on a number line. (p. 5)

absolute-value equation (AB-suh-loot-VAL-yoo i-KWAY-zhuhn) An equation that has a number, or variable, within absolute-value bars. (p. 58)

absolute-value function (AB-suh-loot-VAL-yoo FUHNGK-shuhn) A nonlinear function whose graph forms a "V" that opens up or down. (p. 138)

absolute-value inequality (AB-suh-loot-VAL-yoo in-i-KWOL-uh-tee) An inequality that contains an absolute-value expression. (p. 84)

Addition Property of Equality (uh-DISH-uhn PROP-ur-tee UHV i-KWOL-uh-tee) For real numbers a, b, and c, if $a = b$, then $a + c = b + c$. (p. 44)

Addition Property of Inequality (uh-DISH-uhn PROP-ur-tee UHV *in*-i-KWOL-uh-tee) If a, b, and c are real numbers and $a < b$, then $a + c < b + c$. These statements are also true if $<$ is replaced by $\le$, $>$, or $\ge$. (p. 72)

Additive Identity Property (AD-i-tiv eye-DEN-ti-tee PROP-ur-tee) The property that states that the sum of any number and zero equals that number; $a + 0 = a$. (p. 20)

Additive Inverse Property (AD-i-tiv IN-vurss PROP-ur-tee) The property that states that the sum of two inverse (opposite) numbers equals zero; $a + (-a) = 0$. (p. 5)

algebra tiles (AL-juh-bruh TYELZ) Manipulatives used to model algebraic expressions or polynomials. (p. 178)

algebraic equation (*al*-juh-BRAY-ik i-KWAY-zhuhn) An equation that contains numbers and variables with operation symbols. (p. 40)

algebraic expression (*al*-juh-BRAY-ik ek-SPRESH-uhn) A mathematical expression that contains numbers and variables with operation symbols. (p. 16)

a_n (AY SUHB EN) The nth term of a sequence. (p. 103)

angle of depression (ANG-guhl UHV di-PRESH-uhn) The angle whose vertex is at the eye of an observer and whose sides lie on a horizontal line and on the observer's line of sight *downward* to an object. (p. 296)

angle of elevation (ANG-guhl UHV el-uh-VAY-shuhn) The angle whose vertex is at the eye of an observer and whose sides lie on a horizontal line and on the observer's line of sight *upward* to an object. (p. 296)

arithmetic sequence (*a*-rith-MET-ik SEE-kwuhnss) A number sequence in which each term is found by adding the same number to each previous term. (p. 103)

Associative (grouping) Property (uh-SOH-shee-uh-tiv [GROOP-ing] PROP-ur-tee) Changing the grouping of the addends, or factors, does not change the sum, or product. For all real numbers a, b, and c, $(a + b) + c = a + (b + c)$ and $(ab)c = a(bc)$. (p. 20)

asymptote (AS-im-*toht*) A line that the graph of a function gets closer and closer to. (p. 330)

axis of symmetry (AK-siss UHV SIM-uh-tree) A line that divides a graph into two congruent parts; a vertical line that runs through the vertex of a parabola. (pp. 138, 248)

B

back-to-back stem-and-leaf plot (BAK-TOO-BAK STEM-AND-LEEF PLOT) A type of stem-and-leaf plot, also known as a double stem-and-leaf plot, that compares two sets of data by displaying one set of data to the left of the stem and the other to the right. (p. 365)

bias (BYE-uhss) Anything that favors a particular outcome. (p. 359)

biased question (BYE-uhst KWESS-chuhn) A question that suggests or leads to a specific response or excludes a certain group. (p. 360)

biased sample (BYE-uhst SAM-puhl) A sample that is not representative of the population under study. (p. 359)

binomial (bye-NOH-mee-uhl) A polynomial with exactly two terms. (p. 176)

boundary (BOWN-duh-ree) A line that separates a coordinate plane into half-planes. (p. 136)

boundary point (BOWN-duh-ree POYNT) The point on a number line where the graph of a linear inequality in one variable starts. (p. 70)

box-and-whisker plot (BOKS-AND-WISS-kur PLOT) A graph that displays a data set using five key values—lower extreme, lower quartile, median, upper quartile, and upper extreme. There is a box in the middle and whiskers at either side. The quartiles divide the data into four equal parts. (p. 370)

Closure Property (KLOH-zhur PROP-ur-tee) A set of numbers is closed under an operation when that operation is performed on any two numbers from that set and the result is always a number in that set. For all real numbers a and b, $a + b$ and ab are unique real numbers. (pp. 5, 20)

cluster sampling (KLUHSS-tur SAM-pling) The population is divided into groups and a sample is chosen from each group. (p. 359)

coefficient (*koh*-uh-FISH-uhnt) The numerical factor of a term that contains a variable. (p. 16)

combination (*kom*-buh-NAY-shuhn) An arrangement of objects where the order is not important. (p. 392)

common difference (KAH-muhn DIF-ur-uhnss) The difference between any two consecutive terms in an arithmetic sequence; also called *constant difference*. (p. 103)

common ratio (KAH-muhn RAY-shee-oh) The quotient between any two consecutive terms in a geometric sequence; also called the *constant ratio*. (p. 107)

Commutative Property (kuh-MYOO-tuh-tiv PROP-ur-tee) Changing the order of the addends, or factors, does not change the sum, or product. For all real numbers a and b, $a + b = b + a$ and $ab = ba$. (p. 20)

complement (KOMP-luh-muhnt) For a universal set, the set of all elements in the set that are not in a specified subset; in probability, all of the outcomes that are not in the event. (pp. 23, 381)

complementary events (*kom*-pluh-MEN-tuh-ree i-VENTS) Two events that have no outcomes in common, and together they include every outcome in the sample space. (p. 381)

Completeness Property for Points on the Number Line (kuhm-PLEET-niss PROP-ur-tee FOR POYNTS ON THUH NUHM-bur LINE) Every real number corresponds to exactly one point of a number line, and every point on the number line corresponds to exactly one real number. (p. 4)

complex fraction (kuhm-PLEKS FRAK-shuhn) A fraction that has one or more fractions in the numerator, denominator, or both. (p. 318)

compound event (KOM-pownd i-VENT) In probability, an event made up of two or more simple events. (p. 382)

compound inequality (KOM-pownd *in*-i-KWOL-uh-tee) Two simple inequalities joined by the word AND or OR. (pp. 80, 81)

conditional probability (kuhn-DISH-uhn-uhl *prob*-uh-BIL-uh-tee) A probability that has a condition that may limit the sample space. (p. 388)

conjunction (kuhn-JUHNGK-shuhn) A compound inequality joined by the word AND; solutions that satisfy both parts of the compound inequality are solutions to the conjunction. (p. 80)

constant (KON-stuhnt) A term that does not have variables. (p. 16)

constant of proportionality (KON-stuhnt UHV pruh-POR-shuh-*nal*-uh-tee) A constant ratio of two variables, such as x and y, that are related proportionally. (p. 280)

constant (or direct) variation (KON-stuhnt [OR duh-REKT] vair-ee-AY-shuhn) A relationship described by an equation of the form $y = kx$, where k is a constant nonzero real number. The number k is called the *constant of variation*. (pp. 120, 330)

contradiction (*kon*-truh-DIK-shuhn) A statement whose solution process ends in a false numerical statement; its solution set is the null set. (p. 57)

convenience sample (kuhn-VEEN-yuhnss SAM-puhl) A sample based on the members of the population that are readily available. (p. 359)

conversion factor (kuhn-VUR-zhuhn FAK-tur) A fraction whose numerator and denominator represent the same quantity but use different units; the fraction is equal to 1 because the numerator and denominator are equal. (p. 282)

correlation (*cor*-uh-LAY-shuhn) Describes the relationship between two data sets. (p. 374)

cosine (KOH-sine) If A is an acute angle of a right triangle, $\cos A = \dfrac{\text{leg adjacent to } \angle A}{\text{hypotenuse}}$. (p. 290)

counterexample (KOWN-tur-eg-*zam*-puhl) A case for which a statement is not true. (p. 5)

Cramer's Rule (KRAY-murz ROOL) A method to solve a system of linear equations in terms of determinants. (p. 172)

Cross-Products Rule (CRAWSS-PROD-uhkts ROOL) The product of the *extremes* is equal to the product of the *means*. (p. 190)

cumulative frequency histogram (KYOOM-yuh-luh-tiv FREE-kwuhn-see HISS-tuh-*gram*) A visual summary of a cumulative frequency table. (p. 368)

cumulative frequency table (KYOOM-yuh-luh-tiv FREE-kwuhn-see TAY-buhl) A summary of a data set in which each data value is paired with the sum of the frequencies of all values less than or equal to it. (p. 368)

D

degree of a monomial (di-GREE UHV UH moh-NOH-mee-uhl) The *sum* of the exponents of the variables in the monomial. (p. 177)

degree of a polynomial (di-GREE UHV UH *pol*-ee-NOH-mee-uhl) The *greatest* degree of its terms after the polynomial has been simplified. (p. 177)

dependent events (di-PEN-duhnt i-VENTS) Events in which the outcome of one event affects the probability of the other. (p. 384)

dependent system (di-PEN-duhnt SISS-tuhm) Used to describe a system of equations if both equations in the system describe the same line. (p. 152)

difference of two squares (DIF-ur-uhnss UHV TOO SKWAIRZ) The product of the sum and the difference of the same two terms; $(a + b)(a - b) = a^2 - b^2$. (p. 212)

dimensional analysis (duh-MEN-shuhn-uhl uh-NAL-uh-sis) The process of analyzing units to decide which conversion factor(s) to use when renaming units of measure. (p. 282)

Diophantine equation (dye-uh-FAN-tine i-KWAY-zhuhn) An equation of the form $ax + by = c$, where a, b, and c are integers and have only integer solutions for x and y. (p. 66)

direct variation (duh-REKT vair-ee-AY-shuhn) A linear function that can be written in the form $y = kx$, where k is a nonzero constant called the constant of variation; $y = kx$ or $k = \dfrac{y}{x}, k \neq 0$. (p. 120)

discriminant (diss-KRIM-uh-nuhnt) The expression $b^2 - 4ac$ of the quadratic equation $ax^2 + bx + c = 0, a \neq 0$; it provides important information about the roots of the quadratic equation. (p. 262)

disjoint events (diss-JOYNT i-VENTS) Two events, also known as *mutually exclusive events,* that have no outcomes in common. (p. 386)

disjoint sets (diss-JOYNT SETS) Sets that have no elements in common or that do not intersect. (p. 25)

disjunction (diss-JUHNGK-shuhn) Two simple inequalities joined by the word OR. (p. 82)

Distributive Property (diss-TRIB-yoo-tiv PROP-ur-tee) Multiplying a number by a sum is the same as multiplying the number by each addend of the sum and then adding the products. For all real numbers a, b, and c, $a(b + c) = ab + ac$. (p. 20)

Division Property of Equality (di-VIZH-uhn PROP-ur-tee UHV i-KWOL-uh-tee) For real numbers a, b, and c, $c \neq 0$, if $a = b$, then $\dfrac{a}{c} = \dfrac{b}{c}$. (p. 46)

Division Property of Inequality (di-VIZH-uhn PROP-ur-tee UHV in-i-KWOL-uh-tee) For real numbers a, b, and c, if c is positive, and $a < b$, then $a \div c < b \div c$. If c is negative, and $a < b$, then $a \div c > b \div c$. Similar statements can be written for $a > b$, $a \leq b$, and $a \geq b$. (p. 74)

domain (doh-MAYN) The set of all possible input values of a relation or function, or x-values, in ordered pairs. (p. 41)

E

elimination (i-*lim*-uh-NAY-shuhn) A method for solving a system of linear equations by adding or subtracting the equations to eliminate a variable. (p. 157)

empty (null) set (EMP-tee [NUL] SET) A set with no elements, shown by the symbol { }, or $\varnothing$. (p. 23)

equation (i-KWAY-zhuhn) A statement that two mathematical expressions are equal. (p. 40)

equivalent equations/systems (i-KWIV-uh-luhnt i-KWAY-zhuhnz OR SISS-tuhmz) Equations or systems that have the same solution set. (pp. 42, 158)

evaluate (i-VAL-yoo-ate) To find the value of a numerical or algebraic expression (p. 17)

excluded values (*ek*-SKLOO-did VAL-yooz) Any values of a variable that result in a denominator of 0 must be excluded from the domain of that variable. (p. 306)

experimental probability (ek-*sper*-uh-MENT-al *prob*-uh-BIL-uh-tee) A probability determined by collecting data from an experiment; the ratio of the number of times an event occurs to the total number of trials, or times that the activity is performed. Also known as *empirical probability.* (p. 378)

exponent (ek-SPOH-nuhnt) The number that indicates how many times the base is used as a factor. (p. 10)

exponential decay (*ek*-spoh-NEN-shuhl di-KAY) Occurs when a quantity decreases by the same rate each time period. (p. 344)

exponential function (*ek*-spoh-NEN-shuhl FUHNGK-shuhn) A nonlinear function in which the variable is in the exponent. A function of the form $y = ab^x$, where $a \neq 0, b \neq 1, b > 0$, and x is a real number. (p. 338)

exponential growth (*ek*-spoh-NEN-shuhl GROHTH) Occurs when a quantity is increased by the same rate each time period. (p. 342)

extraneous solution (ek-STRAY-nee-uhss suh-LOO-shuhn) A solution of a derived equation that does not satisfy the original equation. (p. 235)

extreme values (ek-STREEM VAL-yooz) The minimum and maximum values of a data set. (p. 370)

extremes of a proportion (ek-STREEMZ UHV UH pruh-POR-shuhn) In the proportion $a : b = c : d$, the terms a and d. (p. 370)

F

factor a polynomial completely (FAK-tur UH *pol*-ee-NOH-mee-uhl kuhm-PLEET-lee) To express the polynomial as a product of one or more polynomials that cannot be factored further. (p. 201)

factorable (FAK-tuh-ruh-buhl) Used to describe a polynomial if it can be written as a product of factors. (p. 200)

factorial (fak-TOR-ee-uhl) The expression $n!$ is read "n factorial" and represents the product of all positive integers less than or equal to n. (p. 390)

family of functions (FAM-uh-lee UHV FUHNGK-shuhnz) A collection of functions whose graphs have basic characteristics in common. Functions in the same family are transformations of their parent functions. (p. 140)

first quartile (FURST KWOR-tile) The median of the lower half of a data set. (p. 370)

FOIL (FOYL) An acronym for the terms used when multiplying two binomials: the *F*irst, *O*uter, *I*nner, and *L*ast terms. (p. 186)

formula (FOR-myuh-luh) An algebraic, or variable, equation showing relationships among quantities. (p. 60)

frequency table (FREE-kwuhn-see TAY-buhl) A table that shows the frequency of each data value. If the data is divided into intervals, the table shows the frequency of each interval. (p. 366)

function (FUHNGK-shuhn) A special type of relation that pairs each domain value with exactly one range value. (p. 96)

function notation (FUHNGK-shuhn noh-TAY-shuhn) The notation, $f(x)$, used to represent the output of the function f for an input of x. (p. 98)

function rule (FUHNGK-shuhn ROOL) An equation that describes a function. (p. 98)

function table (FUHNGK-shuhn TAY-buhl) A table of ordered pairs that represent solutions of a function. (p. 100)

Fundamental Counting Principle (fuhn-duh-MEN-tuhl KOWNT-ing PRIN-suh-puhl) If one event has m possible outcomes and a second event has n possible outcomes, then there are $m \cdot n$ total possible outcomes for the two events together. (p. 382)

G

geometric sequence (*jee*-uh-MET-rik SEE-kwuhnss) A number sequence in which each term is found by multiplying the previous term by the same number. (p. 107)

graph of an inequality (GRAF UHV AN *in*-i-KWOL-uh-tee) The set of points on a number line, or on a plane, that represents the solution of an inequality. (p. 70)

greatest common monomial factor (GRAYT-ist KOM-uhn mon-OH-me-uhl FAK-tur) The product of all the integer and variable factors that are common to those monomials. (p. 200)

H

half-plane (HAF-PLAYN) One of the two regions on either side of the line separating a coordinate plane. (p. 136)

histogram (HISS-tuh-*gram*) A bar graph that shows the frequency of equal intervals of data with no spaces between the bars unless there is an interval where the frequency is 0. (p. 366)

hyperbola (hye-PUR-buh-luh) The graph of an inverse variation. (p. 330)

hypotenuse (hye-POT-uhn-ooss) The side opposite the right angle in a right triangle. (p. 290)

I

identity (eye-DEN-ti-tee) An equation in which every element of the replacement set (real numbers) makes the equation true. (p. 56)

Identity Property (eye-DEN-ti-tee PROP-ur-tee) Adding 0 to a number or multiplying by 1 does not change the number's value. (p. 20)

inconsistent (in-kuhn-SISS-tuhnt) Used to describe a system of equations where there is no solution. (p. 152)

independent (in-di-PEN-duhnt) Used to describe a system of equations if that system of equations describes two different intersecting lines. (p. 152)

independent events (in-di-PEN-duhnt i-VENTS) Events in which the outcome of one event does not affect the probability of the other. (p. 384)

inequality (*in*-i-KWOL-uh-tee) A mathematical sentence that uses the comparison symbols $<, \leq, >, \geq,$ or $\neq$ to express that two expressions are not equal. (p. 70)

integers (IN-tuh-jerz) The whole numbers and their opposites: $\{\ldots, -3, -2, -1, 0, 1, 2, 3, \ldots\}$. (p. 2)

intercepts (IN-tur-*septs*) The points where a graph crosses the axes. (p. 122)

interquartile range (*in*-tur-KWOR-tile RAYNJ) The range of the middle half of a data set. (p. 371)

intersection of sets (*in*-tur-SEK-shuhn UHV SETS) The *intersection*, $\cap$, of two sets is the set of all elements that are common to both sets. (p. 24)

interval notation (IN-tur-vuhl noh-TAY-shuhn) Shows the endpoints of a solution set. All the real numbers between these endpoints are in the interval. (p. 71)

inverse variation (IN-vurss vair-ee-AY-shuhn) A relationship between two variables in which the product is constant. (p. 330)

irrational number (i-RASH-uh-nuhl NUHM-bur) A number that cannot be expressed in the form $\frac{a}{b}$, where a and b are integers and $b \neq 0$; a nonrepeating and nonterminating decimal. (p. 3)

L

leading coefficient (LEE-ding koh-uh-FISH-uhnt) The coefficient of the first term of a polynomial in standard form. (p. 177)

leg (LEG) In a right triangle, one of the sides adjacent to the right angle. (p. 236)

like terms (LIKE TERMZ) Terms that have exactly the same literal coefficients, raised to the same power. (p. 20)

line of best fit (LINE UHV BEST FIT) A straight line that comes near to as many points of a scatter plot as possible, clearly showing the trend or correlation between two sets of data. (p. 376)

linear equation in standard form/standard form of a linear equation (LIN-ee-ur i-KWAY-zhuhn IN STAN-durd FORM / STAN-durd FORM UHV UH LIN-ee-ur i-KWAY-zhuhn) $Ax + By = C$, where A, B, and C are real numbers, and A and B are not both zeros. (p. 128)

linear function (LIN-ee-ur FUHNGK-shuhn) A function whose graph is a nonvertical line; a function that can be defined by a linear equation, and usually written in the form $y = mx + b$, where m is the slope and b is the y-intercept. (p. 116)

linear inequality (LIN-ee-ur *in*-i-KWOL-uh-tee) An inequality formed when the equal sign of a linear equation is replaced by an inequality symbol, such as $>, <, \geq,$ or $\leq$. (p. 136)

linear transformation (LIN-ee-ur *transs*-fur-MAY-shuhn) A data set involving multiplying by or adding the same number to each member of the data set. (p. 363)

literal coefficient (LIT-ur-uhl *koh*-uh-FISH-uhnt) The variable, or variables, of a term. (p. 16)

literal equation (LIT-ur-uhl i-KWAY-zhuhn) An equation with two or more variables. (p. 61)

lower extreme (LOH-ur ek-STREEM) The least number in the data set; the lower end of the "whisker" of a box-and-whisker plot. (p. 370)

lower quartile (LOH-ur KWOR-tile) The median of the lower half of a set of data; the lower end of the "box" part of a box-and-whisker plot. (p. 370)

M

mapping (MAP-ing) The pairing of the domain and range, or x-coordinate and y-coordinate. (p. 97)

matrix (MAY-triks) The rectangular arrangement of data into rows and columns. (p. 26)

maximum value (MAK-suh-muhm VAL-yoo) The y-value of the vertex of a parabola that opens downward. (p. 247)

mean (MEEN) The average value of a data set. (p. 362)

GLOSSARY

means of a proportion (MEENZ UHV UH pruh-POR-shuhn) In the proportion $a : b = c : d$, the terms b and c. (p. 370)

measures of central tendency (MEZH-urz UHV SEN-truhl TEN-duhn-see) The mean, median, and mode of a data set. (p. 362)

median (MEE-dee-uhn) The middle value, or mean of the two middle values, in an ordered set of data. (p. 362)

minimum value (MIN-uh-muhm VAL-yoo) The y-value of the vertex of a parabola that opens upward. (p. 247)

misleading graph (miss-LEE-ding GRAF) A graph that contains distorting elements, such as art, that make the graph more visually interesting but distort the relationships in the data. (p. 360)

mode (MOHD) The data item that has the greatest frequency in a data set. (p. 362)

monomial (mon-OH-me-uhl) A number, a variable, or the product of a number, and one or more variables with nonnegative exponents. (p. 176)

multiplication equation (*muhl*-tuh-pluh-KAY-shuhn i-KWAY-zhuhn) An equation that contains only the operation of multiplication. (p. 46)

Multiplication Property of Equality (*muhl*-tuh-pluh-KAY-shuhn PROP-ur-tee UHV i-KWOL-uh-tee) For real numbers a, b, and c, $c \neq 0$, if $a = b$, then $ac = bc$. (p. 47)

Multiplication Property of Inequality (*muhl*-tuh-pluh-KAY-shuhn PROP-ur-tee UHV *in*-i-KWOL-uh-tee) If a, b, and c are real numbers, <u>c is positive</u>, and $a < b$, then $ac < bc$. If a, b, and c are real numbers, <u>c is negative</u>, and $a < b$, then $ac > bc$. Similar statements can be written for $a > b$, $a \leq b$, and $a \geq b$. (p. 75)

multiplicative inverse (*muhl*-tuh-PLIK-uh-tiv IN-vurss) The reciprocal of a number. If $a \neq 0$ then $\frac{1}{a}$ is the multiplicative inverse, or reciprocal, of a. (p. 9)

multistep inequality (MUHL-tee-*step in*-i-KWOL-uh-tee) An inequality that involves more than one operation. (p. 76)

mutually exclusive events (MYOO-choo-uhl-ee eks-KLOO-siv i-VENTS) Two events that cannot happen at the same time; also known as *disjoint events*. (p. 386)

N

natural numbers (NACH-ur-uhl NUHM-burz) The numbers that are used in counting; the positive integers. (p. 2)

negative correlation (NEG-uh-tive *kor*-uh-LAY-shuhn) In a scatter plot, as x increases, y decreases. (p. 374)

negative exponent (NEG-uh-tive ek-SPOH-nuhnt) $a^{-n} = \frac{1}{a^n}, a \neq 0$. When a number has a negative exponent, the exponent becomes positive by changing the base to its reciprocal. (p. 11)

negative square root (NEG-uh-tive SKWAIR ROOT) Indicated by writing a negative sign in front of the radical. (p. 2)

nonlinear function (non-LIN-ee-ur FUHNGK-shuhn) A function whose graph is not a straight line. (p. 332)

nonperfect square (non-PUR-fikt SKWAIR) A number that is not the square of a natural number. (p. 3)

number line (NUHM-bur LINE) A line that graphically expresses the real numbers as a series of points distributed about a point arbitrarily designated as zero and in which the magnitude of each number is represented by the distance of the corresponding point from zero. (p. 4)

O

order of operations (OR-dur UHV *op*-uh-RAY-shuhnz) A set of rules for evaluating an expression involving more than one operation. (p. 12)

ordered pairs (OR-durd PAIRZ) Coordinates used to locate a point on a grid; the first number is the x-coordinate, and the second number is the y-coordinate. (p. 94)

outlier (OWT-*lye*-ur) A data item that is much greater or much less than the other items in a data set. (p. 363)

overlapping events (*oh*-vur-LAP-ing i-VENTS) Two events that have common outcomes. (p. 387)

P

parabola (puh-RAB-uh-luh) The graph of a quadratic function. (p. 246)

parallel lines (PA-ruh-*lel* LYENZ) Lines in the same plane that do not intersect. (p. 132)

parent function (PAIR-uhnt FUHNGK-shuhn) The simplest function with the defining characteristics of a family of functions. (p. 142)

Pascal's Triangle (pass-KALZ TRYE-ang-guhl) A geometric arrangement of the binomial coefficients in a triangle. It is named after Blaise Pascal. (p. 196)

percent of change (pur-SENT UHV CHAYNJ) The percent, or rate, a quantity increases or decreases from its original amount. (p. 289)

percent of error (pur-SENT UHV ER-ur) One way to describe how accurate a measurement is. (p. 286)

percentile (pur-SEN-tayhl, -til) A measure that tells what percent of the total items in a data set are at or below a given measure. (p. 372)

perfect square (PUR-fikt SKWAIR) The square of a natural number. (p. 2)

perfect square trinomial (PUR-fikt SKWAIR trye-NOH-mee-uhl) The square of a binomial. (p. 210)

permutation (*pur*-myoo-TAY-shuhn) An arrangement or listing of objects in a specific order. (p. 390)

perpendicular (pur-puhn-DIK-yuh-lur) Intersecting lines at a right angle. (p. 134)

point-slope form (POYNT-SLOHP FORM) An equation of a line written in the form $y - y_1 = m(x - x_1)$, where $P(x_1, y_1)$ is a point on the line and m is the slope of the line. (p. 126)

polynomial (*pol*-ee-NOH-mee-uhl) A monomial or a sum or difference of two or more monomials. (p. 176)

population (*pop*-yuh-LAY-shuhn) The group of people that are included in a survey. (p. 358)

positive correlation (POZ-uh-tiv *kor*-uh-LAY-shuhn) In a scatter plot, as x increases, y increases. (p. 374)

power (POW-ur) A number in exponential form. (p. 10)

prime polynomial (PRIME *pol*-ee-NOH-mee-uhl) A polynomial whose terms do not have a common factor other than 1. (p. 201)

principal square root (PRIN-suh-puhl SKWAIR ROOT) The positive square root of a number. (p. 2)

probability (*prob*-uh-BIL-uh-tee) A measure of the likelihood that an event will occur. (p. 378)

Product Property of Square Roots (PROD-uhkt PROP-ur-tee UHV SKWAIR ROOTS)
$\sqrt{ab} = \sqrt{a} \bullet \sqrt{b}$, where $a \geq 0$ and $b \geq 0$. (p. 226)

proportion (pruh-POR-shuhn) An equation which states that two ratios or rates are equivalent. (p. 284)

proportional (pruh-POR-shuh-nuhl) Used to describe the relationship of y to x when there is a relation between the two variables, x and y, such that $y = ax$, $a \neq 0$. (p. 280)

Pythagorean Theorem (pi-*thag*-uh-REE-uhn THEER-uhm) If a triangle is a right triangle, then the sum of the squares of the legs, a and b, equals the square of the hypotenuse, c; $a^2 + b^2 = c^2$. (p. 236)

Pythagorean triple (pi-*thag*-uh-REE-uhn TRIP-uhl) A set of three positive whole numbers, a, b, and c, that can be the lengths of the sides of a right triangle. (p. 237)

Q

quadratic equation (kwah-DRAT-ik i-KWAY-zhuhn) An equation in the form $ax^2 + bx + c = 0$, where a, b, and c are real numbers and $a \neq 0$. (p. 254)

quadratic formula (kwah-DRAT-ik FOR-myuh-luh) A formula that can be used to solve any quadratic equation. It is derived by solving the standard form of a quadratic equation, $ax^2 + bx + c = 0$, for x by completing the square. (p. 262)

quadratic function (kwah-DRAT-ik FUHNGK-shuhn) A function that can be written in the form, $y = ax^2 + bx + c$, $a \neq 0$. This form is the standard form of a quadratic function. (p. 246)

quadratic polynomial (kwah-DRAT-ik *pol*-ee-NOH-mee-uhl) A polynomial of degree two. (p. 177)

qualitative variables (KWAHL-i-*tay*-tiv VAIR-ee-uh-buhlz) Characteristics that are descriptive and can be separated by category, such as favorite colors. (p. 358)

quantitative variables (KWON-i-*tay*-tiv VAIR-ee-uh-buhlz) Characteristics that can be measured or counted, such as heights or the number of students in each math class. (p. 358)

quartiles (KWOR-tyelz) Values that separate data into four equal parts. (p. 370)

Quotient Property of Square Roots (KWOH-shuhnt PROP-ur-tee UHV SKWAIR ROOTS) For any positive real numbers a and b, $\sqrt{\dfrac{a}{b}} = \dfrac{\sqrt{a}}{\sqrt{b}}$. (p. 232)

R

radical equation (RAD-i-kuhl i-KWAY-zhuhn) An equation that contains a variable within a radicand. (p. 234)

radical function (RAD-i-kuhl FUHNGK-shuhn) A nonlinear function that contains one or more radical expressions with variables in the radicand. (p. 336)

radicand (RAD-i-*kand*) The expression under a radical sign. (p. 2)

random sampling (RAN-duhm SAM-pling) Each individual or population has an equal chance of being selected for a survey. (p. 359)

range (RAYNJ) The set of all possible output values or *y*-coordinates; the difference between the greatest and least values in the set of data. (pp. 94, 362)

rate (RAYT) A ratio that compares two unlike quantities; the percent of a number. (p. 281)

ratio (RAY-shee-oh) A way of comparing two numbers, *a* and *b*, by division. (p. 280)

rational equation (RA-shuh-nuhl i-KWAY-zhuhn) An equation that contains at least one rational expression. (p. 320)

rational exponent (RA-shuh-nuhl ek-SPOH-nuhnt) An exponent that can be expressed as $\frac{m}{n}$ such that if m and n are positive integers and a is a real number, then $a^{\frac{m}{n}} = \left(a^{\frac{1}{n}}\right)^m = \left(\sqrt[n]{a}\right)^m$. (p. 338)

rational expression (RA-shuh-nuhl ek-SPRESH-hun) An expression that is a quotient of two polynomials. (p. 306)

rational function (RA-shuh-nuhl FUHNGK-shuhn) A nonlinear function whose rule includes a quotient of two polynomials in which the denominator has a degree of at least one. (p. 332)

rational number (RA-shuh-nuhl NUHM-bur) A number that can be written in fraction form, $\frac{a}{b}$, where a and b are integers and $b \neq 0$. (p. 2)

rationalizing the denominator (RA-shuh-nuh-*lize*-ing THUH di-NOM-uh-*nay*-tur) A method used to eliminate radicals from the denominator. (p. 232)

real numbers (REEL NUHM-burz) The set of rational numbers and the set of irrational numbers together form the set of real numbers. (p. 4)

reciprocal (ri-SIP-ruh-kuhl) The multiplicative inverse of a number. (p. 9)

recursive formula (ri-KUR-siv FOR-myuh-luh) The formula to find the value of the first term and the rule for finding each term based on the term before. (p. 108)

relation (ri-LAY-shuhn) A set of ordered pairs. (p. 94)

relative error (REL-uh-tiv ER-ur) The percent of error written as a decimal. (p. 286)

repeating decimal (ri-PEET-ing DESS-uh-muhl) A decimal that has a digit or group that repeats without end. (p. 2)

replacement set (domain) (ri-PLAYSS-muhnt SET [doh-MAYN]) The set of all possible numbers that can be used to replace the variable. (p. 41)

representative sample (*rep*-ri-ZEN-tuh-tiv SAM-puhl) When the sample chosen for the survey has characteristics like those of the population. (p. 358)

rise (RIZE) The difference in the *y*-values of two points on a line. (p. 118)

root of an equation (ROOT UHV AN i-KWAY-zhuhn) The solution of an equation. (p. 254)

roster notation (ROS-tur noh-TAY-shuhn) A way of writing a set by listing its elements. (p. 23)

run (RUHN) The difference in the *x*-values of two points on a line. (p. 118)

S

sample (SAM-puhl) A small part of the population used in a survey. (p. 358)

sample space (SAM-puhl SPAYSS) The set of all possible outcomes. (p. 380)

scalar multiplication (SKAY-lur *muhl*-tuh-pluh-KAY-shuhn) When a matrix is multiplied by a real number. (p. 28)

scale (SKAYL) The ratio of a distance in the drawing to the corresponding actual distance in the real object. (p. 284)

scale drawing (SKAYL DRAW-ing) A two-dimensional drawing that accurately represents a real object. (p. 284)

scale factor (SKAYL FAK-tur) A number that tells how much larger or smaller the scale model is than the actual object. (p. 284)

scatter plot (SKAT-ur PLOT) A graph that shows the general relationship, or trend, between two sets of data. (p. 374)

scientific notation (sye-uhn-TIF-ik noh-TAY-shuhn) A way of writing numbers as the product of a number that is at least 1 but less than 10 and a power of 10. (p. 14)

second quartile (SEK-uhnd KWOR-tile) The median of the entire data set and usually referred to as the *median*. (p. 370)

sequence (SEE-kwuhnss) An ordered set of elements that are related by a pattern. (p. 103)

set (SET) A collection of elements. (p. 22)

set-builder notation (SET-BIL-dur noh-TAY-shuhn) A way of writing a set by stating the properties that its elements must satisfy. (p. 23)

simplest radical form (SIM-plist RAD-i-kuhl FORM) When the radicand of the square root has no factors, other than 1, that are perfect squares. (p. 226)

simplest term (lowest term) (SIM-plist TERM [LOH-ist TERM]) A rational expression that has a numerator and denominator with a GCF of 1. (p. 307)

simultaneous equations (*sye*-muhl-TAY-nee-uhss i-KWAY-zhuhnz) A set of two or more equations that have variables in common. (p. 150)

sine (SINE) If A is an acute angle of a right triangle, $\sin A = \dfrac{\text{leg opposite } \angle A}{\text{hypotenuse}}$. (p. 290)

slope (SLOHP) The rate of change between any two points on a line; the ratio of vertical change to horizontal change. (p. 118)

slope-intercept form (SLOHP-IN-tur-*sept* FORM) An equation written in the form of $y = mx + b$, where m is the slope and b is the y-intercept. (p. 122)

solution (suh-LOO-shuhn) The value of the variable that makes the equation or inequality a true sentence. (p. 40)

solution set (suh-LOO-shuhn SET) A set that contains all the values for a variable that make the equation or inequality true. (p. 40)

special product (SPESH-uhl PROD-uhkt) The product that is a perfect square trinomial or a difference of two squares. (p. 210)

square of a binomial (SKWAIR UHV UH bye-NOH-mee-uhl) A perfect-square trinomial; $(a + b)^2 = a^2 + 2ab + b^2$, $(a - b)^2 = a^2 - 2ab + b^2$. (p. 210)

square root (SKWAIR ROOT) One of the two equal factors of a number; the inverse of squaring a number. (p. 2)

square-root function (SKWAIR-ROOT FUHNGK-shuhn) A nonlinear function that contains the independent variable in the radicand. The square-root function is the simplest example of a *radical function*. (p. 336)

standard form (STAN-durd FORM) A polynomial written with the exponents of the variable decreasing from left to right; a linear equation expressed in the form of $Ax + By = C$, where A, B, and C are real numbers and A and B are not equal to 0. (p. 177)

stem-and-leaf plot (STEM-AND-LEAF PLOT) A graph that arranges numerical data in order of place value. Each data item is broken into a stem (digit or digits on the left) and a leaf (digit on the right). (p. 364)

stratified random sample (STRAT-uh-*fide* RAN-duhm SAM-puhl) A sampling method in which the population is divided into similar, nonoverlapping groups. (p. 359)

subset (SUHB-*set*) A set contained within a set; it is denoted by the symbol $\subset$ or $\subseteq$. (p. 22)

Substitution Principle (sub-stuh-TOO-shuhn PRIN-suh-puhl) A method used for solving a system of equations that replaces one variable in one equation with an expression derived from the other equation. (p. 17)

Subtraction Principle (suhb-TRAK-shuhn PRIN-suh-puhl) To subtract any rational number, *add its opposite*. (p. 7)

Subtraction Property of Equality (suhb-TRAK-shuhn PROP-ur-tee UHV i-KWOL-uh-tee) For real numbers a, b, and c, if $a = b$, then $a - c = b - c$. (p. 42)

Subtraction Property of Inequality (suhb-TRAK-shuhn PROP-ur-tee UHV *in*-i-KWOL-uh tee) If a, b, and c are real numbers and $a > b$, then $a - c > b - c$. These statements are also true if $>$ is replaced by $<$, $\leq$, or $\geq$. (p. 73)

survey (SUR-vay) A way to collect data to answer a question. (p. 358)

system of linear equations (SISS-tuhm UHV LIN-ee-ur i-KWAY-zhuhnz) A set of two or more linear equations in the same two or more variables. Also called *simultaneous equations*. (p. 150)

system of linear inequalities (SISS-tuhm UHV LIN-ee-ur *in*-i-KWOL-uh-teez) A set of two or more linear inequalities in the same two or more variables. A graph of the system shows all of its solutions. A solution makes each inequality in the system true. (p. 162)

systematic sampling (*siss*-tuh-MAT-ik SAM-pling) A rule is applied to choose the sample. (p. 359)

T

tangent (TAN-juhnt) If A is an acute angle of a right triangle, $\tan A = \dfrac{\text{leg opposite } \angle A}{\text{leg adjacent to } \angle A}$. (p. 290)

term (TURM) A number, a variable, or the product of a number and one or more variables; each number in a proportion; each figure or number in a sequence. (p. 16)

terminating decimal (TUR-muh-nayt-ing DESS-uh-muhl) A decimal whose digits end. (p. 2)

theoretical probability (*thee*-uh-RET-i-kuhl *prob*-uh-BIL-uh-tee) The probability of an event, $P(E)$, occurring in an experiment with an equally likely outcome. (p. 380)

third quartile (THURD KWOR-tile) The median of the upper half of a data set. (p. 370)

tree diagram (TREE DYE-uh-gram) A diagram showing all possible outcomes of an event or of more than one event. (p. 382)

Triangle Inequality Theorem (TRYE-ang-guhl *in*-i-KWOL-uh-tee THEER-uhm) The theorem stating that the sum of the lengths of any two sides of a triangle is greater than the length of the third side. (p. 90)

trigonometric ratio (*trig*-uh-nuh-MET-rik RAY-shee-oh) A ratio of the lengths of two sides of a right triangle. (p. 290)

Trigonometry (trig-uh-NOM-i-tree) means *the measure of triangles*. The study of trigonometry involves the relationships among the sides and angles of triangles. (p. 290)

trinomial (trye-NOH-mee-uhl) A polynomial with exactly three terms. (p. 176)

U

union of sets (YOON-yuhn UHV SETS) The *union*, ∪, of two sets is the set of all elements that are in either or both sets. (p. 24)

unit rate (YOO-nit RAYT) A rate in which the second term, or denominator, is 1. (p. 281)

universal set (*yoo*-nuh-VUR-suhl SET) The set of all elements being considered, such as the number of people in a survey. (p. 22)

upper extreme (UHP-ur ek-STREEM) The greatest number in the data set; the upper end of the "whisker" of a box-and-whisker plot. (p. 370)

upper quartile (UHP-ur KWOR-tile) The median of the upper half of a set of data; the upper end of the "box" part of a box-and-whisker plot. (p. 370)

V

variable (VAIR-ee-uh-buhl) A letter of the alphabet that represents an unknown number in an algebraic expression or equation. (p. 358)

Venn diagram (VEN DYE-uh-gram) A diagram that uses circles to show how data are related. (p. 4)

vertex (VUR-teks) The point where the left and right parts of a graph, divided by the axis of symmetry, meet; the point at which a parabola changes direction. (pp. 138, 247)

vertical-line test (VUR-tuh-kuhl-LINE TEST) If every vertical line that intersects a graph intersects that graph in exactly one point, then the graph represents a function. (p. 97)

voluntary response sampling (VOL-uhn-ter-ee ri-SPONS SAM-pling) A sample that consists of volunteers who choose to participate. (p. 359)

W

whole numbers (HOHL NUHM-burz) Zero and the counting numbers: {0, 1, 2, 3, 4...}; also called *nonnegative numbers*. (p. 2)

X

x-intercept (EKSS-IN-tur-*sept*) The x-coordinate of the point where the graph crosses the x-axis. (p. 122)

Y

y-intercept (WYE-IN-tur-*sept*) The y-coordinate of the point where the graph crosses the y-axis. (p. 122)

Z

Zero Exponent (ZEER-oh ek-SPOH-nuhnt) $a^0 = 1, a \neq 0$; when a nonzero number has zero as its exponent, its value is 1. (p. 11)

zero of a function (ZEER-oh UHV UH FUHNGK-shuhn) For the function f, any number x, such that $f(x) = 0$. (p. 254)

Zero-Product Property (ZEER-oh-PROD-uhkt PROP-ur-tee) $ab = 0$ if and only if $a = 0$ or $b = 0$, where a and b are real numbers. (p. 254)

Symbols

Numbers and Operations

$a \bullet b, ab$	a times b
$a \div b, \frac{a}{b}$	a divided by b
$\pm$	plus or minus; positive or negative
$=$	is equal to
$\stackrel{?}{=}$	is it equal to?
$\neq$	is not equal to
$\approx$	is approximately equal to
$>$	is greater than
$<$	is less than
$\geq$	is greater than or equal to
$\leq$	is less than or equal to
$...$	continues without end
∞	infinity
a^2	a squared, or a to the second power
$0.\overline{3}$	$0.333 ...$ (repeating decimal)
$\%$	percent
$-a$	the additive inverse or opposite of a
$\frac{1}{a}, a \neq 0$	the reciprocal of a
$a : b$	the ratio of a and b, or $\frac{a}{b}$

Sets, Probability, and Logic

$\cup$	union
$\cap$	intersection
$\{ \}, \varnothing$	the empty set
$\subset, \subseteq$	is a subset of
A'	the complement of A
$P(E)$	probability of an event
$n!$	n factorial $[n \bullet (n-1) \bullet (n-2) \bullet ... \bullet 1]$
$P(n, r)$	permutation of n things taken r at a time
$C(n, r)$	combination of n things taken r at a time
$\wedge$	and, conjunction
$\vee$	or, disjunction
$\rightarrow$	if-then, implication
$\leftrightarrow$	if and only if, biconditional

Geometry and Measurement

$\cong$	is congruent to
$\sim$	is similar to
$\circ$	degree(s)
$\overleftrightarrow{AB}$	line AB
$\overline{AB}$	segment AB
$\overrightarrow{AB}$	ray AB
$\overarc{AB}$	arc AB
$\angle ABC$	angle ABC
AB	length of $\overline{AB}$, distance between A and B
ABC	plane ABC
$\triangle ABC$	triangle ABC
$m\angle ABC$	measure of angle ABC
$||$	is parallel to
$\perp$	is perpendicular to
π	pi (approximately 3.14 or $\frac{22}{7}$)
$\sin A$	sine of angle A
$\cos A$	cosine of angle A
$\tan A$	tangent of angle A

Algebra and Functions

a'	a prime
a^n	a to the nth power
a^{-n}	$\frac{1}{a^n}$ (one over a to the nth power)
a_n	the nth term of a sequence
$a^{\frac{1}{2}}$	$\sqrt{a}$
$\begin{bmatrix} a & b \\ c & d \end{bmatrix}$	matrix
$|x|$	absolute value of x
$[x]$	greatest integer
$\sqrt{x}$	principal (positive) square root of x
$f(x)$	f of x, the value of the function at x
(x, y)	ordered pair

Probability

Theoretical Probability

$$P(E) = \frac{\text{number of favorable outcomes}}{\text{total number of outcomes}}$$

Experimental Probability

$$\text{Exp } P(E) = \frac{\text{number of times the event occurs}}{\text{total number of trials}}$$

Probability of Two Independent Events

$$P(A \text{ and } B) = P(A) \bullet P(B)$$

Probability of Two Dependent Events

$$P(A \text{ and } B) = P(A) \bullet P(B \text{ after } A)$$

Probability of Mutually Exclusive Events

$$P(A \text{ or } B) = P(A) + P(B)$$

Probability of Overlapping Events

$$P(A \text{ or } B) = P(A) + P(B) - P(A \text{ and } B)$$

Measurement Conversions

Length

Metric

1 millimeter (mm) = 0.001 meter (m)		1 dekameter (dam) = 10 meters	
1 centimeter (cm) = 0.01 meter		1 hectometer (hm) = 100 meters	
1 decimeter (dm) = 0.1 meter		1 kilometer (km) = 1000 meters	

Customary

1 foot (ft) = 12 inches (in.)	1 mile (mi) = 5280 feet
1 yard (yd) = 3 feet	1 mile = 1760 yards
1 yard = 36 inches	

Customary to Metric

1 inch = 2.54 centimeters	1 yard ≈ 0.914 meter
1 foot ≈ 0.305 meter	1 mile ≈ 1.61 kilometer

Capacity and Volume

Metric

1 milliliter (mL) = 0.001 liter (L)	1 kiloliter (kL) = 1000 liters

Customary

3 teaspoons (tsp) = 1 tablespoon (tbsp)	1 quart (qt) = 2 pints
1 cup (c) = 8 fluid ounces (fl oz)	1 quart = 4 cups
1 pint (pt) = 2 cups	1 gallon (gal) = 4 quarts

Customary to Metric

1 fluid ounce ≈ 29.6 milliliters	1 quart ≈ 0.946 liter
1 pint ≈ 0.473 liter	1 gallon ≈ 3.78 liters

Mass and Weight

Metric

1 milligram (mg) = 0.001 gram (g)	1 metric ton (t) = 1000 kilograms
1 kilogram (kg) = 1000 grams	

Customary

1 pound (lb) = 16 ounces (oz)	1 ton (T) = 2000 pounds

Customary to Metric

1 ounce ≈ 28.4 grams	1 pound ≈ 454 grams

Temperature

Metric

0° Celsius (C) ...... Water freezes	100° Celsius (C) .... Water boils

Customary

32° Fahrenheit (F) ...... Water freezes	212° Fahrenheit (F) .... Water boils

Time

1 century (cent.) = 100 years (y)	1 leap year = 366 days	1 day = 24 hours (h)
1 year = 12 months (mo)	1 year = 52 weeks (wk)	1 hour = 60 minutes (min)
1 year = 365 days (d)	1 week = 7 days	1 minute = 60 seconds (s)

TABLES

Formula Chart

Perimeter & Circumference	square	$P = 4s$	regular polygon	$P = ns$
	rectangle	$P = 2(\ell + w)$ or $P = 2\ell + 2w$	circle	$C = 2\pi r$ or $C = \pi d$

Area	square	$A = s^2$	trapezoid	$A = \frac{1}{2}(b_1 + b_2)h$
	rectangle	$A = \ell w$ or $A = bh$	regular polygon	$A = \frac{1}{2}aP$
	parallelogram	$A = bh$	circle	$A = \pi r^2$
	triangle	$A = \frac{1}{2}bh$		

Surface Area	cube	$S = 6e^2$	cone	$S = \pi r \ell + \pi r^2$
	prism	$S = Ph + 2B$	sphere	$S = 4\pi r^2$
	rectangular prism	$S = 2(\ell w + \ell h + wh)$	regular pyramid	$S = \frac{1}{2}P\ell + B$
	cylinder	$S = 2\pi rh + 2\pi r^2$		

Volume	cube	$V = e^3$	cylinder	$V = \pi r^2 h$
	rectangular prism	$V = \ell wh$	cone	$V = \frac{1}{3}\pi r^2 h$
	prism	$V = Bh$	sphere	$V = \frac{4}{3}\pi r^3$
	pyramid	$V = \frac{1}{3}Bh$		

nth term of a Sequence	Arithmetic	$a_n = a_{n-1} + d$	Geometric	$a_n = a_{n-1} \cdot r$

Linear Functions	Standard form	$Ax + By = C$	Point-slope form	$y - y_1 = m(x - x_1)$
	Slope-intercept form	$y = mx + b$	Slope Formula	$m = \dfrac{y_2 - y_1}{x_2 - x_1}$

Variation	Direct	$y = kx$ or $k = \dfrac{y}{x}, k \neq 0$	Inverse	$y = \dfrac{k}{x}$ or $k = xy, k \neq 0$

Quadratic Equations	Standard form	$ax^2 + bx + c = 0$	Discriminant	$\sqrt{b^2 - 4ac}$
	Quadratic Formula	$x = \dfrac{-b \pm \sqrt{b^2 - 4ac}}{2a}$	Axis of symmetry	$x = \dfrac{-b}{2a}$

Nonlinear Functions	Absolute-Value Function	$y = |x|$	Rational Function	$y = \dfrac{a}{x}$
	Exponential Function	$y = ab^x$	Radical Function	$y = \sqrt{x}$
	Quadratic Function	$y = ax^2 + bx + c$		

Pythagorean Theorem	right triangle with legs a and b and hypotenuse c	$a^2 + b^2 = c^2$

Trigonometric Ratios

$$\text{sine (sin)} = \frac{\text{opposite leg}}{\text{hypotenuse}}$$

$$\text{cosine (cos)} = \frac{\text{adjacent leg}}{\text{hypotenuse}}$$

$$\text{tangent (tan)} = \frac{\text{opposite leg}}{\text{adjacent leg}}$$

Exponential Growth

$y = ab^x$, $a > 0$ and $b > 1$

Exponential Decay

$y = ab^x$, $a > 0$ and $0 < b < 1$

Distance Formula	$d = \sqrt{(x_2 - x_1)^2 + (y_2 - y_1)^2}$	**Midpoint Formula**	$M = \left(\dfrac{x_1 + x_2}{2}, \dfrac{y_1 + y_2}{2} \right)$

Other Formulas	Simple Interest	$I = prt$	distance traveled	$d = rt$
	Compound Interest Balance	$A = P\left(1 + \frac{r}{n}\right)^{nt}$	percentage proportion	$\dfrac{\text{part}}{\text{whole}} = \dfrac{\text{percent}}{100}$
	Half-life	$A = P(0.5)^t$	percentage = rate $\cdot$ base	$p = rb$

Table of Trigonometric Ratios

Angle	Sin	Cos	Tan	Angle	Sin	Cos	Tan
0°	0.000	1.000	0.000	45°	0.707	0.707	1.000
1°	0.017	1.000	0.017	46°	0.719	0.695	1.036
2°	0.035	0.999	0.035	47°	0.731	0.682	1.072
3°	0.052	0.999	0.052	48°	0.743	0.669	1.111
4°	0.070	0.998	0.070	49°	0.755	0.656	1.150
5°	0.087	0.996	0.087	50°	0.766	0.643	1.192
6°	0.105	0.995	0.105	51°	0.777	0.629	1.235
7°	0.122	0.993	0.123	52°	0.788	0.616	1.280
8°	0.139	0.990	0.141	53°	0.799	0.602	1.327
9°	0.156	0.988	0.158	54°	0.809	0.588	1.376
10°	0.174	0.985	0.176	55°	0.819	0.574	1.428
11°	0.191	0.982	0.194	56°	0.829	0.559	1.483
12°	0.208	0.978	0.213	57°	0.839	0.545	1.540
13°	0.225	0.974	0.231	58°	0.848	0.530	1.600
14°	0.242	0.970	0.249	59°	0.857	0.515	1.664
15°	0.259	0.966	0.268	60°	0.866	0.500	1.732
16°	0.276	0.961	0.287	61°	0.875	0.485	1.804
17°	0.292	0.956	0.306	62°	0.883	0.469	1.881
18°	0.309	0.951	0.325	63°	0.891	0.454	1.963
19°	0.326	0.946	0.344	64°	0.899	0.438	2.050
20°	0.342	0.940	0.364	65°	0.906	0.423	2.145
21°	0.358	0.934	0.384	66°	0.914	0.407	2.246
22°	0.375	0.927	0.404	67°	0.921	0.391	2.356
23°	0.391	0.921	0.424	68°	0.927	0.375	2.475
24°	0.407	0.914	0.445	69°	0.934	0.358	2.605
25°	0.423	0.906	0.466	70°	0.940	0.342	2.747
26°	0.438	0.899	0.488	71°	0.946	0.326	2.904
27°	0.454	0.891	0.510	72°	0.951	0.309	3.078
28°	0.469	0.883	0.532	73°	0.956	0.292	3.271
29°	0.485	0.875	0.554	74°	0.961	0.276	3.487
30°	0.500	0.866	0.577	75°	0.966	0.259	3.732
31°	0.515	0.857	0.601	76°	0.970	0.242	4.011
32°	0.530	0.848	0.625	77°	0.974	0.225	4.331
33°	0.545	0.839	0.649	78°	0.978	0.208	4.705
34°	0.559	0.829	0.675	79°	0.982	0.191	5.145
35°	0.574	0.819	0.700	80°	0.985	0.174	5.671
36°	0.588	0.809	0.727	81°	0.988	0.156	6.314
37°	0.602	0.799	0.754	82°	0.990	0.139	7.115
38°	0.616	0.788	0.781	83°	0.993	0.122	8.144
39°	0.629	0.777	0.810	84°	0.995	0.105	9.514
40°	0.643	0.766	0.839	85°	0.996	0.087	11.430
41°	0.656	0.755	0.869	86°	0.998	0.070	14.301
42°	0.669	0.743	0.900	87°	0.999	0.052	19.081
43°	0.682	0.731	0.933	88°	0.999	0.035	28.636
44°	0.695	0.719	0.966	89°	1.000	0.017	57.290
45°	0.707	0.707	1.000	90°	1.000	0.000	—

Table of Squares and Square Roots

No.	Square	Sq. Root	No.	Square	Sq. Root	No.	Square	Sq. Root
1	1	1.000	51	2601	7.141	101	10,201	10.050
2	4	1.414	52	2704	7.211	102	10,404	10.100
3	9	1.732	53	2809	7.280	103	10,609	10.149
4	16	2.000	54	2916	7.348	104	10,816	10.198
5	25	2.236	55	3025	7.416	105	11,025	10.247
6	36	2.449	56	3136	7.483	106	11,236	10.296
7	49	2.646	57	3249	7.550	107	11,449	10.344
8	64	2.828	58	3364	7.616	108	11,664	10.392
9	81	3.000	59	3481	7.681	109	11,881	10.440
10	100	3.162	60	3600	7.746	110	12,100	10.488
11	121	3.317	61	3721	7.810	111	12,321	10.536
12	144	3.464	62	3844	7.874	112	12,544	10.583
13	169	3.606	63	3969	7.937	113	12,769	10.630
14	196	3.742	64	4096	8.000	114	12,996	10.677
15	225	3.873	65	4225	8.062	115	13,225	10.724
16	256	4.000	66	4356	8.124	116	13,456	10.770
17	289	4.123	67	4489	8.185	117	13,689	10.817
18	324	4.243	68	4624	8.246	118	13,924	10.863
19	361	4.359	69	4761	8.307	119	14,161	10.909
20	400	4.472	70	4900	8.367	120	14,400	10.954
21	441	4.583	71	5041	8.426	121	14,641	11.000
22	484	4.690	72	5184	8.485	122	14,884	11.045
23	529	4.796	73	5329	8.544	123	15,129	11.091
24	576	4.899	74	5476	8.602	124	15,376	11.136
25	625	5.000	75	5625	8.660	125	15,625	11.180
26	676	5.099	76	5776	8.718	126	15,876	11.225
27	729	5.196	77	5929	8.775	127	16,129	11.269
28	784	5.292	78	6084	8.832	128	16,384	11.314
29	841	5.385	79	6241	8.888	129	16,641	11.358
30	900	5.477	80	6400	8.944	130	16,900	11.402
31	961	5.568	81	6561	9.000	131	17,161	11.446
32	1024	5.657	82	6724	9.055	132	17,424	11.489
33	1089	5.745	83	6889	9.110	133	17,689	11.533
34	1156	5.831	84	7056	9.165	134	17,956	11.576
35	1225	5.916	85	7225	9.220	135	18,225	11.619
36	1296	6.000	86	7396	9.274	136	18,496	11.662
37	1369	6.083	87	7569	9.327	137	18,769	11.705
38	1444	6.164	88	7744	9.381	138	19,044	11.747
39	1521	6.245	89	7921	9.434	139	19,321	11.790
40	1600	6.325	90	8100	9.487	140	19,600	11.832
41	1681	6.403	91	8281	9.539	141	19,881	11.874
42	1764	6.481	92	8464	9.592	142	20,164	11.916
43	1849	6.557	93	8649	9.644	143	20,449	11.958
44	1936	6.633	94	8836	9.695	144	20,736	12.000
45	2025	6.708	95	9025	9.747			
46	2116	6.782	96	9216	9.798			
47	2209	6.856	97	9409	9.849			
48	2304	6.928	98	9604	9.899			
49	2401	7.000	99	9801	9.950			
50	2500	7.071	100	10,000	10.000			

TABLES

Key: SU=Skills Update PB=Practice Book

impossible, 378–79, PB 373–74
make predictions, 379
of mutually exclusive events, 386–87, PB 379–80
and odds, 414
outcomes
    Fundamental Counting Principle, find number of using
        the, 382–83, 385, 390, 393, PB 377
    show with tree diagrams, 382–83, 385, PB 377
of overlapping events, 386–87, PB 379–80
theoretical, 380–81, PB 375–76
using a handheld to simulate events, 394–95, PB 387–88

Problem Solving
Applications (Mixed Strategies), 110–11, 220–21, 398–99,
    PB 2, 4, 6, 8, 10, 12, 14, 18, 20, 36, 40, 42, 44, 48, 62, 66, 70,
    72, 74, 92, 94, 96, 98, 99–100, 106, 112, 114, 116, 118, 144,
    154, 166, 170, 172, 176, 178, 192, 196, 204, 208, 211–12,
    218, 222, 224, 226, 230, 232, 240, 246, 248, 252, 254, 256,
    258, 262, 274, 284, 286, 288, 290, 304, 306, 308, 310, 312,
    314, 316, 318, 320, 342, 356, 362, 366, 368, 370, 372, 374,
    376, 378, 380, 382, 384, 386, 391–92
Heuristic model, 34–35, 64–65, 88–89, 110–11, 144–45,
    170–71, 194–95, 220–21, 240–41, 274–75, 300–1, 324–25,
    352–53, 398–99, PB 29–30, 55–56, 79–80, 99–100, 131–32,
    159–60, 185–86, 211–12, 233–34, 267–68, 293–94, 321–22,
    349–50, 391–92
Strategies
    Account for All Possibilities, 202, 226, 240–41,
        PB 233–34, 246, 248, 252, 258, 267, 391, 395
    Adopt a Different Point of View, 274–75, 282, PB 232,
        252, 258, 267–68, 321, 392
    Consider Extreme Cases, 136, 144–45, PB 131–32,
        212, 368
    Find a Pattern, 194–95, 220, PB 8, 10, 30, 79, 96, 98, 154,
        185–86, 188, 211, 267–68, 322, 392
    Guess and Test, 206–7, 284, 300–1, 325, PB 6, 42, 48, 178,
        222, 224, 248, 293–94, 322
    Make a Drawing, 34–35, 50, 58, 65, 221, 281, 324,
        PB 29–30, 92, 178, 230, 240, 254, 256, 262, 286, 288,
        290, 296, 322, 391
    Organize Data, 352–53, PB 349–50, 380, 392, 395
    Reason Logically, 74, 82, 84, 88–89, 110, 160, 221, 257,
        309, 321, 352, PB 79–80, 96, 98–100, 212, 224, 230,
        232, 246, 258, 262, 290, 321, 391
    Solve a Simpler Problem, 60, 64–65, 79, 111, PB 55–56,
        110, 211–12, 392
    Work Backward, 170–71, 211, PB 42, 88, 159–60, 211,
        284, 321

Properties
Closure, 20
equality
    Addition Property of Equality, 44–45, 57, 234–35, 246,
        254–57, PB 147, 151, 227, 261
    Division Property of Equality, 46–49, 57, 234–35, 255,
        296–97, PB 147, 151, 317
    Multiplication Property of Equality, 46–49, 57, 234–35,
        296, PB 151, 227
    Subtraction Property of Equality, 42–43, 57, 234–36, 246,
        254–57, 296–97, PB 145, 147, 151, 227, 261, 303, 317
    Transitive Property of Equality, 71
inequality
    Addition Property of Inequality, 72–73, PB 67–68
    Division Property of Inequality, 74–75, PB 69–70
    Multiplication Property of Inequality, 74–75, PB 69–70
    Subtraction Property of Inequality, 72–73, PB 67–68
    Transitive Property of Inequality, 71

Product Property of Square Roots, 226, 230–33, 239
Quotient Property of Square Roots, 232
real number
    Associative Property of Addition, 20–21, 25, PB 17–18
    Associative Property of Multiplication, 20–21, 25,
        PB 17–18
    Closure Property, 5, 20
    Commutative Property of Addition, 20–21, 25, 246,
        PB 17–18
    Commutative Property of Multiplication, 20–21, 25,
        PB 17–18
    Distributive Property, 20–21, 254, PB 17–18, 47
    Identity Property of Addition, 20–21, PB 17–18
    Identity Property of Multiplication, 20–21, PB 17–18
    Inverse Property of Addition, 5, 20–21, PB 17–18
    Inverse Property of Multiplication, 20–21, PB 17–18
    Zero Product Property, 254–57, 306–9, PB 249, 253, 261,
        303–5, 319

Proportions
apply to scale drawings/models, 284–85, PB 279–80
constant of proportionality, 280
Cross-Products Rule (cross multiplication), 280, 284–85
defined, 280
graph, 281
terms
    extremes, 280
    means, 280

Pythagorean Theorem
apply, 236–37, 292–93, PB 229–30
Converse of the Pythagorean Theorem, 237
defined, 236
extending to three dimensions, 242–43, PB 235–36
Pythagorean triples, 237

Quadrants, 93, 407–8 (SU)

Quadratic equations
discriminant, 262–63, PB 257–58
graph, 254, 256
in standard form, 254
solutions (roots of the equation or zeros of the function),
    254
solve
    by completing the square, 260–61, PB 255–56
    by factoring, 254–57, PB 249–52
    verbal problems involving, 258–59, PB 253–54
    with the Quadratic Formula, 264–65, 269, PB 259–60
zero-product property, 254–57, 267, 306, PB 249–52

Quadratic Formula
discriminant, 262–63, PB 257–58
using to solve quadratic equations, 264–65, PB 259–60

Quadratic functions
defined, 246
domain/range, 247–49, PB 244–46
families of, 272–73, PB 265–66
parabolas (*see also* Parabolas), 246–53, PB 243–48
graphs of, 250–53, PB 247–48
minimum/maximum values, 247, PB 243–44
using a handheld to graph, 272–73, PB 265–66

Quadrilaterals, 412 (SU)

Quartiles, 370–71, 373, PB 367–68

Quotient Property of Square Roots, 232

Radical equations, 234–35, PB 227–28

Radical expressions
add/subtract, 228–29, PB 223–24
multiply/divide, 230–33, PB 225–26
simplify
find a perfect square then continue to simplify, 226–27, PB 221–22
find the greatest perfect square, 226–27, PB 221–22
graph ordered pairs, 336–37, PB 335–36

Radical functions
graph
find domain and range, 336–37, PB 335–36
function table, make a, 336–37, PB 335–36

Rate
rename/convert using conversion factors, 282–83
unit price, 282
unit rate, 281, 283

Rational equations, 320–23, PB 317–20

Rational exponents, 338

Rational expressions
factoring the numerator and denominator, 306–7, PB 303–04
combine, with like denominators, 314–15, PB 311–12
combine, with unlike denominators, 316–17
defined, 306
divide, 312–13, PB 309–10
identify excluded values, 307–9
multiply, 310–11, PB 307–8
simplify
factoring a trinomial, 308–9, PB 305–6
factoring by grouping, 308–9, PB 305–6
factoring the difference of two squares, 308–9, PB 305–6

Rational functions
defined, 332
graph
function table, make a, 332–35, PB 333–34
graph ordered pairs, 332–35, PB 333–34
identify asymptotes, 332–35, 346–47, PB 333–34, 343–44
using a handheld, 346–49, PB 343–46
parent function/family of functions, 332–33, 335

Rational numbers, 2–3, PB 1–2

Ratios
defined, 280, PB 277
forms
fraction, 280–81, 283, PB 277
word, 280, PB 277
proportions and, 280
simplest form, 280, PB 277
trigonometric, 290–91, PB 285–86

Real numbers
absolute value of, 5
add with like/unlike signs, 6–7, PB 5–6
additive inverse, 5, 20, PB 17
classify, 4–5, PB 3–4
Closure Property, 4–5, PB 3–4
compare and order on a number line, 4, PB 3–4
divide, 8–9, PB 7–8
find absolute value and additive inverse of, 4–5, PB 3–4
graph, 4, PB 3–4
multiply, 8–9, PB 7–8
properties of, 20–21, PB 17–18

set of, the, 4
subtract with like/unlike signs, 7, PB 5–6

Reasoning
analyze information, 8, 10, 12, 16, 22, 28–29, 32, 34–35, 40, 42, 46, 50, 54, 58, 60, 64–65, 72, 74, 76, 88–89, 96, 100, 104, 106, 110–11, 120, 122, 128, 144–145, 150, 154, 156, 165, 170–71, 178, 182, 184, 186, 190, 194–95, 210, 212, 220–21, 228, 234, 240–41, 258, 264, 268–69, 274–75, 283–84, 287–89, 292, 294, 296–97, 300–1, 320, 324–25, 330, 338, 342, 345, 351–53, 398–99, PB 29, 55, 79, 99, 131, 159, 185, 211, 233, 267, 293, 321, 349, 393
classify/sort, 4, 22–25, 66, 176–77, 381, 387, 390–95, PB 19–20, 102, 169–70, 380, 383–86
communicate (*see* Discuss and Write; Tell About It; Write About It)
compare/contrast, 12, 14, 16–17, 19, 23, 70–87, 112–13, 372–73, PB 65–78, 101–2, 369–70
deductive reasoning/conclusions, 254, 304
justify/verify
logic/logical reasoning, 5, 74, 82, 84, 88–89, 110, 144, 160, 221, 257, 309, 321, 352, PB 79–80, 96, 98–100, 212, 224, 230, 232, 246, 258, 262, 290, 321, 391
reasonableness of solution, 6–9, 43, 45, 49, 53, 57, 59, 234–35, 269, PB 5–6
validity of results, 34–35, 64–65, 88–89, 110–11, 144–45, 170–71, 194–95, 220–21, 240–41, 274–75, 300–1, 324–25, 352–53, 398–99, PB 29, 55, 79, 99, 131, 159, 185, 211, 233, 267, 293, 321, 349, 393
mathematical, 92, 114, 198, 244, 356, PB 83, 163, 189, 353
predictions (make), 114, 142–43, 253, 273, 345, 378–79, PB 120, 266, 342, 344, 373–74
problem solving (*see* Problem Solving, Applications; Problem Solving, Strategies)
proportional reasoning, 284–85, PB 279–80
spatial reasoning, 109, 112–13, 184–85, 212, 235–36, 242–43
true/false, 4, 40–41, 57, 69, 72–73, 77, 86–87, 162, 235, 253, 285, PB 39–40, 47, 60, 77, 90, 104, 120, 123–24, 150, 153, 164, 190, 202, 216, 272, 298, 326, 354, 388
visual reasoning, 2, 22–25, 34, 46, 50, 94–95, 97, 99, 105, 178–79, 197, 221, 408–12(SU)
write a rule, 100–1, 104, 114, 330, PB 93–94, 271

Relations
domain and range, 94–95, PB 89–90
functions and, 96–98, PB 91–92
represent as a mapping diagram, 94–95, 97–98, PB 90–91
represent using a rule, 94–95, 98, PB 89, 92

Relative error, 286–87, PB 281–82

Review
Check Your Progress, online @ www.progressinmathematics.com (*see also* Assessment, *Check Your Progress*)
Cumulative Review (*see* Assessment, *Cumulative Review*)
Do You Remember? (*see* Do You Remember?)
Skills Update (*see* Skills Update)
Spiral Review (*see* Spiral Review)
Tell About It (*see* Tell About It)
Test Preparation, end-of-lesson feature (*see* Assessment, *Test Preparation*)
Write About It (*see* Assessment, *Write About It*)

Right triangles
angle of depression, 295
angle of elevation, 295
bias, 359–60
solving a, 292–93, PB 287–88